EARTH

AN INTRODUCTION TO PHYSICAL GEOLOGY   FOURTH CANADIAN EDITION

Edward J. Tarbuck

Frederick K. Lutgens

Cameron J. Tsujita
Western University

Stephen R. Hicock
Western University

PEARSON

Toronto

Editor-in-Chief: Michelle Sartor
Acquisitions Editor: Cathleen Sullivan
Marketing Manager: Marlene Olsavsky
Program Manager: Darryl Kamo
Project Manager: Kimberley Blakey
Developmental Editor: Paul Donnelly
Media Editor: Ben Zaporazan
Media Producer: Daniel Szabo
Production Services: Harleen Chopra®, Cenveo Publisher Services
Permissions Project Manager: Marnie Lamb
Photo Permissions Research: Zoe Milgram, QBS Learning
TextPermissions Research: Haydee Hidalgo, Electronic Publishing Services, Inc.
Art Director: ZenaDenchik
Cover Designer: Alex Li
Interior Designer: Nesbitt Graphics
Cover Image: J. David Andrews/Masterfile

Credits and acknowledgments for material borrowed from other sources and reproduced, with permission, in this textbook appear on the appropriate page within the text.

Original edition published by Pearson Education, Inc., Upper Saddle River, New Jersey, USA. Copyright © 2013 Pearson Education, Inc. This edition is authorized for sale only in Canada.

If you purchased this book outside the United States or Canada, you should be aware that it has been imported without the approval of the publisher or the author.

10 9 8 7 6 5 4 3 2 CKV

Library and Archives Canada Cataloguing in Publication

Tarbuck, Edward J., author
    Earth : an introduction to physical geology / Edward J. Tarbuck, Frederick K. Lutgens, Dennis Tasa, Cameron J. Tsujita, Stephen R. Hicock. — Fourth Canadian edition.

Revision of: Earth : an introduction to physical geology / Edward J. Tarbuck ... [et al.] 3rd Canadian ed.

Includes bibliographical references and index.
ISBN 978-0-13-704776-5 (pbk.)

    1. Physical geology—Textbooks. I. Title.

QE28.2.T37 2014   551   C2013-907524-0

ISBN 978-0-32-186543-4

BRIEF CONTENTS

CONTENTS

"Smokey the Bear"
Hat

A NOTE TO STUDENTS FROM THE CANADIAN AUTHORS

Welcome to the fourth Canadian edition of *Earth: An Introduction to Physical Geology*. We are excited to be your personal guides on your journey into the fascinating world of geology. Some of you may have already glimpsed some of our tour stops—perhaps in a high school course, in a television documentary, on the news, or even first-hand. We hope the content of this textbook will strike a chord with you in terms of how it connects with these experiences, and that it will enhance your future encounters with geology, whether in pondering the source of graphite in your pencil, watching a volcanic eruption or earthquake on the news, or simply enjoying scenery on a vacation.

We became involved with this book for three reasons. First, we feel it is important for Canadian students to have a book that has direct relevance to them as citizens of Canada. Second, co-authoring a book provides us, as teachers, with an opportunity to reach students beyond the gates of our academic institution. And third, we love geology and feel privileged to share our enthusiasm for what we do as geologists.

As both authors and teachers, we are aware that while some students will have some background in geology, this will be a new experience for many of you. Thus, we have stood by our conviction to keep this an *introductory-level* textbook, and have done our best to keep the language simple and straightforward, to guide you through the concepts step by step, and to provide clear explanations of technical terms.

All of the changes we made to this book since the last edition were done with one focus—to improve its educational value for *you, the student*. We want you to feel that you got your money's worth in buying this book. While our editors, and many geology instructors across Canada, offered valuable suggestions on revising this book, it was comments from students (that would be you!) that guided our overall approach. The main student suggestion was to shorten the book, making the text more "to the point" with more focus on fundamental concepts and less space taken up with details of non-essential issues. This fourth edition, shorter and more concise than its predecessors, is as much a product of your input as it is of our commitment to producing the best introductory geology text we can offer.

Another suggestion was to discuss geology in a way that is more relevant to students than what typically exists in textbooks, and preferably relating to popular culture. In response we offer special-interest boxes entitled Geology and Popular Media that focus on the portrayal of geology in Hollywood movies. We hope they will interest and entertain you without adding too much reading.

So here we go. Make sure to buckle up, as we will travel from the top of the atmosphere to Earth's core and from the highest mountains to the ocean floor. We will encounter processes operating from the subatomic level to those affecting our entire planet; and we will witness the development of Earth, from the time of its birth about 4.6 billion years ago to the present. We hope this trip will heighten your awareness about how we, as humans, fit into this complex system of rock, gases, water, life, and energy—how Earth provides resources we depend on, and how our use of these resources affects our planet. Above all, we hope you enjoy this journey of learning.

Sincerely, your authors,
Cam Tsujita and S. R. Hicock

Earth is a very small part of a vast universe. It is but one small planet orbiting a middle-aged, average-sized star (among billions of others), in one of an estimated 400 billion galaxies. But as the old saying goes, "good things come in small packages." In spite of being unremarkable in many ways, Earth stands out as being the only planet known to host complex life. Earth, the "Goldilocks planet" of our solar system, has just the right combination of conditions and ingredients necessary to support biologic activity: not too hot, not too cold; not too wet, not too dry; and so forth. The science of geology serves as the foundation for understanding how Earth formed, how it developed, how it works, and how we, as complex life forms, relate to the processes that have rendered Earth a unique, life-sustaining planet.

Media reports are constant reminders that our planet is highly dynamic, and since the publication of the third Canadian edition of *Earth* in 2012, the world has witnessed many examples of Earth's powerful forces. In 2013 alone, spectacular displays of volcanic activity were reported from Italy (Mt. Etna), Indonesia (Kelimutu), Kamchatka (Tolbachik), and Japan (Sakurajima).

Between 2012 and 2013, the world also witnessed the tragic devastation caused by natural disasters such as earthquakes in Iran (August 2012), Guatemala/Mexico (December 2012), and Santa Cruz Islands in the South Pacific (February 2013); floods in India, Bangladesh, Nigeria, and Philippines (August 2012), and Australia (January 2013); and landslides in Colombia and Kenya (December 2012) and Philippines (March 2013). All of these events caught human populations off guard. In order to be better prepared for such events, we must gain an awareness of their underlying causes and their frequency of occurrence over long periods of time. Geology can aid in the understanding of where, why, and how natural disasters occur, and how we can lessen their impact on human populations through long-range planning.

Impacts of human activities on Earth's environment have also remained in the public eye since the last edition. Environmental issues and disasters related to our use of Earth's resources, such as global warming, climate change, and the frequency of extreme weather events, continue to intensify. Geology is important in this context because it yields clues to help us understand, prevent, and repair environmental problems. Just as an auto mechanic must have a good working knowledge of the interactions among the parts in a car in order to fix it, knowledge of our planet is critical to our well-being and is, indeed, vital to our survival.

The primary function of this fourth Canadian edition is to serve as a meaningful, non-technical, up-to-date primer for college and university students taking their first course in geology. A main goal of *Earth* is to complement and reinforce the basic geologic principles and concepts learned in class.

DISTINGUISHING FEATURES

Readability

The language of the book is straightforward and written so it can be understood by the layperson. Clear, readable discussions with a minimum of technical language are the rule. Frequent headings and subheadings help students follow discussions and identify the important ideas presented in each chapter. Large portions of the text were rewritten line-by-line or deleted in an effort to make the material more concise, more understandable, and more relevant to a Canadian audience.

Illustrations and Photographs

Geology is a highly visual science. Therefore, photographs and artwork are essential to an introductory book. *Earth* contains hundreds of photographs, of which many are new to this fourth edition. These have been carefully selected to aid understanding, add relevance and tangibility, and, where possible, infuse geologic concepts with a Canadian perspective. The illustrations in *Earth* are renowned for their quality. This edition features a selection of SmartFigures, which are described below, as well as some new or redesigned line art by Cam Tsujita that illustrate concepts more clearly and realistically than ever before.

Focus on Learning

When a chapter has been completed, three useful devices help students review: Chapter Summary, Review Questions, and a Glossary in MasteringGeology (www.masteringgeology.com) to clarify the spelling and meaning of common terms.

Special Interest Boxes

At appropriate places throughout the book, special interest boxes with icons appear relating to five themes: Earth as a System, People and the Environment, Canadian Profile, Understanding Earth, and Geology and Popular Media. These themes and boxes serve as threads that weave through the chapters and help tie them together while enhancing the main text material.

Maintaining a Focus on Basic Principles and Instructor Flexibility

The organization of chapters in this textbook is intended to be a compromise between the traditional approach of covering plate tectonics as a culmination of the understanding of geologic principles, and the more "systems-based" approach where plate tectonics is covered at the beginning of the text. This book's organization accommodates the study of minerals and rocks in the laboratory (which usually comes early in an introductory-level geology course), while exploring how each component fits into the basic idea of plate tectonics. By revisiting plate tectonics after covering the fundamentals (minerals, rocks, time, etc.), we believe that students will have a better appreciation of why plate tectonics is the central paradigm of modern geology.

The book begins with a rudimentary view of geology and a brief glimpse of plate tectonics as a general concept. We then turn to a discussion of Earth materials, from minerals to rocks. Next is the element of time—how time is classified, how Earth materials can be dated, and the sheer immensity of geologic time as revealed in the geologic record. From there, we examine how rocks are deformed and the dynamic nature of Earth's surface and interior as observed in earthquakes. We then examine the ocean floor and the mechanisms that move tectonic plates. Following that, we revisit plate tectonics in greater detail, when students are ready to appreciate how the "little pictures" fit into the "big picture."

Next the book turns its focus to Earth's surficial processes, including mass wasting, streams, groundwater, glaciation, wind, and waves and currents. Because these processes are gravity-driven (i.e., influenced by elevation and topography changes caused by plate tectonics), these topics are intentionally covered after plate tectonics.

Finally, we discuss mineral and energy resources from the viewpoints of resource use and value, and in the context of the environment. Because resource exploration is often viewed as the "bottom line" of geology, we felt it appropriate to cover that topic in the final chapter—from a uniquely Canadian perspective.

NEW TO THE FOURTH CANADIAN EDITION

Major changes to this edition are listed below.

New Concise Approach

- There is a greater focus on the fundamental principles of geology.

- The length of the book has been substantially reduced, enhancing readability and reducing paper use.
- Concise definitions and streamlined explanations have been increased to improve readability and comprehension.

New Examples and Explanations

- There are now more Canadian examples and better photographs to emphasize the relevance of concepts to Canadian students.
- Coverage of headlining events of geologic and environmental significance has been updated, including eruptions of Java's Mount Merapi and under Iceland's Eyjafjallajökull ice cap (Chapter 4), the devastating earthquake and tsunami in Japan (Chapter 10), new solar farms in Ontario, and the status of tidal turbines in the Bay of Fundy (Chapter 20)—all of which occurred since the third edition came out.

New and Improved Pedagogy

- **SmartFigures—Art That Teaches:** Inside every chapter are a number of SmartFigures. Just use your smartphone to scan the QR code next to such a figure, and the art comes alive! Prepared and narrated by Professor Callan Bentley, each three- to four-minute feature is a mini-lesson that examines and explains the concepts illustrated by the figure. It is truly art that teaches. For those without smartphones, SmartFigures are also available via www.masteringgeology.com and the eText.
- Also included are improved custom graphics by Cam Tsujita that help students visualize concepts described in the text.

Integration with Web-Based Activities and Animations

- **MasteringGeology** (www.masteringgeology.com) contains two sets of web-based activities and animations: GEODe: Earth; and Geoscience Animations to add a dynamic aspect to learning.
- **GEODe: Earth** is a dynamic program that reinforces key concepts with animations, tutorials, and interactive exercises.
- **Geoscience Animations** include over 60 animations to visualize key geologic processes.
- All GEODe: Earth activities and Geoscience Animations, organized by chapter, are listed on MasteringGeology.

THE TEACHING AND LEARNING PACKAGE

A comprehensive traditional and new supplements package accompanies the book and uses electronic media.

MasteringGeology

Each new copy of *Earth*, fourth Canadian edition, comes with a Student Access Code for MasteringGeology. MasteringGeology delivers engaging, dynamic learning opportunities—focused on course objectives and responsive to each student's progress—that are proven to help students absorb course material and understand difficult concepts.

- MasteringGeology provides a rich and flexible set of course materials to get instructors started quickly.

- MasteringGeology provides quick and easy access to information on student performance against learning outcomes. Instructors can quickly add their own learning outcomes to track student performance.

- The Mastering Geology gradebook and diagnostic tools capture the step-by-step work of every student, providing unique insight into class performance.

- Assignable items include the following:

  - **SmartFigures** bring key chapter illustrations to life! Found throughout the book, SmartFigures are sophisticated, annotated illustrations that are also narrated videos. The SmartFigure videos are accessible on mobile devices via scannable QuickResponse (QR) codes printed in the text and through the Study Area in MasteringGeology.

  - **GigaPan® Activities** take advantage of the GigaPan high-resolution panoramic picture technology developed by Carnegie Mellon University in conjunction with NASA. Photos and accompanying questions correlate with concepts in the student book.

  - **Encounter Earth Activities** provide interactive exploration of geology concepts using Google Earth™. Students work through the activities in Google Earth and then test their knowledge by answering the assessment questions, which include hints and specific wrong-answer feedback.

  - **Animation Activities** illuminate the most difficult-to-understand topics in geology. The animation activities include audio narration, a text transcript, and assignable multiple-choice questions with specific wrong-answer feedback.

  - **GeoTutor Activities** consist of sophisticated, high-impact visuals that ask students to demonstrate their knowledge by synthesizing and analyzing core concepts using higher-order thinking skills.

  - Concept Check questions, Give It Some Thought questions, Reading questions, and Test Bank questions are also included.

- MasteringGeology includes a Study Area for students to access all of their study resources. The Study Area includes geoscience animations, GEODe activities, *In the News* RSS feeds, Self-Study Quizzes, Weblinks, Glossary, Flashcards, and an optional Pearson eText.

See www.masteringgeology.com

CourseSmart

CourseSmart goes beyond traditional expectations—providing instant, online access to the textbooks and course materials you need at a lower cost for students. And even as students save money, you can save time and hassle with a digital eTextbook that allows you to search for the most relevant content at the very moment you need it. Whether it's evaluating textbooks or creating lecture notes to help students with difficult concepts, CourseSmart can make life a little easier. See how when you visit www.coursesmart.com/instructors.

Pearson eText

Pearson eText gives students access to the text whenever and wherever they have access to the internet. eText pages look exactly like the printed text, offering powerful new functionality for students and instructors. Users can create notes, highlight text in different colours, create bookmarks, zoom, click hyperlinked words and phrases to view definitions, and view in single-page or two-page view. Pearson eText allows for quick navigation to key parts of the eText using a table of contents and provides full-text search. The eText may also offer links to associated media files, enabling users to access videos, animations, or other activities as they read the text.

INSTRUCTOR'S RESOURCES

The authors and publisher have been pleased to work with a number of talented people who produced an excellent supplements package, which can be downloaded from the Pearson Canada catalogue.

Instructor's Manual

The Instructor's Manual has been designed to help seasoned and new professors alike, offering in each chapter an introduction to the chapter, outline, learning objectives/focus on concepts, and answers to review questions and suggested quiz questions.

Test Bank

This extensive test bank contains multiple-choice, true/false, and short-answer questions, a selection of which you can link to actual figures and photos from the text. This is available as a Word File and as a TestGen ® computerized test generator.

PowerPoint® Presentations

These presentations average 40 slides per chapter, consisting of customizable lecture outlines with supporting art.

Image Library

All the photos, art, and tables from the text, in order, loaded into PowerPoint slides.

The Geoscience Animation Library

This library includes animations that illuminate many difficult-to-visualize topics of physical geology. Created through a unique collaboration among five of Pearson's leading geoscience authors, these animations represent a significant leap forward in lecture presentation aids.

Pearson Custom Library

For enrolments of at least 25 students, you can create your own textbook by choosing the chapters that best suit your own course needs. To begin building your custom text, visit www.pearsoncustomlibrary.com. You may also work with a dedicated Pearson Custom editor to create your ideal text—publishing your own original content or mixing and matching Pearson content. Contact your local Pearson Representative to get started.

peerScholar

Firmly grounded in published research, peerScholar is a powerful online pedagogical tool that helps develop your students' critical and creative thinking skills. peerScholar facilitates this through the process of creation, evaluation, and reflection. Working in stages, students begin by submitting a written assignment. peerScholar then circulates their work for others to review, a process that can be anonymous or not depending on your preference. Students receive peer feedback and evaluations immediately, reinforcing their learning and driving the development of higher-order thinking skills. Students can then re-submit revised work, again depending on your preference. Contact your Pearson Representative to learn more about peerScholar and the research behind it.

Technology Specialists

Pearson's technology specialists work with faculty and campus course designers to ensure that Pearson technology products, assessment tools, and online course materials are tailored to meet your specific needs. This highly qualified team is dedicated to helping schools take full advantage of a wide range of educational resources, by assisting in the integration of a variety of instructional materials and media formats. Your local Pearson Education sales representative can provide you with more details on this service program.

ACKNOWLEDGEMENTS

Revising a textbook is a mammoth task that demands input from many talented individuals. It is largely due to the consistently superior work of the publishing team at Pearson Canada that we enthusiastically accepted the challenge of co-authoring this fourth Canadian edition of *Earth*.

We are indebted to many friends and colleagues who generously contributed material and reviews to various editions of *Earth*; such enthusiasm for this project is a testament to the dedication of Canadian geologists in promoting geo-literacy in this country. Above all, we tip our hats to our students, whose insightful questions and comments ultimately improve how we teach.

Many colleagues unselfishly contributed material for the Canadian Profile boxes. Thanks are extended especially to Claudia Cochrane, Matt Devereux, David Eaton, John Gosse, Brian Hart, Richard Léveillé, Mike Powell, Rob Schincariol, Gordon Southam, Vic Tyrer, Gordon Winder, and Grant Young.

Several colleagues and other individuals were also very generous in providing photographs for all Canadian editions of *Earth*, and in many cases allowed us to use multiple images from their personal collections. We thank all who donated their images for the greater cause of enhancing the tangibility of concepts discussed in this book.

Special thanks go to those colleagues who prepared in-depth reviews for the fourth Canadian edition of *Earth*. Their critical comments and thoughtful input helped guide our work and strengthen the text, even in the smallest details. We wish to thank the following reviewers:

Mary-Helen Armour, York University
Mary Lou Bevier, University of British Columbia
Luke Copland, University of Ottawa
Jaroslav Dostal, Saint Mary's University
Cliff Shaw, University of New Brunswick
Attila M. Zsaki, Concordia University

We would also like to acknowledge the publishing team at Pearson Canada. Many thanks are due to Cathleen Sullivan, acquisitions editor, who brought us on board; and Paul Donnelly, our developmental editor, who patiently coordinated this project. We also thank the production team, led by Kimberly Blakey; copyeditor Sally Glover; proofreader Colleen Ste. Marie; permissions researcher Marnie Lamb; and technical reviewer Philip Giles for their outstanding work. The professionalism and high standard for detail that you have all demonstrated during the production of this book is deeply appreciated. Thanks also to editorial director Gary Bennett for having steadfast faith in us and the value of this product.

Cam extends his heartfelt thanks to his father (James Tsujita), mother (Lilly Tsujita), sister (Kimberly Kaszas), and brother-in-law (George Kaszas), who have provided unwavering support throughout his academic career. Special thanks to Cam's wife, Erica Tsujita, and his three sons, Jeremy, Casey, and Warner, who persevered through his long work hours during the preparation of this textbook. Cam also thanks all the students who inspired the work in this textbook.

Steve gives heartfelt thanks to his wife, Fran, for her patience and understanding when work on the textbook meant spending evenings and weekends away from home.

Cam Tsujita and Steve Hicock

AN INTRODUCTION TO GEOLOGY AND PLATE TECTONICS

1

The glacier-capped peaks of the Canadian Rocky Mountains attest to the geologic processes that have shaped the Canadian landscape. (Photo by vlad_g/Fotolia)

The spectacular eruption of a volcano, the terror caused by an earthquake, the magnificent scenery of a mountain valley, and the destruction created by a landslide* are all subjects for the **geologist** (Figure 1.1). The study of geology deals with many fascinating and practical questions about our physical environment. What forces produce mountains? Will there soon be a great earthquake on the Canadian west coast? What was the Ice Age like? Will there be another? How are ore deposits formed? Should we look for water here? Is strip mining practical in this area? Where is the best place to drill the next oil well?

THE SCIENCE OF GEOLOGY

The subject of this text is **geology**, from the Greek *geo*, "Earth," and *logos*, "discourse." It is the science that pursues an understanding of planet Earth. Geology is traditionally divided into two broad areas—physical and historical. **Physical geology**, the primary focus of this book, examines the materials composing Earth to gain an understanding of the many processes that operate both on and beneath its surface. The aim of **historical geology**, conversely, is to understand the origin of Earth and its development through time. Thus, it strives to establish an orderly, chronologic arrangement of the multitude of physical and biologic changes that have occurred in the geologic past.

It is challenging to understand Earth because our planet is a dynamic body with many interacting parts and a complex history. Throughout its long existence, Earth has been changing and will continue to do so in the future. Sometimes the changes are rapid and violent, as when earthquakes or volcanic eruptions occur. Conversely, change can take place so slowly that it goes unnoticed during a lifetime. Scales of size and space also vary greatly among the phenomena that geologists study. Sometimes they must focus on phenomena that are submicroscopic, and at other times they must deal with features that are continental or global in scale.

A great deal of geology is based on observations and experiments conducted outdoors in the field. Typically, this information comes from **outcrops** (e.g., Figure 1.1), where bedrock is exposed at the surface. But geology is also done in the laboratory, where, for example, the study of various Earth materials provides insights into many basic processes. Frequently, geology requires an application of knowledge from physics, mathematics, chemistry, and biology. Geology is a science that seeks to expand our knowledge of the natural world and our place in it. This basic philosophy has endured since the time of the pioneers of geology, including knighted Canadian geologist Sir William Logan (Box 1.1). Finally, geology is applied by mining and energy companies that are vital to Canada's economy and that provide well-paying jobs to Canadian geology students.

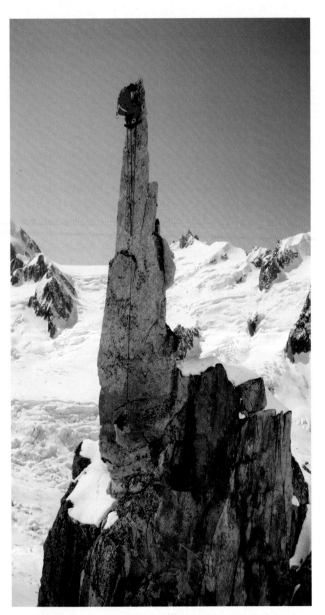

Figure 1.1 These sharp peaks in the French Alps are being sculpted by alpine glaciers. Geologists study the processes that create and modify these mountains. (Photo by St. Clair Renard, Felix/Getty Images)

Throughout this book, the term landslide *is used informally, in a general sense, to describe various gravity-driven slope processes that are classified in Chapter 14.*

CANADIAN PROFILE
Sir William Logan: Canada's Premier Geologist

by C. Gordon Winder*

In a 1998 list of the 100 most important Canadians in history, a geologist was cited as the number-one scientist. William Edmond Logan (1798–1875) was born in Montreal, the third child and second son of Scottish immigrants (see Figure 1.A). His education started in Montreal and finished in Edinburgh. In 1816, he registered for medicine at the University of Edinburgh and completed the first year. He had the highest mark in his geometry class of 200 students and was awarded a brass octant, engraved with his name.

In 1817, Logan started working in London for his uncle, a commodity broker. He travelled to Northern Ireland, Paris, Spain (to view copper deposits), and Rome, where his diary records types of building stone. He was reading the available geology books and continued with lessons in geometry, languages, painting, and the flute.

In 1830, Logan's uncle purchased a copper smelter at Swansea, Wales, and Logan was appointed business manager. Coal was mined around Swansea, but the supply was sporadic. Logan started mapping the area's geology. He used precise surveying instruments and his map proved to be so superior that the British Geological Survey adopted it as its official map. On the basis of upright petrified tree trunks and stumps in the strata, he proposed a theory for the origin of coal, a theory that is still valid today.

In the early 1840s, the Government of Canada decided to establish a geologic survey. Logan applied for the directorship, was appointed on April 20, 1842, and was headquartered in Montreal. In 1843, he measured the rocks with coal at Joggins, Nova Scotia. In 1844, he examined the Gaspé Peninsula, looking for coal. His collections of rock chips and fossils were wrapped in paper; he counted paces and used a Rochon micrometer to measure distance, a compass for direction, and mercury barometers for elevation; he recorded his observations in leather-bound notebooks during the evenings beside a campfire.

His accommodation was a blanket thrown over saplings, and he was assisted by Aboriginal people, who moved the camp and constructed birchbark canoes. He ate salt pork, sea biscuits, berries, fish, birds, and wild game, and drank tea with sugar. On one occasion, local people, puzzled by this aimlessly wandering mumbler, attempted to deliver him to an insane asylum.

In subsequent years, Logan traversed the Ottawa River to Lake Temiskaming, surveyed the areas around Lake Superior and Lake Huron for copper and iron deposits, and studied the complex geology of the Quebec Eastern Townships, where copper deposits were being explored. No coal deposit was ever discovered.

Logan trained his assistants himself. Alexander Murray was a retired naval officer who mapped southern Ontario (including the Petrolia oil fields) and later the area north of Lake Huron. Sterry Hunt was a university-trained chemist who analyzed rocks, minerals, and water. Elkanah Billings, a lawyer and amateur paleontologist, identified fossils. Logan had two mapmakers and a handyman, who was once mistaken for the survey director in his elegant clothes. The director, commonly dressed in field clothes, looked more like a handyman.

Logan drew attention to Canada's potential mineral wealth at international exhibitions in London (1851) and Paris (1855). The Canadian rock and mineral specimens were the largest and most spectacular at the exhibitions. In January 1856, he was knighted by Queen Victoria and was

Figure 1.A   Sir William Logan.
(Photo reproduced with the permission of Library and Archives Canada)

the first individual born in Canada to be so honoured. He received numerous other awards in his lifetime.

As the Geological Survey director, Logan did administrative work, including writing field reports, doing cost accounting, answering letters (including some from swindlers), and sending requests to the government for funds. Occasionally, the government reduced the funding; Logan, convinced the Geological Survey was essential, paid the additional costs with his own money. Logan wrote the four copies of all reports, scientific and administrative, by hand. He worked day and night in the Survey office and had a folding chair that, with blankets, served as a bed—though some people wondered if he ever slept. His worn-out field boots lined the walls.

In 1863, a 983-page text, *Geology of Canada*, was published and contained a small atlas with a coloured geologic map of Canada, including parts of Newfoundland, the Maritime provinces, the adjacent areas of the United States, and areas west of Lake Superior. In 1869, a large-scale map was published; all copies were hand-coloured, probably by Logan, which contributed to his eye strain.

On November 30, 1869, Logan retired as the Geological Survey director and went to Llechryd, Wales, to live with his sister Eliza. Each summer he returned to the Eastern Townships to examine the complex geology. He died in Wales on June 22, 1875, and is buried in the Anglican churchyard at Cilgerran, Wales. His name was given to Canada's highest mountain, Mount Logan (5959 metres), located in the southwest corner of Yukon.

*"Sir William Logan" by C. Gordon Winder. C. Gordon Winder is a professor emeritus in the Department of Earth Sciences at Western University.

Geology, People, and the Environment

The primary focus of this book is to help you develop an understanding of basic geologic principles, but along the way, we will explore numerous important relationships between people and the natural environment. Many of the problems and issues addressed by geology are of practical value.

Natural hazards are a part of living on Earth. On any given day they adversely affect millions of people worldwide and are responsible for staggering damage. Among the hazardous Earth processes studied by geologists are volcanoes, floods (e.g., Figure 1.2), earthquakes, landslides, and tsunamis. Of course, geologic hazards are simply *natural* processes; they become hazards only when people try to live where these processes occur (Figure 1.3).

Resources represent another important focus of geology and include water and soil, a great variety of metallic and nonmetallic minerals, and energy. Together, they form the very foundation of modern civilization. Geology deals not only with the formation and occurrence of these vital resources but also with maintaining their supplies and the environmental impact of their extraction and use.

Complicating all environmental issues is rapid world population growth and most people's aspiration to a better standard of living. This means an increasing demand for resources and a growing

Figure 1.2 Two geologic hazards are represented in this image. On June 21, 2013 following heavy rain the Bow River overflowed its banks and flooded downtown Calgary. The floating tree was uprooted by mass wasting of the river bank. (Photo © Rosanne Tackaberry/Alamy)

Figure 1.2 This is an image of Italy's Mt. Vesuvius in September 2000. This major volcano is surrounded by the city of Naples and Bay of Naples. In 79 C.E., Vesuvius explosively erupted, burying the towns of Pompeii and Herculanaeum in volcanic ash. Will it happen again? (False colour image is 40 km wide) (Image courtesy of NASA)

pressure for people to dwell in environments that have significant geologic hazards.

Geologic processes have an impact on people, but we humans can dramatically influence geologic processes as well. For example, river flooding is natural, but the magnitude and frequency of flooding can be changed significantly by human activities, such as clearing forests, building cities, and constructing dams. Unfortunately, natural systems do not always adjust to artificial changes in ways that we can anticipate. Thus, an alteration to the environment that is intended to benefit society often has the opposite effect.

Some Historical Notes about Geology

The nature of Earth—its materials and processes—has been a focus of study for centuries. Writings about such topics as fossils, gems, earthquakes, and volcanoes date back more than 2300 years to the early Greeks, whose primitive ideas survived through the Middle Ages.

CATASTROPHISM In the mid-seventeenth century, James Ussher, Anglican Archbishop of Armagh, Primate of all Ireland, published a major work that had an immediate and a profound influence. A respected scholar of the Bible, Ussher constructed a chronology of human and Earth history in which he determined that Earth was only a few thousand years old, having been created in 4004 BCE. Ussher's treatise earned widespread acceptance among Europe's scientific and religious leaders, and his chronology was soon printed in the margins of the Bible itself.

During the seventeenth and eighteenth centuries the doctrine of **catastrophism** strongly influenced people's thinking about Earth. Briefly stated, catastrophists believed that Earth's landscapes had been shaped primarily by great catastrophes. Features such as mountains and canyons, which today we know take long periods to form, were explained as having been produced by sudden and often worldwide disasters produced by unknown causes that no longer operate. This philosophy was an attempt to force-fit the rates of Earth processes to the then-current ideas on the age of Earth.

UNIFORMITARIANISM Modern geology began in the late eighteenth century when James Hutton, a Scottish physician and gentleman farmer, published his *Theory of the Earth*. In this work, Hutton put forth a fundamental principle that is a pillar of geology today: **uniformitarianism**. It states that the *physical, chemical, and biologic laws that operate today have also operated in the geologic past.** This means that the forces and processes that we observe presently shaping our planet have been at work for a very long time. This idea is summarized in the statement "the present is the key to the past."

---

*From James Hutton, Theory of the Earth, Transactions of the Royal Society of Edinburgh, 1788.

Before Hutton's *Theory of the Earth*, no one had effectively demonstrated that geologic processes occur over extremely long intervals. However, Hutton persuasively argued that forces that appear small could, over long spans, produce effects that were just as great as those resulting from sudden catastrophic events. Unlike his predecessors, Hutton carefully cited verifiable observations to support his ideas.

For example, when he argued that mountains are sculpted and ultimately destroyed by weathering and the work of running water, and that their wastes are carried to the oceans by processes that can be observed, Hutton said, "We have a chain of facts which clearly demonstrates . . . that the materials of the wasted mountains have travelled through the rivers . . . There is not one step in all this progress . . . that is not to be actually perceived." He then went on to summarize this thought by asking a question and immediately providing the answer: "What more can we require? Nothing but time."*

Today the basic tenets of uniformitarianism are just as viable as in Hutton's day. Indeed, we realize more strongly than ever that the present gives us insight into the past and that the physical, chemical,

---

*From James Hutton, Theory of the Earth, Transactions of the Royal Society of Edinburgh, 1788.

and biologic laws that govern geologic processes remain unchanging through time. However, to say that geologic processes in the past were the same as those occurring today is not to suggest that they always had the same relative importance or that they operated at precisely the same rate. Moreover, some important geologic processes are not currently observable, but evidence that they occur is well established. For example, we know that Earth has experienced impacts from large meteorites even though we have no human witnesses. Such events altered Earth's crust, modified its climate, and strongly influenced life on the planet.

The acceptance of uniformitarianism meant understanding that Earth is very old. Although Earth processes vary in intensity, they still take a long time to create or destroy major landscape features (Figure 1.4).

For example, geologists have established that mountains once existed in portions of the present-day Maritimes and Canadian Shield. Today these regions consist of low hills and plains. Erosion (processes that wear land away) gradually destroyed those peaks. Estimates indicate that the North American continent is being lowered at a rate of about three centimetres per 1000 years. At this rate it will take 100 million years for water, wind, and ice to lower mountains that are 3000 metres high.

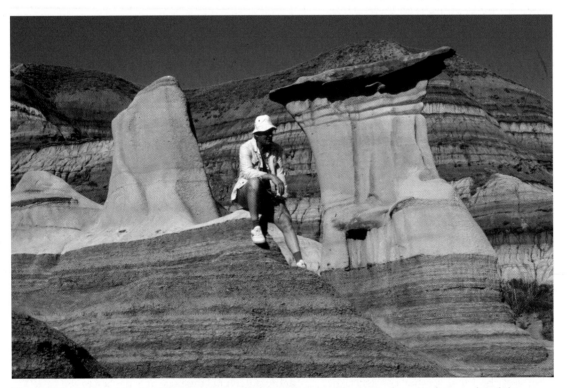

Figure 1.4 Geologist Dr. Gerd Westermann contemplates how weathering and erosion have sculpted the spectacular hoodoos of the Drumheller area in southern Alberta. Some geologic processes act so slowly that changes may not be visible during an entire human lifetime.
(Photo by C. Tsujita)

But even 100 million years is a relatively short span on the time scale of Earth history, for the rock record contains evidence that shows Earth has experienced many cycles of mountain building and erosion. Concerning the ever-changing nature of Earth through great expanses of geologic time, Hutton made a statement that was to become his most famous. In concluding his classic 1788 paper published in the *Transactions of the Royal Society of Edinburgh*, he stated, "The results, therefore, of our present enquiry is, that we find no vestige of a beginning—no prospect of an end."*

In the chapters that follow, we will be examining the materials that compose our planet and the processes that modify it. It is important to remember that although many features of our physical landscape may seem to be unchanging over the decades we observe them, they are nevertheless changing, but on time scales of hundreds, thousands, or even many millions of years.

GEOLOGIC TIME

Although Hutton and others recognized that geologic time is exceedingly long, they had no methods to accurately determine the age of Earth. However, in 1896 radioactivity was discovered. The use of radioactivity for dating was first attempted in 1905 and has been undergoing refinement ever since. Geologists are now able to assign fairly accurate dates to events in Earth history.[†]

For example, we know the dinosaurs became extinct about 66 million years ago. Today the age of Earth is estimated at 4.6 billion years.

---

*From James Hutton, Theory of the Earth, Transactions of the Royal Society of Edinburgh, 1788.

[†]*Chapter 8 is devoted to a much more complete discussion of geologic time.*

Relative Dating and the Geologic Time Scale

During the nineteenth century, long before the advent of radiometric dating, a geologic time scale was developed by using principles of relative dating. **Relative dating** means that events are placed in their proper sequence or order without knowing their age in years. This is done by applying such principles as the **law of superposition** (*super* = over, *positum* = to place), which states that in layers of sedimentary rocks or lava flows, the youngest layer is on top and the oldest is on the bottom (assuming that nothing has turned the layers upside down, which sometimes happens; see Chapter 8).

Fossils, the remains or traces of prehistoric life (Figure 1.5), were also essential to the development of the geologic time scale. Fossils are the basis for the **principle of fossil succession**, which states that *fossil organisms succeed one another in a definite and determinable order, and therefore any time span can be recognized by its fossil content*. This principle was laboriously worked out over decades by collecting fossils from countless rock layers around the world. Once established, it allowed geologists to identify rocks of the same age in widely separated places and to build the geologic time scale shown in Figure 1.6.

Notice that units with the same designations do not necessarily extend for the same number of years. For example, the Cambrian Period lasted just over 50 million years, whereas the Silurian Period spanned less than 30 million years. As we will emphasize again in Chapter 8, this situation exists because the basis for establishing the time scale was not the regular rhythm of a clock, but the changing character of life forms through time. Numeric ages were added long after the time scale was established. A glance at Figure 1.6 also reveals that the Phanerozoic

Figure 1.5 A Armoured head region of a primitive Devonian fossil fish from Quebec. **B.** An Ordovician trilobite from the Georgian Bay area of Ontario. (Photo **A** courtesy of Terry Ciotka/Canada Fossils Inc.; photo **B** by Denis Tetreault)

A   B

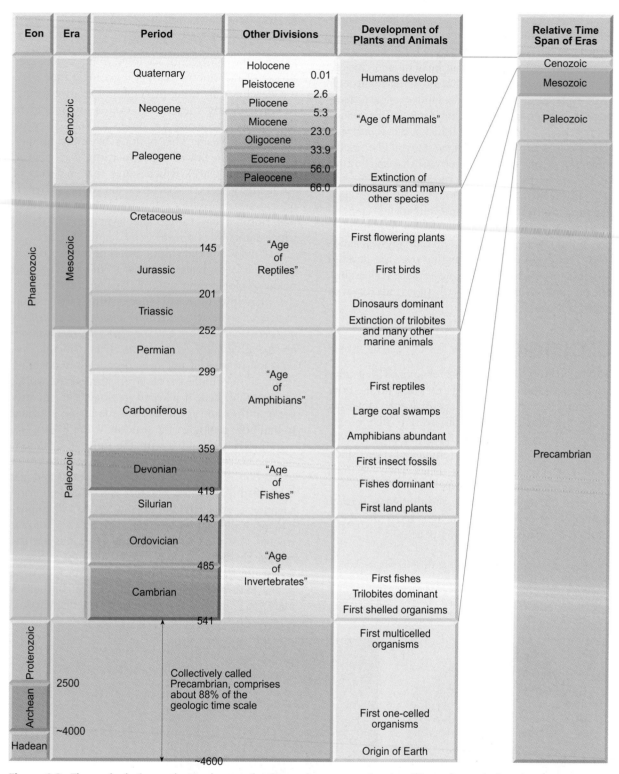

Figure 1.6 The geologic time scale. Numbers on the time scale represent time in millions of years before the present. These ages were added long after the time scale had been established by using relative dating techniques. The Precambrian accounts for more than 88 percent of geologic time.
(Adapted from the International Commission on Stratigraphy. Chart drafted by K. M. Cohen, S. Finney, and P. L. Gibbard.
© International Commission on Stratigraphy, January 2013. By kind permission of the International Union of Global Services.)

Eon is divided into many more units than earlier eons even though it encompasses only about 12 per cent of Earth history. The meagre fossil record for the earlier eons is the primary reason for the lack of detail on this portion of the time scale. Without abundant fossils, geologists lose their primary tool for subdividing geologic time.

The Magnitude of Geologic Time

The concept of geologic time is new to many non-geologists. People are accustomed to dealing with increments of time that are measured in hours, days, weeks, and years. History books commonly examine events over spans of centuries, but even a century is difficult to appreciate fully. For most of us, someone or something that is 90 years old is *very old*, and a 1000-year-old artifact is *ancient*.

By contrast, those who study geology must routinely deal with vast time spans—millions or billions (thousands of millions) of years. When viewed in the context of Earth's 4.6-billion-year history, a geologic event that occurred 100 million years ago may be characterized as "recent" by a geologist, and a rock sample that has been dated at 10 million years may be called "young."

An appreciation for the magnitude of geologic time is important in the study of geology because many processes are so gradual that vast spans of time are needed before significant changes occur.

How long is 4.6 billion years? If you were to begin counting at the rate of one number per second and continued 24 hours a day, seven days a week and never stopped, it would take about two lifetimes (150 years) to reach 4.6 billion!

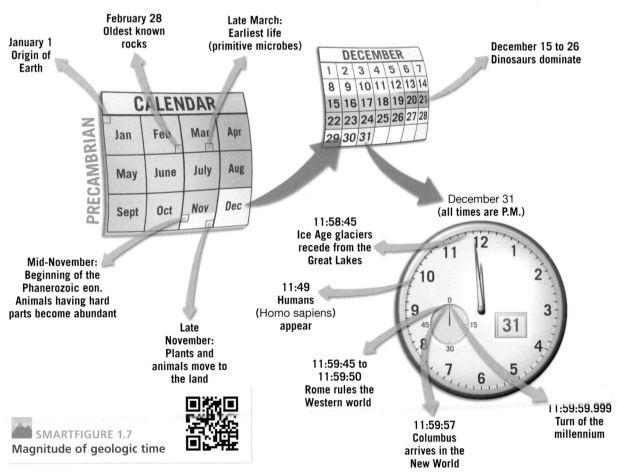

What if we compress the 4.6 billion years of Earth history into a single year?

January 1
Origin of Earth

February 28
Oldest known rocks

Late March:
Earliest life
(primitive microbes)

December 15 to 26
Dinosaurs dominate

December 31
(all times are P.M.)

11:58:45
Ice Age glaciers recede from the Great Lakes

11:49
Humans
(Homo sapiens)
appear

Mid-November:
Beginning of the Phanerozoic eon. Animals having hard parts become abundant

Late November:
Plants and animals move to the land

11:59:45 to 11:59:50
Rome rules the Western world

11:59:57
Columbus arrives in the New World

11:59:59.999
Turn of the millennium

SMARTFIGURE 1.7
Magnitude of geologic time

Figure 1.7 The 4.6 billion years of Earth history squeezed into just one year. (Adapted from J. Clague and R. Turner, *Vancouver, City on the Edge: Living with a Dynamic Geological Landscape*. [Vancouver, BC: Tricouni Press, 2003. Permission from Tricouni Press Ltd.])

As another interesting basis for comparison, we can try to imagine Earth's entire 4.6 billion year history compressed into a single year Figure 1.7. In this context, we would expect the oldest known rocks to form by the end of February, a full two months after Earth's birth date. Earth's first life forms, in the form of simple microbes, would appear near the end of March. It would take nearly eight more months for more complex life forms with hard parts to appear (in mid-November). We might visualize plants and animals living on land by late November, and dinosaurs ruling the land for a brief time from mid- to late December (only to die out by Boxing Day (December 26).

Flash forward to late New Year's Eve, when Humans (*Homo sapiens*) appear 11 minutes before midnight, after which Ice Sheets briefly march across the Canadian landscape, ultimately receding from the Great Lakes at 11:59 pm. Rome ruled the western world for 5 seconds (11:59:45 to 11:59:50), Columbus discovered North America 3 seconds before midnight, and we celebrated the turn of the last millenium a mere second before New Year's Day.

The foregoing is just one of many analogies that have attempted to convey the magnitude of geologic time. Although helpful, all of them—no matter how clever—can only begin to help us comprehend the vast expanse of Earth history and the enormous number of events that have occurred. Nevertheless, now that you have some notion of the evolution of geologic thinking, and of Earth's antiquity, we will briefly review how scientists think our planet came to be and how it is layered, before we peek at the major geologic development of the twentieth century—plate tectonics. Later in the book we present details of plate tectonics, which frames the context in which other topics are discussed.

EARLY EVOLUTION OF EARTH

Recent earthquakes caused by displacements of Earth's **crust** and lava erupted from active volcanoes represent only the latest in a long line of events by which our planet has attained its present form and structure. The geologic processes operating in Earth's interior can be best understood when viewed in the context of much earlier events in Earth's history.

Origin of Planet Earth

According to astronomers, Earth's story began about 13.7 billion years ago with the *Big Bang*, an incomprehensibly large explosion that sent all matter of the universe flying outward at incredible speeds. In time, the debris from this explosion, which was almost entirely hydrogen and helium, began to cool and condense into the first stars and galaxies. It was in one of these galaxies, the Milky Way, that our solar system and planet Earth took form.

Earth, along with other planets, several dozen moons, and numerous smaller bodies, revolves around the Sun. The orderly nature of our solar system leads most researchers to conclude that Earth and the other planets formed at essentially the same time and from the same primordial material as the Sun. The **nebular theory** suggests that the bodies of our solar system evolved from an enormous rotating cloud called the *solar nebula*, composed mostly of hydrogen and helium, with a small percentage of the heavier elements (Figure 1.8).

About 5 billion years ago this huge cloud of gases and minute particles began to gravitationally contract (what triggered the collapse is not known). As this slowly spiralling nebula contracted, it rotated faster and faster for the same reason ice skaters do when they draw their arms toward their bodies. Eventually the inward pull of gravity came into balance with the outward force caused by the rotational motion of the nebula (Figure 1.8). By this time the once vast cloud had assumed a flat disk shape with a large concentration of material at its centre called the *protosun* (pre-Sun).

During the collapse, gravitational energy was converted to thermal energy (heat), causing the temperature of the inner portion of the nebula to dramatically rise. However, the formation of the Sun marked the end of the period of contraction and thus the end of gravitational heating. Temperatures in the region where the inner planets now reside began to decline. The decrease in temperature caused those substances with high melting points to coalesce (join together). Such materials as iron and nickel and the elements of which the rock-forming minerals are composed—silicon, calcium, sodium, and so forth—formed metallic and rocky clumps that orbited the Sun. Repeated collisions caused these fragments to coalesce into larger asteroid-sized bodies, which in a few tens of millions of years accreted into the four inner planets, including Earth. Not all of these clumps of matter were incorporated into the *protoplanets* (pre-planets). Those that remained in orbit are called *asteroids* and *meteoroids*, and become *meteorites* when they survive an impact with Earth.

Formation of Earth's Layered Structure

As material accumulated to form Earth (and for a short period afterward), the high-velocity impact of nebular debris and the decay of radioactive elements

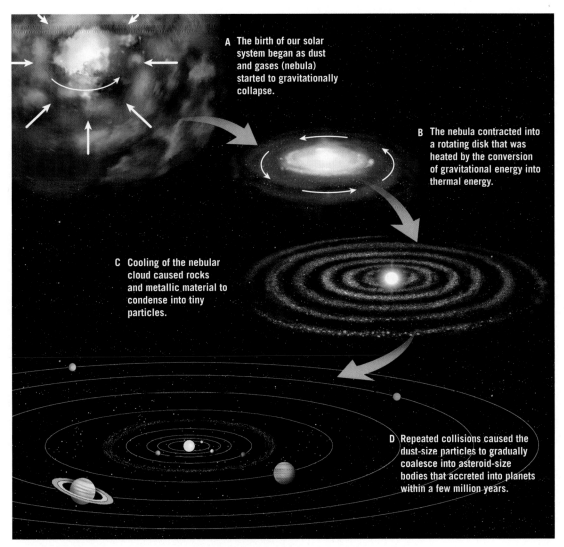

A The birth of our solar system began as dust and gases (nebula) started to gravitationally collapse.

B The nebula contracted into a rotating disk that was heated by the conversion of gravitational energy into thermal energy.

C Cooling of the nebular cloud caused rocks and metallic material to condense into tiny particles.

D Repeated collisions caused the dust-size particles to gradually coalesce into asteroid-size bodies that accreted into planets within a few million years.

Figure 1.8 Nebular theory. **A.** A huge rotating cloud of dust and gases (nebula) begins to contract. **B.** Most of the material is gravitationally swept toward the centre, producing the Sun. However, owing to rotational motion, some dust and gases remain orbiting the central body as a flattened disk. **C.** The planets begin to accrete from the material that is orbiting within the flattened disk. **D.** In time most of the remaining debris collects into the planets and their moons.

SMARTFIGURE 1.8
Nebular theory
Formation of the solar system according to the nebular theory.

caused the temperature of our planet to steadily increase. During this time of intense heating, Earth became hot enough to melt iron and nickel. Melting produced liquid blobs of heavy metal that sank toward the centre of the planet. This process occurred rapidly on the scale of geologic time and produced Earth's dense, iron-rich **core**.

The early episode of heating resulted in another process of chemical differentiation, whereby melting formed buoyant masses of molten material that rose toward the surface, where they solidified to produce a primitive **crust**. These rocky materials were enriched in oxygen and oxygen-seeking elements, particularly silicon and aluminum, along with lesser amounts of calcium, sodium, potassium, iron, and magnesium. In addition, some heavy metals, such as gold, lead, and uranium, which have low melting points or were highly soluble in the ascending molten masses, were scavenged from Earth's interior and concentrated in the developing crust. This early period of chemical segregation established the three basic divisions of Earth's interior: the iron-rich *core*, the thin *primitive crust*, and Earth's largest layer, called the **mantle**, which is located between the core and crust and is also dominated by iron, magnesium, and oxygen-seeking elements.

An important consequence of this early interval of chemical differentiation is that large volumes of gases were allowed to escape from Earth's interior, as happens today during volcanic eruptions. By this process a primitive atmosphere gradually evolved. It was on this planet, with this atmosphere, that life as we know it came into existence. We will elaborate on Earth's interior after we introduce the most important development in geologic thinking in recent times—plate tectonics.

PLATE TECTONICS: A GEOLOGIC PARADIGM

Earth is a dynamic planet! If we could go back in time a few hundred million years, we would find the face of our planet dramatically different from what we see today. There would be no Great Lakes, Rocky Mountains, or prairies. Moreover, we would find continents having different sizes and shapes and located in different positions than today's land masses. In contrast, over the past few billion years, the Moon's surface has remained essentially unchanged—only a few craters have been added.

Within the past several decades a great deal has been learned about the workings of our dynamic planet. This episode has witnessed an unequalled revolution in our understanding of Earth. The revolution began in the early part of the twentieth century with the radical proposal by Alfred Wegener (Figure 1.9) of **continental drift**—the idea that the continents moved about the face of the planet. This proposal contradicted the established view that the continents and ocean basins are permanent and stationary features on the face of Earth. For that reason, the notion of drifting continents was received with great skepticism and even ridicule. More than 50 years passed before enough data were gathered to transform this controversial hypothesis into a **paradigm** (comprehensive theory held with a very high degree of confidence and respect) that wove together the basic processes known to operate on Earth. The paradigm that finally emerged, called **plate tectonics** (*tekton* = to build), provided geologists with the first comprehensive model of Earth's internal workings.*

Thus, the paradigm of plate tectonics did not appear overnight; it evolved gradually over several decades from its first incarnation as continental drift. We'll briefly review Wegener's evidence, then introduce the main components of the plate tectonics paradigm.

Continental Drift: An Idea Before Its Time

The idea that continents, particularly South America and Africa, fit together like pieces of a jigsaw puzzle originated with the development of reasonably

Plate tectonics can be defined as the composite of various ideas explaining the observed motion of Earth's lithosphere through the mechanisms of subduction and sea-floor spreading, which in turn generate Earth's major features, including continents and ocean basins (terms will be explained shortly).

Figure 1.9 Alfred Wegener shown waiting out the 1912–1913 Arctic winter during an expedition to Greenland, where he made a 1200-kilometre traverse across the widest part of the island's ice sheet. (Photo courtesy of bpk, Berlin/Bildarchiv Preussischer/Art Resouce, NY)

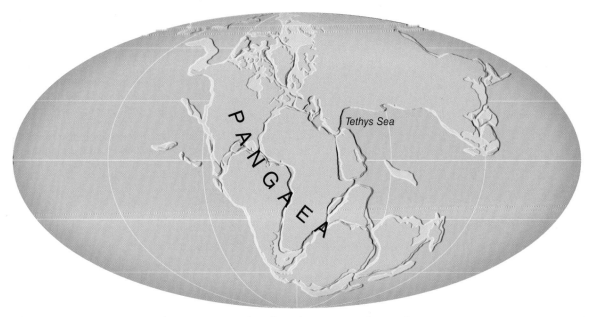

Figure 1.10   Reconstruction of Pangaea as it is thought to have appeared 200 million years ago.

accurate world maps. However, little significance was given to this idea until 1915, when Alfred Wegener, a German meteorologist and geophysicist, published *The Origin of Continents and Oceans*. In this book, Wegener set forth the basic outline of his radical hypothesis of continental drift.

Wegener suggested that a single *supercontinent* called **Pangaea** (*pan* = all, *gaea* = Earth) once existed (Figure 1.10). He further hypothesized that about 200 million years ago this supercontinent began breaking into smaller continents, which then "drifted" to their present positions, based on the following evidence.

FIT OF THE CONTINENTS Like a few others before him, Wegener first suspected that the continents might once have been joined when he noticed the remarkable similarity between the coastlines on opposite sides of the South Atlantic. However, his use of present-day shorelines to make a fit of the continents was challenged immediately by other Earth scientists. These opponents correctly argued that shorelines are continually modified by erosional, depositional, and tectonic processes.

Many years later, a much better approximation of the true outer boundary of the continents was used—the seaward edge of the **continental shelf**, a gently sloping platform of continental material extending from the shore. Today the continental shelf lies submerged, its edge a few hundred metres below sea level. In the early 1960s, Sir Edward Bullard and two associates produced a map that attempted to fit the edges of the continental shelves

of South America and Africa at a depth of 900 metres. The remarkable fit that was obtained is shown in Figure 1.11. Although the continents overlap in a few places, these are regions where streams have deposited large quantities of sediment, thus enlarging the continental shelves.

Figure 1.11   This figure shows the best fit of South America and Africa along the seaward edge of the continental shelf at a depth of about 900 metres. The areas where continental blocks overlap appear in brown. (Adapted from A. G. Smith, "Continental Drift." In *Understanding the Earth*, edited by I. G. Gass, 1972)

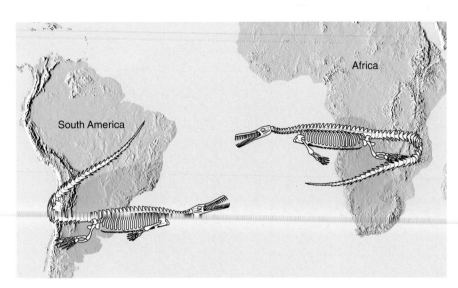

Figure 1.12 Fossils of *Mesosaurus* (their regions of occurrence indicated in green), have been found on both sides of the South Atlantic Ocean and nowhere else in the world. Fossil remains of this and other organisms on the continents of Africa and South America appear to link these land masses during the late Paleozoic Era and early Mesozoic Era.

FOSSIL EVIDENCE To add credibility to his argument for the existence of the supercontinent Pangaea, Wegener cited the distribution of the fossil fern *Glossopteris*. This plant, identified by its large seeds that could not be blown very far, was known to be widely dispersed in Africa, Australia, India, and South America during the late Paleozoic Era. Later, fossil remains of *Glossopteris* were discovered in Antarctica as well. Wegener also learned that these seed ferns and associated flora grew only in a subpolar climate. Therefore, he concluded that the land masses must have been joined, because they are presently located in climatic zones that are far too diverse to support these cold-loving plants. For Wegener, fossils were convincing evidence that a supercontinent had existed.

Wegener also came across an article citing fossil evidence for the existence of a land bridge connecting South America and Africa. Through a search of the literature, Wegener learned that most paleobotanists (scientists who study the fossilized remains of plants) agreed that some type of land connection was needed to explain the existence of identical fossils on widely separated land masses. This requirement was particularly true for late Paleozoic and early Mesozoic life forms.

Wegener cited documented cases of several fossil organisms that had been found on different land masses but that could not have crossed the vast oceans presently separating the continents. The classic example is *Mesosaurus*, a presumably aquatic, snaggle-toothed reptile whose fossil remains are limited to eastern South America and southern Africa (Figure 1.12). If *Mesosaurus* had been able to swim well enough to cross the vast South Atlantic Ocean, its remains should be more widely distributed. As this was not the case, Wegener argued that South America and Africa must have been joined somehow.

How did other scientists during Wegener's era explain the discovery of identical fossil organisms in places separated by thousands of kilometres of open ocean? The idea of land connections was the most widely accepted solution to the problem of migration (Figure 1.13). We know, for example, that during the recent Ice Age, the lowering of sea level allowed animals to cross the narrow Bering Strait between Asia and North America. Was it possible that land bridges once connected Africa and South America? We are now quite certain that land bridges of this magnitude did not exist. If they had, their remnants should still lie below sea level, but they are nowhere to be found.

ROCK TYPE AND STRUCTURAL SIMILARITIES Anyone who has worked a jigsaw puzzle knows that in addition to the pieces fitting together, the picture must be continuous as well. The picture that must match in the continental drift puzzle is one of rock types and mountain belts found on the continents. If the continents were once together, as the supercontinent Pangaea, the rocks found in a particular region on one continent should closely match in age and type with those found in adjacent positions on the adjoining continent.

Such evidence exists in the form of mountain belts that terminate at one coastline, only to reappear on a land mass across the ocean. For instance, the mountain belt that includes the Appalachians trends northeastward through eastern North America and disappears off the coast of Newfoundland and Labrador (Figure 1.14A). Mountains of comparable age and structure are found in the British Isles and Scandinavia. When these land masses are reassembled, as in Figure 1.14B, the mountain chains form a nearly continuous belt.

Figure 1.13 These sketches by John Holden illustrate various explanations for the occurrence of similar species on land masses that are presently separated by vast oceans.
(Reprinted with permission of John Holden)

Wegener was very satisfied that the similarities in rock structure on both sides of the Atlantic linked these land masses. In his own words, "It is just as if we were to refit the torn pieces of a newspaper by matching their edges and then check whether the lines of print run smoothly across. If they do, there is nothing left but to conclude that the pieces were in fact joined in this way."*

*A. Wegener, The Origin of Continents and Oceans. Translated from the 4th revised German edition of 1929 by J. Birman (London: Methuen, 1966).

PALEOCLIMATIC EVIDENCE Because Alfred Wegener was a meteorologist by profession, he was keenly interested in obtaining paleoclimatic (*palaios* = ancient, *climatic* = climate) data in support of continental drift. His efforts were rewarded when he found evidence for apparently dramatic global climatic changes. In particular, he learned of ancient glacial deposits that indicated that near the end of the Paleozoic Era (between 300 million and 220 million years ago), ice sheets covered extensive areas of the Southern Hemisphere. Layers of ancient glacial rock called *tillite*, of the same age,

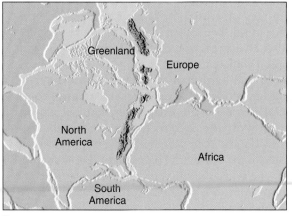

A   B

Figure 1.14 Matching mountain ranges across the North Atlantic. **A.** The Appalachian Mountains trend along the eastern flank of North America and disappear off the coast of Newfoundland and Labrador. Mountains of comparable age and structure are found in the British Isles and Scandinavia. **B.** When these land masses are placed in their pre-drift locations, these ancient mountain chains form a nearly continuous belt. These folded mountain belts formed roughly 300 million years ago as the land masses collided during the formation of the supercontinent of Pangaea.

Figure 1.15 **A.** The supercontinent Pangaea, showing the area covered by glacial ice 300 million years ago. **B.** The continents as they are today. White areas contain evidence of the old ice sheet.

were found in southern Africa and South America, as well as in India and Australia. Below these beds of glacial rock lay striated and grooved rock. In some locations the striations and grooves indicated that the ice had moved from what is now the sea onto land. Much of the land area containing evidence of this late Paleozoic glaciation presently lies within 30 degrees of the equator in a subtropical or tropical climate.

Could Earth have gone through an episode of sufficient cooling to have generated extensive continental ice sheets in what is presently a tropical region? Wegener rejected this explanation because during the late Paleozoic Era, large tropical swamps existed in the Northern Hemisphere. These swamps, with their lush vegetation, eventually became the major coalfields of eastern North America, Europe, and Siberia.

Wegener believed that a more plausible explanation for the late Paleozoic glaciation was provided if the land masses were fitted together as a supercontinent, with South Africa centred over the South Pole (Figure 1.15). This would account for

the conditions necessary to generate extensive expanses of glacial ice over much of the Southern Hemisphere. At the same time, this geography would place today's northern land masses nearer the equator and account for their vast coal deposits. Wegener was so convinced that his explanation was correct that he wrote, "This evidence is so compelling that by comparison all other criteria must take a back seat."

How does a glacier develop in hot, arid Australia? How do land animals migrate across wide expanses of open water? As compelling as this evidence may have been, 50 years passed before most of the scientific community would accept it and the logical conclusions to which it led. Unfortunately Alfred Wegener perished on the Greenland Ice Sheet in 1930 and did not live to see his idea vindicated.

PLANET OF SHIFTING PLATES

According to the plate tectonics model, the **lithosphere**, the "sphere of rock" that consists of the crust and the uppermost (brittle) part of the mantle (see details on pages 21–22), is broken into smaller units called plates. These rigid slabs of lithosphere are mobile and continually change shape and size over time as they interact with other plates. As shown in Figure 1.16, seven major lithospheric plates are recognized. They are the North American, South American, Pacific, African, Eurasian, Australian-Indian, and Antarctic plates. Intermediate-size plates include the Caribbean, Nazca, Philippine, Arabian, Cocos, Juan de Fuca, and Scotia plates. In addition, over a dozen smaller plates not shown in Figure 1.16 have been identified. Note that several large plates include an entire continent plus a large area of sea floor (for example, the South American plate). However, none of the plates are defined entirely by the margins of a single continent.

The lithospheric plates move relative to one another at a very slow but continuous rate that averages about five centimetres a year. This movement is ultimately driven by the unequal distribution of heat within Earth, resulting in mantle **convection** (*con* = with, *vect* = carried). Hot material found deep in the mantle moves slowly upward and serves as one part of our planet's internal convective system. Concurrently, cooler, denser slabs of lithosphere descend back into the mantle, setting Earth's rigid outer shell in motion. Ultimately, the titanic movements of Earth's lithospheric plates generate earthquakes, create volcanoes, and deform large masses of rock into mountains.

Plate Boundaries

Lithospheric plates move as coherent units relative to all other plates. Although the interiors of plates may experience some deformation, all major interactions among individual plates (and therefore most deformation) occurs along their *boundaries*. In fact, the first attempts to outline plate boundaries were made by using the locations of earthquakes. Later work showed that plates are bounded by three distinct types of boundaries, which are distinguished by the type of relative movement they exhibit. These boundaries are depicted at the bottom of Figure 1.16 and briefly described here:

1. At **divergent boundaries**, plates move apart, resulting in upwelling of material from the mantle, perhaps to create new sea floor (Figure 1.16A). Plate spreading (divergence) occurs mainly at a **mid-ocean ridge** (e.g., Mid-Atlantic Ridge, East Pacific Rise) but can also occur under rift valleys on continents. This mechanism has created the floor of the Atlantic Ocean during the past 160 million years and is appropriately called **sea-floor spreading**. Along mid-ocean ridges molten

rock emerges and the oceanic lithosphere is elevated and buoyant because it is hot and occupies more volume than do cooler rocks. Worldwide, this interconnected ridge system extends for more than 70 000 kilometres through all major ocean basins. As new lithosphere is formed along the oceanic ridge, it is slowly yet continually displaced away from the zone of upwelling along the ridge axis. In addition, cooling causes the hot material just below the sea floor to strengthen (become more rigid), thereby adding to the thickness of the plate (oceanic lithosphere in this case). Therefore, as that part of the plate moves farther away from the mid-ocean ridge with sea-floor spreading, it becomes older, cooler, and thicker.

2. In **convergent boundaries**, plates move together, resulting in the descent (consumption) of oceanic lithosphere into the mantle (Figure 1.16B), or two continental margins collide to create a major mountain system (see Chapter 12). Although new lithosphere is continually being added at the oceanic ridges, the planet is not growing in size—its total surface area remains essentially constant. To accommodate the newly created lithosphere, older oceanic plates return to Earth's interior along *convergent boundaries*. As two plates slowly converge, the leading edge of an oceanic slab is bent downward, allowing it to slide beneath the other slab by a process called **subduction**. Plate margins at which oceanic crust is being consumed are called **subduction zones**.

3. In **transform fault boundaries**, plates slide past each other without the production or destruction of lithosphere (Figure 1.16C). These faults form in the direction of plate movement and were first discovered in association with offsets in oceanic ridges by Canadian John Tuzo Wilson. Although most transform faults are located along oceanic ridges, some slice through the continents (e.g., San Andreas Fault, Alpine Fault of New Zealand) and can cause devastating earthquakes.

If you examine Figure 1.16, you can see that each large plate is bounded by a combination of these boundaries. Movement along one boundary requires that adjustments be made at the others.

Now that you have the basic idea of continental drift and plate tectonics, we will leave this topic to examine the internal structure, major spheres, and dominant surface features of our planet. In subsequent chapters we relate topics to plate tectonics, and in Chapter 12 we revisit the paradigm in detail (including paleomagnetic evidence), after gaining more background knowledge of minerals, rocks, dating methods, and internal Earth processes.

Figure 1.16 Mosaic of rigid lithospheric plates that constitute Earth's outer shell. (From W. B. Hamilton, U.S. Geological Survey)

EARTH'S INTERNAL STRUCTURE

The segregation of material that began early in Earth's history resulted in the formation of three layers defined by their chemical composition: the crust, mantle, and core. Earth can also be divided into layers based on physical properties such as whether the layer is solid or liquid and how weak or strong it is (see Chapter 10). Knowledge of both types of layered structures is essential to our understanding of basic geologic processes, such as plate tectonics, volcanism, earthquakes, and mountain building (Figure 1.17).

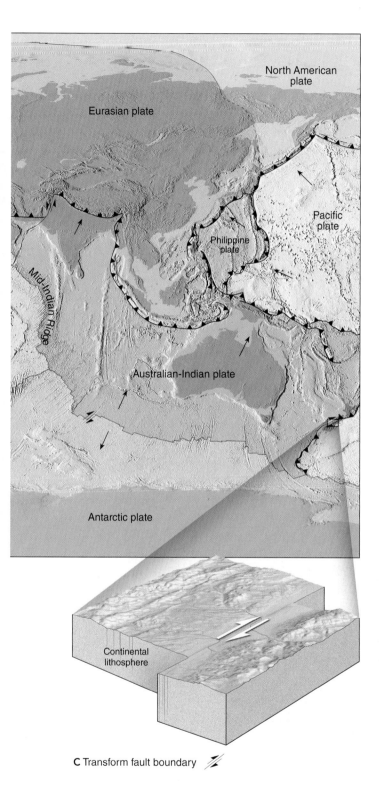

C Transform fault boundary

Continental lithosphere

Layers Defined by Composition

CRUST The crust, Earth's comparatively thin, rocky outer skin, is generally divided into oceanic and continental crust. The oceanic crust averages seven kilometres thick and composed of dark rocks called *basalt* (see Chapter 3). By contrast, the continental crust averages 35 kilometres thick but may exceed 70 kilometres in some mountainous regions. Unlike the oceanic crust, which has a relatively homogeneous chemical composition, the continental crust consists of many rock types. The upper crust has an average composition similar to a rock called *granite* (see Chapter 3), whereas the composition of the lowermost continental crust is more similar to basalt. Continental rocks have an average density of about 2.7 g/cm^3, and some have been discovered in the Canadian Shield that are more than 4 billion years old. The rocks of the oceanic crust are generally younger (180 million years or less) and denser (about 3.0 g/cm^3) than continental rocks.*

MANTLE More than 82 percent of Earth's volume is contained in the mantle, a solid rocky shell that extends to a depth of 2900 kilometres. The boundary between the crust and mantle represents a marked change in chemical composition. The dominant rock type in the uppermost mantle is *peridotite* (see Chapter 3), which has a density of 3.3 g/cm^3. At greater depth peridotite changes by assuming a more compact crystalline structure and hence a greater density.

CORE The composition of the core is thought to be an iron-nickel alloy with minor amounts of oxygen, silicon, and sulphur—elements that readily form compounds with iron. At the extreme pressure found in the core, this iron-rich material has an average density of nearly 11 g/cm^3 and approaches 14 times the density of water at Earth's centre.

Layers Defined by Physical Properties

Earth's interior is characterized by a gradual increase in temperature, pressure, and density with depth. Estimates put the temperature at a depth of 100 kilometres at between 1200°C and 1400°C, whereas the temperature at Earth's centre may exceed 6700°C. Clearly, Earth's interior has retained much of the energy acquired during its formative years, despite the fact that heat is continuously transferred to the surface, where it is lost to space. The increase in pressure with depth causes a corresponding increase in rock density.

The gradual increase in temperature and pressure with depth affects the physical properties and hence the mechanical behaviour of Earth materials. When a substance is heated, its chemical bonds weaken and its mechanical strength (resistance to deformation) is reduced. If the temperature exceeds the melting point of an Earth material, the material's chemical

---

Liquid water at sea level has a density of 1.0 g/cm^3; therefore, the density of basalt is three times that of water.

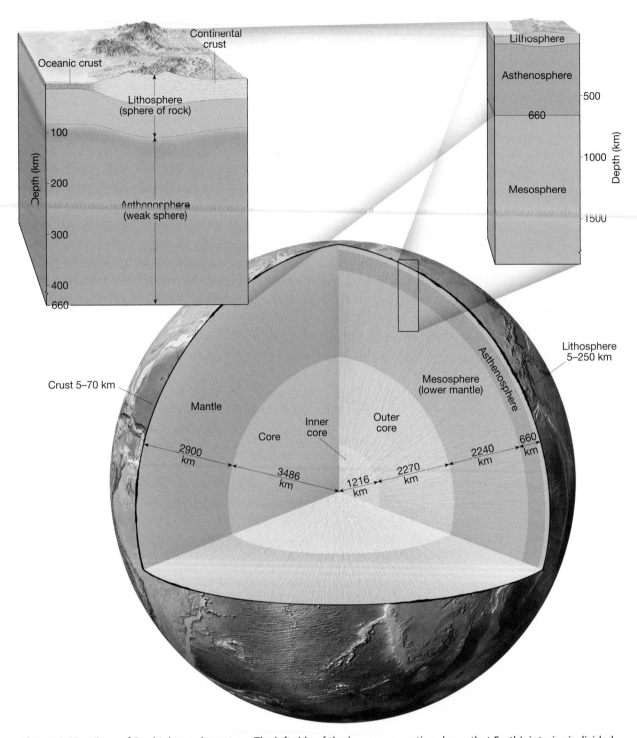

Figure 1.17 Views of Earth's layered structure. The left side of the large cross-section shows that Earth's interior is divided into three different layers based on compositional differences: the crust, mantle, and core. The right side of the large cross-section depicts the five main layers of Earth's interior, based on physical properties and hence mechanical strength: the lithosphere, asthenosphere, mesosphere, outer core, and inner core. The block diagram above the large cross-section shows an enlarged view of the upper portion of Earth's interior.

bonds break and melting ensues. If temperature were the only factor that determined whether a substance melted, our planet would be a molten ball covered with a thin, solid outer shell. However, pressure also increases with depth and tends to increase rock strength. Furthermore, because melting is accompanied by an increase in volume, it occurs at higher temperatures with depth because of greater confining pressure. Thus, depending on the physical environment (temperature and pressure), a particular Earth material may behave like a brittle solid, deform in a puttylike manner, or even melt and become liquid.

Earth can be divided into five main layers based on physical properties and hence mechanical strength: the lithosphere, asthenosphere, mesosphere (lower mantle), outer core, and inner core.

LITHOSPHERE AND ASTHENOSPHERE Earth's outermost layer (the lithosphere) consists of the crust and uppermost mantle and forms a relatively cool, rigid, and brittle shell. Although this layer is composed of materials with markedly different chemical compositions, it tends to act as a unit that exhibits rigid behaviour, mainly because it is cool and thus strong. The lithosphere averages about 100 kilometres in thickness but may be more than 250 kilometres thick below the older portions of the continents (Figure 1.17). Within the ocean basins, the lithosphere is only a few kilometres thick along the oceanic ridges but increases to perhaps 100 kilometres in regions of older and cooler oceanic crust.

Beneath the lithosphere, in the upper mantle (to a depth of about 410 kilometres) lies the soft, comparatively weak **asthenosphere** ("weak sphere"). The top portion of the asthenosphere has a temperature/pressure regime that results in a small amount of melting. Within this very weak zone the lithosphere is mechanically detached from the layer below. The result is that the lithosphere is able to move independently of the asthenosphere.

It is important to emphasize that the strength of various Earth materials is a function of both their composition and the temperature and pressure of their environment. You should not get the idea that the entire lithosphere behaves like a brittle solid similar to rocks found on the surface. Rather, the rocks of the lithosphere get progressively hotter and weaker (more easily deformed) with increasing depth. At the depth of the uppermost asthenosphere, the rocks are close enough to their melting temperatures (some melting may actually occur) that they are very easily deformed. Thus, the uppermost asthenosphere is weak because it is near its melting point, just as hot wax is weaker than cold wax.

MESOSPHERE OR LOWER MANTLE Below the zone of weakness in the uppermost asthenosphere, increased pressure counteracts the effects of higher temperature, and the rocks gradually strengthen with depth. Between the depths of 410 kilometres and 2900 kilometres a more rigid layer is found, called the **mesosphere** (*middle sphere*) or **lower mantle**. Despite their strength, the rocks of the mesosphere are still very hot and capable of very gradual flow, an essential component of the heat transfer mechanism that drives plate tectonics.

INNER AND OUTER CORE The core, which is composed mostly of an iron-nickel alloy, is divided into two regions that exhibit very different mechanical strengths. The **outer core** is a *liquid layer* 2270 kilometres thick. It is the convective flow of metallic iron within this zone that generates Earth's magnetic field (Box 1.2). The **inner core** is a sphere with a radius of 1216 kilometres. Despite its higher temperature, the material in the inner core is stronger (because of immense pressure) than the outer core and behaves like a *solid*.

From the plate tectonics introduction, we can see that Earth's internal processes are intimately connected with what goes on at our planet's surface, which we will look at next.

EARTH'S SPHERES

A view of Earth, such as the one in Figure 1.18A, provided the Apollo 8 astronauts and the rest of humanity with a unique perspective of our home. Seen from space, Earth is breathtaking in its beauty and startling in its solitude. Such an image reminds us that our home is, after all, a planet—small, self-contained, and fragile—and that we, as living beings on this planet, are subject to whatever fate may befall it.

The closer view of Earth in Figure 1.18B reveals it is much more than rock and soil. In fact, the most conspicuous features are not the continents but the swirling clouds suspended above the surface and the vast global ocean. These features emphasize the importance of air and water to our planet and help us appreciate why the physical environment is traditionally divided into three major parts: the water portion of our planet, the hydrosphere; Earth's gaseous envelope, the atmosphere; and, of course, the solid Earth, which geologists call the geosphere.

Earth's surface is characterized by continuous interactions as air comes in contact with rock, rock with water, and water with air. Moreover, the biosphere (plant and animal life) interacts with each of the three physical realms and is an equally integral part of the planet. Thus, Earth can be thought of as consisting of four major spheres: the hydrosphere, atmosphere, biosphere, and geosphere.

The interactions among Earth's four spheres are uncountable. The photo on the cover of this book and Figure 1.19 provide us with examples. The shoreline is an obvious meeting place for rock, water, and air. Ocean waves created by the drag of air moving across open water break against the rocky shore. The force of the water can be powerful and the erosional work that is accomplished can be great.

Hydrosphere

Earth is sometimes called the *blue* planet. Liquid water, more than anything else, makes Earth special. The **hydrosphere** is a dynamic mass of water that is

BOX
1.2   UNDERSTANDING EARTH
Why Does Earth Have a Magnetic Field?

Anyone who has used a compass to find direction knows that Earth's magnetic field has a north pole and a south pole. In many respects our planet's magnetic field resembles that produced by a simple bar magnet. Invisible lines of force pass through Earth and out into space while extending from one pole to the other (Figure 1.B). A compass needle, which is a small magnet free to move about, becomes aligned with these lines of force and points toward the magnetic poles. Note that Earth's magnetic poles do not coincide exactly with the geographic poles. The north magnetic pole is located in northern Canada, in the Arctic Ocean, while the south magnetic pole is located near Antarctica in the Indian Ocean south of Australia.

In the early 1960s, geophysicists learned that Earth's magnetic field periodically (every million years or so) reverses polarity; that is, the north magnetic pole becomes the south magnetic pole, and vice versa. The cause of these reversals is apparently linked to the fact that Earth's magnetic field experiences long-term fluctuations in intensity. Recent calculations indicate that the magnetic field has weakened by about 5 percent over the past century. If this trend continues for another 1500 years, Earth's magnetic field will become very weak or even nonexistent.

It has been suggested that the decline in magnetic intensity is related to changes in the convective flow in the core. In a similar manner, magnetic reversals may be triggered when something disturbs the main convection pattern of the fluid core. After a reversal takes place, the flow is re-established and builds a magnetic field with opposite polarity.

Magnetic reversals are not unique to Earth. The Sun's magnetic field regularly reverses polarity, having an

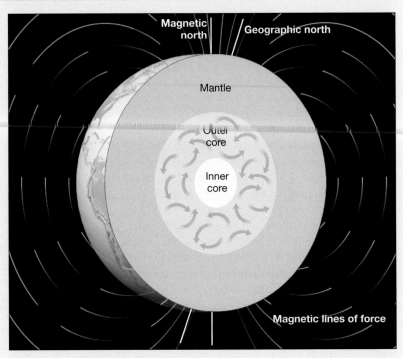

Figure 1.B Earth's magnetic field is thought to be generated by convection of molten iron alloy in the liquid outer core.

average period of about 22 years. These solar reversals are closely tied to the well-known 11-year sunspot cycle.

When Earth's magnetic field was first described in 1600, it was thought to originate from permanently magnetized materials located deep within Earth. We have since learned that except for the upper crust, the planet is much too hot for magnetic materials to retain their magnetism. Furthermore, permanently magnetized materials are not known to vary their intensity in a manner that would account for the observed long-term waxing and waning of Earth's magnetic field.

The details of how Earth's magnetic field is produced are still poorly understood. Nevertheless, most investigators agree that the gradual flow of molten iron in the outer core is important to the process. The most

widely accepted view proposes that the core behaves like a self-sustaining *dynamo*, a device that converts mechanical energy into magnetic energy. The driving forces of this system are Earth's rotation and the unequal distribution of heat in the interior, which propels the highly conductive molten iron in the outer core. As the iron churns in the outer core, it interacts with Earth's magnetic field. This interaction generates an electric current, just as moving a wire past a magnet creates a current in the wire. Once established, the electric current produces a magnetic field that reinforces Earth's magnetic field. As long as the flow within the molten iron outer core continues, electric currents will be produced and Earth's magnetic field will be sustained. This is important not only for navigation, but it also protects us from our Sun's harmful solar wind.

A   B

Figure 1.18 **A.** View that greeted the Apollo 8 astronauts as their spacecraft emerged from behind the Moon. **B.** Africa and Arabia are prominent in this image of Earth taken from Apollo 17. The tan cloud-free zones over the land coincide with major desert regions. The band of clouds across central Africa is associated with a much wetter climate that in places sustains tropical rainforests. The dark blue of the oceans and the swirling cloud patterns remind us of the importance of the oceans and the atmosphere. Antarctica, a continent covered by glacial ice, is visible over the South Pole. (Photos by NASA)

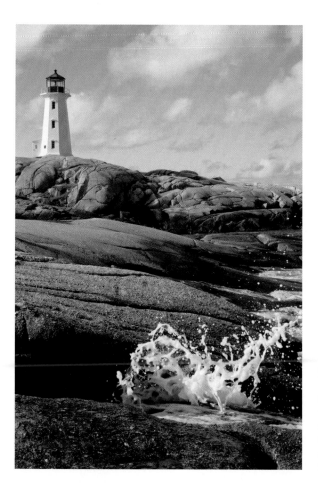

continually on the move, evaporating from the oceans to the atmosphere, precipitating on the land, and returning to the ocean again. The global ocean is certainly the most prominent feature of the hydrosphere (Figure 1.18B), blanketing nearly 71 percent of Earth's surface to an average depth of about 3800 metres. It accounts for about 97 percent of Earth's water. However, the hydrosphere also includes the fresh water found underground and in streams, lakes, and glaciers that are responsible for sculpting and creating many of our planet's varied landforms.

Atmosphere

Earth is surrounded by a life-giving gaseous envelope called the **atmosphere**. Compared with the geosphere, the atmosphere is thin and tenuous (Figure 1.18B). Fifty percent lies below an altitude of 5.6 kilometres, and 90 percent occurs within just 16 kilometres of Earth's surface. By comparison,

Figure 1.19 The shoreline is one obvious meeting place for rock, water, and air. The rocks that dominate this scene were smoothed by ocean waves created by the force of moving air. The calm conditions apparent in this photograph of Peggy's Cove, Nova Scotia, are deceptive, for the force of the water can be powerful during storms, and the erosional work that is accomplished can be great. (Photo © Natalia Bratslavsky/Fotolia)

Earth's lithosphere averages 100 kilometres in thickness! Despite its modest dimensions, this thin blanket of air is a crucial part of the planet. It not only provides the air that we breathe but also protects us from the Sun's intense heat and dangerous ultraviolet radiation. The energy exchanges that continually occur between the atmosphere and Earth's surface and between the atmosphere and space produce the effects we call weather and climate. Without weather and climate there would be no weathering and little erosion of Earth's surface.

Biosphere

The **biosphere** includes all life on Earth. It is concentrated near the surface in a zone that extends from the ocean floor upward for several kilometres into the atmosphere. Plants and animals depend on the physical environment for the basics of life. However, organisms do more than just respond to their physical environment. Through countless interactions, life forms help maintain and alter their physical environment. Without life, the makeup and nature of the geosphere, hydrosphere, and atmosphere would be very different.

Geosphere

Lying beneath the atmosphere and oceans is the geosphere. Much of our study of the geosphere focuses on more accessible surface features that we will briefly examine next before concluding the chapter by considering Earth as a system with a rock cycle.

THE FACE OF EARTH

The two principal divisions of Earth's surface are the continents and the ocean basins (Figure 1.20). A significant difference between these two areas is their relative levels. The average elevation of the continents above sea level is about 840 metres, whereas the average depth of the oceans is about 3800 metres. Thus, the continents stand, on average, 4640 metres above the level of the ocean floor.

Although land and sea meet at the shoreline, this is not the boundary between the continents and the ocean basins; the real boundary is marked by the outer edge of the continental shelf, a gently sloping platform of continental material that extends seaward from the shore. A glance at Figure 1.20 shows that the width of the continental shelf is variable. For example, it is broad along the East and Arctic coasts of North America but relatively narrow along the Pacific margin of the continent.

The boundary between the continents and the deep-ocean basins lies along the **continental slope**, which is a steep drop-off that extends from the outer edge of the continental shelf to the floor of the deep ocean (Figure 1.20). Using this as the dividing line, we find that about 60 percent of Earth's surface is represented by ocean basins, and the remaining 40 percent by continents.

Continents

The most prominent topographic features of the continents are young linear mountain belts located principally in two zones. The circum-Pacific belt (the region surrounding the Pacific Ocean) includes the mountains of the western Americas and continues into the western Pacific in the form of volcanic island arcs. Island arcs are active mountainous regions composed largely of deformed volcanic rocks and include the Aleutian Islands, Japan, the Philippines, and New Guinea.

The other major mountain belt extends eastward from the Alps through Iran and the Himalayas, and then bends southward into Indonesia. Careful examination of mountainous terrains reveals that most are places where thick sequences of rocks have been squeezed and highly deformed as if placed in a gigantic vice.

Older mountain ranges are also found on the continents. Examples include the Appalachians in eastern North America and the Urals in Russia. Their formerly lofty peaks are now worn low, the result of millions of years of erosion. Still older are the stable continental interiors. Within these stable interiors are areas known as **shields**, extensive and relatively flat expanses composed largely of crystalline, granite-like rocks. Radiometric ages of minerals contained in some shield rocks exceed 4 billion years. Even these oldest-known rocks exhibit evidence of enormous forces that have folded and deformed them.

Ocean Basins

The ocean-basin floor has a wide diversity of features, including linear chains of volcanoes, deep canyons, and large plateaus. The topography is nearly as varied as that on the continents.

The ocean basins contain one of the most prominent topographic features on Earth: the oceanic ridge system. Figure 1.20 shows the Mid-Atlantic Ridge and the East Pacific Rise, parts of this system. This broad elevated feature forms a continuous belt that winds for more than 70 000 kilometres around the globe in a manner similar to the seam of a baseball. Rather than consisting of highly deformed rock, such as most of the mountains found on the continents, the oceanic ridge system consists of layer upon layer of volcanic rock that has been fractured and uplifted.

The ocean floor also contains extremely deep depressions that can exceed 11 000 metres below sea level. Although these deep-ocean **trenches** are

Figure 1.20 Major physical features of some continents and ocean basins. The diversity of features on the ocean floor is as great as on the continents.

relatively narrow and represent only a small fraction of the ocean floor, they are very significant features. Some trenches are located adjacent to young mountains that flank the continents. For example, the Peru–Chile Trench off the west coast of South America parallels the Andes Mountains (Figure 1.20). Other trenches parallel linear island chains called volcanic island arcs.

EARTH AS A SYSTEM

As we study Earth, it becomes clear that our planet can be viewed as a dynamic body with many separate but interacting parts or *spheres*. The hydrosphere, atmosphere, biosphere, and geosphere and all of their components can be studied separately. However, the parts are not isolated. Each is related in some way to the others to produce a complex and continuously interacting whole that we call the *Earth system*.

A **system** is a group of interacting, or interdependent, parts that form a complex whole. Most of us hear and use the term frequently. We may service our car's cooling *system*, make use of the city's transportation *system*, and be a participant in the political *system*. A news report might inform us of an approaching weather *system*. Further, we know that Earth is just a small part of a large system known as the *solar system*.

Figure 1.21 When Mount St. Helens erupted in May 1980, the area shown here was buried by a volcanic mudflow. Now plants are re-established and new soil has formed. (Photo by Terry Donnelly/ Alamy Images)

The parts of the Earth system are linked: a change in one part can produce changes in any or all of the other parts. For example, when a volcano erupts, lava from Earth's interior may flow out at the surface and block a nearby valley. This new obstruction influences the region's drainage system by creating a lake or causing streams to change course. The large quantities of volcanic ash and gases that can be emitted during an eruption might be blown high into the atmosphere and influence the amount of solar energy that can reach Earth's surface. The result could be a drop in air temperatures over the entire hemisphere. Where the surface is covered by lava flows (or a thick layer of volcanic ash), existing soils are buried. This causes the soil-forming processes to begin anew to transform the new surface material into soil (Figure 1.21). The Earth system is characterized by processes that vary on spatial scales from fractions of millimetres to thousands of kilometres. Time scales for Earth's processes range from milliseconds to billions of years.

The Earth system is powered by energy from two sources. The Sun drives external processes that occur in the atmosphere, in the hydrosphere, and at Earth's surface. Weather and climate, ocean circulation, and erosional processes are driven by energy from the Sun. Earth's interior is the second source of energy. Heat remaining from when our planet formed, and heat that is continuously generated by radioactive decay, powers the internal processes that produce volcanoes, earthquakes, and mountains.

Humans are *part of* the Earth system—a system in which the living and nonliving components are entwined and interconnected. Therefore, our actions produce changes in all of the other parts. When we burn gasoline and coal, build seawalls along the shoreline, dispose of our wastes, and clear the land, we cause other parts of the system to respond, often in unforeseen ways. Throughout this book you will learn about many of Earth's subsystems: the hydrologic system, the tectonic (mountain-building) system, and the rock cycle, to name a few. Remember that these components *and we humans* are all part of the Earth system.

The Rock Cycle: Part of the Earth System

The Earth system has a nearly endless array of cycles (e.g., water, chemical, biologic) in which matter is recycled over and over again. The cycle that involves the processes by which one type of rock changes to another is called the **rock cycle**. It helps us understand the origin of igneous, sedimentary, and metamorphic rocks (see Chapters 3, 6, and 7) and to see that each type is linked to the others by the processes that act on and within the planet.

THE BASIC CYCLE We will begin our look at the rock cycle at the bottom of Figure 1.22. *Magma* is molten material that forms in certain environments of Earth's interior where temperatures and pressures are such that rock melts. Once formed, magma migrates upward into Earth's outer layer or crust. Eventually, magma cools and solidifies. This process, called *crystallization*, can occur either beneath the surface or, following a volcanic eruption, at the surface. In either situation the resulting rocks are called **igneous rocks** (*ignis* = fire, *ous* = full of).

If igneous rocks are exposed at the surface, they will undergo *weathering*, in which the day-to-day influences of the atmosphere slowly disintegrate and decompose rocks. The materials that result are often moved downslope by gravity (see Chapter 14) before being picked up and transported by any of a number of erosional agents: running water, glaciers, wind, or waves (see Chapters 15–19). Eventually, these particles and dissolved substances are deposited as **sediment**. Although most sediment ultimately comes to rest in the ocean, other sites of deposition

ROCK CYCLE

Viewed over long time spans,
rocks are constantly forming,
changing, and reforming.

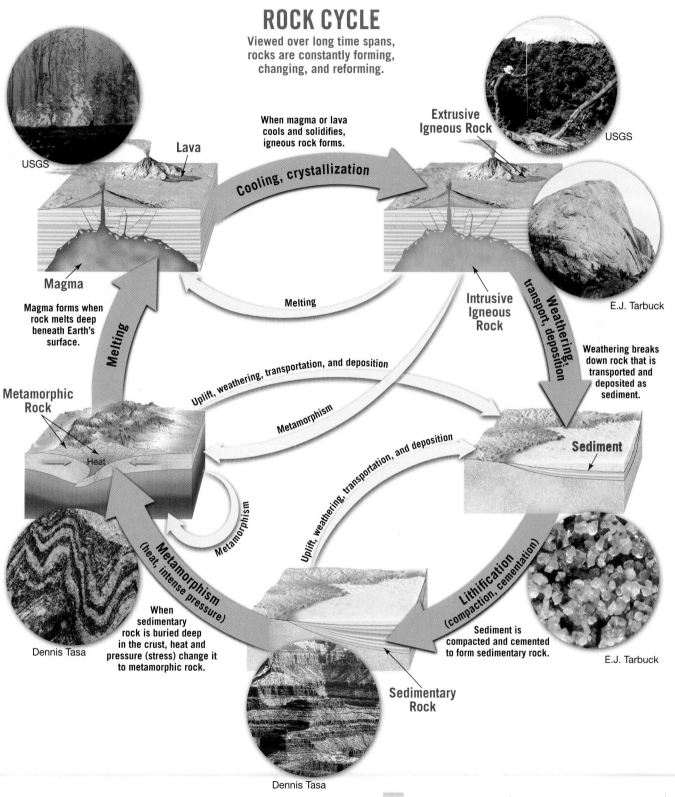

When magma or lava
cools and solidifies,
igneous rock forms.

Cooling, crystallization

Extrusive
Igneous Rock

USGS

USGS

Lava

Magma

Melting

Magma forms when
rock melts deep
beneath Earth's
surface.

Melting

Intrusive
Igneous
Rock

E.J. Tarbuck

Weathering, transport, deposition

Weathering breaks
down rock that is
transported and
deposited as
sediment.

Uplift, weathering, transportation, and deposition

Metamorphic
Rock

Heat

Metamorphism

Metamorphism

Sediment

Uplift, weathering, transportation, and deposition

Metamorphism
(heat, intense pressure)

Metamorphism

Lithification
(compaction, cementation)

When
sedimentary
rock is buried deep
in the crust, heat and
pressure (stress) change it
to metamorphic rock.

Sediment is
compacted and cemented
to form sedimentary rock.

E.J. Tarbuck

Dennis Tasa

Sedimentary
Rock

Dennis Tasa

Figure 1.22 Viewed over long spans, rocks are constantly
forming, changing, and re-forming. The rock cycle helps
us understand the origin of the three basic rock groups.
Arrows represent processes that link each group to the
others.

SMARTFIGURE 1.22
The rock cycle

include river floodplains, swamps, desert basins, and dunes.

Next, the sediments undergo *lithification*, a term meaning "conversion into rock." Sediment is usually lithified into **sedimentary rock** when compacted by the weight of overlying layers or when cemented as percolating water fills the pores (open spaces between particles) with mineral matter.

If the resulting sedimentary rock is buried deep within Earth and involved in the dynamics of mountain building, or intruded by a mass of magma, it will be subjected to great pressures and intense heat. The sedimentary rock will react to the changing environment and turn into the third rock type, **metamorphic rock** (*meta* = change, *morph* = form). When metamorphic rock is subjected to additional pressure changes or to still higher temperatures, it will melt, creating magma, which will eventually crystallize into igneous rock.

Processes driven by heat from Earth's interior are responsible for creating igneous and metamorphic rocks. Weathering and erosion—external processes powered by a combination of energy from the Sun and gravity—produce the sediment from which sedimentary rocks form.

ALTERNATIVE PATHS The paths shown in the basic cycle (purple arrows in Figure 1.22) are not the only ones that are possible. Indeed, other paths are just as likely to be followed as those described in the preceding section. These alternatives are indicated by the blue arrows in Figure 1.22.

Igneous rocks, rather than being exposed to weathering and erosion at Earth's surface, may remain deeply buried. Eventually, these masses may be subjected to the strong compressional forces and high temperatures associated with mountain building. When this occurs, they are transformed directly into metamorphic rocks.

Metamorphic and sedimentary rocks, as well as sediment, do not always remain buried. Rather, overlying layers may be stripped away, exposing the once-buried rock. When this happens, the material is attacked by weathering processes and turned into new raw materials for sedimentary rocks.

Although rocks might seem to be unchanging masses, the rock cycle clearly shows that they are not. The changes, however, take time—great amounts of geologic time (see Chapter 8).

In the remaining chapters we will examine in more detail the workings of our dynamic planet in the context of plate tectonics and the rock cycle. In Chapter 2 we will start this process with the basic building blocks of rocks—the minerals.

CHAPTER SUMMARY

- Two areas of geology are *physical geology* (Earth's materials and processes) and *historical geology* (Earth's development through time). Geology includes natural hazards, resources, and human influences on our planet.
- *Uniformitarianism* is most simply expressed as "the present is the key to the past."
- The *nebular theory* describes a large cloud of dust and gases contracting to form our solar system.
- The *continental drift hypothesis* is based on the premise that continents are capable of breaking up, changing their positions over time, and reassembling. The last major continental breakup occurred approximately 200 million years ago when the supercontinent Pangaea split into smaller land masses. These land masses drifted apart, forming today's arrangement of continents.

- *Plate tectonics* holds that Earth's outer lithosphere consists of several plates that interact to cause earthquakes, volcanoes, and mountain building. Plate boundaries include those that are *divergent* (plates move apart), *convergent* (plates move together), and *transform* (plates slide past each other).
- Chemically, Earth is divided into thin outer crust, solid mantle, and dense core.
- Physically, Earth's layers are the cool, rigid *lithosphere*; weaker *asthenosphere*; hot, rigid *mesosphere*; liquid outer core; and solid inner core. Earth can also be divided into four spheres: geosphere (solid Earth), hydrosphere (water), atmosphere (gases), and biosphere (life).
- Large-scale features on Earth that directly reflect plate tectonic processes include continents with

mountains and shields, ocean basins with trenches, and the oceanic ridge system. At edges of continents are continental shelves and steeper *continental slopes.*

• The Sun drives external processes while heat from Earth's interior powers internal processes

such as volcanoes and earthquakes. The *rock cycle* helps us visualize how rocks transform from one type to another.

MasteringGeology   www.masteringgeology.com

Looking for additional review and test prep materials? Visit the Study Area in MasteringGeology to enhance your understanding of this chapter's content by accessing a variety of resources, including

Self-Study Quizzes, Geoscience Animations, GEODe Tutorials, RSS feeds, flashcards, weblinks, self-study quizzes, and an optional Pearson eText.

REVIEW QUESTIONS

1. How did James Hutton's concept of uniformitarianism change the way people previously thought about rates of geologic processes (such as the uplift or erosion of mountains) and, ultimately, about the Earth's age (in Hutton's time, assumed to be quite youthful and no more than a few thousand years old)?

2. Name and describe Earth's internal divisions classified by their composition versus those classified by their physical properties.

3. Name Earth's four major physical realms or "spheres" and describe the significance of each as components of the larger system we call Earth.

4. Describe four independent lines of evidence used by Alfred Wegener to support his early ideas on continental drift—most importantly, the concept that Earth's present-day continents are redistributed fragments of a much larger land mass that began to split apart about 200 million years ago.

5. Explain why plate tectonics is considered a paradigm and why its relatively recent acceptance (over the past several decades) is often referred to as a scientific "revolution."

6. Essentially, how do igneous, sedimentary, and metamorphic rocks fit into the rock cycle?

MINERALS: THE BUILDING BLOCKS OF ROCKS

Orange-red crystals of garnet (variety: grossular) and smaller crystals of yellowish-green pyroxene (variety: diopside) from the Jeffrey Mine, Asbestos, Quebec. (Photo by Mineral Masterpiece)

CHAPTER OUTLINE

Minerals
The Composition of Minerals
The Structure of Minerals
Physical Properties of Minerals
Mineral Classes

Earth's crust and oceans are the source of a wide variety of useful and essential minerals (Figure 2.1). In fact, practically every manufactured product contains materials obtained from minerals. Most people are familiar with the common uses of many basic metals, including aluminum in beverage cans, copper in electrical wiring, and gold and silver in jewellery. However, some people are not aware that pencil lead contains the greasy-feeling mineral graphite and that talcum powder comes from the mineral talc. Moreover, many do not know that drill bits covered with diamonds are employed by dentists to drill through tooth enamel, or that the common mineral quartz is the source of silicon for computer chips. As the mineral requirements of modern society grow, the need to locate additional supplies of useful minerals also grows and becomes more challenging.

All processes studied by geologists are in some way dependent on the properties of minerals. Volcanic eruptions, plate tectonics and mountain building, weathering and erosion, and even earthquakes involve rocks and minerals. A basic knowledge of Earth materials is therefore essential to understanding all geologic phenomena.

MINERALS

We start with **mineralogy** because minerals are the building blocks of rocks. Geologists define **minerals** as any naturally occurring inorganic solids that possess an orderly internal structure and a definite chemical composition. Thus, for any Earth material to be considered a mineral it must exhibit the following characteristics:

1. It must occur naturally.
2. It must be a solid at surface temperatures and pressures.

Figure 2.1 Canadian mineral samples. **A.** Aragonite (as ammolite; fossil mother of pearl) from Lethbridge, Alberta. **B.** Microcline (variety: amazonite) from Lac Sairs, Quebec. **C.** Sodalite from Bancroft, Ontario. **D.** Gold (on quartz) from Louvricourt Mines, Quebec. **E.** Phlogopite from Baffin Island, Nunavut. **F.** Beryl (variety: emerald) from Quadeville, Ontario. **G.** Quartz (variety: amethyst) from Loon, Ontario. **H.** Chabazite from Wasson's Bluff, Nova Scotia. **I.** Gypsum (variety: selenite) from Swift Current Creek, Saskatchewan. (Photos **A–G** by C. Tsujita; photos **H** and **I** by Arnim Walter)

3. It must possess an orderly internal structure; that is, its atoms must be arranged in a definite pattern.

4. It must have a definite chemical composition that can vary within specified limits.

5. It is *usually* inorganic (although mineral formation can, in some cases, be mediated by biologic processes).

When geologists use the term *mineral*, they only consider those substances that meet these five criteria. Consequently, synthetic diamonds and other useful materials produced by chemists are not considered minerals. Rocks, however, are more loosely defined. Simply, a **rock** is any solid mass of mineral or mineral-like matter that occurs naturally as part of our planet. A few rocks are composed of one mineral. Limestone, for example, is composed of impure masses of the mineral calcite. However, most rocks, like granite (shown in Figure 2.2), occur as aggregates of different minerals, each of which retains its characteristic physical and chemical properties. Here, the term *aggregate* implies that the minerals are joined in such a way that the properties of each mineral are retained. Note that you can easily distinguish the mineral constituents of the sample of granite shown in Figure 2.2.

Some rocks are composed of nonmineral matter. These include the volcanic rocks *obsidian* and *pumice*, composed of noncrystalline, glassy substances; and *coal*, which consists of organic matter.

Because the properties of rocks are determined largely by the chemical composition and internal structure of the minerals they contain, we will first study minerals in this chapter, and then the major rock types in subsequent chapters.

THE COMPOSITION OF MINERALS

Elements

Each of Earth's approximately 4660 minerals is uniquely defined by its combination of chemical composition and internal structure. In other words, every sample of the same mineral contains the same *elements* joined together in a consistent, repeating pattern. At present, 118 elements are known. Of these, 90 are naturally occurring (Figure 2.3). Some minerals, such as gold and sulphur, consist entirely of one element. However, most minerals are a combination of two or more elements joined to form a

Granite
(Rock)

Quartz
(Mineral)

Hornblende
(Mineral)

Orthoclase feldspar
(Mineral)

Figure 2.2 Most rocks are aggregates of several kinds of minerals.
(Photos by E. J. Tarbuck)

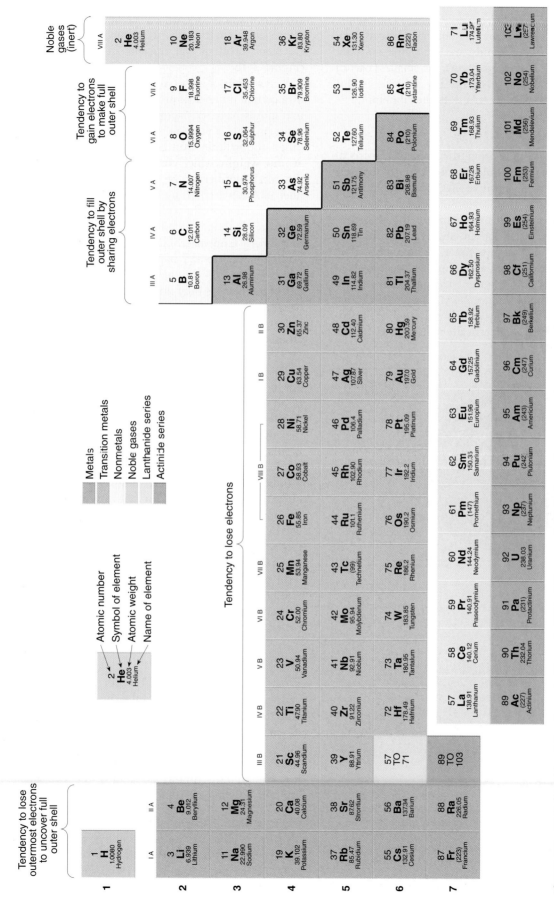

Figure 2.3 Periodic table of the elements. Elements 104 to 118 are synthetic and not shown.

chemically stable and electrically neutral compound. To understand better how elements combine to form molecules and compounds, we must first consider the **atom** (*a* = not, *tomos* = cut), the smallest part of matter that cannot be chemically split. It is this extremely small particle that does the combining.

Atomic Structure

The central part of an atom, the nucleus, consists of a bundle of particles called **protons and neutrons**. Each proton has a positive electrical charge while each neutron has no charge. Both types of particles are about equal in size and density. Together they constitute nearly all of an atom's mass. Rapidly orbiting the nucleus are tinier, lighter, negatively charged particles called **electrons** that occupy what may be visualized as concentric, spherically shaped energy level **shells** (Figure 2.4A). In any given atom, the number of electrons equals the number of protons, resulting in an electrically neutral state for the

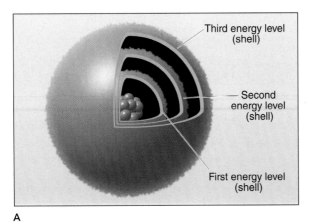

Third energy level
(shell)

Second
energy level
(shell)

First energy level
(shell)

A

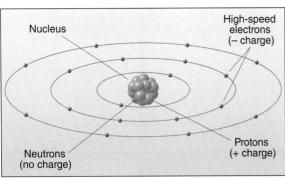

Nucleus

High-speed
electrons
(– charge)

Neutrons
(no charge)

Protons
(+ charge)

B

Figure 2.4 Two models of the atom. (Note that these models are not drawn to scale.) **A.** Model of an atom showing spherically shaped, concentric electron energy level shells surrounding a central nucleus of protons and neutrons. Electrons are minuscule in size compared with protons and neutrons, and the relative space between the nucleus and electron shells is much greater than illustrated. **B.** A more simplified view of the atom, depicting high-speed electrons orbiting the nucleus in a single plane.

atom as a whole. To make it easier to visualize the electrons in their shells, it is convenient to depict electrons orbiting the nucleus in a single plane (Figure 2.4B).

An atom of a specific element is characterized by a certain number of protons. For example, all carbon atoms have six protons, all oxygen atoms have eight protons, and so forth. This unique number is called the **atomic number**. This differs from the **atomic weight**, which corresponds approximately to the total number of protons and neutrons in its nucleus (each accounting for one unit of mass), plus a comparatively miniscule mass contribution from electrons. It should be noted that while the number of protons (and matching number of electrons) is explicitly represented in the periodic table of elements (Figure 2.3) by the atomic number, the number of neutrons is only implied as part of the atomic weight. Determining the approximate number of neutrons merely requires the subtraction of the atomic number from the atomic weight.

For most elements, the stability of their atoms is dictated by the number of electrons present in their energy level shells. The innermost shell of an atom can hold a maximum of two electrons. Shells surrounding this innermost shell can hold a maximum of eight electrons. For atoms of elements with more than two electrons, the most stable electron configuration occurs when the number of electrons in the outermost shell equals eight. This requirement for stability is satisfied in atoms of the so-called "noble gases" (e.g., argon), which are the least chemically active elements. Other elements—those with fewer than eight electrons in their outermost shell—tend to combine with other atoms in order to achieve this stable configuration. Such combination is achieved through the interaction of the outermost electrons, called **valence electrons**.

Bonding

Elements combine with each other to form a wide variety of more complex substances. The strong attractive force linking atoms together is called a *chemical bond*. When chemical bonding joins two or more elements together in definite proportions, the substance is called a **compound**. Minerals are chemical compounds. In this book only the two main types of bonding are summarized.

IONIC BONDS Perhaps the easiest type of bond to visualize is an **ionic bond**. In ionic bonding, one or more electrons are transferred from one atom to another. Simply, one atom gives up some electrons and the other receives them. A common example of

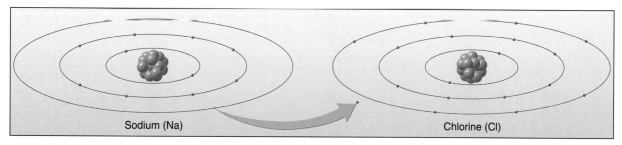

Figure 2.5 Chemical bonding of sodium and chlorine through the transfer of the lone outer electron from a sodium atom to a chlorine atom. The result is a positive sodium ion (Na⁺) and a negative chloride ion (Cl⁻). Bonding to produce sodium chloride (NaCl) is due to electrostatic attraction between the positive and negative ions.

ionic bonding is the joining of sodium (Na) and chlorine (Cl) to produce sodium chloride (NaCl or common table salt). This bond is shown in Figure 2.5. Notice that sodium gives up a single electron to chlorine to form an electrically neutral compound. Once electron transfer occurs, the atoms themselves are no longer electrically neutral. By giving up one electron, a neutral sodium atom becomes *positively charged*. Similarly, by acquiring one electron, the neutral chlorine atom becomes *negatively charged*. Such atoms, which have an electrical charge because they have a deficit or surplus of electrons, are called **ions**. An atom that picks up an extra electron and becomes negatively charged is called an *anion*. An atom that loses an electron and becomes positively charged is called a *cation*.

We know that ions with like charges repel and those with unlike charges attract. Thus, an *ionic bond* is the attraction of oppositely charged ions to one another, producing an electrically neutral compound. Figure 2.6 illustrates the arrangement of

sodium and chloride ions in ordinary table salt. Notice that salt consists of alternating sodium and chloride ions, positioned in such a manner that each positive ion is attracted to and surrounded on all sides by negative ions, and vice versa. This arrangement maximizes the attraction between ions with unlike charges, while minimizing the repulsion between ions with like charges. Thus, *ionic compounds consist of an orderly arrangement of oppositely charged ions assembled in a definite ratio that provides overall electrical neutrality*.

The properties of a chemical compound are *dramatically different* from the properties of the elements composing it. For example, chlorine is a green, poisonous gas that is so toxic it was used during World War I as a chemical weapon. Sodium is a soft, silvery metal that reacts vigorously with water and, if held in your hand, can burn severely. Together, however, these atoms produce the compound sodium chloride (table salt), a clear crystalline solid that is essential for human life. This example illustrates an

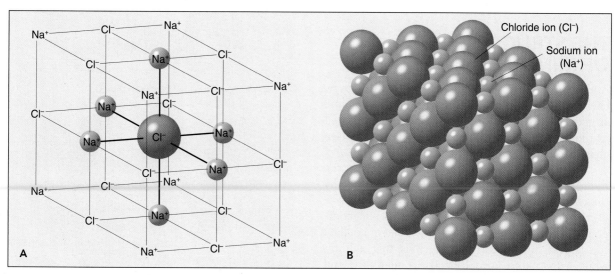

Figure 2.6 Schematic diagrams illustrating the arrangement of sodium and chloride ions in table salt. **A.** Structure has been opened up to show arrangement of ions. **B.** Actual ions are closely packed.

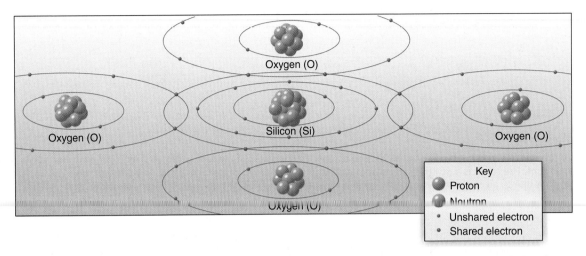

Figure 2.7 Silica, the basic building block of all silicate minerals, consists internally of a central silicon atom that shares a pair of electrons with each of four neighbouring oxygen atoms, forming strong covalent bonds. This diagram, depicting all atoms in a single plane, is a two-dimensional representation of what is actually a three-dimensional structure—the silica tetrahedron (depicted later in Figure 2.21).

important difference between a rock and a mineral. Most *minerals* are *chemical compounds* with unique properties that are very different from the elements that compose them. Most *rocks*, however, are *mixtures* of minerals, with each mineral retaining its own identity.

COVALENT BONDS Not all atoms combine by transferring electrons to form ions. Other atoms *share* electrons to form a bond that is stronger than the ionic bond. For example, the most common mineral group, the silicates, contains the element silicon, which readily forms covalent bonds with oxygen. Figure 2.7 illustrates the sharing of a pair of electrons between one silicon and four oxygen atoms to form a single unit (building block) of silica, $(SiO_4)^{4-}$.

THE STRUCTURE OF MINERALS

A mineral is composed of an ordered array of atoms chemically bonded to form a particular crystalline structure. This orderly packing of atoms is reflected in the regularly shaped objects we call crystals (see chapter-opening photo).

For those compounds formed by ions, the internal atomic arrangement is determined partly by the charges on the ions, but even more so by the size of the ions involved. To form stable ionic compounds, each positively charged ion is surrounded by the largest number of negative ions that will fit, while maintaining overall electrical neutrality, and vice versa. Figure 2.8 shows ideal packing arrangements for ions of various sizes.

Let's examine the geometric arrangement of sodium and chloride ions in the mineral halite (common salt; Figure 2.9). We see in Figure 2.9A that the sodium and chloride ions pack together to form a cube-shaped internal structure (Figure 2.9B). Also note that the orderly arrangement of ions found at the atomic level (Figure 2.9C) is reflected on a much larger scale in the cube-shaped halite crystals shown in Figure 2.9D. Like halite, all samples of a particular mineral contain the same elements, joined together in the same orderly arrangement.

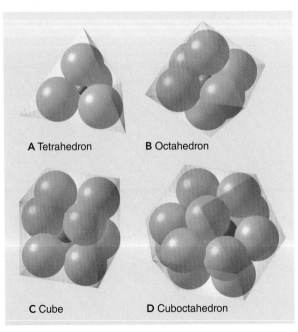

Figure 2.8 Ideal geometric packing for positive (blue) and negative (orange) ions of various size ratios.

A Sodium and Chloride ions

B Building block of the mineral halite

C Intergrown crystals of the mineral halite

D Collection of building blocks (crystal)

Figure 2.9 The structure of sodium chloride. **A, B.** The orderly arrangement of sodium and chloride ions in the mineral halite. **C, D.** The orderly arrangement at the atomic level produces the regularly shaped salt crystals shown in this photograph. (Photo **C** by E.J. Tarbuck)

Some elements are able to join together in more than one type of geometric arrangement. This means that two or more minerals can share the same chemical composition and yet exhibit very different physical characteristics. Minerals of this type are said to be **polymorphs** (*poly* = many, *morph* = form). Graphite and diamond are good examples of polymorphism because they both consist exclusively of carbon yet have drastically different properties (Figure 2.10). Graphite is the soft, grey material of which pencil lead is made, whereas diamond is the hardest known mineral. They are different because of how they are formed. Diamonds form at depths approaching 200 kilometres, where the compact structure shown in Figure 2.10A is produced by extreme pressures. Graphite, conversely, forms under low pressure and temperature and consists of sheets of carbon atoms that are widely spaced and weakly held together (Figure 2.10B). Because these carbon sheets will easily slide past one another, graphite makes an excellent lubricant.

Scientists have learned that by heating graphite under high pressure, they can produce diamonds. Although synthetic diamonds are generally not gem quality, they have many industrial uses.

In nature, some minerals transform from one polymorph into another when changes in temperature and pressure occur in their surrounding environment. For example, when rocks containing *olivine* are carried to greater depths by a subducting plate, the olivine will convert to a more compact form called *spinel*.

PHYSICAL PROPERTIES OF MINERALS

Minerals are solids formed primarily by inorganic processes. Each mineral has an orderly arrangement of atoms (crystalline structure) and a definite chemical composition, which give it a unique set of physical properties. Some properties, such as those described below, can be directly observed and/or tested by simple means and therefore are especially useful in mineral identification.

Crystal Habit (Shape)

Crystal habit is the external expression of a mineral that reflects the orderly internal arrangement of atoms. Figure 2.11A illustrates the characteristic habit of the iron-bearing mineral pyrite.

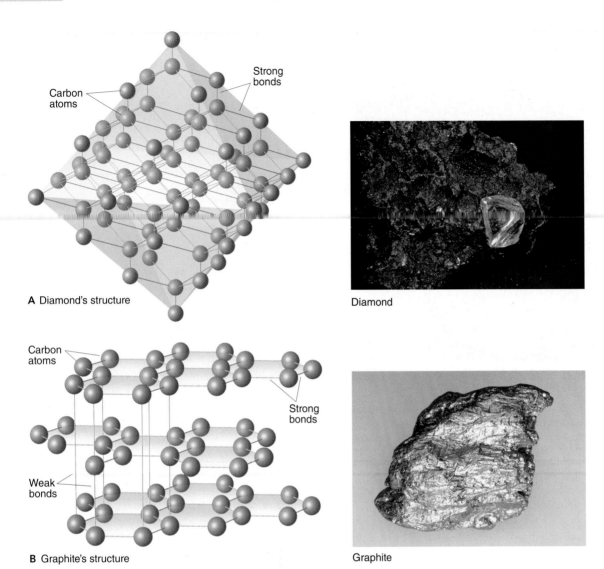

Figure 2.10   Comparing the structures of diamond and graphite. Both are natural substances with the same chemical composition: carbon atoms. Nevertheless, their internal structure and physical properties reflect the fact that each forms in a very different environment. **A.** All carbon atoms in diamond are covalently bonded into a compact, three-dimensional framework, which accounts for the extreme hardness of the mineral. **B.** In graphite the carbon atoms are bonded into sheets that are joined in a layered fashion by very weak electrical forces. These weak bonds allow the sheets of carbon to readily slide past each other, making graphite soft and slippery, and thus useful as a dry lubricant.
(Photo **A** by E. R. Degginger/Science Source; photo **B** by E. J. Tarbuck)

Generally, when a mineral can form without space restrictions, it will develop individual crystals with well-formed crystal faces. Some minerals, such as quartz, have a distinctive crystal habit (Figure 2.11B). However, the growth of individual crystals is often interrupted by competition for space, resulting in an intergrown mass of crystals lacking obvious crystal habit. This is one of the reasons why you must be able to recognize other diagnostic mineral properties, such as those described below, to identify minerals accurately.

Lustre

Lustre is the appearance or quality of light reflected from the surface of a mineral crystal. Some minerals such as pyrite (Figure 2.11A) look like polished metal and have a *metallic lustre*. Others, such as quartz (Figure 2.11B), have a *nonmetallic lustre* and can be further described as vitreous (glassy, as in the case of quartz), pearly, silky, resinous, or earthy (dull). Still other minerals appear somewhat metallic in lustre and are said to be submetallic.

A

B

Figure 2.11   Crystal habit is the external expression of a mineral's orderly internal structure. **A.** Pyrite, commonly known as "fool's gold," often forms cubic crystals. They may exhibit parallel lines (striations) on the faces. **B.** Quartz sample that exhibits well-developed hexagonal crystals with pyramid-shaped ends.
(Photo **A** courtesy of E. J. Tarbuck; photo **B** © theartofphoto/Fotolia)

Colour

Although **colour** of a mineral specimen is often obvious, it is not always diagnostic. For example, pure quartz is clear and colourless (see Figure 2.11B), but the addition of slight impurities (e.g., iron, chromium) can impart hues of purple (amethyst, as shown in Figure 2.1), pink (rose quartz), yellowish orange (citrine), or even dark brown to black (smoky quartz) (Figure 2.12).

Streak

Streak is the colour of a mineral in its powdered form and is obtained by rubbing the mineral across a piece of unglazed porcelain known as a *streak plate* (Figure 2.13). Although the colour of a mineral can vary from sample to sample, the streak (e.g., reddish brown in hematite) usually does not and is therefore a more reliable property.

Figure 2.12   Because of the presence of slight impurities, minerals, such as quartz, can occur in a wide range of colours.
(Photo courtesy of E. J. Tarbuck)

Figure 2.13   Although the colour of a mineral may not be helpful in identification, the streak, which is the colour of the powdered mineral, can be very useful.
(Photo by Dennis Tasa/Pearson Education)

TABLE **2.1** Mohs Scale of Relative Hardness		
Relative Scale	**Mineral**	**Hardness of Some Common Objects**
10 (Hardest)	Diamond	
9	Corundum	
8	Topaz	
7	Quartz	6.5 streak plate
6	Potassium feldspar	5.5 glass, knife blade
5	Apatite	
4	Fluorite	4.5 wire nail
3	Calcite	3 copper penny
2	Gypsum	2.5 fingernail
1 (Softest)	Talc	

Source: From Friederich Mohs, Versuch einer Elementar-Methode, (Wien, 1812).

Hardness

One of the most useful properties is **hardness**, a measure of a mineral's resistance to abrasion or scratching. By rubbing a mineral of unknown hardness against one of known hardness, or vice versa, a numeric value can be obtained by using the **Mohs scale** of relative hardness. This scale consists of 10 minerals arranged in order from 1 (softest) to 10 (hardest), as shown in Table 2.1.

Any mineral of unknown hardness can be compared with the scale minerals or with other objects of known hardness. A fingernail has a hardness of 2.5; a copper penny, 3.5; and a piece of glass, 5.5. Gypsum is 2, and can be scratched with your fingernail; calcite is 3 and will scratch your fingernail but will not scratch glass. Quartz will scratch glass and diamond can scratch itself or any other mineral.

Cleavage

Cleavage (*kleiben* = carve) is the tendency of a mineral to break along planes of weak bonding. Minerals that have cleavage can be identified by the distinctive smooth surfaces produced when the minerals are broken.

The simplest type of cleavage occurs in micas. Because they have weak bonds in one planar direction, they cleave to form thin, flat sheets. Some minerals reveal several cleavage planes when broken; others show poor cleavage; and still others, such as quartz, have no cleavage at all.

When minerals break evenly in multiple directions, cleavage is described as the *number of planes* exhibited and the *angles at which they meet*, as depicted in Figure 2.14).

Do not confuse cleavage with crystal habit (shape). When a mineral exhibits cleavage, it will break into pieces that all have *the same geometry*. By contrast the quartz crystals shown in Figure 2.11B do not have cleavage. If broken, they fracture into shapes that do not resemble each other or the original crystals.

Fracture

Minerals having chemical bonds of similar strength in all directions, and therefore lacking the ability to cleave along certain planes within their crystals, may still break or **fracture** in a distinctive manner. Quartz, for example, breaks to form smooth curved surfaces resembling broken glass or the interior of a seashell. This is called *conchoidal fracture* (Figure 2.15). Some minerals break into splinters or fibres. Most minerals, however, fracture irregularly, producing uneven fracture.

Specific Gravity

Specific gravity is a number representing the ratio of the weight of a mineral to the weight of an equal volume of water. For example, if a mineral weighs three times as much as an equal volume of water, its specific gravity is 3. If a mineral feels as heavy as common rocks you have handled, its specific gravity will probably be somewhere between 2.5 and 3. Some metallic minerals have a specific gravity two or three times that of common rock-forming minerals. Galena, which is mined for lead (Figure 2.16), has a specific gravity of roughly 7.5, whereas the specific gravity of 24-karat gold is approximately 20.

Other Properties of Minerals

In addition to the properties already discussed, there are others that are diagnostic of certain minerals. For example, halite is ordinary salt so it is quickly identified with your tongue. Thin sheets of mica will bend and elastically snap back. Gold is malleable and can be easily shaped. Talc feels soapy and graphite feels greasy. Magnetite has a high iron content and is attracted to a magnet. Also, many sulphur-bearing minerals smell like rotten eggs when rubbed or scratched.

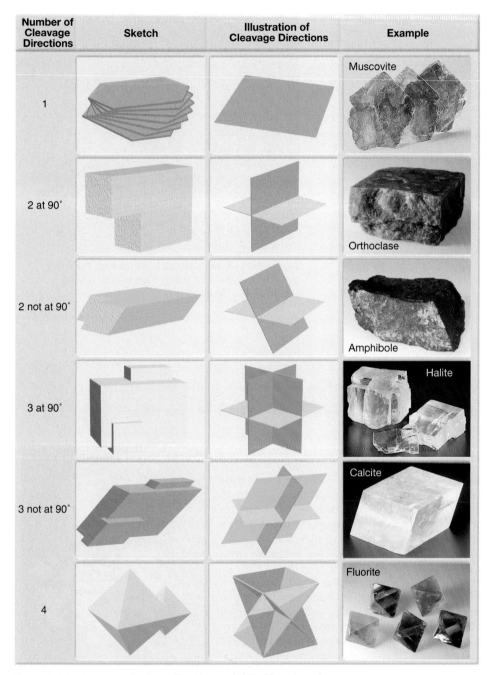

Number of Cleavage Directions	Sketch	Illustration of Cleavage Directions	Example
1			Muscovite
2 at 90°			Orthoclase
2 not at 90°			Amphibole
3 at 90°			Halite
3 not at 90°			Calcite
4			Fluorite

Figure 2.14 Common cleavage directions exhibited by minerals. (Photos courtesy of E. J. Tarbuck)

Some minerals exhibit special optical properties. For example, when a transparent piece of calcite is placed over printed material, the letters appear twice (Figure 2.17). This optical property is known as *double refraction*.

Another diagnostic property of calcite is that it reacts vigorously when brought into contact with acid; any rock containing calcite will immediately effervesce (fizz) when a drop of dilute hydrochloric acid is applied to it (Figure 2.18).

MINERAL CLASSES

Approximately 4660 minerals have been named and new ones are identified each year, but only a few dozen are common. Collectively, these few

Figure 2.15 Conchoidal fracture. The smooth curved surfaces result when minerals break in a glasslike manner. (Photo by E. J. Tarbuck)

Figure 2.16 Galena is lead sulphide and, like other metallic ores, has a relatively high specific gravity. (Photo by E. J. Tarbuck)

GEOLOGY AND POPULAR MEDIA
Kryptonite Discovered! . . . Sort Of

Kryptonite, the fictional substance eagerly sought by villains determined to take over the world, has figured so prominently in comic books, radio, television programs, and movies that it is difficult to imagine a Superman adventure without it. The nature of kryptonite has changed frequently over the history of the Superman franchise, and has been a specific element (not to be confused with the real element of the same name), a metal alloy, a type of rock (as meteorites), and a mineral. Likewise, the colour of kryptonite has varied, although the green variety, valued for its strength-sapping effects on Superman, has been, by far, the most widely cited. In some stories, kryptonite is simply rock fragments derived from Superman's exploded home planet Krypton; in others it was created from the nuclear explosion that *caused* Krypton's destruction. But such inconsistencies aside, it is well-established that Superman's powers are significantly weakened if he comes into close contact with kryptonite. In the 2006 movie

Superman Returns, the composition of kryptonite is revealed when the camera zooms in to the empty glass case (in the Metropolis Museum) from which Lex Luthor has stolen this precious material. Written on the specimen name plate is *sodium lithium boron silicate hydroxide with fluorine*.

Enter the Rio Tinto Group, a mineral exploration company working in the Jadar Valley of Serbia. Discovered in drill cores obtained in 2006 were compact masses of a mineral that had not been previously described. A sample was sent to mineralogist Chris Stanley of the Natural History Museum (London, UK), who, with help from the National Research Council of Canada, established that it was a new mineral species, composed of *sodium lithium boron silicate hydroxide*. By sheer coincidence, the new mineral (later named jadarite; Figure 2.A) turned out to have a nearly identical chemical composition to the latest flavour of kryptonite featured in *Superman Returns* (minus fluorine). But despite the chemical similarity to

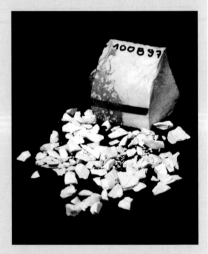

Figure 2.A Core sample of jadarite, a newly discovered mineral with nearly the same chemical composition as the fictional kryptonite—Superman's least favourite substance. (Photo courtesy of C. Tsujita)

kryptonite, this new mineral is neither green nor radioactive. It doesn't glow on its own either (although it does fluoresce a pretty pinkish-orange colour under ultraviolet light). So Superman is safe . . . for now.

Figure 2.17 A transparent specimen of calcite showing the property of double refraction. (Photo by S. R. Hicock)

Figure 2.18 Calcite vigorously effervesces when brought into direct contact with acid. (Photo by C. Tsujita)

make up most rocks of Earth's crust and, as such, are classified as *rock-forming minerals. Eight elements* make up the bulk of these minerals, and represent more than 98 percent (by weight) of continental crust (Figure 2.19). In order of abundance, they are: oxygen (O), silicon (Si), aluminum (Al), iron (Fe), calcium (Ca), sodium (Na), potassium (K), and magnesium (Mg).

Silicon and oxygen combine to form the framework of the most common mineral class, the **silicates**. The next most common mineral class is the carbonates, of which calcite is the most prominent member. We will first discuss the silicates and then look at the other mineral classes.

The Silicates

Every silicate mineral contains the elements oxygen and silicon. Other than quartz and its polymorphs, a silicate mineral includes one or more other common elements that are needed to produce electrical neutrality. Together, these additional elements give rise to hundreds of varieties of silicate minerals, each with unique physical and chemical properties that can, on the one hand, be extremely useful to humans, while on the other, be potentially hazardous to our health.

THE SILICON–OXYGEN TETRAHEDRON All silicates have the same fundamental building block, the **silicon–oxygen tetrahedron** (*tetra* = four, *hedra* = a base). This structure consists of four oxygen ions (each with a 2– charge) surrounding a much smaller silicon ion with a 4+ charge (Figure 2.20). The

silicon–oxygen tetrahedron is therefore a complex ion $(SiO_4)^{4-}$ with an overall charge of 4–.

These tetrahedra join together to become neutral compounds through the addition of cations (Figure 2.21). In this way, a chemically stable structure is produced, consisting of individual tetrahedra linked by cations.

MORE COMPLEX SILICATE STRUCTURES Tetrahedra can link with other tetrahedra (by sharing oxygen ions) to form *single chains*, *double chains*, or *sheet structures* (Figure 2.22). The joining of tetrahedra in each of these configurations results from the

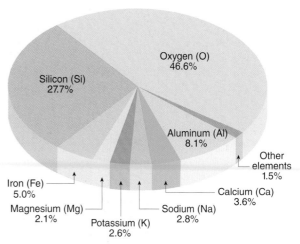

Figure 2.19 Relative abundance of the eight most abundant elements in continental crust.

Figure 2.20 Two representations of the silicon–oxygen tetrahedron. **A.** The four large spheres represent oxygen ions, and the blue sphere represents a silicon ion. The spheres are drawn in proportion to the radii of the ions. **B.** An expanded view of the tetrahedron using rods to depict the bonds that connect the ions.

sharing of a different number of oxygen atoms between silicon atoms in adjacent tetrahedra.

To understand better how this sharing takes place, select one of the silicon ions (small blue spheres) near the middle of the single-chain structure shown in Figure 2.22B. This silicon ion is completely surrounded by four larger oxygen ions (you are looking *through* one of the four to see the blue silicon ion). Of the four oxygen ions, two are joined to other silicon ions, whereas the other two are not shared this way. *It is the linkage across the shared oxygen ions that joins the tetrahedra as a chain structure.* Now examine a silicon ion near the middle of the sheet structure and count the number of shared and unshared oxygen ions surrounding it (Figure 2.22D). The increase in the degree of sharing accounts for the sheet structure. Other silicate structures exist, and the most common has all of the oxygen ions shared to produce a complex three-dimensional framework (Figure 2.22E).

The ratio of oxygen ions to silicon ions differs in each of the silicate structures. The isolated tetrahedron has four oxygen ions for every silicon ion (Figure 2.22A). In the single chain, the oxygen-to-silicon ratio is 3:1, and in the three-dimensional framework, this ratio is 2:1. As more of the oxygen ions are shared, the percentage of silicon in the structure increases. Silicate minerals are therefore described as having a high or low silicon content based on their ratio of oxygen to silicon. This difference in silicon content is important, as you will see in Chapter 3. Except for quartz (SiO_2), the basic structure (chains, sheets, or three-dimensional frameworks) of most silicate minerals has a net negative charge. Therefore, metal cations are required to bring the overall charge into balance and to serve as the "mortar" that holds these structures together. The cations that most often link silicate structures are iron (Fe^{2+}), magnesium (Mg^{2+}), potassium (K^+),

Figure 2.21 Relative sizes and electrical charges of ions of the eight most common elements in Earth's crust. These are the most common ions in rock-forming minerals.

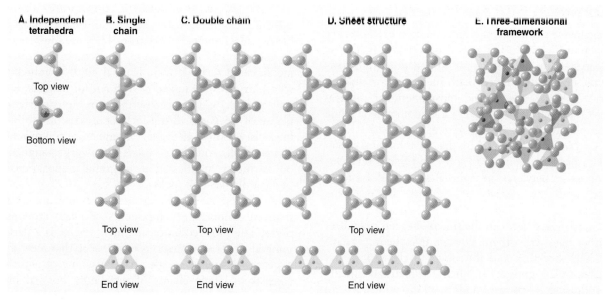

Figure 2.22 Five types of silicate structures. **A.** Independent tetrahedra. **B.** Single chains. **C.** Double chains. **D.** Sheet structures. **E.** Three-dimensional framework.

sodium (Na^+), aluminum (Al^{3+}), and calcium (Ca^{2+}). These positively charged ions bond with the unshared oxygen ions that occupy the corners of the silica tetrahedra.

Figure 2.21 shows that each of these cations has a particular atomic size and a particular charge. Generally, ions of approximately the same size are able to substitute freely for one another. For instance, ions of iron (Fe^{2+}) and magnesium (Mg^{2+}) are nearly the same size and substitute for each other without altering the mineral structure. This also holds true for calcium and sodium ions, which can occupy the same site in a crystalline structure. In addition, aluminum (Al^{3+}) often substitutes for silicon in the silicon–oxygen tetrahedron.

Thus, individual specimens of a particular mineral can contain various amounts of substituting elements. Such a mineral is expressed by a chemical formula with parentheses to show the variable component. For example, the chemical formula for the mineral olivine, a magnesium-iron silicate, is written as $(Mg,Fe)_2SiO_4$. The iron (Fe^{2+}) and magnesium (Mg^{2+}) cations in olivine freely substitute for each other. At one extreme, olivine may contain iron without magnesium (Fe_2SiO_4, or iron silicate), and at the other, iron is lacking (Mg_2SiO_4, or magnesium silicate). Between these end members, any ratio of iron to magnesium is possible. Thus, olivine, as well as many other silicate minerals, is actually a *group* of minerals with a range of composition between the two end members.

In certain substitutions, the ions that interchange do not have the same electrical charge. For instance, when calcium (Ca^{2+}) substitutes for sodium (Na^+), the structure gains a positive charge. One way in which this substitution is accomplished, while still maintaining overall electrical neutrality, is the simultaneous substitution of aluminum (Al^{3+}) for silicon (Si^{4+}). This particular substitution occurs in the mineral plagioclase feldspar, which is a member of the most abundant group of minerals found in Earth's crust. The end members of this particular feldspar series are a calcium–aluminum silicate (anorthite, $CaAl_2Si_2O_8$), and a sodium–aluminum silicate (albite, $NaAlSi_3O_8$).

Figure 2.21 shows that among the major constituents of the silicate minerals, only oxygen is an anion (negatively charged). Because oppositely charged ions attract (and similarly charged ions repel), the chemical bonds that hold silicate structures together form between oxygen and oppositely charged cations. Thus, cations arrange themselves so that they can be as close as possible to oxygen while remaining as far apart from each other as possible. Because of its small size and high charge (4+), the silicon (Si) cation forms the strongest bonds with oxygen. Aluminum (Al) is more strongly bonded to oxygen than are calcium (Ca), magnesium (Mg), iron (Fe), sodium (Na), or potassium (K), but not as strongly as silicon. In many ways, aluminum plays a role similar to that of silicon by being the central ion in the basic tetrahedral structure.

Common Silicate Minerals

The major silicate groups and common examples are given in Figure 2.23. The feldspars (*feld* = field, *spar* = crystal) are by far the most abundant silicate minerals, composing more than 50 percent of Earth's crust. Quartz, the second most abundant mineral in continental crust, is the only common mineral made completely of silicon and oxygen.

Notice in Figure 2.23 that each mineral group has a particular silicate *structure* and that a relationship exists between the internal structure of a mineral and the *cleavage* it exhibits. Because the silicon–oxygen bonds are strong, silicate minerals tend to cleave between the silicon–oxygen structures rather than across them. For example, the micas have a sheet structure and thus tend to cleave into flat plates (see Figure 2.14). Quartz, which has equally strong silicon–oxygen bonds in all directions, has no cleavage and fractures instead.

Silicate minerals readily form (crystallize) when magma cools and solidifies (as discussed in Chapter 1). This cooling can occur at or near Earth's surface (low temperature and pressure) or at great depths (high temperature and pressure). The environment during crystallization and the chemical composition of the magma determines, to a large degree, which minerals are produced. For example, the silicate mineral olivine crystallizes at high temperatures, whereas quartz crystallizes at much lower temperatures, so the two do not coexist.

In addition, some silicate minerals form at Earth's surface from the weathered products of existing silicate minerals. Still other silicate minerals are formed under the extreme pressures associated with mountain building. Each silicate mineral, therefore, has a structure and a chemical composition that *indicate the conditions under which it formed*. Thus, by carefully examining the mineral constituents of rocks, geologists can often determine the circumstances under which the rocks formed.

We will now examine some of the most common silicate minerals, which we divide into two major categories on the basis of their chemical makeup.

FERROMAGNESIAN (DARK) SILICATES The **dark silicates,** or **ferromagnesian silicates**, are those minerals containing ions of iron (iron = *ferro*) or magnesium or both in their structure. Because of their iron content, ferromagnesian silicates are dark in colour and have a greater specific gravity, between 3.2 and 3.6, than nonferromagnesian silicates. The most common dark silicate minerals are olivine, the pyroxenes, the amphiboles, the dark mica (biotite), and dark garnet.

The *olivine* group of high-temperature silicate minerals are black to olive-green and have a glassy lustre and a conchoidal fracture. They are important components of Earth's mantle. The structure of olivine is characterized by individual silica tetrahedra whose oxygens are linked to iron and/or magnesium ions by ionic bonds. Because there are no consistent planes of weakness within its overall structure, olivine lacks a distinct cleavage. Olivine more commonly forms small, rounded crystals than large, angular ones, which is manifested in the granular appearance of most olivine-rich rocks.

The *pyroxenes* are a group of complex minerals that are important components of dark igneous rocks. The most common member, *augite*, is a dark mineral with two directions of cleavage that meet at a nearly 90-degree angle. Its crystalline structure consists of single chains of tetrahedra bonded by ions of iron and magnesium. Because the silicon–oxygen bonds are stronger than the bonds joining the adjacent silicate chain, augite cleaves parallel to (between) the silicate chains. Augite is one of the dominant minerals in basalt, a common igneous rock of oceanic crust and volcanic areas on continents.

Amphibole is a chemically complex group of minerals whose most common member is *hornblende* (Figure 2.24). Hornblende is usually dark green to black and has two directions of cleavage. In contrast to augite, whose two cleavage directions intersect at 90 degrees, hornblende always cleaves at angles of approximately 60 and 120 degrees (Figure 2.25). As in pyroxene minerals, the cleavage angles in amphibole minerals reflect preferential breakage along ionic bonds between the silica chains, which are significantly weaker than the strong covalent bonds within the silica chains themselves. Because the double chains of silica tetrahedra are wider than single chains, the planes of weakness in amphibole minerals intersect at a wider angle (120 degrees) than in pyroxene minerals (90 degrees). Another distinguishing feature of hornblende is that it often forms elongate crystals, in contrast with augite, which tends to form rather stubby, blocky crystals. Hornblende crystals are often visible as dark flecks scattered among the lighter-coloured crystals of feldspar and quartz in igneous rocks such as granite.

Biotite is the dark, iron-rich member of the mica group. Like other micas, biotite possesses a sheet structure that gives it excellent cleavage in one direction (perfect basal cleavage). Biotite also has a shiny black appearance that helps distinguish it from the other dark ferromagnesian minerals. Like amphibole, biotite is also a common constituent of igneous rocks, including granite.

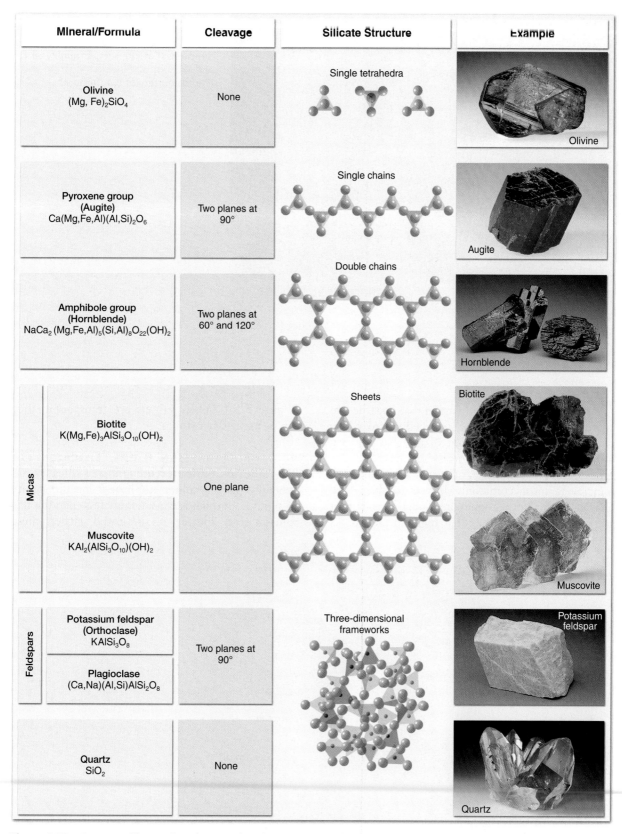

Mineral/Formula	Cleavage	Silicate Structure	Example
Olivine $(Mg, Fe)_2SiO_4$	None	Single tetrahedra	Olivine
Pyroxene group (Augite) $Ca(Mg,Fe,Al)(Al,Si)_2O_6$	Two planes at 90°	Single chains	Augite
Amphibole group (Hornblende) $NaCa_2 (Mg,Fe,Al)_5(Si,Al)_8O_{22}(OH)_2$	Two planes at 60° and 120°	Double chains	Hornblende
Micas Biotite $K(Mg,Fe)_3AlSi_3O_{10}(OH)_2$	One plane	Sheets	Biotite
Micas Muscovite $KAl_2(AlSi_3O_{10})(OH)_2$	One plane	Sheets	Muscovite
Feldspars Potassium feldspar (Orthoclase) $KAlSi_3O_8$	Two planes at 90°	Three-dimensional frameworks	Potassium feldspar
Feldspars Plagioclase $(Ca,Na)(Al,Si)AlSi_2O_8$	Two planes at 90°	Three-dimensional frameworks	Potassium feldspar
Quartz SiO_2	None	Three-dimensional frameworks	Quartz

Figure 2.23 Common silicate minerals. Note that the complexity of the silicate structure increases from top to bottom. (Photos by Dennis Tasa/Pearson Education)

Figure 2.24 Hornblende variety of amphibole. Hornblende is a common dark silicate mineral having two cleavage directions that intersect at roughly 60° and 120°.
(Photo courtesy of E. J. Tarbuck)

← 5 cm →

Garnet is similar to olivine in that its structure is composed of individual tetrahedra linked by metallic ions. Also like olivine, garnet has a glassy lustre, lacks cleavage, and possesses conchoidal fracture. Although the colours of garnet are varied, this mineral is most commonly brown to deep red. Garnet readily forms equidimensional crystals that are most commonly found in metamorphic rocks

(Figure 2.26). When garnets are transparent, they can be used as gemstones.

NONFERROMAGNESIAN (LIGHT) SILICATES The **light silicates,** or **nonferromagnesian silicates,** are generally light in colour and have a specific gravity of about 2.7, which is considerably less than the ferromagnesian silicates. As indicated earlier, these

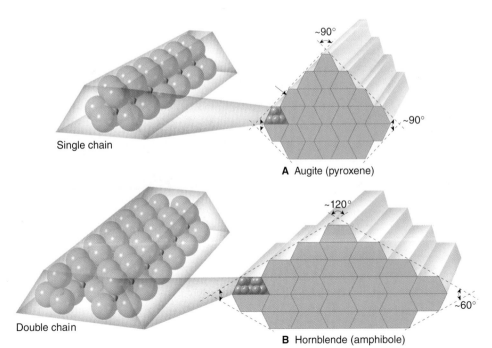

Single chain

A Augite (pyroxene)

~90°

~90°

Double chain

B Hornblende (amphibole)

~120°

~60°

Figure 2.25 Cleavage angles for augite and hornblende.

Figure 2.26 A deep-red garnet crystal embedded in a light-coloured, mica-rich metamorphic rock. (Photo by E. J. Tarbuck)

Figure 2.27 Sample of the mineral orthoclase feldspar. (Photo by E. J. Tarbuck)

differences are mainly attributable to the presence or absence of iron and magnesium. The light silicates contain varying amounts of aluminum, potassium, calcium, and sodium rather than iron and magnesium.

Muscovite is a common member of the mica group. It is light in colour and has a pearly lustre. Like other micas, muscovite has excellent cleavage in one direction. In thin sheets, muscovite is transparent to translucent, a property that accounts for its use in windows during the Middle Ages (called Muscovy glass). Because muscovite is very shiny, it can often be identified by the sparkle it gives a rock. If you have ever looked closely at beach sand, you may have seen the glimmering brilliance of the mica flakes scattered among the other sand grains.

Feldspar, the most common mineral group, can form under a very wide range of temperatures and pressures, a fact that partially accounts for its abundance. All feldspars have similar physical properties: They have two planes of cleavage meeting at or near 90-degree angles, are relatively hard (6 on the Mohs scale), and have a lustre that ranges from glassy to pearly. As one component in a rock, feldspar crystals can be identified by their rectangular shape and rather smooth, shiny faces (Figure 2.27).

Two different feldspar structures exist. *Orthoclase* is a type of feldspar that contains potassium ions in its structure and is therefore often called *potassium feldspar*. The other type, *plagioclase feldspar*, contains both sodium and calcium ions that can freely substitute for each other during crystallization.

Orthoclase feldspar is usually light cream to salmon pink, whereas the plagioclase feldspars tend to range from white to grey to blue-green. However, colour should not be used to distinguish these two types. A more reliable method is to look for fine, parallel, scratch-like lines called *striations* that are commonly present on cleavage planes of plagioclase feldspar but absent in orthoclase feldspar (Figure 2.28).

Quartz is the only common silicate mineral that consists entirely of silicon and oxygen. As such, the term *silica* is applied to quartz, which has the chemical formula SiO_2. As the structure of quartz contains a ratio of two oxygen ions (O^{2-}) for every silicon ion (Si^{2+}), no other positive ions are needed to attain neutrality.

Figure 2.28 These parallel lines, called striations, are a distinguishing characteristic of the plagioclase feldspars. (Photo by E. J. Tarbuck)

In quartz a three-dimensional framework is developed mainly through the sharing of oxygens by adjacent silicon ions. The bonds in quartz are primarily the strong silicon–oxygen (covalent) type, rendering it hard and resistant to weathering. As mentioned above, quartz lacks cleavage, but exhibits conchoidal fracture. Pure quartz is clear and colourless and, if allowed to solidify in an open space without interference, can form hexagonal crystals with pyramid-shaped ends (e.g., Figure 2.11B). However, like most other clear minerals, quartz is commonly coloured by the inclusion of various ions (impurities) and often forms without developing good crystal faces. The most common varieties of quartz are milky (white), smoky (grey), rose (pink), amethyst (purple), and rock crystal (clear) (Figure 2.12).

Clay is a term used to describe a variety of complex minerals that, like the micas, have a sheet structure. The clay minerals are generally very fine-grained and can be studied only microscopically. Most clay minerals originate as products of the chemical weathering of other silicate minerals (mainly feldspars). Thus, clay minerals make up a large percentage of the surface material we call soil. Because of the importance of soil in agriculture, and because of its role as a supporting material for buildings, clay minerals are extremely important to humans.

One of the most common clay minerals is *kaolinite*, which is used in the manufacture of fine chinaware and in the production of high-gloss paper, such as that used in this textbook. Further, some clay minerals absorb large amounts of water, which allows them to swell to several times their normal size. These swelling clays have been used as thickening additives to milkshakes in fast-food restaurants, as clumping agents in cat litter, and in several other ingenious ways.

Important Nonsilicate Minerals

Other mineral classes are scarce when compared with the silicates, although many are extremely important geologically and economically. Table 2.2 lists examples of several nonsilicate mineral classes of economic value. A discussion of a few of the more common nonsilicate rock-forming minerals follows.

The *carbonate minerals* are much simpler structurally than are the silicates. This mineral class is composed of the carbonate ion (CO_3^{2-}) and one or more kinds of cations. The two most common carbonate minerals are *calcite*, $CaCO_3$ (calcium carbonate); and *dolomite*, $CaMg(CO_3)_2$ (calcium–magnesium carbonate). Because these minerals are similar both physically and chemically, they are difficult to distinguish from each other. Both have a vitreous lustre, a hardness of 3 to 4, and nearly perfect rhombic cleavage (in three directions, not at 90 degrees; see Figure 2.14). They can, however, be distinguished by using dilute hydrochloric acid. As noted earlier, calcite reacts vigorously with this acid; dolomite reacts much more slowly. Calcite and dolomite are usually found together as the primary constituents in the sedimentary rocks limestone (in which calcite dominates) and dolostone (in which dolomite dominates). Limestone has numerous economic uses as road aggregate, building stone, and the main ingredient in portland cement.

Three other nonsilicate minerals found in sedimentary rocks are *halite*, *sylvite*, and *gypsum*.

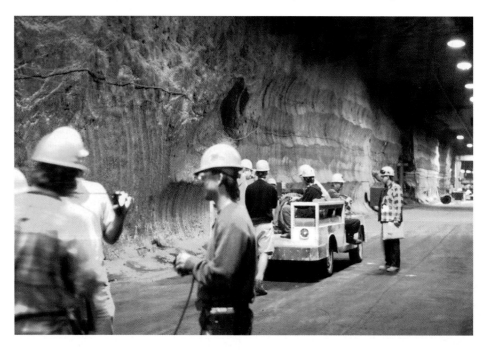

Figure 2.29 Thick beds of potash (potassium-rich salt deposit) in an underground mine in Saskatchewan. (Photo by Jisuo Jin)

TABLE 2.2 Common Nonsilicate Mineral Classes

Class	Member	Formula	Economic Use
Oxides	Hematite	Fe_2O_3	Ore of iron, pigment
	Magnetite	Fe_3O_4	Ore of iron
	Corundum	Al_2O_3	Gemstone, abrasive
	Ice	H_2O	Solid form of water
	Chromite	$FeCr_2O_4$	Ore of chromium
	Ilmenite	$FeTiO_3$	Ore of titanium
Hydroxides	Limonite	$FeO(OH) \bullet nH_2O$	Ore of iron, pigments
	Bauxite	$Al(OH)_3 \bullet nH_2O$	Ore of aluminum
Sulphides	Galena	PbS	Ore of lead
	Sphalerite	ZnS	Ore of zinc
	Pyrite	FeS_2	Sulphuric acid production
	Chalcopyrite	$CuFeS_2$	Ore of copper
	Bornite	Cu_5FeS_4	Ore of copper
	Cinnabar	HgS	Ore of mercury
Sulphates	Gypsum	$CaSO_4 \bullet 2H_2O$	Plaster
	Anhydrite	$CaSO_4$	Plaster
	Barite	$BaSO_4$	Drilling mud
Native elements	Gold	Au	Trade, jewellery
	Copper	Cu	Electrical conductor
	Diamond	C	Gemstone, abrasive
	Sulphur	S	Sulpha drugs, chemicals
	Graphite	C	Pencil lead, dry lubricant
	Silver	Ag	Jewellery, photography
	Platinum	Pt	Catalyst
Halides	Halite	$NaCl$	Common salt
	Fluorite	CaF_2	Component of steelmaking
	Sylvite	KCl	Fertilizer
Carbonates	Calcite	$CaCO_3$	Portland cement, lime
	Dolomite	$CaMg(CO_3)_2$	Portland cement, lime
	Malachite	$Cu_2CO_3(OH)_2$	Gemstone
	Azurite	$Cu_3(CO_3)_2(OH)_2$	Pigment
Phosphates	Apatite	$Ca_5(PO_4)_3(F,Cl,OH)$	Fertilizer
	Turquoise	$CuAl_6(PO_4)_4(OH)_8 \bullet 4H_2O$	Gemstone

These minerals are commonly found in thick layers, which are the last vestiges of ancient seas and saline lakes that have long since evaporated (Figure 2.29). Like limestone, they are important nonmetallic resources. Halite is the mineral name for common table salt (NaCl), whereas sylvite (KCl) is the principal mineral of potash used in fertilizers. Gypsum ($CaSO_4 \bullet 2H_2O$), calcium sulphate with water bound into the structure, is the mineral from which plaster and other similar building materials are made.

A number of other minerals are prized for their economic value (see Table 2.2 and Box 2.2). Included in this category are the ores of metals, such as hematite (iron), sphalerite (zinc), and galena (lead); the native (free-occurring, not in compounds) elements, including gold, silver, and carbon (diamonds); and a host of others, such as fluorite, corundum, and uraninite (a uranium source).*

---

*For more on the economic significance of these and other minerals, see Chapter 20.

BOX
2.2   UNDERSTANDING EARTH

Gemstones

Precious stones have been prized since antiquity. But misinformation abounds regarding gems and their mineral makeup. This stems partly from the ancient practice of grouping precious stones by colour rather than by mineral makeup. For example, *rubies* and red *spinels* are very similar in colour, but they are completely different minerals. Classifying by colour led to the more common spinels being passed off as rubies to royalty. Even today, with modern identification techniques, common *yellow quartz* is sometimes sold as the more valuable gemstone *topaz*.

Figure 2.B Australian sapphires showing variation in cuts and colours. (Photo by Fred Ward/Black Star)

Naming Gemstones

Most precious stones have common names that are different from their parent mineral. For example, *sapphire* is one of two names given to the mineral *corundum*. Minute amounts of foreign elements can produce vivid sapphires of nearly every colour (Figure 2.B). Traces of titanium and iron in corundum produce the most-prized: blue sapphires. When corundum contains a sufficient quantity of chromium, it exhibits a brilliant red colour, and the gemstone is called *ruby*. If a specimen is not suitable as a gem, it simply goes by the mineral name *corundum*. Because of its hardness, corundum that is not of gem quality is often crushed and sold as an abrasive. Most natural rubies and sapphires have been heated and recrystallized to enhance their clarity and colour.

To summarize, when corundum exhibits a red hue, it is called *ruby*, but if it exhibits any other colour, the gemstone is called *sapphire*. Whereas corundum is the base mineral for two gemstones, quartz is the parent of more than a dozen gemstones. Table 2.A lists some well-known gemstones and their parent minerals.

What Constitutes a Gemstone?

When found in their natural state, most gemstones are dull and would be passed over by most people as just another rock. Gems must be cut and polished by experienced professionals before their true beauty is displayed (Figure 2.B). Only those mineral specimens that are of such quality that they can command a price in excess of the cost of processing are considered gemstones.

TABLE **2.A**	Important Gemstones	
Gemstone	**Mineral Name**	**Prized Hues**
Precious		
Diamond	Diamond	Colourless, yellows
Emerald	Beryl	Greens
Opal	Opal	Brilliant hues
Ruby	Corundum	Reds
Sapphire	Corundum	Blues
Semiprecious		
Alexandrite	Chrysoberyl	Variable
Amethyst	Quartz	Purples
Cat's-eye	Chrysoberyl	Yellows
Chalcedony	Quartz (agate)	Banded
Citrine	Quartz	Yellows
Garnet	Garnet	Reds, greens
Jade	Jadeite or nephrite	Greens
Moonstone	Feldspar	Transparent blues
Peridot	Olivine	Olive greens
Smoky quartz	Quartz	Browns
Spinel	Spinel	Reds
Topaz	Topaz	Purples, reds
Tourmaline	Tourmaline	Reds, blue-greens
Turquoise	Turquoise	Blues
Zircon	Zircon	Reds

Gemstones can be divided into two categories: precious and semi-precious. A *precious* gemstone has beauty, durability, size, and rarity, whereas a *semiprecious* gemstone generally has only one or two of these qualities. The gemstones traditionally held in highest esteem are diamonds, rubies, sapphires, emeralds, and some varieties of opal (Table 2.A). All other gemstones are classified as semi-precious. However, large high-quality specimens of semi-precious stones often command a very high price.

Today translucent stones with evenly tinted colours are preferred. The most favoured hues are red, blue, green, purple, rose, and yellow. The most-prized stones are pigeon-blood rubies, blue sapphires, grass-green emeralds, and canary-yellow diamonds. Colourless gemstones are generally less than desirable, except for diamonds that display flashes of colour known as fire.

The durability of a gemstone depends on its hardness; that is, its resistance to abrasion by objects normally encountered in everyday living. For good durability, gemstones should be as hard as or harder than quartz as defined by the Mohs scale of hardness. One notable exception is opal, which is comparatively soft (hardness of 5 to 6.5) and brittle. Opal's esteem comes from its "fire," which is a display of a variety of brilliant colours, including greens, blues, and reds.

It seems to be human nature to treasure what is rare. In the case of gemstones, large high-quality specimens are much rarer than smaller stones. Thus, large rubies, diamonds, and emeralds, which are rare in addition to being beautiful and durable, command the very highest prices.

In the chapters that follow we will see that minerals combine under different pressure and temperature conditions in the rock cycle (see Chapter 1) to form various rocks. Some minerals are found together because they are formed under similar conditions and/or have similar chemical compositions.

CHAPTER SUMMARY

- A mineral is a natural, usually inorganic solid with a chemical structure that gives it unique physical properties. Most rocks are aggregates of minerals. Building blocks of minerals are elements. An atom is the smallest particle having characteristics of an element. Each atom has a nucleus containing protons (positive charges) and neutrons (no charges). Surrounding the nucleus are electrons (negative charges).

- In ionic bonds electrons are transferred between atoms resulting in net positive or negative charged ions. In covalent bonds atoms share electrons. Mineral properties include crystal habit, lustre, colour, streak, hardness, cleavage, fracture, specific gravity, and others used to tell minerals apart.

- Oxygen, silicon, aluminum, iron, calcium, sodium, potassium, and magnesium make up most of the common minerals and over 98 percent of continental crust.

- The most common mineral class is the silicates, all of which contain silicon–oxygen tetrahedra. Tetrahedra can be linked in chains (pyroxene, amphibole), sheets (micas), or networks (feldspar, quartz) bonded by iron, magnesium, potassium, sodium, aluminum, and calcium cations.

- Common nonsilicate classes include carbonates (e.g., calcite), oxides (e.g., hematite), sulphides (e.g., sphalerite), sulphates (e.g., gypsum), halides (e.g., halite), and native elements (e.g., gold).

MasteringGeology

www.masteringgeology.com

Looking for additional review and test prep materials? Visit the Study Area in MasteringGeology to enhance your understanding of this chapter's content by accessing a variety of resources, including

Self-Study Quizzes, Geoscience Animations, GEODe Tutorials, RSS feeds, flashcards, weblinks, self-study quizzes, and an optional Pearson eText.

REVIEW QUESTIONS

1. List the three main particles of an atom and explain how they differ from one another. What are the characteristics a material must have in order to be considered a true mineral?

2. Based on the criteria outlined in this chapter, could ice be considered a mineral? Discuss.

3. What is the difference between a mineral and a rock?

4. Explain the difference between ionic and covalent bonding.

5. What is the difference between silicon, silica, and silicate?

6. What is the difference between cleavage and fracture?

7. How would you determine whether a flat surface on a mineral crystal is a crystal face or a cleavage plane?

8. If you were given a mineral specimen of unknown hardness and a full set of minerals (and other materials) of known hardness, how would you determine the hardness of the "unknown" mineral using Mohs scale as a guide?

9. What are the main types of silicate structures (i.e., the manner in which silica units are arranged and/or linked within mineral crystals) represented in (a) the ferromagnesian mineral groups (olivine, pyroxene, amphibole, and biotite mica), (b) the feldspars, and (c) quartz?

IGNEOUS ROCKS

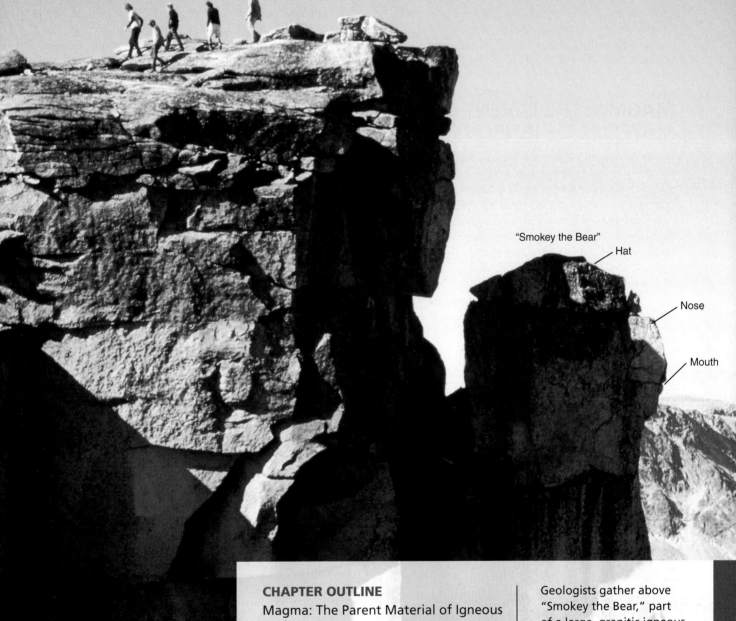

"Smokey the Bear"

Hat

Nose

Mouth

Geologists gather above "Smokey the Bear," part of a large, granitic igneous intrusion in Cathedral Provincial Park in south-central British Columbia. (Photo by Peter Rotheisler)

Igneous rocks make up the bulk of Earth's crust. In fact, with the exception of Earth's core, the remaining solid portion of our planet is basically a huge mass of igneous rocks that is partially covered by a thin veneer of sedimentary and metamorphic rocks. Consequently, a basic knowledge of igneous rocks is essential to our understanding of the structure, composition, and internal workings of our planet.

MAGMA: THE PARENT MATERIAL OF IGNEOUS ROCK

In our discussion of the rock cycle (Chapter 1), it was pointed out that **igneous rocks** (*ignis* = fire) form as molten rock cools and solidifies. Abundant evidence indicates that the parent material for igneous rocks—called *magma*—is formed by a process called **partial melting**. Partial melting occurs at various levels within Earth's crust and upper mantle to depths of perhaps 250 kilometres. We will explore the origin of magma in the next section.

Once it is formed, a magma body buoyantly rises toward the surface because it is less dense than the surrounding rocks. Occasionally molten rock breaks through, producing a volcanic eruption. Magma that reaches Earth's surface is called **lava**. The lava fountain shown in Figure 3.1 was produced when escaping gases propelled molten rock from a magma chamber. Sometimes magma is explosively ejected from a vent, producing a catastrophic eruption. However, not all volcanic eruptions are as violent as this. Some volcanoes emit quiet outpourings of very fluid lava.

Igneous rocks that form when magma solidifies *at the surface* are classified as **extrusive** (*ex* = out, *trudere* = thrust), or **volcanic** (after the fire god Vulcan). Extrusive igneous rocks are abundant in western portions of the Americas, including the volcanic cones of the Cascade Range and the extensive lava flows of the Columbia Plateau. In addition, many oceanic islands, such as the Hawaiian chain, are composed almost entirely of volcanic igneous rocks.

Magma that loses its mobility before reaching the surface eventually crystallizes at depth. Igneous rocks that *form at depth* are termed **intrusive** (*in* = into, *trudere* = thrust), or **plutonic** (after Pluto, the god of the lower world in classical mythology). A body of plutonic rock is called a **pluton**. Intrusive igneous rocks

Figure 3.1 Recent eruption of Hawaii's Kilauea Volcano. (Photo by U.S. Geological Survey)

would not be exposed at the surface if portions of the crust were not uplifted and the overlying rocks stripped away by erosion. Exposures of intrusive igneous rocks occur in many places, including much of western and central British Columbia, the St. Lawrence region of Quebec (e.g., Mount Royal in Montreal), the highlands of the Maritimes, and in the Sweetgrass Hills area of Montana just south of Alberta. Very ancient igneous intrusions are also exposed throughout the Canadian Shield, which includes much of Nunavut; the Northwest Territories; much of Manitoba, Ontario, and Quebec; and parts of Alberta and Saskatchewan.

Generating Magma from Solid Rock

Most magma probably originates from melting in Earth's mantle and plate tectonics play a major role in the generation of most magma. The greatest amount of igneous activity occurs at divergent plate boundaries, often in association with sea-floor spreading. Substantial amounts of magma are also produced at subduction zones, where oceanic lithosphere descends into the mantle. The magma generated here contains components of the mantle as well as subducted crust and subducted sediments. In addition, some magma appears to be generated deep in the mantle where it is not influenced directly by plate motions.

Based on available scientific evidence, *Earth's crust and mantle are composed primarily of solid, not molten, rock*. Although the outer core is a fluid, its iron-rich material is very dense and remains deep within Earth. So what is the source of magma that produces igneous activity?

Geologists conclude that magma originates when essentially solid rock, located in the crust and upper mantle, melts. The most obvious way to generate magma from solid rock is to raise the temperature above the rock's melting point.

ROLE OF HEAT Workers in underground mines know that temperatures get higher as they go deeper. Although the rate of temperature change varies from place to place, it *averages* about 25C° per kilometre in the *upper* crust. This change in temperature with depth is known as the **geothermal gradient** (Figure 3.2). Estimates indicate that the temperature at a depth of 100 kilometres ranges between 1200°C and 1400°C. At these high temperatures, rocks in the lower crust and upper mantle are near their melting points; they are very hot but still essentially solid.

Enough additional heat can be generated within the crust or upper mantle to produce some magma in several ways. First, at subduction zones, friction generates heat as huge slabs of lithosphere slide past one another. Second, crustal rocks are

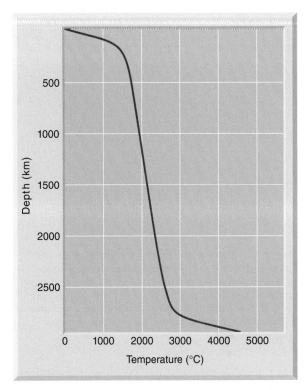

Figure 3.2 This graph illustrates the estimated temperature distribution for the crust and mantle. Notice that temperature increases significantly from the surface to the base of the lithosphere (100-kilometre depth) and that the temperature gradient (rate of change) is much less in the mantle. Because the temperature difference between the top and bottom of the mantle is relatively small, geologists conclude that slow convective flow (hot material rising and cool material sinking) must occur in the mantle.

heated as they descend into the mantle during subduction. Third, hot mantle rocks can rise and intrude crustal rocks. Although all of these processes generate some magma, the quantities produced are relatively small and the distribution is very limited.

As you will see, the vast bulk of magma forms without the aid of an additional heat source. Rock that is near its melting point can begin to melt if the confining pressure drops or if **volatiles** (fluids, gases) are introduced. We will now consider the roles that pressure and volatiles play in generating magma.

ROLE OF PRESSURE If temperature were the only factor that determined whether or not rock melts, our planet would be a molten ball covered with a thin, solid outer shell. This, of course, is not the case. The reason is that pressure also increases with depth.

Melting, which is accompanied by an increase in volume, *occurs at higher temperatures at depth* because of greater confining pressure (Figure 3.3). Consequently, an increase in confining pressure causes a rise in the rock's melting temperature. Conversely, reducing confining pressure lowers a

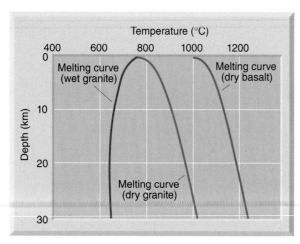

Figure 3.3 Idealized melting temperature curves. These curves portray the minimum temperatures required to melt rock within Earth's crust. Notice that dry granite and dry basalt melt at higher temperatures with increasing depth. By contrast, the melting temperature of wet granite actually decreases as the confining pressure increases.

rock's melting temperature. When confining pressure drops enough, **decompression melting** is triggered. This can occur when rock *ascends* as a result of convective upwelling, thereby moving into zones of lower pressure. (Recall that even though the mantle

is a solid, it does flow at very slow rates over millions of years.) This process is responsible for generating magma along ocean ridges where plates are rifting apart (Figure 3.4).

ROLE OF VOLATILES Water and other volatiles (mainly gases) cause rock to melt at lower temperatures. Further, the effect of volatiles is magnified by increased pressure. Consequently, "wet" rock buried at depth has a much lower melting temperature than does "dry" rock of the same composition and under the same confining pressure (see Figure 3.3). Therefore, in addition to a rock's composition, its temperature, depth (confining pressure), and water content determine whether it exists as a solid or liquid.

Volatiles play an important role in generating magma in regions where cool slabs of oceanic lithosphere descend into the mantle (Figure 3.5). As an oceanic plate sinks, both heat and pressure drive water from the subducting crustal rocks. These volatiles, which are very mobile, migrate into the wedge of hot mantle that lies above. This process is believed to lower the melting temperature of mantle rock sufficiently to generate some melt. Laboratory studies have shown that the melting point of basalt can be lowered by as much as 100C° by the addition of only 0.1 percent water.

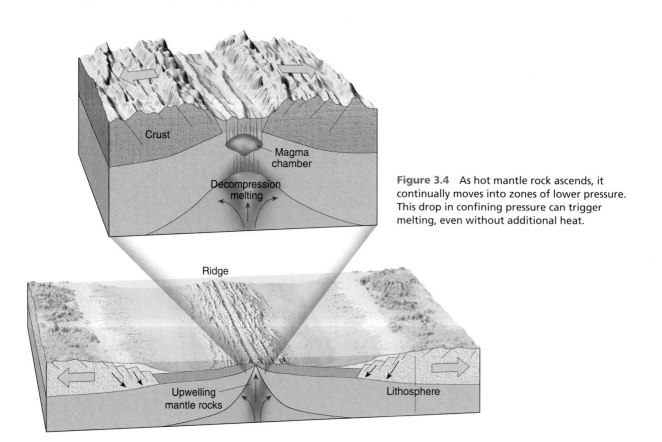

Figure 3.4 As hot mantle rock ascends, it continually moves into zones of lower pressure. This drop in confining pressure can trigger melting, even without additional heat.

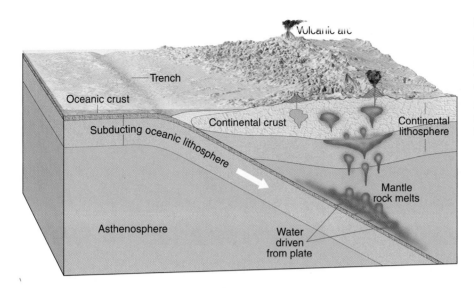

Figure 3.5 As a plate of oceanic lithosphere descends into the mantle, water and other volatiles are driven from the subducting crustal rocks. These volatiles lower the melting temperature of mantle rock sufficiently to generate melt.

When enough mantle-derived **mafic** (from *ma*gnesium and *fer*rum, the Latin name for iron) magma forms, it will buoyantly rise toward the surface. In a continental setting, mafic magma may pond beneath crustal rocks, which have a lower density and are already near their melting temperature. This pooling can result in some melting of the crust and the formation of a secondary, silica-rich or **felsic** (from *fel*dspar and *silica*) magma.

In summary, magma can be generated under three sets of conditions: (1) *heat* can be added, for example, by a magma body from a deeper source intruding and melting crustal rock; (2) *a decrease in pressure* (without the addition of heat) can result in *decompression melting*; and (3) the *introduction of volatiles* (mainly water) can lower the melting temperature of mantle rock sufficiently to generate magma.

The Nature of Magma

Magma is completely or partly molten material that, on cooling, solidifies to form an igneous rock. Most magmas consist of three distinct parts: a liquid component, a solid component, and a gaseous phase.

The liquid portion, called **melt**, is composed of mobile ions of those elements commonly found in Earth's crust. Melt is made up mostly of ions of silicon and oxygen, as well as lesser amounts of aluminum, potassium, calcium, sodium, iron, and magnesium.

The solid components (if any) in magma are silicate minerals that have already crystallized from the melt. As a magma body cools, the size and number of crystals increases. During the last stage of cooling, a magma body is mostly a crystalline solid with only minor amounts of melt.

Water vapour (H_2O), carbon dioxide (CO_2), and sulphur dioxide (SO_2) are the most common volatile components of magma and are confined by the immense pressure exerted by the overlying rocks. These volatiles are dissolved within the melt and will readily vaporize (form a gas) at surface pressures. Volatiles remain part of the magma either until it moves near the surface (low-pressure environment), or until the magma body is essentially crystallized, at which time any remaining volatiles freely migrate away. These hot fluids play an important role in metamorphism and will be considered further in Chapter 7.

From Magma to Crystalline Rock

As magma cools, the ions in the melt begin to lose their mobility and arrange themselves into orderly crystalline structures. This process, called **crystallization**, generates various silicate minerals that reside within the remaining melt.

When magma cools, it is generally the silicon and oxygen atoms that link together first to form silicon–oxygen tetrahedra, the basic building blocks of the silicate minerals (Chapter 2). As magma continues to lose heat to its surroundings, the tetrahedra join with each other and with other ions to form embryonic crystal nuclei. Slowly, each nucleus grows as ions lose their mobility and join the crystalline network.

The earliest formed minerals have space to grow and tend to have better developed crystal faces than do the later ones that fill the remaining space. Eventually, all of the melt is transformed into a solid mass of interlocking silicate minerals that we call an igneous rock (Figure 3.6).

A

B

Figure 3.6 **A.** Close-up of interlocking crystals in a coarse-grained igneous rock. The largest crystals are about 1 centimetre in length. **B.** Photomicrograph (photo taken through a microscope) of interlocking crystals in a coarse-grained igneous rock. (Photos by E. J. Tarbuck)

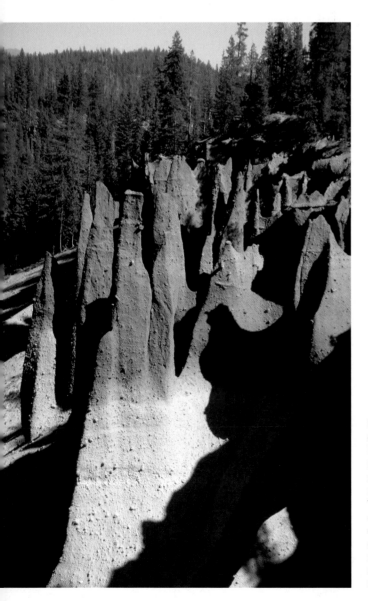

As you will see later, the crystallization of magma is much more complex than just described. Whereas a single compound, such as water, crystallizes at a specific temperature, solidification of magma, with its diverse chemistry, spans a temperature range of at least 200C°. During crystallization, the composition of the melt continually changes as ions are selectively removed and incorporated into the earliest formed minerals. If the melt should separate from the earliest formed minerals, its composition will be different from that of the original magma. Thus, a single magma can generate rocks with widely differing compositions. Consequently, a great variety of igneous rocks exist.

HOW MAGMAS EVOLVE

Because of the large variety of igneous rocks, it is logical to assume that an equally large variety of magmas also exist. However, geologists have observed that a single volcano can extrude a number of lavas that exhibit quite different compositions (Figure 3.7). Data of this type led geologists to examine the

Figure 3.7 Ash and pumice ejected during a large eruption of Mt. Mazama (Crater Lake). Notice the gradation from light-coloured, silica-rich ash near the base to dark-coloured rocks at the top. It is likely that before this eruption the magma began to segregate as the less dense silica-rich (felsic) magma migrated toward the top of the magma chamber. The zonation seen in the rocks resulted because a sustained eruption tapped deeper and deeper levels of the magma chamber. Thus, this rock sequence is an inverted representation of the compositional zonation in the magma body; that is, the magma from the top of the chamber erupted first and is found at the base of these ash deposits and vice versa. (Photo by E. J. Tarbuck)

BOX
3.1

CANADIAN PROFILE
Norman Bowen and His Reaction Series

Based on his high-temperature, high-pressure experiments and microscopic studies of igneous rocks (Figure 3.A), Norman Bowen's reaction series provides a visual representation of the order in which minerals crystallize from a magma of average composition (see Figure 3.8). This model assumes that the magma cools slowly at depth in an otherwise unchanging environment. Notice that Bowen's reaction series is divided into two branches: a discontinuous series and a continuous series. Discontinuous refers to the changing crystal structures of minerals within the series, whereas all the minerals in the continuous series have the same crystal structure.

Discontinuous Reaction Series

The upper left branch of Bowen's reaction series, called the *discontinuous reaction series*, indicates that as a magma cools, olivine is the first mineral to crystallize. Once formed, olivine chemically reacts with the remaining melt to form pyroxene (see Figure 3.8). In this reaction, olivine, which is composed of individual silicon–oxygen tetrahedra, incorporates more silica into its structure, thereby linking its tetrahedra into single-chain structures of pyroxene. (Note: Pyroxene has a lower crystallization temperature than olivine and is more stable at lower temperatures.) As the magma body cools further, pyroxene crystals react with the melt to generate the double-chain structure of amphibole, which in turn reacts with the melt to form the sheet-silicate biotite. These reactions do not usually run to completion, so various amounts of each mineral in the series may exist at any given time.

In fact, some minerals, such as biotite, may never form.

Continuous Reaction Series

The right branch of the reaction series, called the *continuous reaction series*, illustrates that calcium-rich plagioclase feldspar crystals react with the sodium ions in the melt to become progressively more sodium rich (see Figure 3.8). Here, the sodium ions diffuse into the feldspar crystals and displace the calcium ions in the crystal lattice.

During the last stage of crystallization, after much of the magma has solidified, potassium feldspar forms. Finally, if the remaining melt has excess silica, the mineral quartz forms.

Testing Bowen's Reaction Series

During an eruption of Hawaii's Kilauea volcano in 1965, mafic lava poured into a pit crater, forming a lava lake that became a natural laboratory for testing Bowen's reaction series. When the surface of the lava lake cooled enough to form a crust, geologists drilled through it into the magma and periodically removed samples that were quenched to preserve the melt and minerals that were growing within it. By sampling the lava at successive stages of cooling, a history of crystallization was recorded.

As Bowen's reaction series predicts, olivine crystallized early but later ceased to form and was partly resorbed into the cooling melt. (In a larger magma body that cooled more slowly, we would expect most, if not all, of the olivine to react with the melt and change to pyroxene.) Most importantly, the melt changed composition throughout the course of

Figure 3.A Norman Levi Bowen (1887–1956), studying his reaction series with a polarizing microscope. Bowen was born in Kingston, Ontario, graduated from Queen's University, completed his Ph.D. at MIT, then spent most of his professional life at the Geophysical Laboratory, Carnegie Institution, Washington, DC. He was considered the leading expert on igneous rocks.
(Photo courtesy of the Geophysical Laboratory, Carnegie Institution of Washington)

crystallization. In contrast to the original mafic lava, which contained about 50 percent silica (SiO_2), the final melt contained more than 75 percent silica and had a composition similar to granite.

Although the lava in this setting cooled rapidly compared with rates experienced in deep magma chambers, it was slow enough to verify that minerals do crystallize in a systematic fashion that roughly parallels Bowen's reaction series. Further, had the melt been separated at any stage in the cooling process, it would have formed a rock with a composition much different from that of the original lava.

---

possibility that magma might change (evolve) and thus become the parent to a variety of igneous rocks. To explore this idea, a pioneering investigation into the crystallization of magma was carried out by Canadian scientist N. L. Bowen (Box 3.1) in the first quarter of the twentieth century.

Bowen's Reaction Series and the Composition of Igneous Rocks

Recall that ice freezes at a single temperature whereas magma crystallizes through at least 200C° of cooling. In a laboratory setting Bowen and his co-workers

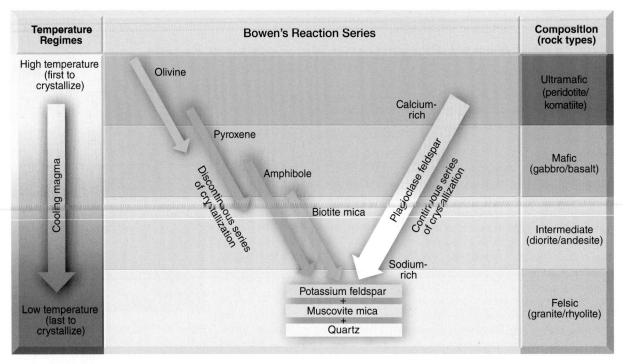

Temperature Regimes	Bowen's Reaction Series	Composition (rock types)

Figure 3.8 Bowen's reaction series shows the sequence in which minerals crystallize from magma. Note that each rock group consists of minerals that crystallize in the same temperature range.

demonstrated that as a mafic magma cools, minerals tend to crystallize in a systematic fashion based on their melting points. As shown in Figure 3.8, the first mineral to crystallize from a mafic magma is the ferromagnesian mineral olivine. Further cooling generates calcium-rich plagioclase feldspar as well as pyroxene, and so forth down the diagram.

During the crystallization process, the composition of the liquid portion of the magma continually changes. For example, at the stage when about a third of the magma has solidified, the melt will be nearly depleted of iron, magnesium, and calcium because these elements are constituents of the earliest-formed minerals. The removal of these elements from the melt will cause it to become enriched in sodium and potassium. Further, because the original mafic magma contained about 50 percent silica (SiO_2), the crystallization of the earliest-formed mineral, olivine, which is only about 40 percent silica, leaves the remaining melt richer in SiO_2. Thus, the silica component of the melt becomes enriched as the magma evolves.

MAGMATIC DIFFERENTIATION Bowen demonstrated that minerals crystallize from magma in a systematic fashion. At one or more stages during crystallization, a separation of the solid and liquid components of a magma can occur. One example is called **crystal settling**. This process occurs when

the earlier-formed minerals are denser (heavier) than the liquid portion and sink toward the bottom of the magma chamber (Figure 3.9), thereby becoming separated from the melt. When the remaining melt solidifies—either in place or in another location if it migrates into fractures in the surrounding rocks—it will form a rock with a chemical composition much different from the parent magma (Figure 3.9). The formation of one or more secondary magmas from a single parent magma is called **magmatic differentiation**.

At any stage in the evolution of a magma, the solid and liquid components can separate into two chemically distinct units. Further, magmatic differentiation within the secondary melt can generate additional chemically distinct fractions. Consequently, magmatic differentiation and separation of the solid and liquid components at various stages of crystallization can produce several chemically diverse magmas and ultimately a variety of igneous rocks (see Figure 3.9). Bowen also demonstrated that if the solid components of a magma remain in contact with the remaining melt, they will chemically react and evolve into the next mineral in the sequence shown in Figure 3.8. For this reason, this arrangement of minerals became known as **Bowen's reaction series** (see Box 3.1).

Figure 3.8 depicts the sequence in which minerals crystallize from a magma of average

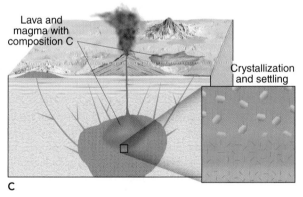

Figure 3.9 Illustration of how a magma evolves as the earliest-formed minerals (those richer in iron, magnesium, and calcium) crystallize and settle to the bottom of the magma chamber, leaving the remaining melt richer in sodium, potassium, and silica (SiO_2). **A.** Emplacement of a magma body and associated igneous activity generates rocks that have a composition similar to that of the initial magma. **B.** After a time, crystallization and settling changes the composition of the melt, while generating rocks that have a composition quite different from the original magma. **C.** Further magmatic differentiation results in another more highly evolved melt with its associated rock types.

composition under laboratory conditions. However, we find that minerals that form in the same general temperature regime in Bowen's reaction series are also found together in the same igneous rocks. For example the minerals quartz, potassium feldspar, and muscovite are located in the same region of Bowen's

diagram, and are typically found together as major constituents of the plutonic igneous rock granite. Thus Bowen's work was a major breakthrough in understanding igneous rocks. However, later work showed that magmatic differentiation by crystal settling alone cannot account for the entire compositional spectrum of igneous rocks; other mechanisms must be involved.

ASSIMILATION Once a magma body forms, its composition can change through the incorporation of foreign material. For example, as magma migrates upward, it may incorporate some of the surrounding host rock, a process called **assimilation** (Figure 3.10). This process can operate in a near-surface environment, where rocks are brittle. As the magma pushes upward, stress causes numerous cracks in the overlying rock. The force of the injected magma is often sufficient to dislodge blocks of "foreign" rock and incorporate them into the magma body. In deeper environments, the magma may be hot enough to simply melt and assimilate some of the surrounding host rock, which is near its melting temperature.

MAGMA MIXING Another means by which the composition of a magma body can be altered is called **magma mixing**. This process occurs whenever one magma body intrudes another (Figure 3.10). Once combined, convective flow can stir the two magmas and generate a fluid with an intermediate composition. Magma mixing can occur during the ascent of two chemically distinct magma bodies, when the more buoyant mass overtakes the slower moving mass.

In summary, Bowen successfully demonstrated that through crystal settling and magmatic differentiation, a single parent magma can generate several mineralogically different igneous rocks. Thus, this process, in concert with magma mixing and contamination by crustal rocks, accounts in part for the great diversity of magmas and igneous rocks. We will next look at another important process, partial melting, which also generates magmas that have varying compositions.

Partial Melting and Magma Formation

Recall that the crystallization of a magma occurs over a temperature range of at least 200C°. As you might expect, melting, the reverse process, spans a similar temperature range. As rock begins to melt, those minerals with the lowest melting temperatures melt first. If melting continues, minerals with higher

Assimilation of country rock

Crystallization and settling

Figure 3.10 This illustration shows three ways that the composition of a magma body can be altered: magma mixing, assimilation of host (country) rock, and crystallization and settling (magmatic differentiation).

melting points begin to melt and the composition of the magma steadily approaches the overall composition of the rock from which it was derived. Most often, however, melting is not complete. The incomplete melting of rocks is known as partial melting, a process that produces most, if not all, magma.

Notice in Figure 3.8 that rocks with a felsic composition are composed of minerals with the lowest melting (crystallization) temperatures—namely, quartz and potassium feldspar. Also note that as we move up Bowen's reaction series, the minerals have progressively higher melting temperatures and that olivine, which is found at the top, has the highest melting point. When a rock undergoes partial melting, it will form a melt that is enriched in ions from minerals with the lowest melting temperatures. The unmelted crystals are those of minerals with higher melting temperatures. Separation of these two fractions would yield a melt with a chemical composition that is richer in silica and nearer to the felsic end of the spectrum than the rock from which it was derived.

FORMATION OF A MAFIC MAGMA Most mafic magmas probably originate from partial melting of *peridotite*, a dark-coloured igneous rock that is thought to be the main constituent of the upper mantle. Mafic magmas that originate from direct melting of mantle rocks are called *primary* magmas because they have not yet evolved. Melting to produce these mantle-derived magmas can be triggered by a reduction in confining pressure (decompression melting). This can occur, for example, where mantle

rock ascends as part of slow-moving convective flow at mid-ocean ridges (see Figure 3.4). Recall that mafic magmas can also be generated at subduction zones, where water driven from the descending slab of oceanic crust promotes partial melting of mantle rocks (see Figure 3.5).

Because most mafic magma forms between 50 and 250 kilometres below the surface, we might expect that this material would cool and crystallize at depth. However, as mafic magma migrates upward, the confining pressure steadily diminishes and reduces its melting temperature. As you will see in the next chapter, environments exist in which mafic magmas ascend rapidly enough that the heat loss to the surrounding environment is offset by the drop in the melting temperature. Consequently, large outpourings of mafic lavas are common at Earth's surface. In some situations, however, mafic magmas that are comparatively dense will collect beneath crustal rocks and crystallize at depth.

FORMATION OF ANDESITIC AND FELSIC MAGMAS
Intermediate and felsic magmas are found only within, or adjacent to, continental margins (Figure 3.5). Interactions between mantle-derived mafic magmas and more silica-rich components of Earth's crust generate these magmas. For example, as a mafic magma migrates upward, it may melt and assimilate some of the crustal rocks through which it ascends.

The result is the formation of a more silica-rich magma of **intermediate composition** or **andesitic composition** (between mafic and felsic).

Figure 3.11 Eruption in 1996 of Mount Ruapehu, Tongariro National Park, New Zealand. Volcanoes that border the Pacific Ocean are fed largely by magmas that have intermediate to felsic compositions. These silica-rich magmas often erupt explosively, generating large plumes of volcanic dust and ash. (Photo © NHPA/Photoshot)

Magma of intermediate composition can also evolve from a mafic magma by the process of magmatic differentiation. Recall from our discussion of Bowen's reaction series that as mafic magma solidifies, it is the silica-poor ferromagnesian minerals that crystallize first. If these iron-rich components are separated from the liquid by crystal settling, the remaining melt, now enriched in silica, will have a composition more akin to andesite. These evolved (changed) magmas are termed *secondary magmas*.

Felsic rocks are found in much too large a quantity to be generated solely from the magmatic differentiation of primary mafic magmas. Most likely they are the end product of the crystallization of an intermediate magma, or the product of partial melting of silica-rich continental rocks. The heat to melt crustal rocks often comes from hot mantle-derived mafic magmas that formed above a subducting plate within the crust.

Felsic melts are higher in silica and thus more viscous (thicker) than other magmas. Felsic magmas are also formed at lower temperatures than other magmas. Therefore, in contrast to mafic magmas that frequently produce vast outpourings of lava, felsic magmas usually lose their mobility before reaching the surface and tend to produce large plutonic bodies. On those occasions when silica-rich magmas do reach the surface, explosive eruptions, such as from Mount Ruapehu in New Zealand (Figure 3.11) and Mount St. Helens in Washington State (which famously blew its top in 1980), are the result.

IGNEOUS COMPOSITIONS

Igneous rocks are mainly composed of silicate minerals. Furthermore, the mineral makeup of a particular igneous rock is ultimately determined by the chemical composition of the magma from which it crystallizes. Recall that magma is composed largely of the eight elements that are the major constituents of the silicate minerals. Chemical analysis shows that silicon and oxygen (usually expressed as the silica [SiO_2] content of a magma) are by far the most abundant constituents of igneous rocks. These two elements, plus ions of aluminum (Al), calcium (Ca), sodium (Na), potassium (K), magnesium (Mg), and iron (Fe), make up roughly 98 percent by weight of most magmas. In addition, magma contains small amounts of many other elements, including titanium and manganese, and trace amounts of much rarer elements, such as gold, silver, and uranium.

As magma cools and solidifies, these elements combine to form two major groups of silicate minerals. The dark (or ferromagnesian) silicates are rich in iron or magnesium or both and comparatively low in silica. Olivine, pyroxene, amphibole, and biotite mica (Figure 3.8) are the common dark silicate minerals of Earth's crust. By contrast the light (or nonferromagnesian) silicates contain greater amounts of potassium, sodium, and calcium rather than iron and magnesium. As a group these minerals are richer in silica than are the dark silicates. The light silicates include quartz, muscovite mica, and the most abundant mineral group, the feldspars. The feldspars make up at least 40 percent of most igneous rocks.

Felsic versus Mafic Compositions

Despite their great compositional diversity, igneous rocks (and the magmas from which they form) can be divided into broad groups according to their proportions of light and dark minerals (Figure 3.12). At one end of the continuum are rocks composed almost entirely of light-coloured silicates: quartz and feldspar. Igneous rocks in which these are the dominant minerals are said to be felsic. In addition to quartz and feldspar, most felsic rocks contain about 10 percent dark silicate minerals, usually biotite mica and amphibole. Felsic rocks are rich in silica (about 70 percent) and are major constituents of the continental crust. Because granite is the most common type of felsic rock, some geologists refer to felsic rocks as having a **granitic** composition.

Rocks that contain substantial dark silicate minerals and calcium-rich plagioclase feldspar (but no quartz) are said to be mafic (Figure 3.12). This is because they contain a high percentage of ferromagnesian minerals. Because of their iron content, mafic rocks are typically darker and denser than felsic rocks. Mafic rocks are also referred to as having a **basaltic** composition because the most common rock type of this composition is basalt. Mafic rocks make up the ocean floor as well as many of the

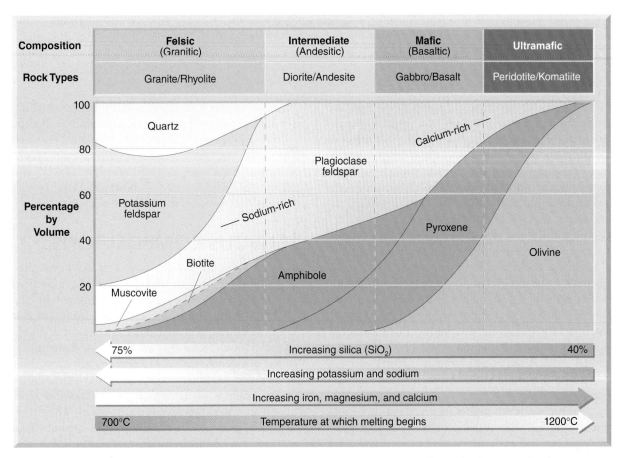

Figure 3.12 Mineralogy of common igneous rocks and the magmas from which they form. The first named rock type in each pair is the intrusive form; the second is its extrusive equivalent (same mineralogy). (After Dietrich, Daily, and Larsen)

volcanic islands located within the ocean basins, and they are also found on the continents.

Other Compositional Groups

As you can see in Figure 3.12, rocks with a composition between felsic and mafic are said to have an intermediate or andesitic composition, after the common volcanic rock *andesite*. Intermediate rocks contain at least 25 percent dark silicate minerals, mainly amphibole, pyroxene, and biotite mica, with the other dominant mineral being plagioclase feldspar. This important category of igneous rocks is associated with volcanic activity that is commonly confined to the margins of the continents (see Figure 3.5).

Another important igneous rock, peridotite, contains mostly olivine and pyroxene and thus falls on the opposite side of the compositional spectrum from felsic rocks (see Figure 3.12). Because peridotite is composed almost entirely of ferromagnesian minerals, its chemical composition is referred to as **ultramafic**. Although ultramafic rocks are rare at Earth's surface, peridotite is believed to be the main constituent of the upper mantle. The volcanic equivalent of peridotite is komatiite.

Silica Content as an Indicator of Composition

An important aspect of the chemical composition of igneous rocks is their silica (SiO_2) content. Recall that silicon and oxygen are the two most abundant elements in igneous rocks. Typically the silica content of crustal rocks ranges from a low of about 40 percent in ultramafic rocks to a high of more than 70 percent in felsic rocks (Figure 3.12). The percentage of silica in igneous rocks actually varies in a systematic manner that parallels the abundance of other elements. For example, rocks comparatively low in silica contain large amounts of iron, magnesium, and calcium. By contrast, rocks high in silica contain very small amounts of those elements but are enriched instead in sodium and potassium. Consequently, the chemical makeup of an igneous rock can be inferred directly from its silica content.

Further, the amount of silica present in magma strongly influences its behaviour. Felsic magma, which has a high silica content, is quite viscous and exists as a liquid at temperatures as low as 650°C. Conversely, mafic magmas are low in silica and are generally more fluid. Also, mafic magmas crystallize at higher temperatures than felsic magmas and are completely solid when cooled to 1000°C.

In summary, igneous rocks can be divided into broad groups according to the proportions of light and dark minerals they contain. Felsic rocks, which are almost entirely composed of the light-coloured minerals quartz and feldspar, are at one end of the compositional spectrum (Figure 3.12). Mafic rocks, which contain abundant dark silicate minerals in addition to plagioclase feldspar, make up the other major igneous rock group of Earth's crust. Between these groups are rocks with an intermediate (andesitic) composition, while ultramafic rocks, which lack light-coloured minerals, lie at the other end of the compositional spectrum from felsic rocks.

Although the crystallization of magma is complex, it is nevertheless possible to classify igneous rocks based on their mineral composition and the conditions under which they formed. Their environment during crystallization can be roughly inferred from the size and arrangement of the mineral grains, a property called *texture*. Consequently, *igneous rocks are most often classified by their mineral composition and texture*. We will consider these two rock characteristics in the following sections.

IGNEOUS TEXTURES

The term **texture** is used to describe the overall appearance of a rock based on the size, shape, and arrangement of its interlocking crystals (Figure 3.13). Texture is an important characteristic because it reveals a great deal about the environment in which the rock formed. This permits geologists to make inferences about a rock's origin while working in the field (Figure 3.13A), where sophisticated equipment is not available.

Factors Affecting Crystal Size

Three factors contribute to the textures of igneous rocks: (1) *the rate at which magma cools* (e.g., glassy texture), (2) *the amount of silica present*, and (3) *the amount of volatiles in the magma* (e.g., pegmatitic texture). Of these, the rate of cooling is the dominant factor, but like all generalizations, this one has numerous exceptions.

A very large magma body located at great depth will cool over perhaps tens or hundreds of thousands of years as it slowly loses heat to its surroundings. Slow cooling permits ions to join one of the existing crystalline structures. Consequently, slow cooling promotes the growth of fewer but larger crystals.

Conversely, if cooling occurs rapidly (for example, in a thin lava flow), the ions quickly combine to form crystals. The result is a mass of small, but very numerous, intergrown crystals. In the extreme, when molten material is quenched quickly, there may not be sufficient time for the ions to arrange into a crystalline network. Rocks that consist of unordered ions are referred to as **glass**.

Figure 3.13 Igneous rock textures. **A.** Outcrop of dark basalt (solidified lava flow) intruded by pink bodies of granite on Baffin Island (note backpack for scale). **B.** Aphanitic (fine-grained) hand specimen of basalt. **C.** Phaneritic (coarse-grained) hand specimen of granite. **D.** Porphyritic (large crystals embedded in a finer-grained groundmass). **E.** Glassy (cooled too rapidly to form crystals). Photomicrographs (the coloured circular photos taken through a microscope; see Box 3.2) are magnified about 27 times. (Photo **A** by S. R. Hicock; photos **B–E** by E. J. Tarbuck)

BOX

3.2

UNDERSTANDING EARTH
Thin Sections and Rock Identification

Igneous rocks are classified on the basis of their mineral composition and texture. When analyzing specimens, geologists examine them closely to identify the minerals present and to determine the size and arrangement of the interlocking crystals. When out in the field, geologists use megascopic techniques to study rocks. The *megascopic* characteristics of rocks are those features that can be determined with the unaided eye or by using a low-magnification (x10) hand lens. When practical to do so, geologists collect hand samples that can be taken back to the laboratory, where *microscopic*, or high-magnification, methods can be employed. Microscopic examination is important to identify trace minerals, as well as those textural features that are too small to be visible with the unaided eye.

Because most rocks are not transparent, microscopic work requires the preparation of a very thin slice of rock known as a *thin section* (Figure 3.B). First, a saw containing diamonds embedded in its blade is used to cut a narrow slab from the sample. Next, one side of the slab is polished by using grinding powder and then cemented to a microscope slide. Once the mounted sample is firmly in place, the other side of it is ground to a thickness of about 0.03 millimetres. When a slice of rock is that thin, it is usually transparent. Nevertheless, some metallic minerals, such as pyrite and magnetite, remain opaque.

Once produced, thin sections are examined under a *polarizing microscope*. Such an instrument has a polarized light source beneath the stage so that light can be transmitted upward through the thin section in one (plane-polarized) or two (cross-polarized) directions. Because minerals have crystalline structures that influence polarized light, this procedure allows for even the smallest components of a rock to be identified. Part C of Figure 3.B is a photomicrograph (photo taken through a microscope)

A Hand sample of granite

B Thin section

Quartz

Feldspar

Biotite

C Photomicrograph taken with polarized light, magnified about 27 times

Figure 3.B Thin sections are very useful in identifying the mineral constituents in rocks. **A.** A slice of rock is cut from a hand sample by using a diamond saw. **B.** This slice is cemented to a microscope slide and ground until it is transparent to light (about 0.03 millimetres thick). **C.** A thin section of granite viewed under cross-polarized light.
(Photos by E. J. Tarbuck)

of a thin section of granite shown under cross-polarized light. The mineral constituents are identified by their unique optical properties. In addition to assisting in the study of igneous rocks, microscopic techniques are also used in analyzing sedimentary and metamorphic rocks.

Types of Igneous Textures

The effect of cooling on rock textures is fairly straightforward: rapid cooling tends to generate small crystals, whereas slow cooling promotes the growth of large crystals. We will consider the other two factors affecting crystal growth as we examine the major textural types.

APHANITIC (FINE-GRAINED) TEXTURE Igneous rocks that form at the surface or as small masses within the upper crust where cooling is relatively rapid possess a very fine-grained texture termed **aphanitic** (*a* = not, *phaner* = visible). By definition, the crystals that make up aphanitic rocks are so small that individual minerals can only be distinguished with the aid of a microscope (Figure 3.13B). Because mineral identification is not possible, we commonly characterize fine-grained rocks as being light, intermediate, or dark in colour. Using this system of grouping, light-coloured aphanitic rocks are those containing primarily light-coloured nonferromagnesian silicate materials and so forth (see the section titled "Common Silicate Minerals" in Chapter 2).

Commonly seen in many aphanitic rocks are the voids left by gas bubbles that attempt to escape as lava solidifies. These spherical or elongate openings are called *vesicles*, and the rocks that contain them are said to have a **vesicular texture**. Rocks that exhibit a vesicular texture usually form in the upper zone of a lava flow, where cooling occurs rapidly enough to "freeze" the lava, thereby preserving the cavities produced by the expanding gas bubbles (Figure 3.14).

PHANERITIC (COARSE-GRAINED) TEXTURE When large masses of magma slowly solidify far below the surface, they form igneous rocks that exhibit a coarse-grained texture described as **phaneritic** (*phaner* = visible). These coarse-grained rocks consist of a mass of intergrown crystals, which are roughly equal in size and large enough so that the individual minerals can be identified without the aid of a microscope (Figure 3.13C). Geologists often use a small magnifying lens to aid in identifying coarse-grained minerals. Because phaneritic rocks form deep within Earth's crust, their exposure at Earth's surface results only after erosion removes the overlying rocks that once surrounded the magma chamber.

PORPHYRITIC TEXTURE A large mass of magma located at depth may require tens to hundreds of thousands of years to solidify. Because different minerals crystallize at different temperatures (as well as at differing rates), it is possible for some crystals to become quite large before others even begin to form.

If magma containing some large crystals should change environments—for example, by erupting at the surface—the remaining liquid portion of the lava would cool relatively quickly. The resulting rock, which has large crystals embedded in a matrix of smaller crystals, is said to have a **porphyritic texture** (Figures 3.13D and 3.22A). The large crystals in such a rock are referred to as **phenocrysts** (*pheno* = show, *cryst* = crystal), whereas the matrix of smaller crystals is called **groundmass**. A rock with such a texture is termed a **porphyry**.

GLASSY TEXTURE During some volcanic eruptions, molten rock is extruded into water or ejected into the atmosphere, where it is quenched quickly. Rapid cooling of this type may generate rocks having a **glassy** texture. As we indicated earlier, glass results when unordered ions are "frozen" before they are able to form crystals. *Obsidian*, a common type of natural glass, is similar in appearance to a dark chunk of manufactured glass (Figure 3.13E).

Lava flows composed of obsidian several tens of metres thick occur in some places (Figure 3.15).

Figure 3.14   Vesicular texture displayed in an outcrop of solidified lava. Vesicles are small holes left by escaping gas bubbles.
(Reproduced with the permission of Natural Resources Canada 2010, courtesy of the Geological Survey of Canada. Photo by C. J. Hickson.)

Figure 3.15   This obsidian flow was extruded from a vent along the south wall of Newberry Caldera, Oregon. Note the road for scale. (Photo by E. J. Tarbuck)

Thus, rapid cooling is not the only mechanism by which a glassy texture can form. As a general rule, magmas with high silica content tend to form long, chainlike structures before crystallization is complete. These structures in turn impede ionic transport and increase the magma's viscosity. *Viscosity* is a measure of a fluid's resistance to flow.

A magma that is rich in silica may be extruded as an extremely viscous mass that eventually solidifies to form obsidian. By contrast, a magma that is low in silica forms very fluid lavas that on cooling usually generate fine-grained crystalline rocks. However, the surface of silica-poor lava may be quenched rapidly enough to form a thin, glassy skin. Moreover, Hawaiian volcanoes sometimes generate lava fountains, which spray mafic lava tens of metres into the air. Such activity can produce strands of volcanic glass called *Pele's hair*, after the Hawaiian goddess of volcanoes.

PYROCLASTIC (FRAGMENTAL) TEXTURE Some igneous rocks are formed from the consolidation of individual rock fragments that are ejected during a violent volcanic eruption. The ejected particles might be very fine ash, molten blobs, or large angular blocks torn from the walls of the vent during the eruption. Igneous rocks composed of these rock fragments are said to have a **pyroclastic** or **fragmental texture** (Figure 3.16).

A common type of pyroclastic rock called *welded tuff* is composed of fine fragments of glass that remained hot enough during their flight to fuse together on impact. Other pyroclastic rocks are composed of fragments that solidified before impact

and became cemented together at some later time. Because pyroclastic rocks are made of individual particles or fragments rather than interlocking crystals, their textures often appear to be more similar to sedimentary rocks than to other igneous rocks.

PEGMATITIC TEXTURE Under special conditions, exceptionally coarse-grained igneous rocks, called **pegmatites**, may form. These rocks, which are composed of interlocking crystals, most larger than a centimetre in diameter, are said to have a **pegmatitic texture**. Most pegmatites are found as small masses around the margins of large plutons or in thin dykes and veins that extend into the adjacent host rock.

Figure 3.16   Pyroclastic (fragmental) texture. This volcanic rock consists of angular rock fragments embedded in a light-coloured matrix of ash. (Photo by E. J. Tarbuck)

Pegmatites form in the late stages of crystallization, when water and other volatiles, such as chlorine, fluorine, and sulphur, make up an unusually high percentage of the melt. Because ion migration is enhanced in these fluid-rich environments, the crystals that form are abnormally large. Thus, the large crystals in pegmatites are not the result of inordinately long cooling histories: rather, they are the consequence of the fluid-rich environment in which crystallization takes place.

The composition of most pegmatites is similar to that of granite. Thus, pegmatites contain large crystals of quartz, feldspar, and muscovite. However, some contain significant quantities of comparatively rare and hence valuable minerals.

NAMING IGNEOUS ROCKS

As was stated previously, igneous rocks are most often classified, or grouped, on the basis of their mineral composition and texture (Figure 3.17). The various igneous textures result mainly from different cooling histories, whereas the mineral composition of an igneous rock is the consequence of the chemical makeup of its parent magma. Because igneous rocks are classified on the basis of their mineral composition and texture, two rocks may have similar mineral constituents but have different textures and hence different names. For example, granite, a coarse-grained plutonic rock, has a fine-grained volcanic equivalent called *rhyolite*. Although these rocks are mineralogically the same, they have different cooling histories and do not look at all alike (Figure 3.18).

Felsic (Granitic) Igneous Rocks

GRANITE Granite is perhaps the best known of all igneous rocks (Figure 3.18A). This is partly because of its natural beauty, which is enhanced when it is polished, and partly because of its abundance in the continental crust. Slabs of polished granite are commonly used for tombstones, monuments, and construction. Kenora, Ontario, and Maplewood, Nova Scotia, are well-known areas in Canada where granite is quarried.

Chemical Composition	Felsic (Granitic)	Intermediate (Andesitic)	Mafic (Basaltic)	Ultramafic
Dominant Minerals	Quartz Potassium feldspar Sodium-rich plagioclase feldspar	Amphibole Sodium- and calcium-rich plagioclase feldspar	Pyroxene Calcium-rich plagioclase feldspar	Olivine Pyroxene
Accessory Minerals	Amphibole Muscovite Biotite	Pyroxene Biotite	Amphibole Olivine	Calcium-rich plagioclase feldspar
Rock Colour (based on % of dark minerals)	0% to 25%	25% to 45%	45% to 85%	85% to 100%

TEXTURE					
Phaneritic (coarse-grained)		Granite	Diorite	Gabbro	Peridotite
Aphanitic (fine-grained)		Rhyolite	Andesite	Basalt	Komatiite (rare)
Porphyritic		"Porphyritic" precedes any of the above names whenever there are appreciable phenocrysts			
Glassy		Obsidian (compact glass) Pumice (frothy glass)			Uncommon
Pyroclastic (fragmental)		Tuff (fragments smaller than 2 mm) Volcanic Breccia (fragments larger than 2 mm)			

Figure 3.17 Classification of the major groups of igneous rocks based on their mineral composition and texture. Phaneritic (coarse-grained) rocks are plutonic, solidifying deep underground. Aphanitic (fine-grained) rocks are volcanic, or solidify as shallow, thin plutons (plutonic outcrops).

←2 cm→

←2 cm→

A Granite

B Rhyolite

Close up

Close up

Figure 3.18   A. Granite, one of the most common phaneritic igneous rocks. **B.** Rhyolite, the aphanitic equivalent of granite, is less abundant.
(Photos by E. J. Tarbuck)

Granite is a phaneritic rock composed of about 20 percent quartz and roughly 65 percent feldspar, mostly potassium- and sodium-rich varieties. Quartz crystals, which are irregular in shape, are commonly glassy and clear to light grey in colour. By contrast, feldspar crystals are not as glassy, are generally white to grey or salmon pink, and exhibit a rectangular rather than irregular shape. When potassium feldspar is dominant and dark pink in colour, granite appears almost reddish (Figure 3.13A). This variety is popular as a building stone. However, the feldspar grains are commonly white to grey so that when mixed with lesser amounts of dark silicates, granite appears light grey in colour.

Other minor constituents of granite are muscovite and some dark silicates, particularly biotite and amphibole. Although the dark components make up less than 10 percent of the volume of most granites, dark minerals appear to be more prominent than their percentage would indicate.

Granite can also have a porphyritic texture (Figure 3.13D). These specimens contain feldspar crystals of a centimetre or more in length that are scattered among the finer-grained groundmass of quartz, feldspar, and amphibole.

Granite and other related crystalline rocks are often the by-products of mountain building (as in the Coast Mountains of British Columbia). Because granite is very resistant to weathering, it frequently forms the core of eroded mountains (chapter-opening photo and Figure 3.19).

Granite is an abundant rock. However, it has become common practice among geologists to apply the term *granite* to any coarse-grained intrusive rock composed predominantly of light silicate materials that contain quartz. We will follow this practice for the sake of simplicity. You should keep in mind that this use of the term *granite* covers rocks that have a wide range of mineral compositions.

RHYOLITE Rhyolite is the extrusive equivalent of granite and, like granite, is composed essentially of the light-coloured silicates (Figure 3.18B). This fact accounts for its colour, which is usually buff to pink or occasionally very light grey. Rhyolite is aphanitic and frequently contains glass fragments and voids, indicating rapid cooling in a surface environment. When rhyolite contains phenocrysts, they are small and composed of either quartz or potassium feldspar. In contrast to granite, which is widely distributed as large plutonic masses, rhyolite deposits are less common and generally less voluminous. Yellowstone Park is one well-known exception. Here rhyolite lava flows and thick ash deposits of similar composition are extensive.

Figure 3.19   Stawamus Chief, a large igneous monolith located near Squamish, British Columbia. Granite bedrock is exposed over much of the area, whose steep rock faces attract climbers from around the world. (Photo by Gunter Marx/Alamy)

OBSIDIAN Obsidian is a dark-coloured glassy rock that usually forms when silica-rich lava is quenched quickly (Figure 3.20). In contrast to the orderly arrangement of ions characteristic of minerals, *the ions in glass are unordered*. Consequently, glassy rocks such as obsidian are not composed of minerals in the strict sense.

Although usually black or reddish-brown in colour (Figure 3.20), obsidian has a high silica content. By itself, silica is clear like window glass; the dark colour results from the presence of metallic ions. If you examine a thin edge of a piece of obsidian, it will be nearly transparent. Because of its excellent conchoidal fracture and ability to hold a sharp, hard edge, obsidian was a prized material from which Aboriginal peoples chipped tools for hunting (e.g., arrow and spear points) and for cutting tough materials such as animal hide.

PUMICE *Pumice* is a volcanic rock with a frothy texture. Usually found with obsidian, pumice forms when large amounts of gas escape through lava to generate a grey, frothy mass (Figure 3.21). Because of the large percentage of voids, many samples of pumice will float when placed in water. Flow lines are commonly visible in pumice, indicating that some movement occurred before solidification was complete. Moreover, pumice and obsidian can often be found interlayered.

Intermediate (Andesitic) Igneous Rocks

ANDESITE *Andesite* is a medium-grey fine-grained rock of volcanic origin. Its name comes from South America's Andes Mountains, where numerous volcanoes are composed of this rock type. Other volcanic structures encircling the Pacific Ocean are also of andesitic composition. Andesite commonly exhibits a porphyritic texture (Figure 3.22). When this is the case, the phenocrysts are commonly light, rectangular crystals of plagioclase feldspar or black, elongate amphibole crystals. Andesite often resembles rhyolite, so identification usually requires microscopic examination to verify the mineral makeup. Andesite contains minor amounts of quartz, whereas rhyolite is composed of about 25 percent quartz.

A Obsidian flow

B Hand sample of obsidian

Figure 3.20 Obsidian is a dark-coloured, glassy rock formed from silica-rich lava. The scene in photo **A** shows the base of a lava dome south of Mono Lake, California. (Photos by E. J. Tarbuck)

A Andesite porphyry

B Close up

Figure 3.22 Andesite porphyry. **A.** Hand sample of andesite porphyry, a common volcanic rock.
B. Photomicrograph of a thin section of andesite porphyry to illustrate texture. Notice that the few large crystals (phenocrysts) are surrounded by much smaller crystals (groundmass).
(Photos by E. J. Tarbuck)

Figure 3.21 Pumice, a glassy rock containing numerous vesicles.
(Photo by E. J. Tarbuck)

←2 cm→

Diorite

Close up

Figure 3.23 Diorite is a phaneritic igneous rock of intermediate composition. The white crystals are plagioclase feldspar and the black crystals are amphibole and biotite.
(Photo by E. J. Tarbuck)

DIORITE *Diorite* is the plutonic equivalent of andesite. It is a coarse-grained intrusive rock that looks somewhat similar to grey granite. However, it can be distinguished from granite by the absence of visible quartz crystals and a higher percentage of dark silicate minerals. The mineral makeup of diorite is primarily sodium-calcium plagioclase feldspar and amphibole, with lesser amounts of biotite. Because the light-coloured feldspar grains and dark amphibole crystals appear to be roughly equal in abundance, diorite has a salt-and-pepper appearance (Figure 3.23).

Mafic (Basaltic) and Ultramafic Igneous Rocks

BASALT *Basalt* is a very dark green to black fine-grained volcanic rock composed primarily of pyroxene and calcium-rich plagioclase feldspar, with lesser amounts of olivine and amphibole (Figure 3.24A). Porphyritic basalt commonly contains small light-coloured feldspar phenocrysts or glassy-appearing olivine phenocrysts embedded in a dark groundmass.

Basalt is the most common extrusive igneous rock (Figure 3.24A). Many volcanic islands, such as

the Hawaiian Islands and Iceland, are composed mainly of basalt (Figure 3.25). Further, the upper layers of the oceanic crust consist of basalt. In Canada, areas of south-central British Columbia were the sites of significant basaltic outpourings. Farther south, in Oregon and Washington, basalt flows have accumulated to thicknesses approaching 3 kilometres (see Figure 4.23).

GABBRO *Gabbro* is the intrusive equivalent of basalt (Figure 3.24B). Like basalt, it is very dark green to black in colour and composed primarily of pyroxene and calcium-rich plagioclase feldspar. Although gabbro is not a common constituent of the continental crust, it undoubtedly makes up a significant percentage of the oceanic crust. Here large portions of the magma found in subsurface magma chambers that once fed basalt flows eventually solidified at depth to form gabbro.

PERIDOTITE The upper mantle is dominated by a phaneritic rock called peridotite (Figure 3.24C), which has an ultramafic composition; it is primarily composed of olivine, pyroxene, and calcium-rich plagioclase feldspar. Occurrences of peridotite are limited to rare slivers of mantle rock that are pushed up to Earth's surface in some forms of mountain building, and to small chunks of material that are transported to the surface by basaltic (mafic) magma.

Pyroclastic Rocks

Pyroclastic rocks are composed of fragments ejected during a volcanic eruption. One of the most common pyroclastic rocks, called *tuff*, is composed mainly of tiny ash-size fragments (smaller than two millimetres) that are later cemented together (Figure 3.26). In situations where the ash particles remained hot enough to fuse, the rock is called *welded tuff*. Although welded tuff consists mostly of tiny glass shards, it may contain walnut-size pieces of pumice and other rock fragments.

Welded tuffs blanket vast portions of once volcanically active areas of western North America. Some of these tuff deposits are hundreds of metres thick and extend for tens of kilometres from their source. Most formed millions of years ago as volcanic ash spewed from large volcanic structures (calderas) in an avalanche style, spreading laterally at speeds approaching 100 kilometres per hour.

Pyroclastic rocks composed mainly of particles larger than ash are called *volcanic breccia*. The particles in volcanic breccia can consist of streamlined fragments that solidified in air, blocks broken from the walls of the vent, crystals, and glass fragments.

A Basalt

Close up

B Gabbro

Close up

C Peridotite

Figure 3.24 These dark-coloured mafic and ultramafic rocks are composed primarily of pyroxene and calcium-rich plagioclase. **A.** Basalt is aphanitic and a very common extrusive rock. **B.** Gabbro, the phaneritic equivalent of basalt, is less abundant. **C.** Peridotite is an ultramafic phaneritic rock.
(Photos **A** and **B** by E. J. Tarbuck; photo **C** by S. R. Hicock)

Figure 3.25 Fluid mafic lava moving down the slopes of Hawaii's Kilauea Volcano.
(Photo by U.S. Geological Survey)

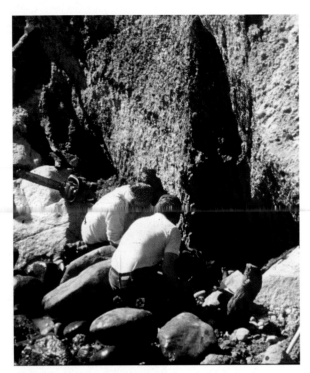

Figure 3.26   River bank exposure of a tuff deposit resting on white granite bedrock in Lillooet Valley, British Columbia. Although composed mainly of ash-sized particles, this tuff also contains walnut-sized balls of light-coloured pumice. Pyroclastic constituents of this size are called lapilli (see details in Chapter 4). Note also the brown stump of a tree that was killed and buried by the pyroclastic material (near the lower right-hand corner of the photograph).
(Photo by S. R. Hicock)

Unlike most igneous rock names, such as granite and basalt, the terms *tuff* and *volcanic breccia* do not imply mineral composition. Thus, they are frequently used with a composition modifier, such as, for example, rhyolite tuff.

INTRUSIVE IGNEOUS BODIES

As stated earlier in this chapter, bodies of plutonic igneous rock, formed by the intrusion and solidification of magma at depth, are called **plutons**. Because all plutons form out of view beneath Earth's surface, they can be studied only after uplift and erosion have exposed them. The challenge lies in reconstructing the events that generated these structures millions or even hundreds of millions of years ago.

Nature of Plutons

Plutons occur in a great variety of sizes and shapes. Some of the most common types are illustrated in Figure 3.27. Some of these structures have a tabular (tabletop) shape, others are massive (shapeless), and some cut across existing (host) rocks while others form when magma is injected between sedimentary layers. Plutons are classified according to their shape as either **tabular** or **massive** and by their orientation with respect to the host rock. Intrusive rocks are said to be **discordant** (*discordare* = to disagree) if they cut across existing rocks and **concordant** (*concordare* = to agree) if they form parallel to sedimentary layers. Many of the largest intrusive bodies are the remnants of magma chambers that once fed ancient volcanoes. Large intrusive bodies of particular significance in Canada include plutons in the Coast Mountains of British Columbia, the Monteregian intrusions around Montreal in Quebec, interior Nova Scotia, and the Sweetgrass Hills just south of Alberta.

Dykes

Dykes are tabular discordant plutons produced when magma is injected into fractures (Figures 3.27 and 3.28). The force of the magma can farther separate the walls of the fracture. Once crystallized, these wall-like structures range from less than 1 centimetre to more than 1 kilometre thick and the largest ones are hundreds of kilometres long. Most dykes, however, are a few metres thick (Figure 3.28) and extend laterally for no more than a few kilometres.

Dykes are commonly found in groups (e.g., Mackenzie Dyke Swarm of the Canadian Shield) that served as vertical pathways for magma that fed ancient lava flows. The parent pluton is generally not observable. Some dykes are found radiating, like spokes on a wheel, from an eroded volcanic neck (e.g., Figures 3.27B and 4.26). In these situations as magma rose it generated fissures through the volcano out of which lava flowed.

Sills

Tabular concordant plutons form when magma is injected along sedimentary bedding surfaces and are called **sills** (Figures 3.27B and 4.26). Horizontal sills are the most common (e.g., Purcell Sill of Waterton Lakes National Park, Alberta), but sills can occur in other orientations if the sedimentary layers within which they are hosted have been tilted. Because of their relatively uniform thickness and large areal extent, sills tend to be the products of fluid mafic magmas in shallow environments.

In many respects, sills closely resemble buried lava flows. Both are tabular and commonly exhibit columnar jointing (Figure 3.30). **Columnar joints** form as igneous rocks cool and develop shrinkage fractures that produce elongate, pillar-like columns.

A Emplacement of igneous structures

B Crystallization and erosion

C Extensive uplift and erosion

Figure 3.27 Illustrations showing basic igneous bodies. **A.** This block diagram shows the relationship between volcanism and intrusive igneous activity. **B.** This view illustrates the basic plutons, some of which have been exposed by erosion long after their formation. **C.** After millions of years of uplift and erosion, a batholith is exposed at the surface.

When interpreting the geologic history of a region, it is important to distinguish between sills and buried lava flows. Fortunately, under close examination these two phenomena can be readily distinguished. The upper portion of a buried lava flow usually contains voids produced by escaping gas bubbles (vesicular texture; see Figure 3.14), and only the rocks beneath a lava flow show evidence of baking. Sills, however, form when magma has been forcefully intruded between sedimentary layers. Thus, fragments of the overlying rock can be found only in sills. Lava flows, conversely, are extruded before the overlying strata are deposited. "Baked" zones in the rock above and below are trademarks of a sill and are only found on the rock below a lava flow, not on the overlying rock.

A   B

Figure 3.28 Light- and dark-coloured dykes. **A.** Dykes of felsic composition cut through dark-coloured mafic volcanic rocks near Lakelse, British Columbia. **B.** Dark-coloured dyke of mafic composition cuts through light-coloured granitic rock north of Sudbury, Ontario.
(Photos by S. R. Hicock)

Laccoliths

Laccoliths (*lakkos* = pond, *lithos* = stone) are similar to sills because they form when magma intrudes between sedimentary layers in a near-surface environment. However, the magma that generates laccoliths is more viscous and collects as a blister-like mass that arches the overlying strata upward (see Figure 3.27B). Consequently, a laccolith can occasionally be detected because of the dome-shaped bulge it creates at the surface. Most

A

B

Figure 3.29 **A.** The dark-coloured rock layer in this photograph is a sill made of gabbro. It is located in the Upper Brock River Canyon, near Paulatuk, Northwest Territories. **B.** Mount McKay near Thunder Bay, Ontario, is a resistant mafic sill (upper part) that rests on weaker sedimentary rocks (lower part).
(Photo **A** Reproduced with the permission of the Minister of Public Works and Government Services Canada, 2013, and courtesy of Natural Resources Canada; photo **B** courtesy of Kris Olynyk)

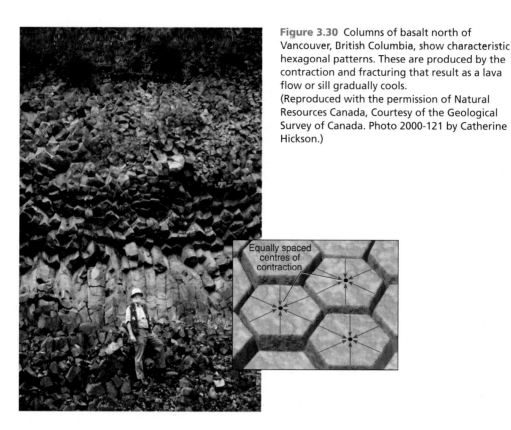

Figure 3.30 Columns of basalt north of Vancouver, British Columbia, show characteristic hexagonal patterns. These are produced by the contraction and fracturing that result as a lava flow or sill gradually cools.
(Reproduced with the permission of Natural Resources Canada, Courtesy of the Geological Survey of Canada. Photo 2000-121 by Catherine Hickson.)

Equally spaced centres of contraction

large laccoliths are probably not much wider than a few kilometres.

Batholiths

By far the largest intrusive igneous bodies are **batholiths** (*bathos* = depth, *lithos* + stone). Most commonly, batholiths occur in groups that form extensive belts several hundreds of kilometres long and up to 100 kilometres wide, as shown in Figure 3.31.

By definition, a plutonic body must have a surface exposure greater than 100 square kilometres to be considered a batholith. Smaller plutons of this type are termed **stocks**. Many stocks appear to be portions of batholiths that are not very exposed.

Batholiths usually consist of rock types having felsic to intermediate chemical composition, as in Nova Scotia. Smaller batholiths can be rather simple structures composed almost entirely of one rock type. However, studies of large batholiths have shown that they consist of several distinct plutons that were intruded over millions of years. The Sierra Nevada batholith formed nearly continuously over 130 million years, ending about 80 million years ago.

Batholiths may compose the core of mountain systems. After uplifting, erosion has removed the surrounding rock, thereby exposing the resistant igneous body (see Figure 3.19 and Chapter 3 opening photo). Large expanses of granitic rock also occur in the stable interiors of the continents, such as the Canadian Shield. These relatively flat exposures are the remains of ancient mountains that have long since been levelled by uplift and erosion. The exposed rocks that make up the batholiths of youthful mountain ranges, such as B.C.'s Coast Mountains, were generated near the top of a magma chamber, whereas in shield areas, the roots of former mountains and, thus, the lower portions of batholiths are exposed. In Chapter 13 we will further consider the role of igneous activity as it relates to mountain building.

EMPLACEMENT OF BATHOLITHS An interesting problem geologists faced was trying to explain how large granitic batholiths came to reside within only moderately deformed sedimentary and metamorphic rocks. What happened to the rock that was displaced by these igneous masses? How did the magma body make its way through several kilometres of solid rock?

We know that magma rises because it is less dense than the surrounding rock, much like a cork held at the bottom of a container of water will rise when it is released. But Earth's crust is made of solid rock. Nevertheless, at depths of several kilometres, where temperature and pressure are high, even solid rock can deform by flowing. Thus, at great depths, a mass of buoyant, rising magma can forcibly make

Figure 3.31 Granitic batholiths that occur along the western margin of North America. These gigantic, elongate bodies consist of numerous plutons that were emplaced during the past 150 million years of Earth history.

room for itself by pushing aside the overlying rock. As the magma continues to move upward, some of the host rock that was shouldered aside will fill in the space left by the magma body as it passes.[*]

As a magma body nears the surface, it encounters relatively cool, brittle rock that is not easily pushed aside. Farther upward movement is accomplished by *stoping*. In this process, fractures that develop in the overlying host rock allow magma to rise and dislodge blocks of rock. Once incorporated into the magma body, these blocks may melt, thereby altering the composition of the magma body (assimilation). Eventually, the magma body will cool sufficiently so that upward movement comes to a halt. Evidence supporting the fact that magma can move through solid rock occurs in the form of **xenoliths**. Xenoliths are unmelted pieces of the host rock found in the pluton after it has been exhumed by erosion.

---

[*]An analogous situation occurs when a can of oil-based paint is left in storage. The oily component of the paint is less dense than the pigments used for coloration; thus, oil collects into drops that slowly migrate upward, while the heavier pigments settle to the bottom.

CHAPTER SUMMARY

- *Igneous rocks* include those that are *extrusive*, forming at Earth's surface as lava flows and as pyroclastic deposits result from volcanic activity, and those that are *intrusive*, occurring as plutonic bodies formed below Earth's surface. Magma forms in the crust and mantle by raising temperature, decreasing pressure, or adding *volatiles*.

- Slow cooling and crystallization forms large crystals, while rapid cooling forms small ones and even glass.
- In a magma chamber, heavier minerals with higher melting points form earlier (*Bowen's reaction series*) and tend to sink to the bottom (*crystal settling*) as the melt gains a lighter composition

(*magmatic differentiation*). Composition can also change by *assimilation* or *magma mixing*.

- Igneous rocks are divided into three main compositional groups that are readily identified by their relative proportions of light- and dark-coloured minerals. *Felsic* igneous rocks are dominated by light-coloured minerals, whereas *mafic* igneous rocks are dominated by dark-coloured minerals, and *intermediate* igneous rocks contain approximately equal proportions of both.

- The other major criterion on which igneous rocks are classified is texture, the basic types being *phaneritic* (with visible crystals), *aphanitic* (tiny crystals), *porphyritic* (larger phenocrysts imbedded in a finer groundmass), and *glassy*.

- The names of igneous rocks embody both compositional characteristics and texture. For example, granite is always felsic and phaneritic, whereas its extrusive counterpart, rhyolite, is felsic and aphanitic. Together, these characteristics provide a basis for interpreting how a particular igneous rock formed.

- Intrusive igneous bodies tend to be *tabular* (sheet-like) or *massive* and are *discordant* (cut across) or *concordant* (parallel) to host rocks.

- *Dykes* are tabular, discordant plutons, whereas *sills* are tabular, concordant bodies that tend to intrude between rock layers. *Laccoliths* are like sills but arch overlying strata upward, similar to a blister. *Batholiths* are large igneous bodies that can cover hundreds to thousands of square kilometres; they commonly make up the cores of mountains.

MasteringGeology

Looking for additional review and test prep materials? Visit the Study Area in MasteringGeology to enhance your understanding of this chapter's content by accessing a variety of resources, including Self-Study Quizzes, Geoscience Animations, GEODe Tutorials, RSS feeds, flashcards, weblinks, self-study quizzes, and an optional Pearson eText.

REVIEW QUESTIONS

1. How does magma differ from lava?

2. How do heat, pressure, and volatiles influence the ability of rock to melt?

3. What is partial melting?

4. Why does magma rise toward Earth's surface rather than sink?

5. How does the texture of an igneous rock relate to the conditions under which it formed (e.g., above versus below Earth's surface)?

6. How does the manner in which magma is generated at a convergent boundary differ from that at a divergent boundary? How is this reflected in the composition of igneous rocks that tend to form in these settings?

7. What is Bowen's reaction series and how does it relate to the presence of certain mineral types in igneous rocks of different composition (e.g., ultramafic, mafic, intermediate, or felsic) and to the sequence in which these minerals crystallize?

8. Describe the differences in the manner dykes, sills, laccoliths, and batholiths are formed and explain why these plutonic bodies tend to form in areas of the world that are volcanically active.

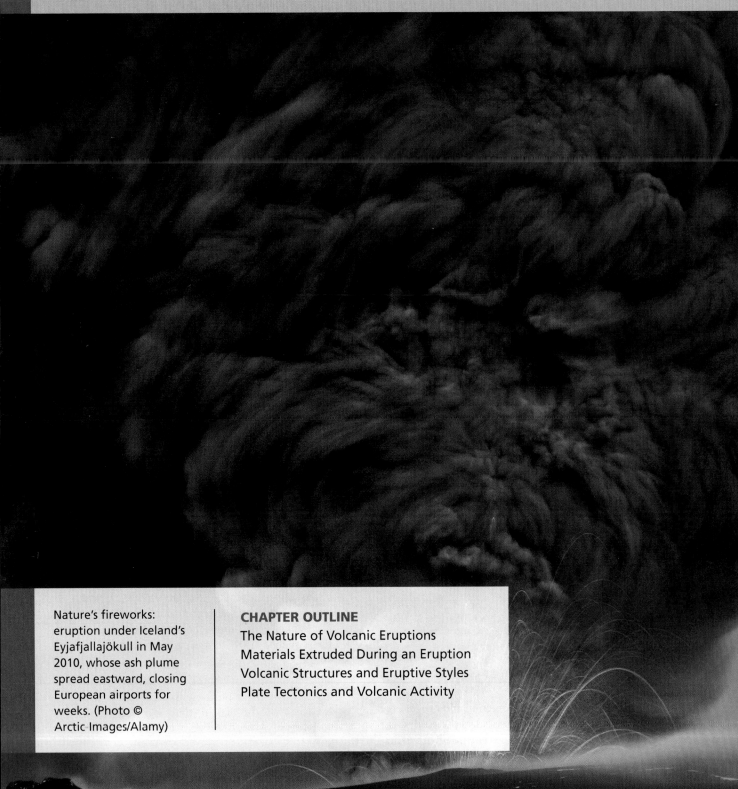

4 VOLCANOES AND VOLCANIC PROCESSES

Nature's fireworks: eruption under Iceland's Eyjafjallajökull in May 2010, whose ash plume spread eastward, closing European airports for weeks. (Photo © Arctic Images/Alamy)

CHAPTER OUTLINE
The Nature of Volcanic Eruptions
Materials Extruded During an Eruption
Volcanic Structures and Eruptive Styles
Plate Tectonics and Volcanic Activity

Figure 4.1 Sunrise view of the most destructive eruption of Indonesia's Mount Merapi in 100 years.
(Photo by Tom Pfeiffer/www.VolcanoDiscovery.com)

"The heat surrounded us and there was white smoke everywhere!" recalled a survivor of Mount Merapi's most devastating eruption in a century (Figure 4.1). In early November 2010 central Java's active volcano killed about 350 people as rocks, ash, and debris rained from the sky in Indonesia. Homes were burned and incinerated cattle littered the scorched flanks of the volcano. The main blast could be heard 20 kilometres away and followed a devastating tsunami that had slammed the west coast of Indonesia the day before, killing more than 400. The heavy grey ash plume rose 12 kilometres into the air, darkened the sky, and blanketed trees, cars, and roads 240 kilometres away.

Global atmospheric darkening and cooling also accompanied the largest and deadliest eruptions in recorded history: Mount Tambora (1815) and Krakatoa (1883), both in Indonesia. In fact, 1816 is known as "the year without a summer" when crops failed, livestock died, and the worst famine of the nineteenth century occurred in the northern hemisphere.

Not all volcanic eruptions are as violent as these. Some volcanoes, such as Sicily's Mount Etna and Hawaii's Kilauea, generate relatively quiet outpourings of fluid lavas. These "gentle" eruptions occasionally include fountains of incandescent lava sprayed hundreds of metres into the air, producing spectacular but usually harmless lava fountains (Figure 4.2). The longest and largest of Kilauea's eruptions began in 1983, has destroyed 180 homes, and remains active; Etna is erupting as we write this.

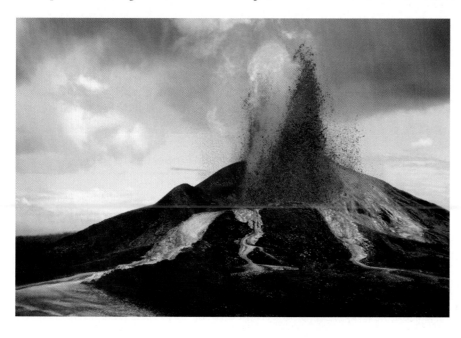

Figure 4.2 Fluid mafic lava erupting near Kilauea Volcano, Hawaii.
(Photo © Greg Vaughn/Alamy)

Figure 4.3 Mount Garibaldi, located in southwest British Columbia. Garibaldi has been dormant since the last Ice Age and has suffered some erosion since then. Mt. Cayley, north of Garibaldi, erupted about 2600 years ago. (Photo by David P. Lewis/ Shutterstock)

Why do volcanoes like Mount Garibaldi (Canada, Figure 4.3) and Lassen Peak (United States) erupt explosively, whereas others, like Kilauea, are relatively quiet? Why do volcanoes occur in chains, like the Aleutian Islands of Alaska or the Cascade Range in western North America? Why do some volcanoes form on the ocean floor, while others occur on the continents? This chapter will deal with these and other questions as we explore the nature and movement of magma and lava.

THE NATURE OF VOLCANIC ERUPTIONS

Volcanic activity is commonly perceived as a process that produces a picturesque, cone-shaped structure that periodically erupts in a violent manner (Box 4.1). Although some eruptions are very explosive, many are not. What determines whether a volcano extrudes

magma violently or gently? The primary factors include the magma's *composition*, its *temperature*, and the amount of *dissolved gases* it contains. To varying degrees, these factors affect the magma's mobility, or **viscosity** (*viscos* = sticky). The more viscous the material, the greater its resistance to flow. (For example, maple syrup is more viscous than water.) Magma associated with an explosive eruption is much more viscous than magma extruded in a quiescent manner.

Factors Affecting Viscosity

The mobility of lava is strongly influenced by temperature. As lava cools and begins to congeal, the flow decreases in mobility and eventually halts. Furthermore, the chemical composition of the magma is important. Recall from Chapter 3 that a major difference among various igneous rocks is their silica (SiO_2) content (Table 4.1). Likewise, a *magma's viscosity is directly related to its silica content.*

TABLE 4.1 Magmas Have Different Compositions, Which Cause Their Properties to Vary

Composition	Silica Content	Viscosity	Gas Content	Tendency to Form Pyroclastics	Volcanic Landform
Mafic (basaltic) magma	Least (~50%)	Least	Least (1%–2%)	Least	Shield volcanoes Basalt plateaus Cinder cones
Intermediate (andesitic) magma	Intermediate (~60%)	Intermediate	Intermediate (3%–4%)	Intermediate	Composite cones
Felsic (granitic) magma	Most (~70%)	Greatest	Most (4%–6%)	Greatest	Volcanic domes Pyroclastic flows

Dante's Peak was based on the violent eruption of Mount St. Helens in 1980 and starred Pierce Brosnan as volcanologist Harry Dalton. Scientifically, this is one of the better disaster movies. The film is set in the Cascade Range of Washington State, which does contain active composite cone volcanoes, including St. Helens. Dalton monitors earthquake tremors and does various tests on soil and water that a volcanologist would do in an active volcanic area (except for the robot in the crater). Waters in the area would have turned acidic and the volcano would have produced volcanic ash that blocked out the sun and damaged engines in aircraft, as well as devastating mudflows that choked rivers and took out bridges. However, lake water would not have become acidic enough to eat through the bottom of the aluminum boat in a few minutes, nor would the town's water supply get contaminated in that short time. In the scene crossing the lava flow (>1200°C) the tires, gas tank, and upholstery of the vehicle (and Dalton's clothes) would have burst into flame even before reaching the flow.

Largely for the sake of maximizing the visual impact, most movies that have featured volcanoes as agents of destruction have focused entirely on the hazards associated with lava. But while *Dante's Peak* certainly contains the gratuitous lava flow scenes that viewers have come to expect from this kind of disaster movie, it is commendable that some attempt was made in the film to emphasize the destructive potential of pyroclastic flows. The dangers that these superheated, fast-flowing, ground-hugging clouds of volcanic gases and solids pose to human life were graphically demonstrated in 1980, when an estimated 57 lives were claimed by a pyroclastic flow that accompanied a lateral blast on

Figure 4.A Photographer Reid Blackburn, camped approximately 12 kilometres north of the summit of Mount St. Helens, barely reached the shelter of his car before being killed in the lateral blast of superheated gas, ash, and rock fragments that accompanied the collapse of the volcano's northern flank.
(Photo by Dan Dzurisin/U.S Geological Survey)

the northern flank of Mount St. Helens. Among the victims was *National Geographic* photographer Reid Blackburn, who, despite having sought the protection of his car, was killed when the windscreen of the vehicle was shattered under the force of the flow and ultimately rendered Reid helpless against the superheated cloud of volcanic gases and particulates (Figure 4.A). That said, however, contrary to what is depicted in the movie, volcanoes of this type rarely produce both lava and ash during the same eruption, and the lava flows that they *do* produce seldom travel any significant distance from the crater. Furthermore, heavy ash fell more like confetti in the movie (shredded newspaper was used to simulate the falling ash) rather than falling rapidly onto people and car windshields like heavy dust. And finally, volcanic earthquakes are not usually strong enough to destroy

buildings and roads as shown at the start of the film, and would not be capable of heating a hot spring fast enough to boil a person, swimsuit or no swimsuit!

Volcano starred Tommy Lee Jones as emergency official Mike Roark, whose job was to stop lava flowing from a new volcano in Hollywood and to save as many people as he could. This movie ignored scientific accuracy: LA is along the San Andreas fault that does not produce volcanic eruptions; helicopters fly through thick ash that would have stopped their engines (again, volcanoes do not usually produce ash and lava in the same eruption); lava flows around aluminum street lamps that would have melted; and people and cars get so close to the lava that they would have ignited. However, the scene with the train boss burning alive while rescuing the driver is almost realistic.

Figure 4.4 Six-kilometre-high eruption column produced as Cleveland Volcano in Alaska's Aleutian Islands erupted on May 23, 2006.
(Photo by NASA)

The more silica in magma, the greater is its viscosity. The flow of magma is impeded because silica structures link together into long chains, even before crystallization begins. Consequently, because of their high silica content (over 70 percent), felsic (rhyolitic) lavas are very viscous and tend to form comparatively short, thick flows. By contrast, mafic (basaltic) lavas, which contain less silica (about 50 percent), tend to be quite fluid and have been known to travel 150 kilometres or more before congealing.

Importance of Dissolved Gases

Dissolved gases (volatiles) tend to increase the fluidity of magma. On their escape from the magma, gases also provide enough force to propel magma from a volcanic **vent,** a surface opening, or **conduit.**

The summits of volcanoes often begin to inflate months, or even years, before an eruption occurs as magma migrates into a shallow reservoir within the cone. During this phase, dissolved gases tend to migrate upward and accumulate near the top of the magma chamber. When an eruption starts, gas-charged magma moves from the magma chamber and rises through the volcanic vent. As the magma nears the surface, the confining pressure is greatly reduced. This reduction in pressure allows the dissolved gases to be released suddenly, just as opening a warm can of pop will allow carbon dioxide gas bubbles to expand and escape.

Very fluid mafic magmas allow the expanding gases to migrate upward and escape from the vent with relative ease. As they escape, the gases can propel incandescent lava hundreds of metres into the air,

producing lava fountains (see Figure 4.2). Although spectacular, such fountains are mostly harmless and not generally associated with major eruptive events that cause great loss of life and property.

At the other extreme, highly viscous magmas expel jets of hot, ash-laden gases that evolve into buoyant plumes called **eruption columns** that extend thousands of metres into the atmosphere (Figures 4.1, 4.4, and chapter-opening photo). Before such an eruption, an extended period of magmatic differentiation (Chapter 3) occurs, in which iron-rich minerals crystallize and settle out, leaving the upper part of the magma enriched in silica and dissolved gases. As this volatile-rich magma moves up the volcanic vent toward the surface, these gases begin to collect as tiny bubbles. At some point in the vent, this mixture is transformed into a gas jet containing tiny bits of magma that are explosively ejected from the volcano. This type of violent eruption was exemplified by Nevado del Ruiz in Colombia (1985), Mount Pinatubo in the Philippines (1991), and Mount Merapi in Indonesia (2010).

As magma in the upper portion of the vent is ejected, the pressure on the underlying magma drops. Thus, rather than a single "bang," volcanic eruptions are really a series of explosions. The dissolved gases in a viscous magma migrate upward quite slowly. Only within the uppermost portion of the magma body does the gas content build sufficiently to trigger explosive eruptions. Thus, an explosive event is commonly followed by the quiet emission of degassed lavas. However, once this eruptive phase ceases, the process of gas buildup begins anew. This time lag may partially explain the sporadic eruptive patterns of volcanoes that eject viscous lavas.

To summarize, the viscosity of magma, plus the quantity of dissolved gases and the ease with which they can escape, determine the nature of a volcanic eruption. We can now begin to explain the gentle volcanic eruptions of hot, fluid lava in Hawaii and the explosive and sometimes catastrophic eruptions of viscous lava from such volcanoes as Krakatoa, which erupted as recently as 2010.

MATERIALS EXTRUDED DURING AN ERUPTION

Volcanoes can extrude lava, large volumes of gas, and pyroclastic materials (broken rock, lava "bombs," fine ash, and dust), as discussed below.

Lava Flows

Because of their low silica content, hot mafic lavas are usually very fluid. They flow in thin, broad sheets

Figure 4.5   **A.** Typical pahoehoe (ropy) lava flow, Kilauea, Hawaii. **B.** Typical slow-moving aa flow. **C.** Fresh pillow lava off the coast of Hawaii. **D.** Outcrop of solidified pillow lava on south Vancouver Island.
(Photos **A** and **B** by J. D. Griggs/U.S. Geological Survey; photo **C** by U.S. Geological Survey; photo **D** by S. R. Hicock)

or streamlike ribbons. On the island of Hawaii, such lavas have been clocked at speeds of 30 kilometres per hour down steep slopes, but flow rates of 10 to 300 metres per hour are more common. In contrast, the movement of silica-rich (rhyolitic) lava can be too slow to perceive.

When fluid mafic lavas of the Hawaiian type congeal, they commonly form a relatively smooth skin that wrinkles as the still-molten subsurface lava continues to move (Figure 4.5A). These are known as **pahoehoe** (pronounced *pah-hoy-hoy*) **flows** and resemble the twisting braids in ropes.

Another common type of mafic lava, called an **aa** (pronounced *ah-ah*) **flow**, has a surface of rough, jagged blocks with dangerously sharp edges and spiny projections (Figure 4.5B). Active aa flows are

relatively cool and thick and advance at rates from 5 to 50 metres per hour. Moreover, gases escaping from the surface produce numerous voids and sharp spines in the congealing lava. As the molten interior advances, the outer crust is broken further, giving the flow the appearance of an advancing mass of lava rubble.

When lava enters the ocean, or when outpourings of lava actually originate underwater, the flow's outer skin quickly congeals. However, the lava is usually able to move forward by breaking through the hardened surface. This process occurs over and over, generating a pile of elongated structures resembling large pillows stacked atop one another (Figure 4.5C). These structures, called **pillow lavas**, are useful in the reconstruction of Earth

A   B

Figure 4.6   Lava streams that flow in confined channels often develop a solid crust and become flows within lava tubes. **A.** Thurston Lava Tube, Hawaii Volcanoes National Park. **B.** View of an active lava tube as seen through its collapsed roof. (Photo **A** by © CuboImages srl/Alamy; photo **B** by Jeffrey Judd, U.S. Geological Survey)

history (see Figure 4.5D) because they indicate lava flowed under water.

Hardened lava flows commonly contain tunnels that once were channels carrying lava from the volcanic vent to the flow's leading edge. These openings develop in the interior of a flow where temperatures remain high long after the surface congeals. Under these conditions, the still-molten lava within the conduits drains out the lower end, leaving behind the cavelike tunnels called **lava tubes** (Figure 4.6). Lava tubes are important because they allow fluid lavas to advance great distances from their source. Good examples of lava tubes, pahoehoe and aa flows, and a crater are well preserved in Nisga'a Memorial Lava Bed Provincial Park in northwest British Columbia. The eruption of basalt that produced these features 250 years ago destroyed two villages and killed more than 2000 members of the Nisga'a band. Local legend states that the eruption occurred because a child showed disrespect to the salmon, which are vital to the tribe's survival.

Gases

Magmas contain varying amounts of volatiles held by confining pressure, just as carbon dioxide is held in pop or beer; as soon as the pressure is reduced, the gases begin to escape. The gaseous portion of most magmas comprises 1 percent to 6 percent of the total weight, with most of this in the form of water vapour. Although the percentage may be small, the

actual quantity of emitted gas can exceed thousands of tonnes per day.

The composition of volcanic gases is important because they contribute significantly to the gases that make up our planet's atmosphere. Analyses of samples taken during Hawaiian eruptions indicate that the gases are about 70 percent water vapour and 15 percent carbon dioxide, with lesser amounts of sulphur, chlorine, and flourine. Sulphur compounds are easily recognized by their pungent odour. Volcanoes are a natural source of air pollution, including sulphur dioxide, which readily combines with water to form sulphuric acid. For example, Mount Pinatubo (Philippines) erupted in June 1991, injecting up to 27 million tonnes of sulphur dioxide into the atmosphere. The haze of aerosols that remained in the atmosphere after the eruption lowered global temperatures by 0.5C° over the following year. In 2012 Mount Marapi (Sumatra, Indonesia) spewed sulphur-rich ash 1000 metres into the air.

Gases play an important role in creating the narrow passageway, or conduit, that connects the magma chamber to the surface. First, high temperatures and the buoyant force from the rising magma body crack the rock above. Next, high-pressure gases expand the cracks and develop a passageway to the surface. Then hot gases armed with rock fragments erode the walls of the passageway, producing a larger circular conduit as magma moves upward to the surface. Following an eruptive phase, the conduit often becomes choked with congealed magma and debris that was not thrown clear of the vent.

Occasionally, eruptions such as Tambora and Krakatoa emit colossal amounts of volcanic gases that rise high into the atmosphere, where they can reside for several years. Some of these eruptions have an impact on Earth's climate, on a local to regional scale, by spewing volcanic ash and gases into the atmosphere and blocking out sunlight for a short period. However, it has yet to be proven that volcanic eruptions have a long-term impact on global climate.

Pyroclastic Materials

When mafic lava is extruded, dissolved gases escape freely and continually. These gases propel incandescent blobs of lava to great heights (see Figure 4.2). Some of this ejected material lands near the vent and builds a cone-shaped structure, whereas smaller particles tend to be carried great distances by the wind. For example, ash from the 2010 eruption in Iceland (chapter-opening photo) shut down European airports for weeks. By contrast, viscous (granitic) magmas are highly charged with gases; on release, they expand a thousand-fold as they blow pulverized rock, lava, and glass fragments from the vent. The particles produced in both situations are called **pyroclastic materials** (*pyro* − fire, *clast* − fragment). These ejected fragments range in size from dust and sand-sized volcanic ash (less than 2 millimetres) to pieces that weigh several tonnes.

Ash and dust particles are produced from gas-laden viscous magma during an explosive eruption (see Figure 4.4). As magma moves up in the vent, the gases rapidly expand, generating a froth of melt. As the hot gases expand explosively, the froth is blown into very fine glassy fragments. When the hot ash falls, the glassy shards often fuse to form a rock called welded tuff (Chapter 3, Figure 3.26).

Sheets of this material, as well as ash deposits that later consolidate, have covered vast portions of western North America.

Also common are pyroclasts that range from the size of small beads to about the size of walnuts, termed *lapilli* ("little stones"; see Figure 3.26) or *cinders* (2 to 64 millimetres). Particles larger than 64 millimetres in diameter are called *blocks* when they are made of hardened lava and *bombs* when they are ejected as incandescent lava. Because bombs are semi-molten on ejection, they often assume a streamlined shape as they hurtle through the air (Figure 4.7A). Because of their size, bombs and blocks usually fall on the slopes of a cone; however,

they are occasionally propelled far from the volcano by the force of escaping gases. For instance, bombs 6 metres long and weighing about 200 tonnes were blown 600 metres from the vent during an eruption of the Japanese volcano Asama.

So far we have distinguished various pyroclastic materials based largely on the size of the fragments. Some materials are also identified by their texture and composition. In particular, **scoria** is the name applied to vesicular (containing voids) ejecta derived from mafic magma (Figure 4.7B). These black to reddish-brown fragments are generally found in the size range of lapilli. When magma with an intermediate or silica-rich composition generates vesicular ejecta, it is called **pumice** (see Figure 3.21). Pumice is usually lighter in colour and less dense than scoria. Some pumice fragments have so many vesicles that they are light enough to float in water.

Nuée Ardente: A Deadly Pyroclastic Flow

The extrusion of **pyroclastic flows** consisting of hot gases infused with incandescent ash and larger rock fragments can be devastating. The most destructive of these fiery flows, called **nuées ardentes** (also referred to as *glowing avalanches*), are capable of racing down steep volcanic slopes at speeds that can exceed 100 kilometres per hour (Figure 4.8). An infamous one wiped out the port town of St. Pierre on the Caribbean island of Martinique in 1902 (Figure 4.9). Only one of the 28 000 inhabitants (a prisoner protected in a dungeon) survived that devastating eruption of Mont Pelée.

The ground-hugging portion of a nuée ardente is rich in particulate matter, which is suspended by jets of buoyant gases escaping upward through the flow. In addition, air that is overtaken and trapped by an advancing flow can be heated sufficiently to provide buoyancy to the particulate matter of the nuée ardente. Thus, this flow can include large rock fragments as it travels downslope in a nearly frictionless environment. This helps to explain why some nuée ardente deposits are found more than 100 kilometres from their source.

Gravity causes these heavy flows to sweep downslope, much like a snow avalanche. More often, nuées ardentes form from the collapse of tall eruption columns that form over an exploding volcano. Once gravity overcomes the initial upward thrust provided by the escaping gases, the ejecta begin to fall, sending massive amounts of incandescent blocks, ash, and pumice cascading downslope.

Figure 4.7 Volcanic bombs forming during an eruption of Hawaii's Kilauea Volcano. Ejected lava fragments take on a streamlined shape as they sail through the air. The bomb shown in **A** is about 10 centimetres long. **B.** Scoria also gets ejected as abundant holes form by escaping gas bubbles, giving it a vesicular texture.
(**Main** photo by Photovolcanica.com/Shutterstock; photos **A** and **B** by E. J. Tarbuck)

Lahars: Mudflows on Active and Inactive Volcanoes

In addition to violent eruptions, steep-sided volcanoes can generate a type of mudflow referred to by its Indonesian name, **lahar**. These destructive flows occur when volcanic debris becomes saturated with water and rapidly moves down steep volcanic slopes, generally following gullies and stream valleys. Some lahars are triggered when large volumes of ice and snow melt during an eruption. Others are generated when heavy rainfall saturates weathered volcanic deposits. Thus, lahars can occur even when a volcano is *not* erupting.

Figure 4.8 Nuée ardente races down the slope of Mount Merapi (Indonesia) in May 2006. (Photo by Tom Pfeiffer/www.VolcanoDiscovery.com)

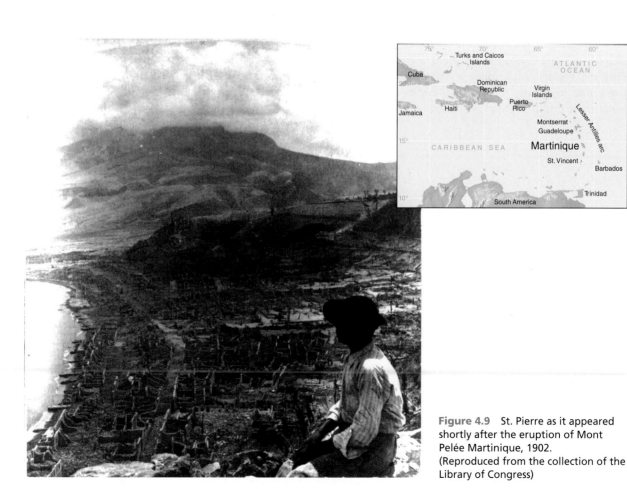

Figure 4.9 St. Pierre as it appeared shortly after the eruption of Mont Pelée Martinique, 1902. (Reproduced from the collection of the Library of Congress)

When Mount St. Helens erupted in 1980, several lahars formed. These flows and accompanying floodwaters raced down the valleys of the north and south forks of the Toutle River at speeds exceeding 30 kilometres per hour. Water levels in the river rose to 4 metres above flood stage, destroying or severely damaging nearly all the homes and bridges along the affected area. Fortunately, the area was not densely populated. This was not the case in 1985, when Nevado del Ruiz, an ice-capped volcano in the Andes, erupted and generated lahars that killed nearly 25 000 people (see the section entitled "Debris Flow" in Chapter 14).

VOLCANIC STRUCTURES AND ERUPTIVE STYLES

The popular image of a volcano is that of a solitary, graceful, snow-capped cone, such as Mount Fujiyama of Japan. These picturesque, conical mountains are produced by explosive volcanic activity that occurred intermittently over thousands, or even hundreds of thousands, of years. However, many volcanoes do not fit this image. Cinder cones are quite small and form during a single eruptive phase that lasts a few days to years. Other volcanic landforms are eroded remnants of former events.

Volcanic landforms come in a wide variety of shapes and sizes, and each structure has a unique eruptive history. Nevertheless, volcanologists have been able to classify volcanic landforms and determine their eruptive patterns. In this section we will consider the general anatomy of a volcano and look at three major volcanic types: shield volcanoes, cinder cones, and composite cones.

Anatomy of a Volcano

Volcanic activity frequently begins when a fissure (crack) develops in the crust as magma moves forcefully toward the surface. As the gas-rich magma moves up this linear fissure, its path is usually localized into a circular conduit, or **pipe**, that terminates at a vent (Figure 4.10). Successive eruptions of lava and/or pyroclastic material, often separated by long periods of inactivity, eventually build the structure we call a **volcano**.

Located at the summit of many volcanoes is a steep-walled depression called a **crater** (*crater* = a bowl). Craters are constructional features that are built upward as ejected fragments collect around the vent to form a doughnut-like structure. Some volcanoes have multiple summit craters, whereas others have very large, more or less circular depressions called **calderas** (*caldaria* = a cooking pot). Calderas are large collapse structures that may or may not form in association with a volcano. (We will consider the formation of various types of calderas later.)

During early stages of growth most volcanic discharges come from a central summit vent. As a volcano matures, material also tends to emerge from fissures that develop along the flanks or base of the volcano. Continued activity from a flank eruption may produce a small **parasitic cone** (*parasitus* = one who eats at the table of another). Mount Etna in

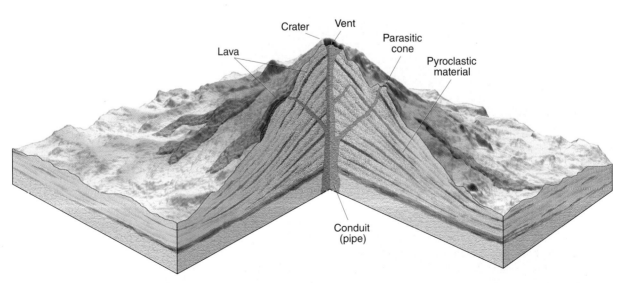

Figure 4.10 Anatomy of a typical composite cone (see also Figures 4.11 and 4.14 for a comparison with a shield and cinder cone, respectively).

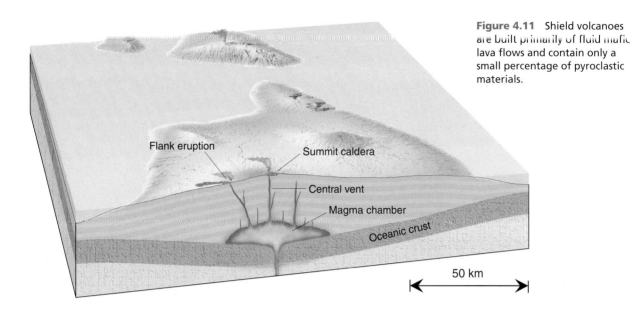

Figure 4.11 Shield volcanoes are built primarily of fluid mafic lava flows and contain only a small percentage of pyroclastic materials.

Flank eruption

Summit caldera

Central vent

Magma chamber

Oceanic crust

50 km

Italy, for example, has more than 200 secondary vents, some of which have built cones. Many of these vents, however, emit only gases and are more appropriately called **fumaroles** (*fumus* = smoke).

Shield Volcanoes

Shield volcanoes are produced by the accumulation of fluid mafic lavas and are broad, slightly domed structures that resemble a warrior's shield (Figure 4.11). Most shield volcanoes have grown up from the deep ocean floor to form islands or seamounts, such as the islands of the Hawaiian chain, Iceland, and the Galapagos. Some shield volcanoes, however, occur on continents. Included in this group are rather massive structures located in East Africa, like Suswa in Kenya.

Extensive study of the Hawaiian Islands confirms that each shield was built from myriad mafic lava flows averaging a few metres thick with less than about 1 percent pyroclastic ejecta. Mauna Loa is one of five overlapping shield volcanoes that together compose the Big Island of Hawaii (Figure 4.12). From its base on the floor of the Pacific Ocean to its summit, Mauna Loa is more than 9 kilometres high, exceeding the height of Mount Everest. This massive pile of basaltic rock has a volume of 80 000 cubic kilometres (Figure 4.13). Most shields are more modest in size: Iceland's Skjaldbreidur is 600 metres high and 10 kilometres across its base. Shield volcanoes also occur on the surface of the planet Mars, the largest of these being Olympus Mons with a diameter of over 500 kilometres and a height of 25 kilometres.

A mature, active shield volcano has a large, steep-sided caldera that occupies its summit. Calderas form when the roof of the volcano collapses as magma from the central magma reservoir migrates to the flanks, often feeding fissure eruptions. In their final stage of growth, mature shields are active more sporadically, with more pyroclastics. The lavas increase in viscosity, resulting in thicker, shorter flows. These eruptions tend to steepen the slope of the summit area, which often becomes capped with clusters of cinder cones. This explains why Mauna Kea, a very mature volcano that has not erupted in recorded history, has a steeper summit than Mauna Loa, which erupted as recently as 1984.

Cinder Cones

As the name suggests, **cinder cones** (also called **scoria cones**) are built from ejected lava fragments that harden while in flight. These fragments range in size from fine ash to bombs but consist mostly of pea- to walnut-size lapilli. Usually a product of relatively gas-rich mafic magma, cinder cones consist of scoria. Occasionally, an eruption of silica-rich magma will generate a cinder cone composed of ash and pumice fragments. Although cinder cones are composed mostly of loose pyroclastic material, they sometimes extrude lava at their base.

Cinder cones have a very simple, distinctive shape determined by the slope that loose pyroclastic material maintains (30 to 40 degrees) as it comes to rest (Figure 4.14). In addition, cinder cones have large, deep craters in relation to the overall size of the structure. Although relatively symmetrical, many

Figure 4.12   Mauna Loa is one of five shield volcanoes that together make up the island of Hawaii. (Photo © Greg Vaughn/Alamy)

cinder cones are elongate, and higher on the side that was downwind during the eruptions.

Cinder cones are usually the product of a single eruptive episode that sometimes lasts only a few weeks and rarely exceeds a few years. Once this event ceases, the magma in the pipe connecting the vent to the magma chamber solidifies, and the volcano never erupts again. Thus, cinder cones are small, usually between 30 metres and 300 metres, and they rarely exceed 700 metres in height (see Figure 4.13C). Canadian volcanoes with cinder cones include Mt. Edziza in British Columbia (Figure 4.14). Probably the most famous cinder cone (Parícutin) erupted in a Mexican cornfield in 1943. A nearby village was eventually buried by pyroclastics and lava flows over the next nine years, leaving only the church towers exposed (Figure 4.15).

Composite Volcanoes

Earth's most picturesque yet potentially dangerous volcanoes are **composite volcanoes** or **stratovolcanoes** (Figure 4.16). Most are located in a relatively narrow zone that rims the Pacific Ocean, appropriately called the *Ring of Fire* (see Figure 4.27). This active zone includes a chain of continental volcanoes that are distributed along the west coast of South and North America, including the large cones of the Andes and the Cascade Range of western North America. The latter group includes Mount St. Helens and Mount Rainier in Washington State and Mount Garibaldi in British Columbia. The most active regions in the Ring of Fire are located along curved belts of volcanic islands situated adjacent to the deep ocean trenches of the northern and western Pacific. This nearly continuous chain of volcanoes stretches from the Aleutian Islands to Kamchatka and from Japan to the Philippines, ending on the North Island of New Zealand.

The classic composite volcano is a large, nearly symmetrical structure composed of both lava and pyroclastic deposits. For the most part, composite volcanoes are the product of gas-rich magma having an andesitic composition. Relative to shields, the silica-rich magmas typical of composite volcanoes can generate thick viscous lavas that travel short distances as well as explosive eruptions that eject huge quantities of pyroclastic material.

The growth of a typical composite volcano begins with both pyroclastic material and lava being emitted from a central vent. As the structure matures, lavas tend to flow from fissures on the lower flanks

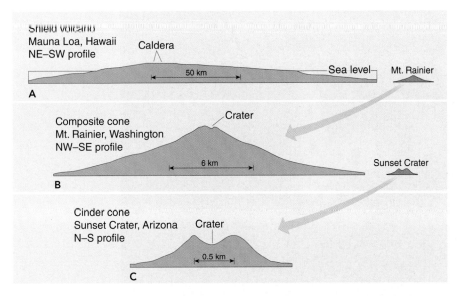

Figure 4.13 Profiles of volcanic landforms. **A.** Profile of Mauna Loa, Hawaii, the largest shield volcano in the Hawaiian chain. Note size comparison with Mount Rainier, Washington, a large composite cone. **B.** Profile of Mount Rainier, Washington. Note how it dwarfs a typical cinder cone. **C.** Profile of Sunset Crater, Arizona, a typical steep-sided cinder cone.

of the cone and may alternate or coincide with explosive eruptions of pyroclastic material from the crater. A typical conical shape, with a steep summit area and more gradually sloping flanks, is partially created by the way that viscous lavas and pyroclastic ejecta contribute to the growth of the volcano. Coarse fragments ejected from the summit crater tend to accumulate around it. Because of their high angle of repose, coarse materials contribute to the steep slopes of the summit area. Finer ejecta are deposited as a thin layer over a large area, which acts to flatten the flank of the volcano. In addition, during the early stages of growth, lavas tend to be more abundant and flow greater distances from the vent than do later lavas. This contributes to the volcano's broad base. As the volcano matures, the short flows that come from the central vent armour and strengthen the summit area. Consequently, steep

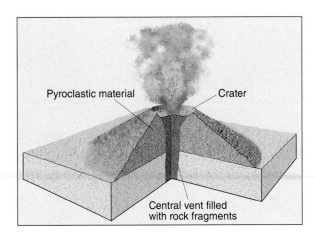

Figure 4.14   Eve Cone, a cinder cone of the Mt. Edziza Volcanic Complex, British Columbia. (Photo © All Canada Photos/Alamy)

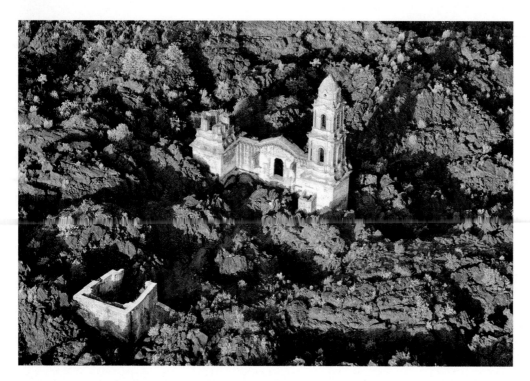

Figure 4.15 The village of San Juan Parangaricutiro (Mexico) engulfed by lava from Parícutin, shown in the background. Only the church towers remain.
(Photo by Michael Collier)

Figure 4.16 These two volcanoes, Pomerape and Parinacota, exhibit the classic shape of a composite volcano. Lauca National Park, Chile.
(Photo © Novarc Images/Alamy)

slopes exceeding 40 degrees are sometimes possible. Parinacota in Chile (Figure 4.16) has the classic form we expect of a composite volcano, with its steep summit and gently sloping flanks.

Most composite volcanoes have a complex history. Huge mounds of volcanic debris surrounding many cones suggest that a large section of the volcano slid downslope as a massive landslide. Others develop horseshoe-shaped depressions at their summits due to explosive eruptions or landslides and eruptions combined, which leave a gaping void on one side of the cone (e.g., Mount St. Helens in 1980).

Living in the Shadow of a Composite Volcano More than 50 volcanoes have erupted in North America in the past 200 years (Figure 4.17). Fortunately, the most explosive of these eruptions, except for Mount St. Helens in 1980, occurred in

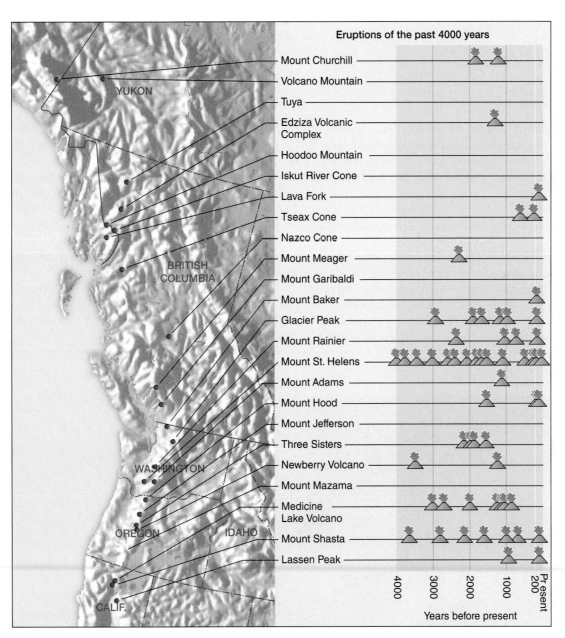

Figure 4.17 The locations of volcanoes along the west coast of North America. Each eruption symbol in the diagram represents from one to several dozen eruptions closely spaced in time.
(Based on Catherine Hickson, "Volcanism in Canada", U.S. Geological Survey and Geological Survey of Canada)

Figure 4.18 Map (20 kilometres across) showing Santorini, the remains of the ancient volcanic island of Thera after the top of the volcano collapsed into the emptied magma chamber following an explosive eruption. The location of the recently excavated Minoan town of Akrotiri is shown. Volcanic eruptions over the past 500 years built the central islands. Despite the fact that another destructive eruption is likely, the city of Phira was built on the flanks of the caldera.

sparsely inhabited regions of Alaska. On a global scale, numerous destructive eruptions have occurred during the past few thousand years, a few of which may have influenced climate and the course of human civilization.

In the case of the Thera composite volcano in the Aegean Sea, all that remains after its catastrophic eruption about 1600 BCE is the scar of the caldera (Santorini in Figure 4.18). It has been suggested that this event gave rise to Plato's legend of the sinking of the island empire of Atlantis that may have occupied Thera. Another famous composite volcano eruption was Italy's Vesuvius, which wiped out the Roman towns of Pompeii and Herculaneum in 79 CE. The casts of victims that were buried by pyroclastic debris during that eruption can be seen today (Figure 4.19). Geologic evidence indicates a super-eruption occurred in Toba, Indonesia, about 73 500 years ago that reached heights of 30 kilometres and spread volcanic ash more than 1000 kilometres away from the volcano. Computer models suggest that, while airborne, the ash drove tropical temperatures to freezing for a period lasting from days to weeks.

Perhaps the most familiar volcanic structure is the composite volcano. But other distinctive and important landforms are also associated with volcanic activity.

Figure 4.19 Plaster casts of several victims of the 79 CE eruption of Mount Vesuvius that destroyed the Roman town of Pompeii. (Photo by Leonard von Matt/Photo Researchers, Inc.)

Figure 4.20 Crater Lake occupies a caldera about 10 kilometres in diameter, formed as a result of the eruption of Mount Mazama (see Figure 4.21). The small cinder cone in the foreground is Wizard Island. (Photo © Greg Vaughn/Alamy)

Calderas

Calderas are large collapse depressions having a more or less circular form (Figure 4.20). Their diameters exceed 1 kilometre, and may be tens of kilometres across. (Those less than 1 kilometre across are called *collapse pits*.) Most calderas are formed by one of the following processes: (1) the collapse of the summit of a large composite volcano following an explosive eruption of silica-rich pumice and ash fragments (Crater Lake type; Figure 4.21); (2) the collapse of the top of a shield volcano caused by subterranean drainage from a central magma chamber (Hawaiian type); and (3) the collapse of a large area, independent of any existing volcanic structures, caused by the discharge of colossal volumes of silica-rich pumice and ash along ring fractures (Yellowstone type).

Another distinctive feature associated with most large calderas is a slow upheaval, or *resurgence*, of the floor of the caldera following an eruptive phase. Thus, these structures consist of a large, somewhat circular depression containing a central elevated region. Most large calderas exhibit a complex history. Geologic evidence suggests that a magma reservoir still exists beneath Yellowstone; thus, another caldera-forming eruption is likely, but not imminent.

Calderas of the type located on the Yellowstone Plateau of northwest Wyoming are among the largest volcanic structures on Earth. Some geologists have compared their destructive force with that of the impact of a small asteroid. Fortunately, no eruption of this type has occurred in recorded history.

Fissure Eruptions and Lava Plateaus

The greatest volume of volcanic material is extruded from fractures in the crust called **fissures** (*fissura* = to split). Rather than building a cone, these long, narrow cracks can extrude a low-viscosity mafic lava (Figure 4.22), blanketing a wide area. The vertical stacking of lava flows produced by successive **fissure eruptions** can lead to immense buildups of basalt totalling hundreds to even thousands of metres in thickness. The extensive Columbia Plateau (Figure 4.23), a 1.5-kilometre-thick pile of

Eruption of
Mount Mazama

Partially emptied
magma chamber

Collapse of
Mount Mazama

Formation of Crater Lake and Wizard Island

Figure 4.21   Sequence of events that formed Crater Lake, Oregon. About 7700 years ago, a violent eruption partly emptied the magma chamber, causing the summit of former Mount Mazama to collapse. Rainfall and groundwater contributed to form Crater Lake, the deepest lake in the United States. Subsequent eruptions produced the cinder cone called Wizard Island.
(After H. Williams, *The Ancient Volcanoes of Oregon*, p. 47. Courtesy of the University of Oregon)

(4.24B). Flows in the Columbia Plateau, for example, are known to extend 150 kilometres from their inferred source. The term **flood basalt** accurately reflects this characteristic. Although not as extensive as those of the Columbian Plateau, flood basalts do occur in parts of Canada, including the Minas Basin (Nova Scotia) and south-central British Columbia (Figure 4.24C), as well as Victoria Island (Northwest Territories and Nunavut) and Axel Heiberg Island (Nunavut).

One of the largest accumulations of flood basalt in the world is the Deccan Traps, a thick sequence of flat-lying basalt flows covering nearly 500 000 square kilometres of west central India. When the Deccan Traps formed about 66 million years ago, nearly 2 million cubic kilometres of lava were extruded in fewer than 1 million years. This event coincided with the demise of the dinosaurs (at the end of the Cretaceous Period), and some believe the two events are connected. Another huge deposit of flood basalts, called the Ontong Java Plateau, is found on the floor of the Pacific Ocean.

Lava Domes

In contrast to mafic lavas, silica-rich (rhyolitic) lavas are so viscous they hardly flow. As the thick lava is "squeezed" out of the vent, it may produce a steep-sided dome-shaped mass of congealed lava called a **lava dome**.

Lava domes typify the late stages of mature, mainly andesitic composite volcano activity. These rhyolitic structures form in the summit crater and as parasitic structures on the flanks of cones following an explosive eruption of gas-rich magma. This is exemplified by the dome that continues to grow from the vent of Mount St. Helens (Figure 4.25). Although most lava domes form in association with existing composite cones or shield volcanoes, some form independently, such as the line of rhyolitic and obsidian domes at Mono Craters, California.

Volcanic Pipes and Necks

Most volcanoes are fed magma through short conduits, called *pipes*, that connect a magma chamber to the surface. In rare cases, deep ultramafic magmas migrate up these structures to produce rocks that are thought to be fairly pristine samples of the mantle. Geologists consider these unusually deep conduits to be "windows" into Earth, for they allow us to view rock normally found only at great depth.

Well-known volcanic pipes are the diamond-bearing structures of South Africa and the Northwest Territories. Here, the rocks filling the pipes

approximately 300 individual basalt flows, is a classic example of such a buildup.

Because it is very fluid, the basaltic lava erupting from a volcanic fissure (Figure 4.24A) can flow laterally in sheets over considerable distances

Figure 4.22 Lava extruded along the East Rift Zone, Kilauea, Hawaii. (Photo © Greg Vaughn/Alamy)

originated at depths of at least 150 kilometres, where pressure is high enough to generate diamonds and other high-pressure minerals. The task of transporting essentially unaltered magma (along with diamond inclusions) through 150 kilometres of solid rock is exceptional and accounts for the scarcity of natural diamonds (see Chapter 20).

Volcanoes on land are continually being lowered by weathering and erosion. Cinder cones are easily eroded, because they are composed of unconsolidated materials. However, all volcanoes eventually succumb to relentless erosion. As erosion progresses, the rock occupying the volcanic pipe is commonly more resistant and may remain standing

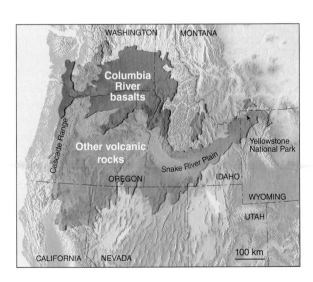

Figure 4.23 Volcanic areas that compose the Columbia Plateau in the U.S. Pacific Northwest. The Columbia River basalts cover an area of nearly 200 000 square kilometres. Activity here began about 17 million years ago as lava began to pour out of large fissures, eventually producing a basalt pile with an average thickness of nearly 1.5 kilometres. (After U.S. Geological Survey)

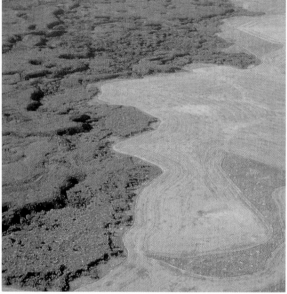

B

Figure 4.24 Basaltic fissure eruption. **A.** Lava fountaining from a fissure and formation of fluid lava flows called flood basalts. **B.** Photo of basalt flows near Idaho Falls. **C.** Plateau basalts exposed in canyon walls of Chasm Provincial Park, south-central British Columbia. The canyon was carved by meltwater at the end of the Ice Age.
(Photo **B** by John S. Shelton; photo **C** © Radius Images/Alamy)

above the surrounding terrain long after most of the cone has vanished. Black Tusk, British Columbia, is such a feature and is called a **volcanic neck** (Figure 4.26).

PLATE TECTONICS AND VOLCANIC ACTIVITY

Geologists have known for decades that the global distribution of volcanism is not random. Most active volcanoes are located along the margins of the ocean basins—most notably along the circum-Pacific belt known as the *Ring of Fire* (Figure 4.27).* Volcanoes

mainly consist of composite cones that emit volatile-rich magma of intermediate (andesitic) composition and occasionally produce awe-inspiring eruptions.

A second group includes islands of deep ocean basins that emit fluid mafic lavas. Among them are active submarine volcanoes that dot the ocean floor as seamounts along oceanic ridges. At these depths the pressures are so great that gases quickly dissolve in seawater. Thus, firsthand knowledge of these eruptions is limited, coming mainly from deep-diving submersibles.

A third group, produced by **intraplate volcanism** (meaning "within the plate"), includes volcanoes in the interiors of continents. The best example is Mount Kilimanjaro in northern Africa. Lava from volcanoes on continents can range from mafic to felsic in composition. Such volcanoes form as a result of magma generation associated with ascending plumes of hot mantle rock. Kilauea in Hawaii belongs to this group. It is situated in the middle of

---

*For our purposes, active volcanoes include those with eruptions that have been dated. At least 700 other cones exhibit geologic evidence that they have erupted within the past 10 000 years and are regarded as potentially active. Further innumerable active submarine volcanoes are hidden from view in the depths of the ocean and are not counted in these numbers.

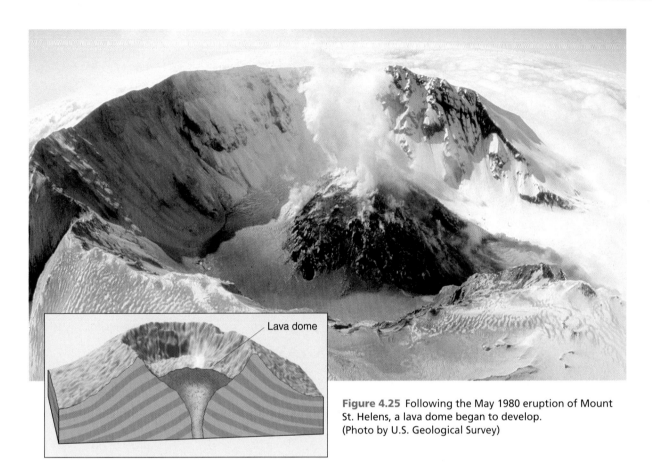

Figure 4.25 Following the May 1980 eruption of Mount St. Helens, a lava dome began to develop. (Photo by U.S. Geological Survey)

Figure 4.26 Black Tusk, British Columbia, is a volcanic neck. This structure, which stands almost 570 metres high, consists of igneous rock that crystallized in the vent of a volcano; the volcano itself has long since been eroded away. (Photo © Wave Royalty Free/Design Pics Inc/Alamy)

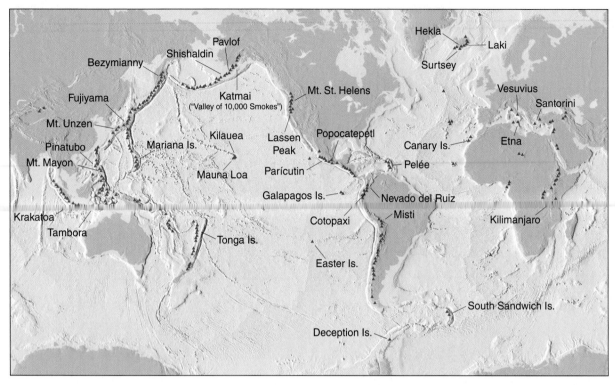

Figure 4.27   Locations of some of Earth's major volcanoes. (Photo © Wave Royalty Free/Design Pics Inc/Alamy)

the vast Pacific plate, thousands of kilometres from the nearest plate boundary. Among other examples are the Canary and Azores islands, Yellowstone, and several volcanic centres in the Sahara Desert of northern Africa. Intraplate volcanoes situated on oceanic lithosphere typically erupt mafic lava, whereas the lava erupted from similar volcanoes on continents can range from mafic to felsic in composition.

Until the late 1960s, geologists had no explanation for the apparently haphazard distribution of continental volcanoes, nor were they able to account for the almost continuous chain of volcanoes that circles the margin of the Pacific basin. The development of plate tectonics theory clarified the picture. Indeed, plate tectonics, magma generation, and volcanism are intimately connected and will be further discussed in Chapters 11 through 13.

CHAPTER SUMMARY

- Volcanic eruptions are controlled by the magma's composition, temperature, and amount of dissolved gases. Magma viscosity is related to silica content: more silica, more viscous. Dissolved gases increase magma fluidity and propel molten material from the volcano's *vent*.
- Extruded materials include *pahoehoe* (braided) and *aa* (blocky) lava; gases; *pyroclastics* (ash, pumice, lapilli, cinders, blocks, and bombs); *nuées ardentes*; and *lahars*.
- Broad *shield volcanoes* are built by fluid mafic lava flows; *cinder cones* are made of pyroclastics; and

composite volcanoes are composed of both materials. Most volcanoes are fed by conduits (*pipes*), whose eroded remnants stick out as *volcanic necks*. Nearly circular *calderas* commonly result from collapse following explosive eruption. Most volcanic material is extruded from *fissures* to form extensive *flood basalts*.

- Most active volcanoes are near plate boundaries (oceanic ridges, subduction zones) and in plate interiors above mantle plumes.

MasteringGeology
www.masteringgeology.com

Looking for additional review and test prep materials? Visit the Study Area in MasteringGeology to enhance your understanding of this chapter's content by accessing a variety of resources, including

Self-Study Quizzes, Geoscience Animations, GEODe Tutorials, RSS feeds, flashcards, weblinks, self-study quizzes, and an optional Pearson eText.

REVIEW QUESTIONS

1. List three factors that determine the nature of a volcanic eruption. What role does each play?

2. Why do volcanoes at convergent plate boundaries (e.g., along the west coast of North America) tend to be more explosive and pose a greater threat to people than those at divergent plate boundaries?

3. How does the size and shape (profile) of a volcano relate to the characteristics of the materials of which it is composed and, in turn, the behaviour of the eruptions that deposited these materials?

4. Why is the world's circum-Pacific belt (also called the Pacific Rim) commonly referred to as the Ring of Fire?

5. Explain why all recently active volcanoes in Canada are restricted to British Columbia and Yukon.

6. What are fissure eruptions and why do these types of eruptions tend to form flat-lying flows or plateaus rather than volcanic cones?

7. What are lahars and why are they dangerous?

8. What are calderas and how are they formed?

5

WEATHERING AND SOIL

The spectacular badland topography of southern Alberta is a testament to the processes of weathering and erosion. (Photo by Elenathewise/ Fotolia)

CHAPTER OUTLINE

Earth's External Processes
Weathering
Mechanical Weathering
Chemical Weathering
Rates of Weathering
Soil
Controls of Soil Formation
The Soil Profile
Soil Types
Soil Erosion

Before studying sedimentary rocks we must first learn how sediment is produced through weathering. Earth's surface is constantly changing. Rock is disintegrated and decomposed; moved to lower elevations by gravity; and carried away by water, wind, or ice. In this manner, Earth's landscape is sculpted. This chapter focuses on the first step of this ongoing process: weathering. What causes solid rock to crumble, and why does the type and rate of weathering vary from place to place? Soil, an important product of the weathering process and a vital resource, is also examined.

EARTH'S EXTERNAL PROCESSES

Weathering and Soil

Weathering, mass wasting, and erosion are called **external processes** because they occur at or near Earth's surface and are powered by energy from the sun or Earth's gravity. External processes are a basic part of the rock cycle; they transform solid rock into sediment that may transform into sedimentary rocks (Chapter 6).

To most people, the face of Earth appears to be unchanging. In fact, a mere 200 years ago most people fervently believed that mountains, lakes, and deserts were permanent features of a young Earth no more than a few thousand years old. Today, we know that Earth is close to 4.6 billion years old and that mountains eventually wear down, lakes fill with sediment or are drained by streams, and deserts come and go with changes in climate.

Earth is a dynamic body. Some parts of Earth's surface are gradually elevated through plate tectonics, mountain building, and volcanic activity. These **internal processes** derive their energy from Earth's interior. Meanwhile, opposing external processes are continually breaking rock apart (Figure 5.1) through the following processes:

1. **Weathering:** the physical breakdown (disintegration) and chemical alteration (decomposition) of rock at or near Earth's surface

2. **Mass wasting:** the transfer of rock and soil downslope by gravity (Chapter 14)

3. **Erosion:** the physical removal of material by water, ice, or wind (Chapters 15–18)

In this chapter we will focus on rock weathering and the products generated by this activity. However, weathering cannot be easily separated from mass wasting and erosion because they remove the rock debris as weathering breaks rocks apart. Exposure of new material promotes

Figure 5.1 This is an interesting example of the weathering of cross-bedded sandstone in Writing-on-Stone Provincial Park, Davis Coulee, Alberta. When weathering accentuates differences in rocks, spectacular landforms are sometimes created. As the rock gradually disintegrates and decomposes, mass wasting and erosion remove the products of weathering. (Photo by Rudi Meyer)

further disintegration and decomposition of the rock.

WEATHERING

Weathering and Soil

Weathering goes on all around us, but it seems so slow and subtle that it is easy to underestimate its importance. However, weathering is an essential part of the rock cycle and thus a key process in the Earth system.

All materials are subject to weathering. Consider, for example, the fabricated product concrete. A newly poured concrete sidewalk has a smooth, fresh look. However, a few years later the same sidewalk will appear chipped, cracked, and rough, with pebbles exposed at the surface. Roots of nearby trees may heave and buckle the concrete as well. The same natural processes that break apart a concrete sidewalk also break down rock.

Mechanical weathering (sometimes referred to as *physical weathering*) is accomplished by physical forces that break rock into smaller and smaller pieces without changing the rock's mineral composition. **Chemical weathering** involves a chemical transformation of rock into one or more new compounds. These two concepts can be illustrated with a piece of paper. As an analogy, paper can be disintegrated by tearing it into smaller and smaller pieces, whereas decomposition occurs when the paper is burned.

Weathering is the response of Earth materials to a changing environment. For instance, after millions of years of uplift and erosion, the rocks overlying a large, intrusive igneous body (pluton) may be removed, exposing it at the surface (see Figures 3.19, 5.4, and 5.5). This mass of crystalline rock—formed deep below ground where temperatures and pressures are high—is now subjected to a very different and comparatively hostile surface environment. In response, this rock mass will gradually change through processes we call weathering.

In the following sections, we will discuss the various modes of mechanical and chemical weathering. Although we consider these two processes separately, keep in mind that they usually work simultaneously in nature and enhance each other's effectiveness.

MECHANICAL WEATHERING
Weathering and Soil

When a rock undergoes *mechanical weathering*, it is broken into smaller and smaller pieces, each retaining the characteristics of the original material. Figure 5.2 shows that breaking a rock into smaller pieces increases the surface area available for chemical weathering. An analogous situation occurs when sugar is added to tea. A cube of sugar will dissolve much more slowly than will an equal volume of sugar granules because the cube has much less surface area available for dissolution.

In nature, three important physical processes lead to the fragmentation of rock: frost wedging, expansion resulting from unloading, and biologic activity. In addition, although the work of erosional agents (such as wind, glacial ice, and running water) is usually considered separately from mechanical weathering, it is nevertheless important. As these mobile agents move rock debris, they relentlessly disintegrate these materials.

Frost Wedging

Repeated freezing and thawing are important processes of mechanical weathering. Liquid water has the unique property of expanding about 9 percent on freezing because water molecules in the regular crystalline structure of ice are farther apart than they are in liquid water near the freezing point. As a result, water freezing in a confined space exerts tremendous outward pressure on the walls of its container. To verify this, consider an unopened plastic bottle of pop that is placed in the freezer. As the water in the pop freezes, the bottle can crack.

In nature, water works its way into cracks in rock and, on freezing, expands and enlarges these openings. After many freeze–thaw cycles, the rock is broken into angular fragments. This process is appropriately called **frost wedging** (Figure 5.3). Frost wedging is pronounced in mountainous and polor regions where frequent freeze–thaw cycles occur. Here, sections of rock are wedged loose and may tumble into large piles called **talus slopes** that commonly form at the base of steep rock outcrops (Figure 5.3).

Figure 5.2 Chemical weathering can occur only to those portions of a rock that are exposed to the elements. Mechanical weathering breaks rock into smaller and smaller pieces, thereby increasing the surface area available for chemical attack.

4 square units ×
6 sides ×
1 cube =
—
24 square units

1 square unit ×
6 sides ×
8 cubes =
—
48 square units

0.25 square unit ×
6 sides ×
64 cubes =
—
96 square units

Figure 5.3 Frost wedging. As water freezes, it expands, exerting a force great enough to break rock. When frost wedging occurs in such a setting as this, the broken rock fragments fall to the base of the cliff and create a cone-shaped accumulation known as *talus*. **Inset:** This boulder, a glacial erratic in the polar desert conditions of the Northwest Territories, was probably split by frost wedging.
(**Main** photo by David P. Lewis/Shutterstock.; **inset** photo reproduced with the permission of Natural Resources Canada, 2010, courtesy of the Geological Survey of Canada, Photo A94S0069 by C. Jefferson)

Frost wedging also causes great destruction to highways in Canada, particularly in the early spring, when the freeze–thaw cycle is well established. Roadways acquire numerous potholes and are occasionally heaved and buckled by this destructive force. Another type of wedging in rock fractures is caused by the crystallization of salt (such as sodium sulphate, calcium chloride, and sodium chloride) through the evaporation of saline solutions that seep into cracks and joints, especially in hot, arid climates. As the salt crystals grow, they can force the fractures apart and thus contribute to rock disintegration.

Sheeting

When large masses of igneous rock, particularly granite, are exposed by erosion, concentric slabs begin to break loose. The process generating these onion-like layers is called **sheeting**. It is thought that this occurs, at least in part, because of the great reduction in pressure when the overlying rock is eroded away. As the overburden is removed, the outer layers expand more than the rock below and thus separate from the rock body (Figure 5.4). Continued weathering eventually causes the slabs to separate and spall off (flake away), creating an **exfoliation dome** (*ex* = off, *folium* = leaf). Excellent examples of exfoliation domes are Stawamus Chief in British Columbia (see Figure 3.19); Sugarloaf in Rio de Janeiro; and

Half Dome and Liberty Cap in Yosemite National Park in California (Figure 5.5).

Deep underground mining provides us with another example of how rocks behave once the confining pressure is removed. Large rock slabs have been known to explode off the walls of newly cut mine tunnels because of the abruptly reduced pressure. Evidence of this type, plus the fact that fracturing occurs parallel to the floor of a quarry when large blocks of rock are removed, strongly supports the process of unloading as the cause of sheeting.

Although many fractures are created by expansion, others are produced by contraction during the crystallization of magma (see Figure 3.30), and still others by tectonic forces during mountain building. Fractures produced by these activities generally form a definite pattern and are called *joints* (Figure 5.6). Joints allow water to penetrate deeply and start the process of weathering long before the rock is exposed. Finally, fracturing of rocks by frequent drastic temperature changes in deserts has been suggested but not yet proven.

Biologic Activity

Weathering is also accomplished by the activities of organisms, including plants, burrowing animals, and humans. Plant roots and seedlings in search of nutrients and water grow into and expand fractures

C

Figure 5.4 Sheeting is caused by the expansion of crystalline rock as erosion removes the overlying material. When the deeply buried pluton in **A** is exposed at the surface following uplift and erosion in **B**, the igneous mass fractures into thin slabs. **C.** An exhumed pluton on north Baffin Island illustrates the onion-like layers created by sheeting. Note people for scale.
(Photo **C** by S. R. Hicock/Pearson Education)

(Figure 5.7), providing a pathway for water and chemical infiltration. Lichens and mosses attach themselves to bare rock surfaces, thereby enhancing their physical and chemical breakdown.

Burrowing animals further break down rock by moving fresh material to the surface, where physical and chemical processes can more effectively attack it. Decaying organisms also aid in chemical weathering by producing acids that break down minerals, so that rainwater can remove their soluble weathering products.

CHEMICAL WEATHERING
Weathering and Soil

Chemical weathering involves the complex processes that break down rock components and the internal structures of minerals. Such processes convert the constituents to new minerals or release them to the surrounding environment. The original rock decomposes into substances that are stable in the surface environment. Consequently, the products of chemical weathering remain essentially unchanged as long

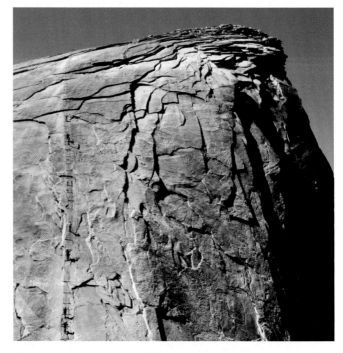

Figure 5.5 Summit of Half Dome, an exfoliation dome in Yosemite National Park, California.
(Photo by Gary Moon/AGE Fotostock)

Figure 5.6 Nearly parallel vertical joints in granitic rock on the south side of Grouse Mountain, British Columbia. (Photo by S. R. Hicock)

as they remain in an environment similar to the one in which they formed.

Water is by far the most important agent of chemical weathering. Pure water alone is a good solvent, and small amounts of dissolved materials result in increased chemical activity for weathering solutions. The major processes of chemical weathering are dissolution, oxidation, and hydrolysis. Water plays a leading role in each.

Dissolution

Perhaps the easiest type of decomposition to envision is the process of **dissolution**. Just as sugar dissolves in water, so too do certain minerals. One of the most water-soluble minerals is halite (common salt), which is composed of sodium and chloride ions. Halite readily dissolves in water because although this compound maintains overall electrical neutrality, the individual ions retain their respective charges.

Moreover, the surrounding water molecules are polar—that is, the oxygen end of the molecule has a small residual negative charge; the end with hydrogen has a small positive charge. As the water molecules come in contact with halite, their negative ends approach sodium ions and their positive ends cluster about chloride ions. This disrupts the attractive forces in the halite crystal and releases the ions to the water solution (Figure 5.8).

Although most minerals are, for all practical purposes, insoluble in pure water, the presence of even a small amount of acid dramatically increases the corrosive force of water. (An acidic solution contains the reactive hydrogen ion, H^+.) In nature, acids are produced by a number of processes. For example, carbonic acid is created when carbon dioxide in the atmosphere dissolves in raindrops. As acidic

Figure 5.7 Roots of cedar trees work their way into fractures in the dolostone that caps the Niagara Escarpment in the Beaver Valley of Ontario. Root wedging widens fractures in rock and aids the process of mechanical weathering. (Photo by C. Tsujita)

Figure 5.8   Illustration of halite dissolving in water.
A. Polar water molecules attack sodium and chloride ions.
B. Once removed, these ions are surrounded and held by a number of water molecules, as shown.

rainwater soaks into the ground, carbon dioxide in the soil may increase the acidity of the weathering solution. Various organic acids are also released into the soil as organisms decay, and sulphuric acid is introduced as acid rain (Box 5.1) and produced by the weathering of pyrite and other sulphide minerals.

Regardless of the source of the acid, this highly reactive substance readily decomposes most rocks and produces certain products that are water soluble. For example, the mineral calcite, $CaCO_3$, which makes up the common building stones marble and limestone, is easily attacked by even a weakly acidic solution:

$$CaCO_3 + (H^+ + HCO_3^-) \rightarrow Ca^{2+} + 2HCO_3^-$$

calcite   carbonic   calcium   bicarbonate
carbonate   acid   ions (soluble) ions (soluble)

During this process, the insoluble calcium carbonate is transformed into soluble products. In nature, over thousands of years, large quantities of limestone are dissolved and carried away by underground water (see Chapter 16). This activity is clearly evidenced by the large number of subsurface caverns found in limestone regions throughout North America. Monuments and buildings made of limestone or marble are also subjected to the corrosive work of acids, particularly in industrial areas that have smoggy, polluted air (see Box 5.1).

The soluble ions from reactions of this type are retained in our underground water supply. These dissolved ions are responsible for the so-called hard water found in many locales. Simply, hard water is undesirable because the active ions react with soap to produce an insoluble material that renders soap nearly useless in removing dirt. To solve this problem, a water softener can be used to remove these ions, generally by replacing them with others that do not chemically react with soap.

Oxidation

Everyone has seen iron and steel objects that rusted when exposed to water (Figure 5.9). The same thing can happen to iron-rich minerals. The process of rusting occurs when oxygen combines with iron to form iron oxide as follows:

$$\textbf{4Fe} + \textbf{3O}_2 \rightarrow \textbf{2Fe}_2\textbf{O}_3$$

iron   oxygen   iron oxide (hematite)

This type of chemical reaction, called **oxidation**,* occurs when electrons are lost from one element during the reaction. In this case, we say that iron was oxidized because it lost electrons to oxygen. Although the oxidation of iron progresses very slowly in a dry environment, the addition of water greatly speeds the reaction.

Oxidation is important in decomposing such ferromagnesian minerals as olivine, pyroxene, and amphibole. Oxygen readily combines with the iron in these minerals to form the reddish-brown iron oxide called *hematite* (Fe_2O_3) or, in other cases, a yellowish-coloured rust called *limonite* [FeO(OH)]. These products are responsible for the rusty colour on the surfaces of dark, iron-rich igneous rocks, such as basalt, as they begin to weather (see Figure 5.11). However, oxidation can occur only after iron is freed

---

*Note that *oxidation* is a term referring to any chemical reaction in which a compound or radical loses electrons; the element oxygen is not necessarily present. Reduction, a chemical reaction in which the compound or ion gains an electron, can occur in water-saturated conditions.

BOX
5.1

EARTH AS A SYSTEM
Acid Precipitation: A Human Impact on the Earth System

Humans are part of the complex interacting whole we call the Earth system. As such, our actions cause changes to all the other parts of the system. For example, by going about our normal activities, we modify the composition of the atmosphere. These atmospheric modifications in turn cause unintended and unwanted changes to occur in the hydrosphere, biosphere, and geosphere. Acid precipitation is one small but significant example.

Decomposing stone monuments and structures are common sights in many cities (Figure 5.A). Although we expect rock to gradually decompose, many of these monuments have succumbed prematurely. An important cause of this accelerated chemical weathering is acid precipitation.

Rain is naturally somewhat acidic (i.e., lower than 7 on the pH scale). When carbon dioxide from the atmosphere dissolves in water, the product is weak carbonic acid. However, the term *acid precipitation* refers to precipitation that is much more acidic than natural, unpolluted rain and snow.

As a consequence of burning large quantities of fossil fuels, such as coal and petroleum products, tens of millions of tonnes of sulphur and nitrogen oxides are released into the atmosphere each year in North America alone. The major sources of these emissions include power-generating plants, industrial processes such as ore smelting and petroleum refining, and vehicles of all kinds. Through a series of complex chemical reactions, some of these pollutants are converted into acids that then fall to Earth's surface as rain or snow. Another portion is deposited in dry form and subsequently converted into acid after coming in contact with precipitation, dew, or fog.

Figure 5.A Acid rain accelerates the chemical weathering of stone monuments and structures, including the Temple of Zeus in Athens, Greece.
(Photo © valerie009/Fotolia)

Northern Europe and eastern North America have experienced widespread acid rain for some time. Studies have also shown that acid rain occurs in many other regions, including western North America, Japan, China, Russia, the rest of Europe, and South America. In addition to local pollution sources, a portion of the acidity found in the northeast United States and eastern Canada originates hundreds of kilometres away in industrialized regions to the south and southwest. This situation occurs because many pollutants remain in the atmosphere for as long as five days, during which time they can be transported great distances.

The damaging environmental effects of acid rain are thought to be considerable in some areas and imminent in others. The best-known effect is an increased acidity in thousands of lakes in Scandinavia and eastern North America. Accompanying this

have been substantial increases in dissolved aluminum leached from the soil by the acidic water, which is toxic to fish. Consequently, some lakes are virtually devoid of fish, and others are approaching this condition. Ecosystems are characterized by many interactions at many levels of organization, which means that evaluating the effects of acid precipitation on these complex systems is difficult and expensive, and far from complete.

In addition to the many lakes that can no longer support fish, research indicates that acid precipitation may also reduce agricultural crop yields and impair the productivity of forests. Acid rain not only harms the foliage but also damages roots and leaches nutrient minerals from the soil. Finally, acid precipitation promotes the corrosion of metals and contributes to the destruction of stone structures.

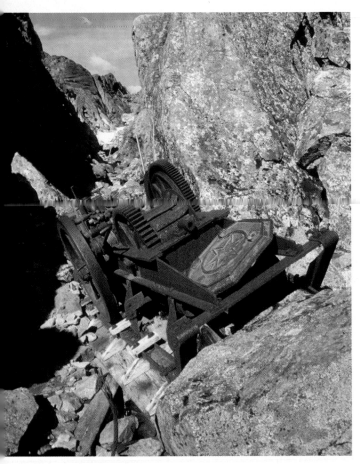

Figure 5.9 Iron reacts with oxygen to form iron oxide, as seen on this rusted tram winch on the Chilkoot Trail, Yukon.
(Photo by Mike Schering)

from the silicate structure by another process, called hydrolysis (explained below).

Another important oxidation reaction occurs when sulphide minerals, such as pyrite, decompose. Sulphide minerals are major constituents in many metallic ores, and pyrite is frequently associated with coal deposits as well. In a moist environment, chemical weathering of pyrite (FeS_2) yields sulphuric acid (H_2SO_4) and iron oxide [$FeO(OH)$]. In many mining locales, this weathering process creates a serious environmental hazard, particularly in humid areas where abundant rainfall infiltrates spoil banks (waste material left after coal or other minerals are removed). This so-called *mine acid* eventually makes its way to streams, killing aquatic organisms and degrading aquatic habitats (see Box 20.2).

Hydrolysis

The most common mineral group, the silicates, is decomposed primarily by the process of **hydrolysis**

(*hydro* = water, *lysis* = to separate), which basically is the reaction of any substance with water. Ideally, the hydrolysis of a mineral would take place in pure water, as some of the water molecules dissociate to form the very reactive hydrogen (H^+) and hydroxyl (OH^-) ions. It is the tiny hydrogen ion that attacks and replaces other larger cations found in the crystal lattice. With the introduction of hydrogen ions into the crystalline structure, the original orderly arrangement of atoms collapses and the mineral decomposes.

In nature, water usually contains other substances that contribute additional hydrogen ions, thereby greatly accelerating hydrolysis. For example, carbon dioxide from the atmosphere and decaying organisms dissolve in water to form carbonic acid that percolates through the soil.

In water, carbonic acid ionizes to form hydrogen ions (H^+) and bicarbonate ions (HCO_3^-). To illustrate how a rock undergoes hydrolysis in the presence of carbonic acid, let's examine the chemical weathering of granite, a common continental rock. Recall that granite consists mainly of quartz and potassium feldspar. The weathering of the potassium feldspar component of granite is as follows:

$$\underset{\text{potassium feldspar}}{2KAlSi_3O_8} + \underset{\text{carbonic acid}}{2(H^+ + HCO_3^-)} + \underset{\text{water}}{H_2O} \rightarrow$$

$$\underset{\substack{\text{kaolinite}\\\text{(residual clay)}}}{Al_2Si_2O_5(OH)_4} + \underset{\substack{\text{potassium}\\\text{ion}}}{2K^+} + \underset{\substack{\text{bicarbonate}\\\text{ions}}}{2HCO_3^-} + \underset{\text{silica}}{4SiO_2}$$
$$\underbrace{\hspace{5cm}}_{\text{in solution}}$$

In this reaction, the hydrogen ions (H^+) attack and replace potassium ions (K^+) in the feldspar structure, thereby disrupting the crystalline network. Once removed, the potassium is available as a nutrient for plants or becomes the soluble salt potassium bicarbonate ($KHCO_3$), which may be incorporated into other minerals or carried to the ocean.

The most abundant product of the chemical breakdown of potassium feldspar is the clay mineral kaolinite. Clay minerals are the end products of weathering and are very stable under surface conditions. Consequently, clay minerals make up a high percentage of the inorganic material in soils. Moreover, the most abundant sedimentary rock, shale, contains a high proportion of clay minerals. Industrial uses of clay minerals are presented in Chapter 20.

In addition to the formation of clay minerals during the weathering of potassium feldspar, some silica is removed from the feldspar structure and carried away by groundwater. This dissolved silica will eventually precipitate, producing nodules of chert or flint, or it will fill in the pore spaces between grains of sediment, or it will be carried to the ocean, where microscopic animals will remove it from the water to build hard silica shells.

To summarize, the weathering of potassium feldspar generates a residual clay mineral, a soluble salt (potassium bicarbonate), and some silica, which enters into solution.

Quartz, the other main component of granite, is very resistant to chemical weathering; it remains substantially unaltered when attacked by weak acidic solutions. As a result, when granite weathers, the feldspar crystals dull and slowly turn to clay, releasing the once interlocked quartz grains, which still retain their fresh, glassy appearance. Although some of the quartz remains in the soil, much is eventually transported to the sea or to other sites of deposition, where it becomes the main constituent of such features as sandy beaches and sand dunes. In time these quartz grains may be lithified to form the sedimentary rock *sandstone* (Chapter 6).

Table 5.1 lists the weathered products of some of the most common silicate minerals. Remember that silicate minerals make up most of Earth's crust and that these minerals are composed mostly of only eight elements. When chemically weathered, the silicate minerals yield sodium, calcium, potassium, and magnesium ions that form soluble products, which can be removed by groundwater. The element iron combines with oxygen, producing relatively insoluble iron oxides, most notably hematite and limonite, which give soil a reddish-brown or yellowish colour. Under most conditions, the three remaining elements—aluminum, silicon, and oxygen—join with water to produce residual clay minerals. However, even the highly insoluble clay minerals are very slowly removed by subsurface water.

Alterations Caused by Chemical Weathering

As noted earlier, the most significant result of chemical weathering is the decomposition of unstable minerals and the generation or retention of those materials that are stable at Earth's surface. This accounts for the predominance of certain minerals in the surface material we call soil.

In addition to altering the internal structure of minerals, chemical weathering causes physical changes as well. For instance, when angular rock fragments are attacked by water flowing through joints, the fragments tend to take on a spherical shape. The gradual rounding of the corners and edges of angular blocks is illustrated in Figure 5.10. The corners are attacked most readily because of the greater surface area for their volume as compared with the edges and faces. This process, called **spheroidal weathering**, gives the weathered rock a more rounded or spherical shape (Figure 5.10).

Sometimes during the formation of spheroidal boulders, successive shells separate from the rock's main body (Figure 5.11). Eventually the outer shells break off, allowing the chemical weathering activity to penetrate deeper into the boulder. This spherical scaling results because as the minerals in the rock weather to clay, they increase in size through the addition of water to their structure. This increased bulk exerts an outward force that causes concentric layers of rock to break loose and fall off.

Hence, chemical weathering does produce forces great enough to cause mechanical weathering. This type of spheroidal weathering in which shells spall off should not be confused with the phenomenon of sheeting discussed earlier. In sheeting, the fracturing occurs as a result of unloading, and the rock layers that separate from the main body are largely unaltered at the time of separation.

RATES OF WEATHERING
Weathering and Soil

Several factors influence the type and rate of rock weathering. We have already seen how mechanical weathering affects the rate of weathering. By breaking rock into smaller pieces, the amount of surface area exposed to chemical weathering increases. Other important factors examined here include the roles of rock characteristics and climate.

TABLE 5.1 Products of Weathering

Mineral	Residual Products	Material in Solution
Quartz	Quartz grains	Silica
Feldspars and Micas	Clay minerals	Silica K+, Na+, Ca²⁺
Amphibole (hornblende)	Clay minerals Limonite Hematite	Silica Ca²⁺, Mg²⁺
Olivine	Limonite Hematite	Silica Mg²⁺

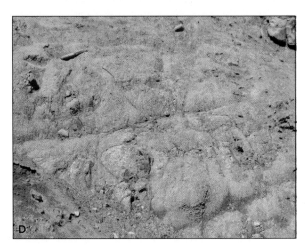

Figure 5.10 Spheroidal weathering of extensively jointed rock. **A.** Water moving through the joints begins to enlarge them. **B, C.** Because the rocks are attacked more on the corners and edges, they eventually take on a spherical shape. The photo in **D** shows spheroidal weathering of granitic rock on the south side of Grouse Mountain, British Columbia. Note knife for scale. (Photo **D** by S. R. Hicock)

Figure 5.11 Successive shells are loosened as the weathering process continues to penetrate ever deeper into this ancient lava flow on south Vancouver Island. Note the orange oxidation on the surface of the basalt sphere (underneath the piece of rock held in hand). (Photo by S. R. Hicock)

Rock Characteristics

Rock characteristics encompass all of the chemical traits of rocks, including mineral composition and solubility. In addition, any physical features, such as joints, can be important because they influence the ability of water to penetrate rock (see Figures 5.6 and 5.10).

The variations in weathering rates because of the mineral constituents can be demonstrated by comparing old headstones made from different rock types. Headstones of granite, which is composed of silicate minerals, are relatively resistant to chemical weathering. We can see this by examining the inscriptions on the headstones shown in Figure 5.12. In contrast to the granite headstone, the marble headstone shows signs of extensive chemical alteration over a relatively short period. Marble is composed of calcite (calcium carbonate), which readily dissolves in even a weakly acidic solution.

Figure 5.12 An examination of headstones reveals the rate of chemical weathering of diverse rock types. The granite headstone (left) was erected a few years after the marble headstone (right). The inscription date of 1885 on the marble monument is nearly illegible. (Photos by E. J. Tarbuck)

The most abundant mineral group, the silicates, weathers in the order shown in Figure 5.13. The order of silicate mineral weathering is essentially the same as their order of crystallization in Bowen's reaction series (Chapter 3). The explanation for this is related to the crystalline structure of silicate minerals. Silicon–oxygen bonds are very strong. Because quartz is composed entirely of these strong covalent bonds, it is very resistant to weathering. By contrast, olivine has fewer silicon–oxygen bonds and is not nearly as resistant to chemical weathering. Furthermore, olivine crystallizes at a much higher temperature than quartz, whose melting point is closer to weathering temperatures. Because they are already the products of

weathering, oxides, hydroxides, and clay minerals tend to be most resistant to weathering.

Climate

Climatic factors, particularly temperature and moisture, are crucial to the rate of rock weathering. One important example from mechanical weathering is that the frequency of freeze–thaw cycles greatly affects the amount of frost wedging. Temperature and moisture also exert a strong influence on rates of chemical weathering and on the kind and amount of vegetation present. Regions with lush vegetation generally have a thick mantle of soil rich in decayed organic matter, from which

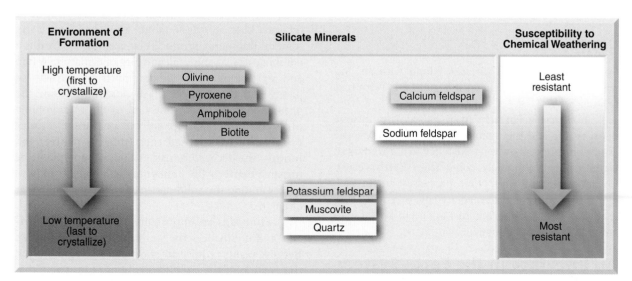

Figure 5.13 The weathering of common silicate minerals. The order in which the silicate minerals chemically weather is essentially the same as their order of crystallization in Bowen's reaction series (Chapter 3).

chemically active fluids containing carbonic acid and humic acids are derived.

The optimum environment for chemical weathering is a combination of warm temperatures and abundant moisture. In polar regions, chemical weathering is ineffective because frigid temperatures keep the available moisture locked up as ice; in arid regions, there is insufficient moisture to foster rapid chemical weathering.

As discussed in Box 5.1, human activities influence the composition of the atmosphere, which in turn affects the rate of chemical weathering.

Differential Weathering

Masses of rock do not weather uniformly; they do so unevenly. This is called **differential weathering**. For example, in Figure 4.26 the durable volcanic neck stands above the surrounding terrain like a stone tower. Figure 5.1 shows an additional example. The results vary in scale from the boldly sculpted surface of the marble headstone in Figure 5.12, to the boldly sculpted exposures of Drumheller, Alberta (Figure 1.4), to the steep cliffs of Mount Robson, Castle Mountain, and Mount Rundle in the Rocky Mountains of Alberta.

Many factors influence the rate of rock weathering. Among the most important are variations in the composition of the rock, including the size of its particles. More resistant rock protrudes as ridges or pinnacles, or as steeper cliffs on an irregular hillside, whereas finer rock, like shale, tends to erode more easily. The number and spacing of joints can also be a significant factor (see Figures 5.6 and 5.10). Differential weathering and subsequent erosion are responsible for creating many unusual and sometimes spectacular rock formations and landforms.

SOIL

Soil covers most land surfaces. Along with air and water, it is one of our most indispensable resources (Figure 5.14).

Soil has accurately been called "the bridge between life and the inanimate world." All life—the entire biosphere—owes its existence to a dozen or so elements that ultimately come from Earth's crust. Once weathering and other processes create soil, plants carry out the intermediary role of assimilating the necessary elements and making them available to animals, including humans.

An Interface in the Earth System

Within the Earth system, soil is an important *interface*—a common boundary at which different

25% air
45% mineral matter
35% water
5% organic matter

Figure 5.14 Soil is an essential resource that we often take for granted. Soil is not a living entity, but it contains a great deal of life. Moreover, this complex medium supports nearly all plant life, which, in turn, supports animal life. The pie chart shows the composition (by volume) of a soil in good condition for plant growth. Although the percentages vary, each soil is composed of mineral and organic matter, water, and air. (Photo © Sascha Burkard/Fotolia)

parts of a system interact. Indeed, it forms where the geosphere, atmosphere, hydrosphere, and biosphere meet. Soil forms through complex environmental interactions among different parts of the Earth system and evolves toward equilibrium with the environment. Soil is sensitive to environmental changes, such as climate, vegetative cover, and animal (including human) activity.

What Is Soil?

Much of Earth's land surface is covered by **regolith** (*rhegos* = blanket, *lithos* = stone), the layer of rock and mineral fragments produced by weathering. **Soil** is a combination of mineral and organic matter, water, and air (Figure 5.14) that supports the growth of plants and develops in place downward from the ground surface. About one-half of the total volume of a good-quality surface soil is a mixture of disintegrated and decomposed rock (mineral matter) and **humus**, the decayed remains of animal and plant life (organic matter). The remaining half consists of pore spaces among the solid particles where air and water circulate.

Humus is an important source of plant nutrients and it enhances the soil's ability to retain water. Because plants require air and water to live and grow, the portion of the soil consisting of pore spaces that allow for the circulation of these fluids is as vital as the solid soil constituents.

Soil water is far from "pure" water; instead, it is a complex solution containing many nutrients. It not only provides the necessary moisture for the chemical reactions that sustain life but also supplies plants with nutrients in a form they can use.

The open spaces not filled with water contain air. This air is the source of necessary oxygen and carbon dioxide for most micro-organisms and plants that live in the soil.

CONTROLS OF SOIL FORMATION

Soil is the product of the complex interplay of several factors, including parent material, time, climate, plants and animals, and topography. Although all these factors are interdependent, their roles will be examined separately.

Parent Material

The source of the weathered mineral matter from which soils develop is called the **parent material** and is a major factor influencing a newly forming soil. Gradually, it undergoes physical and chemical changes as the soil develops. Parent material can either be bedrock or a layer of unconsolidated deposits. When the parent material is bedrock, the soils are termed *residual soils*. By contrast, those developed on unconsolidated sediment transported from elsewhere are called *transported soils* (Figure 5.15)—that is, the soil develops in place on transported parent material, such as the glacial deposits that cover much of Canada.

The nature of the parent material influences soils in two ways. First, the type of parent material will affect the rate of weathering and thus the rate of soil formation. Also, because unconsolidated deposits are already partly weathered with more surfaces available, soil development on such material progresses more rapidly than on bedrock. Second, the chemical makeup of the parent material affects the soil's fertility. This influences the character of the natural vegetation the soil can support.

Similar soils are often produced from different parent materials and dissimilar soils can develop from the same parent material. For example, an organic-rich soil formed on granite in a temperate climate, such as Nova Scotia or northern Ontario, will be quite different from a soil formed on granite in a desert.

Residual soil is developed on bedrock

No soil development because of very steep slope

Transported soil is developed on unconsolidated deposits

Thinner soil on slope because of erosion

Unconsolidated deposits

Bedrock

Figure 5.15 The parent material for residual soils is the underlying bedrock, whereas transported soils form on unconsolidated deposits. Also note that as slopes become steeper, soil becomes thinner. (Photos by E. J. Tarbuck)

Time

If weathering has been going on for a comparatively short time, the character of the parent material determines to a large extent the characteristics of the soil. However, as weathering processes continue, the influence of parent material on soil is overshadowed by the other soil-forming factors, especially climate. As a rule, the longer a soil has been forming, the thicker it becomes and the less it resembles the parent material.

Climate

Climate is considered to be the most influential control on soil formation, especially temperature and precipitation, whose variations determine whether chemical or mechanical weathering will dominate. They also greatly influence the rate and depth of weathering. For instance, a hot, wet climate may produce a thick layer of chemically weathered soil in the same amount of time that a cold, dry climate produces a thin mantle of mechanically weathered debris. The amount of precipitation influences the degree to which various materials are leached from the soil, thereby affecting soil fertility. Finally, climatic conditions are an important control on the type of plant and animal life present.

Plants and Animals

The types and abundance of organisms present have a strong influence on the physical and chemical properties of a soil. Such phrases as *prairie soil, forest soil*, and *tundra soil* are common.

Plants and animals supply organic matter to the soil. Certain bog soils are composed almost entirely of organic matter, whereas desert soils might contain less than 1 percent. When organic matter is decomposed, important nutrients are supplied to plants, animals, and microorganisms living in the soil. Consequently, soil fertility is in part related to the amount of organic matter present. Furthermore, the decay of plant and animal remains causes the formation of various organic acids that hasten the weathering process. Organic matter also absorbs water and thus aids water retention in a soil.

Micro-organisms, including fungi, bacteria, and single-celled protozoa, play an active role in the decay of plant and animal remains. The end product is humus, an earthy-looking material that no longer resembles the plants and animals from which it is formed. In addition, certain micro-organisms aid soil fertility because they have the ability to convert atmospheric nitrogen into soil nitrogen.

Earthworms and other burrowing animals mix the mineral and organic portions of a soil. Earthworms, for example, feed on organic matter and thoroughly mix soils in which they live, often moving and enriching tonnes per hectare each year. Burrows and holes also aid the passage of water and air through the soil.

Topography

On steep slopes, soils are often poorly developed because little water soaks in and, as a result, the moisture content of the soil may be insufficient for vigorous plant growth. Further, because of accelerated erosion on steep slopes, the soils are thin or at times nonexistent (Figure 5.15).

In contrast, poorly drained and waterlogged soils found in lowlands have a much different character. Such soils are usually thick and dark due to the large quantity of organic matter that accumulates because saturated conditions retard the decay of vegetation. The optimum terrain for soil development is a flat to undulating upland surface, which produces good drainage, minimum erosion, and sufficient infiltration of water into the soil.

Although this section deals separately with each of the soil-forming factors, remember that they all interact to form soil. No single factor is responsible for a soil's character; it is the combined influence of parent material, time, climate, plants and animals, and topography.

THE SOIL PROFILE

Because soil-forming processes operate from the surface downward, variations in composition, texture, structure, and colour gradually evolve at varying depths. These vertical differences, which usually become more pronounced as time passes, form distinctive zones or layers known as **horizons**. A vertical section through all of the soil horizons, as would be observed in a trench, constitutes the **soil profile** (Figure 5.16).

Figure 5.17 presents an idealized view of a well-developed soil profile with five distinct horizons. From the surface downward, they are designated as *O, A, E, B,* and *C*. These five horizons are common in soil profiles of temperate regions. The characteristics and extent of development of horizons vary in different environments. Thus, different localities can exhibit soil profiles that contrast greatly with one another.

The *O* soil horizon consists largely of organic material, whereas the layers beneath it consist mainly of mineral matter. The upper portion of the *O* horizon is primarily plant litter, such as loose leaves and other organic debris that are still recognizable. By contrast, the lower portion of the *O* horizon is made

Figure 5.16 A soil profile is a vertical cross-section from the surface down to the parent material. Well-developed soils show distinct layers called horizons. In this photo an upper brown *O* horizon rests on a white *E* horizon, rusty *B* horizon, then yellowish *C* horizon above greyish parent material.
(By permission of Agriculture and Agri-Food Canada)

up of partly decomposed organic matter (humus) with no identifiable plant structures. In addition to plants, the *O* horizon is teeming with microscopic life, including bacteria, fungi, protozoa, and insects, that contribute oxygen, carbon dioxide, and organic acids to the developing soil.

Underlying the organic-rich *O* horizon is the *A* horizon. This zone is largely mineral matter, yet biologic activity is high, and up to 30 percent humus can be present. Together, the *O* and *A* horizons make up what is commonly called the *topsoil*. Below the *A* horizon, the *E* horizon is a light-coloured layer that contains little organic material. As water percolates downward through this zone, finer particles are carried away, a process called **eluviation** (*elu* = get away from, *via* = a way). Downward percolation of water also dissolves soluble inorganic soil components and carries them to deeper zones. This process is called **leaching**.

Immediately below the *E* horizon is the *B* horizon, or *subsoil*. Much of the material removed from the *E* horizon by eluviation is deposited in the *B* horizon, or *zone of accumulation*. The accumulation of the fine clay particles enhances water retention in the subsoil. The *O*, *A*, *E*, and *B* horizons together constitute the **solum**, or "true soil." It is in the solum that the soil-forming processes are active and that living roots and other plant and animal life are largely confined.

Below the solum and above the unaltered parent material is the *C* horizon, a layer characterized by partially altered parent material. Whereas the *O*, *A*, *E*, and *B* horizons bear little resemblance to the parent material, it is easily identifiable in the *C* horizon (Figure 5.16). Although this

O horizon
Loose and partly decayed organic matter

A horizon
Mineral matter mixed with some humus

— Topsoil

E horizon
Light-coloured mineral particles. Zone of eluviation and leaching

Solum or "true soil"

B horizon
Accumulation of clay transported from above

—Subsoil

C horizon
Partially altered parent material

Unweathered parent material

Figure 5.17 Idealized soil profile from a humid climate in the middle latitudes.

material is undergoing changes that will eventually transform it into soil, it has not yet crossed the threshold that separates regolith from soil.

The characteristics and extent of development can vary greatly among soils in different environments. The boundaries between soil horizons can be sharp or gradual. Consequently, a well-developed soil profile indicates that environmental conditions have been relatively stable over an extended time span and that the soil is *mature*.

By contrast, some soils lack horizons altogether. Such soils are called *immature* because soil building has been going on for only a short time. Immature soils are also common on steep slopes, where erosion continually strips away the soil, preventing full development.

SOIL TYPES

There are many ways to classify soils, and literally hundreds of names are applied to soils in different areas of the world. Excluding the poorly developed soils of cold and dry regions, most soils can be classified in the context of three soil types, according to prevailing climatic conditions: pedalfer, pedocal, and laterite.

PEDALFER The term **pedalfer** is derived from the Greek *pedon* (soil) plus the chemical symbols for aluminum (Al) and iron (Fe). As implied by its name, a pedalfer is enriched in iron oxides and aluminum-rich clays in the *B* horizon of the soil profile. This soil type develops in relatively humid temperate climates of Pacific and southeast Canada and the eastern United States. In these areas, rainfall is sufficient to leach soluble minerals, such as calcium carbonate, from the soil and carry iron oxides and clays downward to produce a rusty brown-coloured *B* horizon (Figure 5.16). These soils are organic-rich and are best developed under forest vegetation, where large amounts of decomposing organic matter produce the acid conditions necessary for leaching.

PEDOCAL The term **pedocal** is derived from the Greek *pedon* (soil), plus the first three letters of calcite (calcium carbonate). As the name implies, pedocals are characterized by a high calcium carbonate content. This soil type is found in the prairies of southwest Canada and the western United States, where vegetation is dominated by temperate grassland and brush vegetation. Because chemical weathering is less intense in drier areas, pedocals generally contain less clay than do pedalfers. Water contained in the soil is drawn upward and evaporated, causing

the precipitation of calcium carbonate near the surface. In high concentrations, calcite can be deposited as nodules or a continuous layer within the soil. This type of calcite-cemented soil is known as **hardpan** or **caliche**.

LATERITE In the hot, wet climates of the tropics, soils called **laterites** (after the Latin *latericius*, meaning "brick") may develop. Because chemical weathering is intense under such conditions, these soils are much deeper and denser than soils developing over a similar period in temperate regions. Not only does leaching remove soluble materials, such as calcite, but the great quantities of percolating water also remove much of the silica, resulting in the concentration of the upper soil profile with iron and aluminum. The iron gives the soil a distinctive red colour. As bacterial activity is very high in the tropics, laterites contain practically no humus. This fact, coupled with the highly leached and bricklike nature of these soils, makes laterites poor for growing crops. The infertility of this soil has been demonstrated repeatedly in tropical countries where cultivation has expanded into such areas.

The Canadian Soil Classification System

Although the classification of soils by climate is useful when discussing soils in a global context, it becomes much too general when considering the types of soils specific to a single country, such as Canada. In the Canadian soil classification system, coordinated by the Canadian Soil Classification Working Group, soils are classified in a hierarchical system, similar to that used to study organisms in biology. The levels of hierarchy are, from highest to lowest: orders, great groups, groups, subgroups, families, and series. Attributes of the 10 major categories, or orders, of Canadian soils are summarized in Table 5.2 and their geographic distribution in Canada is shown in Figure 5.18. Other countries use similar classification schemes that are tailored to the climatic conditions and zones of vegetation of those nations.

Ancient Soils: Paleosols

In recent decades, geologists have come to appreciate the significance of *paleosols* ("ancient soils") that record soil-forming conditions of Earth's past. Paleosols serve as valuable indicators of past land areas and many have been found to contain features that are similar to those observed in various modern soils. Such features include traces and remains of plant roots, cracks produced by repeated wetting and

TABLE 5.2 Generalized Descriptions of Canadian Soils According to the Canadian Soil Classification System

Regosolic	Very poor development of *A* and *B* horizons	Areas where mass wasting or repeated influx of parent material prevents significant maturation of soil profile
Chernozemic	Dark, brown- to black-coloured (organic-rich) *A* horizon grading downward into *B* horizon	Cool subarid to subhumid grasslands and forest-grassland transition zones
Brunisolic	Brown-coloured *B* horizon	Young forested areas affected by relatively dry climatic conditions and long winters
Gleysolic	*B* horizon commonly grey or mottled with grey and red	Areas affected by frequent flooding or poor drainage where iron reduction is prevalent
Luvisolic	Strongly leached *A* horizon and a clay-rich *B* horizon	Areas hosting deciduous or mixed forest with moderate to cool climate and calcareous parent material
Podzolic	Poorly decomposed organic layer, strongly leached *A* horizon, clay- and aluminum/iron-rich *B* horizon	Cool, moist, temperate areas dominated by coniferous forest and strongly affected by leaching
Solonetzic	High salt content at or near soil surface, iron-stained *B* horizons, salt-rich *C* horizon	Semi-arid climates where evaporation is extreme; vegetation is dominated by grass or mixed grass-forest cover
Organic	Very high organic content and low mineral content	Cool, wet areas where organic matter accumulation is high
Cryosolic	Layer of permafrost within 1 metre of the soil surface; disruption of soil horizons by repeated freezing and thawing	Tundra landscape dominated by moss and lichens
Vertisolic	Clay-rich, with deep cracks and other disruptive features because of repeated shrinking and swelling	Semi-arid regions of Canadian Prairies underlain by parent material rich in swelling clays; distribution highly localized

Source: Based on Soil Classification Working Group. 1998. The Canadian System of Soil Classification. Agric. and Agri-Food Can. Publ. 1646 (Revised) 187 pp. NRC Research Press, Ottawa.

drying, horizons showing the reduction or oxidation of iron, and beds of caliche.

Specific combinations of such features preserved in any given paleosol can provide information on water content, drainage capacity, fertility, and other attributes of the land area in which the original soil formed. Paleosols have proven particularly useful in studies of glacial–interglacial cycles of the last Ice Age (Figure 5.19A), serving as indicators of fluctuations in temperature and rates of precipitation. To be preserved in the geologic record, a soil must reside in an area where it can be buried. Thus, paleosols developed in lowland or coastal areas are most likely to be preserved (Figure 5.19B).

Land plants were not present before the Paleozoic to contribute to the formation of soils. However, weathered, soil-like horizons containing oxidized iron have been noted in very old rocks. The oldest of such horizons, estimated to be nearly 2 billion years old, are of great geologic significance because they indicate that oxygen levels had reached sufficient concentrations in the atmosphere by that time to allow iron to rust on land.

SOIL EROSION

Soils are just a tiny fraction of all Earth materials, yet they are a vital resource. Because soils are necessary for the growth of rooted plants, they are the very foundation of the human life-support system. Although human ingenuity can increase the agricultural productivity of soils through fertilization and irrigation, soils can also be damaged or destroyed by careless activities. Despite their role in providing food, fibre, and other basic materials, soils are among our most abused resources.

Perhaps this neglect and indifference has occurred because a substantial amount of soil seems to remain even where soil erosion is serious. Nevertheless, although the loss of fertile topsoil may not be obvious to the untrained eye, it is a growing problem as human activities expand and disturb more and more of Earth's surface.

How Soil Is Eroded

Soil erosion is part of the constant recycling of Earth materials that we call the rock cycle (Chapter 1). Once

	Solonetzic
	Chernozemic
	Brunisolic
	Podzolic
	Luvisolic
	Gleysolic
	Organic
	Cryosolic + Ice
	Regosolic

Figure 5.18 Generalized distribution of soil types in Canada according to the Canadian Soil Classification System.
(Soil Order Map of Canada, http://atlas.agr.gc.ca/agmaf/index_eng.html#context=soil-sol_en.xml, Agriculture and Agri-Food Canada ©, 2010. Reproduced with the permission of the Minister of Public Works and Government Services, 2013.)

soil forms, erosional forces, especially water, wind, and gravity, move soil components from one place to another. Every time it rains, raindrops strike the land with surprising force. Each drop acts like a tiny bomb, blasting movable soil particles out of their positions in the soil mass (Figure 5.20).

Then, water flowing across the surface carries away the dislodged soil particles. Because the soil is moved by thin sheets of water, this process is termed *sheet erosion.*

After flowing as a thin, unconfined sheet for a relatively short distance, threads of current typically develop, and tiny channels called *rills* begin to form. When normal farm cultivation cannot eliminate the channels, we know the rills have grown large enough to be called *gullies* (Figure 5.21). Although most dislodged soil particles move only a short distance during each rainfall, substantial quantities eventually leave the fields and make their way downslope to a stream. Once in the stream channel, these soil parti-

cles, which can now be called *sediment,* are transported downstream and eventually deposited.

Rates of Erosion

We know that soil erosion is the ultimate fate of practically all soils. In the past, erosion occurred at slower rates than it does today because more of the land surface was covered and protected by trees, shrubs, grasses, and other plants. However, human activities, such as farming, logging, and construction, which remove or disrupt the natural vegetation, have greatly accelerated the rate of soil erosion. Without the stabilizing effect of plants, the soil is more easily swept away by the wind or carried downslope by sheet erosion.

Natural rates of soil erosion vary greatly from one place to another and depend on soil characteristics as well as on such factors as climate, topography, and type of vegetation. Over a broad area, erosion

A

B

Figure 5.19 **A.** Exhumed rusty paleosol developed on ancient pillow lavas during a warm interglacial episode on south Vancouver Island, early in the last Ice Age. **B.** A paleosol preserved in a Cretaceous coastal plain deposit of British Columbia. In this case, soil development occurred in mudstone with alternating organic-rich (dark-coloured) and organic-poor (light-coloured) layers. The drab colour of the paleosol indicates that iron in the soil was not oxidized, probably because of poor soil drainage on a coastal plain. The thin, dark-coloured lines are fossil plant roots that penetrate through the sedimentary layers of the parent material of the soil. The small increments of the scale bar represent centimetres.
(Photo **A** by S. R. Hicock; photo **B** by Guy Plint)

Figure 5.20 When it is raining, millions of water drops are falling at velocities approaching 10 metres per second (35 kilometres per hour). When water drops strike an exposed surface, soil particles may splash as high as 1 metre into the air and land more than a metre away from the point of raindrop impact. Soil dislodged by splash erosion is more easily moved by sheet erosion.
(Photo courtesy of Soil Conservation Service/U.S. Department of Agriculture)

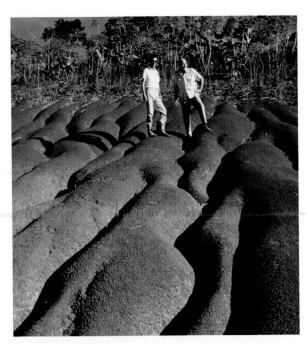

Figure 5.21 Gully erosion in poorly protected laterite soil, southern Colombia.
(Photo by Sandra A. Dunlap/Shutterstock)

caused by surface runoff can be estimated by determining the sediment loads of streams that drain the region. When studies of this kind were made on a global scale, they indicated that before the appearance of humans, sediment transport by rivers to the ocean amounted to more than 9 billion tonnes per year. By contrast, the amount of material currently transported to the sea by rivers is about 24 billion tonnes per year—more than two-and-a-half times the earlier rate.

It is more difficult to measure the loss of soil through wind erosion. Soil removal by wind is generally much less significant than by water erosion, except during periods of prolonged drought. When dry conditions prevail, strong winds can remove large quantities of soil from unprotected fields. Such was the case in the 1930s in the Prairies, a region that came to be called the Dust Bowl (see Box 5.2).

Controlling Soil Erosion

It is estimated that topsoil is eroding faster than it forms on more than one-third of the world's croplands. This means that a renewable resource has become non-renewable in these places. The result is lower productivity, poorer crop quality, reduced agricultural income, and an uncertain future. What can be done?

Simply put, the steeper the slope, the faster the water runs off and the greater the erosion. Thus it is best to leave steep slopes undisturbed, although terraces can slow runoff and decrease soil loss while allowing more water to soak into the ground. On gentle slopes, grass, hay, and crops can be planted parallel to the slope's contours in order to slow runoff and soil loss. Creating smooth, shallow grassed waterways can trap soil and debris washed from fields, protect the surface from wind and water erosion, and even prevent gullies from forming. Finally, planting rows of trees and shrubs as windbreaks can slow the wind and deflect it upward.

PEOPLE AND THE ENVIRONMENT
Return to the Dust Bowl?

During a span of dry years in the 1930s, large dust storms plagued the Canadian Prairies and Great Plains of the United States. Because of the size and severity of these storms, the region came to be called the Dust Bowl, and the decade, the Dirty Thirties. The heart of the Dust Bowl was nearly 40 million hectares in the panhandles of Texas and Oklahoma and adjacent parts of Colorado, New Mexico, and Kansas.

Meanwhile, in Canada, low rainfall rates in the early thirties caused severe shortages of surface water and groundwater. Farmers desperately planted seed in the dry fields only to see it blown away along with the topsoil. Many Canadian farmers fell deeply into debt and moved to cities to look for new jobs. Between the late 1920s and early 1930s, the average income of Prairie families dropped more than 90 percent.

What caused the Dust Bowl? Clearly, the fact that portions of the Prairies and Great Plains experience some of North America's strongest winds is important. However, it was the expansion of agriculture that set the stage for the disastrous period of soil erosion. Thanks to mechanization, cultivation expanded nearly tenfold between the 1870s and 1930. When precipitation was adequate, the soil remained in place. However, the prolonged drought conditions of the 1930s rendered the unprotected fields prone to wind erosion. Only in the late 1930s, when precipitation rates increased, was soil erosion again reduced.

Soil conservation practices have greatly improved since the Dust Bowl era. In particular, farmers

Figure 5.B Dust storm near Edmonton, Alberta, in the summer of 2000. (Photo by L. Peleshok)

minimize tilling and leave a layer of stubble on the ground to reduce soil erosion. Still, the severity of summer droughts (Figure 5.B) in the past couple of decades serves as an eerie reminder of the Dust Bowl years, and 2001 and 2002 were reportedly the driest years in more than a century for parts of Alberta and Saskatchewan, significantly reducing hay and grain productivity. The hay shortage forced many cattle ranchers to sell much of their herd. Forest fires, grasshopper epidemics, and dust storms were commonplace. Despite an abnormally wet summer in 2005, the Prairies again experienced severe drought in 2007, when a heat wave spread over much of western North America during the summer months. Many fear that global warming is contributing to the severe conditions recently witnessed in the Prairies, signalling a possible return to Dust Bowl conditions in the future.

CHAPTER SUMMARY

- *Weathering* is the process that involves the disintegration of rock. *Mechanical weathering* is the physical breakup of rock by *frost wedging* by ice, *unloading* by erosion, and *biologic activity* by roots, and so on. *Chemical weathering* changes rock into different substances through *dissolution*, *oxidation*, and *hydrolysis*.
- Small particles weather faster than large ones; soluble minerals weather faster than silicates; and weathering is faster in hot, wet climates.
- Soil is made of *regolith* (weathered rock materials) and *humus* (decayed organics) and is controlled by *parent material*, time, climate, organisms, and topography.
- Soils develop downward as *O* (organics), *A* (mineral matter), *E* (*leached*), *B* (precipitates), and *C* (altered parent material) horizons. Main soil types are *pedalfer* (iron- and aluminum-rich), *pedocal* (carbonate rich), and *laterites* (leached in tropics).
- Soil erosion is part of the rock cycle and depends mainly on climate, topography, and vegetation.

REVIEW QUESTIONS

1. The processes of weathering and erosion are closely associated, but are not the same thing. Explain how these processes differ.

2. What is the difference between mechanical and chemical weathering, and where in the world would you expect each of these to predominate?

3. How can mechanical weathering enhance the rate at which a given volume of rock is dissolved by chemical weathering? (Hint: Think about surface area.)

4. Explain the differences between the processes of dissolution, oxidation, and hydrolysis and the roles each of these play in weathering.

5. Describe what soil is made of and how the combination of these components distinguish it from regolith.

6. The susceptibility of silicate minerals to destruction by chemical weathering follows the same basic pattern as their order of crystallization in Bowen's reaction series (covered in the previous chapter). Explain why this is so.

7. Describe the distinguishing characteristics of soil horizons *C*, *B*, *E*, *A*, and *O* (in ascending order) and the main processes (physical, chemical, and/or biological) that operate in each.

8. Briefly describe both natural and human-related factors that led to the Dust Bowl of the 1930s (see Box 5.2), and how modern farming practices have since improved soil retention on farmland.

SEDIMENTARY ROCKS

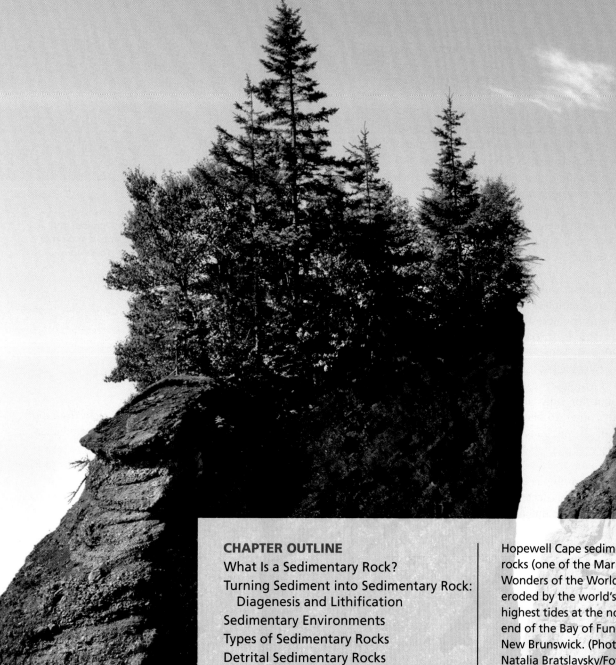

6

Hopewell Cape sedimentary rocks (one of the Marine Wonders of the World) eroded by the world's highest tides at the north end of the Bay of Fundy, New Brunswick. (Photo by Natalia Bratslavsky/Fotolia)

Chapter 5 gave you the background needed to understand the origin of sedimentary rocks, which, among other things, are important in oil and gas exploration (see Chapter 20). Weathering of existing rocks prepares them for erosion by running water, wind, waves, and ice that move weathering products to a new location of deposition. Usually the particles are broken down further during transport. Following deposition, this material is called **sediment**. Upon burial, loose sediment becomes lithified, ultimately transforming it into rock.

WHAT IS A SEDIMENTARY ROCK?

The products of mechanical and chemical weathering are the raw materials (rock fragments, minerals, ions) for sedimentary rocks. The word *sedimentary* is from the Latin *sedimentum* ("to settle"), a reference to solid material settling out of a fluid (water or air). Most sediment is deposited this way. Weathered debris is continuously being swept from bedrock, carried away, and eventually deposited in lakes, river valleys, seas, and countless other places. The particles in a desert sand dune, the mud and plant debris on the floor of a swamp, the gravel in a streambed, and even household dust are examples. As piles of sediment accumulate, the materials near the bottom are compacted. Over long periods, these sediments become cemented together by mineral matter deposited in the spaces between particles, forming solid rock.

Geologists estimate that sedimentary rocks account for only about 5 percent (by volume) of Earth's outer 16 kilometres. However, about 75 percent of all rock outcrops on the continents are sedimentary (Figure 6.1). Therefore, we can think of sedimentary rocks as being a relatively thin and somewhat discontinuous layer in the uppermost portion of the crust. This fact is readily understood when we consider that sediment accumulates at the surface.

The rock layers that sediments eventually form reveal past environments that existed at the surface. By their very nature, sedimentary rocks contain within them indications of past environments in which their particles were deposited and, in some cases, clues to the mechanisms involved in their transport. Sedimentary rocks also contain fossils. It is largely from this group of rocks that geologists must reconstruct Earth's history.

It should be mentioned that many sedimentary rocks are very important economically. Coal, which is burned to provide energy in many countries, is classified in this book as a sedimentary rock. Petroleum and natural gas are associated with sedimentary rocks, as are major sources of iron, aluminum, manganese, fertilizer, and numerous materials essential to the construction industry (more details are given in Chapter 20).

Figure 6.1 These eroded sedimentary rocks near Cheltenham, Ontario, are very colourful. Sedimentary rocks are exposed at the surface more than igneous and metamorphic rocks. Because they contain fossils and other clues about our geologic past, sedimentary rocks are important in the study of Earth history.
(Photo by C. Tsujita)

TURNING SEDIMENT INTO SEDIMENTARY ROCK: DIAGENESIS AND LITHIFICATION

A great deal of change can occur to sediment from the time it is deposited until it becomes a sedimentary rock and is subsequently subjected to the temperatures and pressures that convert it to metamorphic rock. The term **diagenesis** (*dia* = change, *genesis* = origin) is a collective term for all of the chemical, physical, and biologic changes that take place after sediments are deposited but before metamorphism.

Burial promotes diagenesis because as sediments are buried, they are subjected to increasingly higher temperatures and pressures. Diagenesis occurs within the upper few kilometres of Earth's crust at temperatures that are generally between 150°C and 200°C. The upper limit of this range (200°C) marks the threshold between diagenesis and metamorphism, at which point clay minerals begin to re-crystallize to mica.

One example of diagenetic change is *re-crystallization*, the development of more stable minerals from less stable ones. It is illustrated by the mineral aragonite, the less stable form of calcium carbonate ($CaCO_3$). Aragonite is secreted by many marine organisms to produce hard parts such as shells. In some environments, large quantities of these solid materials accumulate as sediment. As burial takes place, aragonite re-crystallizes to the more stable form of calcium carbonate, calcite (the main constituent in the sedimentary rock limestone).

Diagenesis includes **lithification**, the processes by which unconsolidated sediments are transformed into solid sedimentary rocks (*lithos* = stone, *fic* = making). Basic lithification processes include compaction and cementation.

As sediment accumulates, the weight of overlying material compresses the deeper sediments. This process is called **compaction**. The deeper the sediment is buried, the more it is compacted, and the firmer it becomes. As the grains are pressed closer and closer together, there is considerable reduction in **pore space** (the open space between rock particles or within rock fractures) and loss of fluids. For example, when clays are buried beneath several thousand metres of material, the volume of clay can be reduced by as much as 40 percent. As pore space decreases, much of the water that was trapped in the sediments is driven out. Because sands and other coarse sediments are less compressible, compaction is most significant as a lithification process in fine-grained sedimentary rocks.

Cementation is the most important process by which sediments are converted to sedimentary rock. It is a chemical diagenetic change that involves the precipitation of minerals among the individual sediment grains. The cementing materials are carried in solution by water percolating through the pore spaces between particles. Through time, the cement precipitates onto the sediment grains, fills the pore spaces, and joins the particles. Just as the amount of pore space is reduced during compaction, the addition of cement into a sedimentary deposit reduces its porosity as well.

Calcite, silica, and iron oxide are the most common cements. It is often a relatively simple matter to identify the cementing material. Calcite cement will effervesce with dilute hydrochloric acid. Silica is the hardest cement and thus produces the hardest sedimentary rocks. An orange or dark red colour in a sedimentary rock means that iron oxide is present (Figure 6.1).

Most sedimentary rocks are lithified by means of compaction and cementation. However, some initially form as solid masses of intergrown crystals rather than beginning as accumulations of separate particles that later become solid. Other crystalline sedimentary rocks do not begin that way but are transformed into masses of interlocking crystals sometime after the sediment is deposited.

For example, with time and burial, loose sediment consisting of delicate calcareous skeletal debris may be re-crystallized into a relatively dense crystalline limestone. Because crystals grow until they fill all the available space, pore spaces are frequently lacking in crystalline sedimentary rocks. Unless the rocks later develop joints and fractures, they will be relatively impermeable to fluids such as water and oil.

Now that you know basically how sediment turns into rock, we will briefly look at where sediment is deposited or precipitated, before detailing how sedimentary rocks are named and classified.

SEDIMENTARY ENVIRONMENTS

Sedimentary rocks are important in the interpretation of Earth history. By understanding the conditions under which sedimentary rocks form, geologists can often deduce the history of a rock, including information about the origin of its component particles, the method and relative distance of sediment transport, and the nature of the place where the grains eventually came to rest; that is, the environment of deposition.

An **environment of deposition** or **sedimentary environment** is simply a geographic setting where sediment is accumulating. Each site is characterized by a particular combination of geologic processes and environmental conditions. Some kinds of sediment, such as the salt that precipitates from seawater as it evaporates, are solely the product of their sedimentary environment. That is, their component minerals originate and are deposited in the same place. Other sediments accumulate in places far from where they originated, their constituents having been transported great distances by some combination of gravity, water, wind, and ice.

At any given time, the geographic setting and environmental conditions of a sedimentary environment determine the nature of the sediments that accumulate. Therefore, geologists carefully study the sediments in present-day depositional environments because the features they find can also be observed in ancient sedimentary rocks. In fact, this is an application of the principle of *uniformitarianism* (Chapter 1).

By applying a thorough knowledge of present-day conditions, geologists attempt to reconstruct the ancient environments and geographic relations of an area at the time a particular set of sedimentary layers were deposited. Such analyses often lead to the creation of maps that depict the geographic distribution of land and sea, mountains and river valleys, deserts and glaciers, and other environments of deposition.

Types of Sedimentary Environments

Sedimentary environments are commonly placed into one of three categories: continental, transitional (shoreline), or marine. Each category includes many specific subenvironments. Figure 6.2 is an idealized

Beach

Sand dunes

Lake

Estuary

Spit

Tidal flat

Deep-sea fans

Turbidity current

Figure 6.2 Sedimentary environments are those places where sediment accumulates. Each is characterized by certain physical, chemical, and biologic conditions. Because each type of sediment contains clues about the environment in which it was deposited, sedimentary rocks are important in the interpretation of Earth history. A number of important continental, transitional, and marine sedimentary environments are represented in this idealized diagram.
(**Insets** by E. J. Tarbuck)

Alluvial fans

Glacial deposits

Salt
flat

Playa lake

Stream

Swamp

Floodplain

Delta

Lagoon

Reef

Barrier
island

diagram illustrating a number of important sedimentary environments associated with each category. Realize that this is just a sampling of the great diversity of depositional environments. The remainder of this section provides a brief overview of each category. Later, Chapters 14, 15, 17, 18, and 19, as well as portions of Chapter 11, will examine many of these environments in greater detail. Each is an area in which sediment accumulates and in which organisms live and die. Each produces a characteristic sedimentary rock or assemblage that reflects prevailing conditions.

CONTINENTAL ENVIRONMENTS Continental environments are dominated by the erosion and deposition associated with streams. In some cold regions, moving masses of glacial ice replace running water as the dominant process. In arid regions (as well as some coastal settings) wind takes on greater importance. Clearly, the nature of the sediments deposited in continental environments is strongly influenced by climate.

In frigid high-latitude or high-altitude settings, glaciers pick up and transport huge volumes of sediment. Materials deposited directly from ice are typically poorly sorted mixtures of particles that range in size from clay to boulders. Water from melting glaciers transports and re-deposits some of the glacial sediment, creating stratified, sorted accumulations.

Streams are the dominant agent of landscape alteration, eroding more land and transporting and depositing more sediment than any other process. The agitation of sediment by running water within channels of a river system tends to separate sedimentary particles according to density and grain size. As a consequence, sediment deposited in the turbulent headwaters of such a system is commonly dominated by gravel, whereas mud tends to predominate in more distant, and typically less turbulent, parts of a stream's course. Where streams emerge from a mountainous area onto a flatter surface, coarse-grained sediment sourced from the nearby highlands can accumulate at the toe of the slope to form a distinctive cone-shaped feature called an *alluvial fan*. In lowlands distant from such sediment source areas, significant volumes of mud and sand settle out from floodwaters that inundate flat areas of land called *floodplains*.

The work of wind and its resulting deposits are referred to as *aeolian*, after Aeolus, the Greek god of wind. Unlike glacial deposits, aeolian sediments are well sorted. Wind can lift fine dust high into the atmosphere and transport it great distances. Where winds are strong and the surface is not anchored by vegetation, sand transported close to the ground accumulates in *dunes*. Deserts and coasts are common sites for this type of deposition.

In addition to being areas where dunes sometimes develop, desert basins are the sites at which shallow *playa lakes* occasionally form following heavy rains or periods of snowmelt in adjacent mountains. They rapidly dry up, sometimes leaving behind mudflats, evaporites, and other characteristic deposits. In humid regions lakes are more enduring features, and their quiet waters are excellent sediment traps. Small deltas, beaches, and bars form along the lakeshore, with finer sediments coming to rest on the lake floor.

TRANSITIONAL ENVIRONMENTS In transition zones characterized by low gradients or quiet water conditions, fine-grained sediment may be alternately deposited under shallow sheets of water and exposed to air, producing mud-dominated *tidal flats*. At the other extreme, where the shoreline is characterized by energetic wave and current action, sediments delivered to the sea by streams can be repeatedly sorted and deposited to produce a sand or gravel *beach*. Further reworking and redistribution of sand by waves and currents along a shoreline can produce linear sand bodies, such as *spits*, *bars*, and *barrier islands*. Finally, a sheltered, brackish (slightly salty), calm-water area called a *lagoon* may develop behind an offshore bar or reef, within which fine-grained sediments may be deposited.

Deltas are among the most significant deposits associated with transitional environments. The complex accumulations of sediment build outward into the sea when rivers experience an abrupt loss of velocity and drop their load of detritus.

MARINE ENVIRONMENTS Marine depositional environments are divided according to depth. The *shallow marine* environment reaches to depths of about 200 metres and extends from the shore to the outer edge of the continental shelf. The *deep marine* environment lies seaward of the continental shelf in waters deeper than 200 metres.

The shallow marine environment borders all of the world's continents. Its width varies greatly, from practically nonexistent in some places to broad expanses extending as far as 1500 kilometres in other locations. On the average this zone is about 80 kilometres wide. The kind of sediment deposited here depends on several factors, including distance from shore, the elevation of the adjacent land area, water depth, water temperature, salinity, and climate.

Because of the ongoing erosion of the adjacent continent, the shallow marine environment receives huge quantities of land-derived sediment. Where the influx of such sediment is small and the seas are relatively warm, carbonate-rich muds may be the predominant sediment. Most of this material consists of the skeletal debris of carbonate-secreting organisms mixed with inorganic precipitates. Coral *reefs* are also associated with warm, shallow marine environments. In hot regions where the sea occupies a basin with restricted circulation, evaporation triggers the precipitation of soluble materials and the formation of marine evaporite deposits.

Deep marine environments include all the floors of the deep ocean. Far from land masses, tiny particles from many sources remain adrift for long spans. Gradually these small grains "rain" down on the ocean floor, where they accumulate very slowly. Significant exceptions are thick deposits of relatively coarse sediment that occur at the base of the continental slope. These materials are sporadically moved down from the continental shelf by *turbidity currents*—dense, gravity-driven masses of sediment and water—and are deposited as turbidites in *deep-sea fans*.

Sedimentary Facies

By studying a series of sedimentary layers, we can see the changes in environmental conditions that occurred at a particular place with the passage of time. Changes in past environments can also be seen when a single unit of sedimentary rock is traced laterally. This is true because at any one time many different depositional environments can exist over a broad area. For example, when sand is accumulating in a beach environment, finer muds are often being deposited in quieter offshore waters. Still farther out, perhaps in a zone where biologic

activity is high and land-derived sediments are scarce, the deposits consist largely of the calcareous remains of small organisms. In this example, different sediments are accumulating adjacent to one another at the same time. Each unit possesses a distinctive set of characteristics reflecting the conditions in a particular environment. To describe such sets of sediments, the term **sedimentary facies** is used. When a sedimentary unit is examined in cross-section from one end to the other, each facies can grade laterally into another that formed at the same time but that exhibits different characteristics (Figure 6.3).

Now that you have seen where sediments tend to accumulate, and how they are turned into sedimentary rock, you are now ready to study the rocks themselves.

TYPES OF SEDIMENTARY ROCKS

Sediment has three principal sources. First, sediment can originate as solid particles derived from both mechanical and chemical weathering of existing rocks. Deposits of this type are termed *detrital*, and the sedimentary rocks that they form are called **detrital sedimentary rocks**. The second major source of sediment is soluble material produced largely by chemical weathering. When these dissolved substances are precipitated by either inorganic or organic processes, the material is known as chemical sediment and the rocks formed from it are called **chemical sedimentary rocks**. A third sedimentary component is organic matter derived from carbon-rich tissues of once-living things. For example, plant remains that accumulate in a swamp can be buried and altered over time to produce coal, an **organic sedimentary rock**.

Figure 6.3 When a single sedimentary layer is traced laterally, we may find that it is made up of several different rock types. This can occur because many sedimentary environments can exist at the same time over a broad area. The term *facies* is used to describe such sets of sedimentary rocks. Each facies grades laterally into another that formed at the same time but in a different environment.

We will now look at each type of sedimentary rock and some examples of each.

DETRITAL SEDIMENTARY ROCKS

The silicate minerals clay and quartz are the chief constituents of most sedimentary rocks in this category; for this reason, these rocks can also be referred to as *siliciclastic sedimentary rocks.* Recall from Chapter 5 that clay minerals are the most abundant product of the chemical weathering of silicate minerals, especially the feldspars. Clays are fine-grained minerals with sheet-like crystalline structures similar to the micas. The other common mineral, quartz, is abundant because it is extremely durable and resistant to chemical weathering. Thus, when felsic igneous rocks are weathered, individual quartz grains are freed.

Other common minerals in detrital rocks are feldspars and micas. Because chemical weathering rapidly transforms these minerals into new substances, their presence in sedimentary rocks indicates that erosion and deposition were fast enough to preserve some of the primary minerals from the source rock before they could be decomposed.

Particle size is the primary basis for distinguishing various detrital sedimentary rocks (Table 6.1). The sizes of the component grains also provide useful information about environments of deposition (Figure 6.2). Currents of water or air sort the particles by size: The stronger the current, the larger the particle size carried. Gravels, for example, are moved by swiftly flowing rivers as well as by landslides and glaciers. Less energy is required to transport sand; thus, it is common to such features as windblown dunes and some river deposits and beaches. Very little energy is needed to transport clay, so it settles very slowly. Accumulation of these tiny particles is generally associated with the quiet water of a lake, lagoon, swamp, or certain marine environments.

Common detrital sedimentary rocks, in order of increasing particle size, are mudrocks, sandstone, and conglomerate or breccia. We will now look at each type and how it forms.

Shale and Other Mudrocks

Mudrocks, the group of sedimentary rocks that includes shale, mudstone, and siltstone, consist of clay- to silt-sized particles (Figure 6.4) and account for more than half of all sedimentary rocks. Particles in these rocks

TABLE 6.1   Particle Size Classification for Detrital Rocks

Size Range (mm)	Particle Name	Common Sediment Name	Detrital Rock
>256	Boulder		
64–256	Cobble	Gravel	Conglomerate or breccia
4–64	Pebble		
2–4	Granule		
0.062–2	Sand	Sand	Sandstone
0.004–0.062	Silt	Mud	Mudrocks (Shale, mudstone, or siltstone)
<0.004	Clay		

are so small that they cannot be readily identified without strong magnification. Thus, mudrocks are more difficult to study and analyze than most other sedimentary rocks.

The tiny grains in mudrocks indicate that deposition is the result of gradual settling from relatively quiet, non-turbulent currents. Such environments include lakes, river floodplains, lagoons, and portions of the deep-ocean basins (Figure 6.2). Even these "quiet" environments usually experience enough turbulence to keep clay-sized particles suspended almost indefinitely. Consequently, much of the clay is deposited only after the individual particles coalesce to form larger aggregates.

Sometimes the chemical composition of the rock provides additional information. One example is black shale, which is black because it contains abundant organic matter (carbon) and suggests that

Figure 6.4   Shale is a type of mudrock. Mudrocks are by far the most abundant of all sedimentary rocks. Dark shales containing plant remains are relatively common. (Photo by E. J. Tarbuck)

deposition occurred in an oxygen-poor environment such as a swamp, where organic materials do not readily oxidize and decay.

As silt and clay accumulate, they tend to form thin layers called *laminae* (*lamin* = a thin sheet). Initially the particles in the laminae are oriented randomly and abundant pore space is filled with water or other fluids. However, during compaction the clay and silt particles can align almost in parallel and become tightly packed. This rearrangement of grains reduces the size of the pore spaces and forces out much of the water. Once the grains are pressed closely together, the tiny spaces between particles do not readily permit solutions containing cementing material to circulate. Shales are often described as being weak because they are poorly cemented and therefore not well lithified.

The inability of water to migrate between microscopic pore spaces explains why shale commonly forms barriers to the subsurface movement of water and petroleum. Indeed, rock layers that contain groundwater are commonly underlain by shale beds, which block farther downward movement. The opposite is true for underground reservoirs of petroleum. They are commonly capped by shale beds that effectively prevent oil and gas from escaping to the surface.*

It is common to apply the term *shale* to all fine-grained sedimentary rocks, especially in a

---

*The relationship between impermeable beds and the occurrence and movement of groundwater is examined in Chapter 16. Shale beds as cap rocks in oil traps are discussed in Chapter 20.

non-technical context. However, shale is a type of mudrock that can be split into thin layers along closely spaced planes (e.g., the top of the slab in Figure 6.4). This property is termed **fissility** (*fissilis* = something that can be cleft or split). If the rock breaks into chunks or blocks, the name *mudstone* is applied. Another fine-grained rock that is often grouped with shale but lacks fissility is *siltstone*, which is composed largely of silt-sized particles and contains less clay-sized material than shale and mudstone.

Although mudrocks are the most common sedimentary rocks, they are not usually as noticeable because they do not form prominent outcrops as do sandstone and limestone. Rather, mudrocks crumble easily and usually form a cover of soil that hides the unweathered rock below (see differential weathering in Chapter 5). This is illustrated nicely in the Niagara Gorge, where the gentler slopes of weathered shale are quite inconspicuous and overgrown with vegetation, in sharp contrast with the bold cliffs produced by more durable rocks, such as dolostone and sandstone (Figure 6.5).

Although shale beds do not form striking cliffs and prominent outcrops, some deposits have economic value. Certain mudrocks, such as the red shales of the Queenston Formation in the Niagara Escarpment of Ontario, have been a valuable clay source in the brick, pottery, and tile industries for several decades. Clay extracted from mudrocks also represents the raw material for pottery and tile in many parts of the world. More details are given in Chapter 20.

Figure 6.5 Sedimentary rock layers exposed in the walls of the Niagara River valley. Beds of resistant sandstone and dolostone produce bold cliffs. By contrast, weaker, poorly cemented shale crumbles and produces a gentler slope of weathered debris in which some vegetation is growing. This is also a good example of differential weathering, as discussed in Chapter 5.
(Photo by Frank Brunton)

5 cm

Close up

Figure 6.6 Quartz sandstone. After mudrock, sandstone is the most abundant sedimentary rock. Shown in this photo are layers of sandstone exposed in Dinosaur Provincial Park, Alberta. Hand sample photos show the well-sorted, sandy texture of quartz sandstone.
(**Main** photo by Elena Elisseeva/Shutterstock.; **insets** by E. J. Tarbuck)

Sandstone

Sandstone is the name given to rocks in which sand-size grains dominate (Figure 6.6). After shale, sandstone is the most abundant sedimentary rock, accounting for approximately 20 percent of the entire group. Sandstones form in a variety of environments (Figure 6.2) and commonly contain significant clues about their origin, including sorting, particle shape, and composition.

Sorting is the degree of similarity in particle size in a sedimentary rock. For example, if all the grains in a sample of sandstone are about the same size, the sand is considered *well sorted* (Figure 6.6). Conversely, if the rock is a mixture of large and small particles, the sand is considered *poorly sorted*. Deposits of wind-blown sand (Figure 6.7) are usually better sorted than deposits sorted by wave activity. Particles washed by waves are commonly better sorted than materials deposited by streams.

Sediment accumulations that exhibit poor sorting usually result when particles are transported for only a relatively short time and then rapidly deposited. For example, when a turbulent stream reaches the gentler slopes at the base of a steep mountain, its velocity is quickly reduced, and poorly sorted sands and gravels are deposited.

The *roundness* of sand grains, reflecting the degree to which corners and edges of grains have been smoothed down (Figure 6.7B), can also help decipher the history of a sandstone. When streams, winds, or waves move sand and other sedimentary particles, the grains collide with other particles during transport, thereby wearing down surface irregularities. Usually, the degree of rounding reflects the distance, time, or repetition of disturbance involved in the transportation of sediment by currents of air or water. Highly rounded grains indicate that a great deal of abrasion and hence a great deal of transport have occurred.

Very angular grains, on the other hand, imply two things: that the materials were transported only a short distance before they were deposited, and that some other medium may have transported them. For example, when glaciers move sediment, the particles can be made more irregular by the crushing of colliding particles near the base of the glacier.

The length or repetitions of transport by turbulent air and water currents also influences the mineral composition of a sedimentary deposit.

Substantial weathering, long transport, and reworking lead to the gradual destruction of weaker and less stable minerals, including the feldspars and

A. Sorting

Very poorly sorted   Poorly sorted   Well sorted   Very well sorted

B. Roundness

Angular   Subangular   Subrounded   Rounded

C

Figure 6.7 **A.** Sorting is the degree of similarity in particle size. Sediment or sedimentary rock consisting of particles that are nearly all the same size are considered *well-sorted*. Conversely, those composed of particles of many different sizes are considered *poorly sorted*. **B.** Particle shape is described in terms of *roundness* (the degree to which a particle's surface irregularities have been worn down). **C.** The wind-transported sand grains in this sand dune are well sorted and rounded because they are all practically the same size and lack sharp edges (due to having been worn down by repeated collisions with other grains). Athabasca Sand Dunes, Saskatchewan.
(Photo **C** © Radius Images/Alamy)

ferromagnesians. Because quartz is very durable, it is usually the mineral that survives the longest.

The origin and history of sandstone can often be deduced by examining the sorting, roundness, and mineral composition of its constituent grains. Knowing this information allows us to infer that a well-sorted quartz-rich sandstone consisting of highly rounded grains must be the result of a great deal of transport. Such a rock, in fact, may represent several cycles of weathering, transport, and deposition. We can also conclude that a sandstone containing significant amounts of feldspar and angular grains of ferromagnesian minerals underwent little chemical weathering and transport and was probably deposited close to the source area of the particles.

Owing to its durability, quartz is the predominant mineral in most sandstones. When this is the case, the rock may simply be called *quartz sandstone*. When a sandstone contains appreciable quantities of feldspar, the rock is called *arkose*. In addition to feldspar, arkose usually contains quartz and sparkling bits of mica. The mineral composition of arkose indicates that the grains were derived from granitic source rocks. The particles are generally poorly sorted and angular, which suggests short-distance transport and minimal chemical weathering in a relatively dry climate, followed by rapid deposition and burial.

A third variety of sandstone is known as *wacke*. Along with quartz and feldspar, this dark-coloured rock contains abundant rock fragments and matrix. *Matrix* refers to the silt- and clay-sized particles found in spaces between larger sand grains. More than 15 percent of a wacke's volume is matrix. The poor sorting and angular grains characteristic of wacke suggest that the particles were transported

A

B

Close up

Figure 6.8 **A.** As shown in this example near Ville-Marie, Quebec, conglomerate is composed primarily of rounded, gravel-sized particles. Note compass for scale. **B.** Hand specimen of conglomerate.
(Photo **A** by S. R. Hicock; photo **B** by E. J. Tarbuck)

only a relatively short distance from their source area and then rapidly deposited. Before the sediment could be reworked and sorted further, it was buried under additional layers of sediment. Wacke is frequently associated with submarine deposits made by dense sediment-choked torrents called turbidity currents.[*]

Conglomerate and Breccia

Conglomerate consists largely of rounded pebbles and cobbles (Figure 6.8). As Table 6.1 indicates, these particles can range in size from large boulders to particles as small as garden peas. The particles are commonly large enough to be identified as distinctive rock types; thus, they can be valuable in identifying the source areas of sediments. Many conglomerates are poorly sorted because the spaces between the large gravel particles contain trapped sand or mud.

Gravels accumulate in a variety of environments and usually indicate sediment flows down steep slopes or very turbulent currents where only coarse-grained materials settle. Coarse particles in a conglomerate may reflect the action of energetic mountain streams or strong wave activity along a rapidly eroding rocky coast (Figure 6.2). Some glacial and landslide deposits also contain plentiful gravel.

If the large particles are angular rather than rounded, the rock is called *breccia* (Figure 6.9).

Close up

Figure 6.9 When the gravel-sized particles in a detrital rock are angular, the rock is called breccia.
(Photo by E. J. Tarbuck)

---

[*]More on these currents and the graded beds they create is found in the section "Submarine Canyons and Turbidity Currents" in Chapter 11.

Because large particles abrade and become rounded very rapidly during transport, the pebbles and cobbles in a breccia indicate that they did not travel far from their source area before they were deposited.

Thus, like other sedimentary rocks, conglomerates and breccias contain clues to their history. Their particle sizes reveal the strength of the currents that transported them, whereas the degree of rounding indicates how far or how long the particles travelled. The fragments within a sample identify the source rocks that supplied them.

CHEMICAL SEDIMENTARY ROCKS

Chemical sediments derive from material that is carried *in solution* to lakes and seas (Figure 6.2), where some of it precipitates to form chemical sediments. These become rocks such as limestone, rock salt, and potash.

Precipitation occurs in two ways: *inorganic* (*in* = not, *organicus* = life) processes, such as evaporation and chemical activity, or *organic* (life) processes where aquatic organisms form chemical sediments of **biochemical** origin.

One example of inorganic precipitation is the dripstone that decorates many caves (Figure 6.10), and another is the salt left behind as a body of seawater evaporates. With organic precipitation, water-dwelling animals and plants extract dissolved mineral matter to form shells and other hard parts. After the organisms die, their skeletons collect by the millions on the floor of a lake or ocean as biochemical sediment (Figure 6.11). In fact, deposition of carbonate sediment is an integral part of Earth's carbon cycle (Box 6.1).

Limestone

Representing about 10 percent of the total volume of all sedimentary rocks, *limestone* is the most abundant chemical sedimentary rock. It is composed chiefly of calcite ($CaCO_3$) and forms either by inorganic or biochemical processes. The mineral composition of all limestone is similar, yet many different types exist

Figure 6.10 Because many cave deposits are created by the seemingly endless dripping of water over long time spans, they are commonly called *dripstone*. The material being deposited is calcium carbonate ($CaCO_3$) and the rock is a form of limestone called *travertine*. The calcium carbonate is precipitated when evaporation concentrates dissolved salts from a water drop.
(Photo © Chris Howes/Wild Places Photography/Alamy)

← 5 cm →

Close up

Figure 6.11 This rock, called *coquina*, consists of shell fragments; therefore, it has a biochemical origin.
(Photo by E. J. Tarbuck)

BOX
6.1

EARTH AS A SYSTEM
The Carbon Cycle and Sedimentary Rocks

To illustrate the movement of material and energy in the Earth system, we will look at the *carbon cycle* (Figure 6.A). Pure carbon is rare in nature, occurring mainly as diamond and graphite. Most carbon is bonded chemically to other elements to form compounds, such as carbon dioxide, calcium carbonate, and hydrocarbons in coal and petroleum. Carbon is also the basic building block of life as it readily combines with hydrogen and oxygen to form the organic compounds that compose living things.

In the atmosphere, carbon occurs mainly as carbon dioxide (CO_2). Atmospheric carbon dioxide is significant because it is a greenhouse gas, being an efficient absorber of energy emitted by Earth, and thus influences heating of the atmosphere.[*]

Because many processes that operate on Earth involve carbon dioxide, this gas constantly moves into and out of the atmosphere. For example, in photosynthesis, plants absorb carbon dioxide from the atmosphere to produce the organic compounds needed for growth. Animals that consume these plants (or animals that eat these animals) use the compounds as a source of energy and, through the process of

respiration, return carbon dioxide to the atmosphere. (Plants also return some CO_2 to the atmosphere via transpiration.) Further, when plants die and decay or are burned, this biomass is oxidized, and carbon dioxide is returned to the atmosphere.

Not all dead plant material is immediately converted back to carbon dioxide. A small percentage is deposited as sediment. Over geologic time, considerable biomass is buried with sediment. Under the right conditions, some of this biomass is converted to fossil fuel—coal or petroleum. Eventually some of the fuels are recovered (mined or pumped from a well) and burned to run factories and fuel our transportation system. One result of burning fossil fuels is the release of huge quantities of CO_2 into the atmosphere. Thus, CO_2 is transferred from the atmosphere to the biosphere and back again.

Carbon also moves from the geosphere and hydrosphere to the atmosphere and back again. For example, volcanic activity early in Earth's history is thought to be the source of most of the carbon dioxide found in the atmosphere. Carbon dioxide makes its way back to the hydrosphere and then to the solid

Earth by first combining with water to form carbonic acid (H_2CO_3), which then attacks rocks of the lithosphere. One product of this chemical weathering of solid rock is the soluble bicarbonate ion (HCO_3^-), which is carried by groundwater and streams to the ocean. Here, marine organisms extract this dissolved material to secrete calcium carbonate ($CaCO_3$) shells. Dead organisms contribute skeletal remains to the biochemical sediment of the ocean floor and become sedimentary rock. Eventually these rocks may be exposed at Earth's surface, where chemical weathering causes carbon stored in the rock to be released to the atmosphere as CO_2.

In summary, carbon moves among all four of Earth's major spheres. It is essential to every living thing in the biosphere. In the atmosphere, carbon dioxide is an important greenhouse gas. In the hydrosphere, carbon dioxide is dissolved in lakes, rivers, and the ocean. In the lithosphere, carbon is contained in rocks and is stored as organic matter in deposits of coal and petroleum.

_____

[*]*For more on this idea, see the section on "Carbon Dioxide and Global Warming" in Chapter 20.*

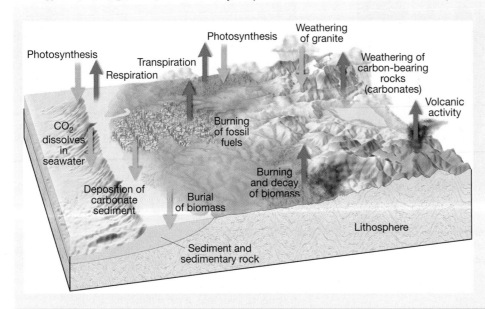

Photosynthesis
Photosynthesis
Weathering of granite
Transpiration
Respiration
Weathering of carbon-bearing rocks (carbonates)
Volcanic activity
CO_2 dissolves in seawater
Burning of fossil fuels
Deposition of carbonate sediment
Burial of biomass
Burning and decay of biomass
Lithosphere
Sediment and sedimentary rock

Figure 6.A Simplified diagram of the carbon cycle with emphasis on the flow of carbon among the atmosphere, hydrosphere, geosphere, and biosphere. The coloured arrows show whether the flow of carbon is into or out of the atmosphere.

B

Figure 6.12 **A.** This modern coral reef is at Bora Bora in French Polynesia. **B.** Paleozoic fossil reef in Arctic Canada containing tubular to cone-shaped corals. (Photo **A** © WaterFrame/Alamy; photo **B** by Jisuo Jin)

because limestones are produced under a variety of conditions. Those forms of biochemical origin are the most common.

ORGANIC LIMESTONES Corals produce large quantities of marine limestone. These relatively simple invertebrate animals secrete a calcareous (calcium carbonate–rich) external skeleton. Although individual coral animals (called *polyps*) are small in size, many create colonies with large calcareous skeletal frameworks that, in turn, build up to form massive structures called *reefs* (Figures 6.12A and 6.2). Other organisms also live with the corals and help cement the entire assemblage into a solid mass.

Certainly the best-known modern reef is Australia's Great Barrier Reef, 2000 kilometres long. Smaller reefs include those in the Bahamas and Florida Keys that have developed in the clear, shallow, warm waters of the tropical and subtropical latitudes. Reefs are not restricted to the present day, and corals have not built all reefs. In Canada, reefs made by microbes are common features in the Precambrian and Early Paleozoic rock successions of the Rocky Mountains and Arctic archipelago. Sponge-like organisms formed small reefs in the Cambrian sequences of British Columbia and Newfoundland and Labrador. Coral-dominated reefs of Silurian and Devonian age occur in rocks of the Niagara Escarpment of Ontario and parts of Arctic Canada

(Figure 6.12B). Significant to Canada's economy, much of Alberta's petroleum is hosted by Devonian reefs that were made chiefly by hard sponges.

Although most limestone is the product of biologic processes, shells and skeletons can re-crystallize before becoming lithified into rock. However, one easily identified biochemical limestone is *coquina*, composed of poorly cemented shells and shell fragments (see Figure 6.11). Limestone consisting of visible shells, shell fragments, and other skeletal components, as well as calcareous mud, is called *fossiliferous limestone*. Another example of limestone is *chalk*, a soft, porous rock made up almost entirely of the hard parts of microscopic marine organisms. Among the most famous chalk deposits are those exposed along the southeast coast of England (Figure 6.13).

INORGANIC LIMESTONES These limestones form when chemical changes, high water temperatures, and/or microbial activity increases the concentration of calcium carbonate to the point that it precipitates. *Travertine* is an example found in caves (see Figure 6.10), where groundwater is the source of the calcium carbonate. As water droplets evaporate in a cavern, salts become concentrated, causing some of the carbon dioxide dissolved in the water to escape, and calcium carbonate to precipitate.

Another type is *oolitic limestone*, composed of small spherical grains called *ooids*. Ooids form in

Figure 6.13 The White Cliffs of Dover. This prominent chalk deposit underlies large portions of southern England as well as parts of northern France. Chalk is made of the skeletal remains of tiny marine organisms. (Photo by David Wall/AGE Fotostock)

shallow marine waters as tiny "seed" particles (commonly small shell fragments) and are moved back and forth by currents. As the grains are rolled about in the warm water, which is supersaturated with calcium carbonate, they become coated with layer upon layer of the precipitate.

Dolostone

Dolostone is composed of the calcium–magnesium carbonate mineral dolomite. Although dolostone can rarely form by direct precipitation from seawater, most dolostone probably originates when magnesium, dissolved in seawater or groundwater, replaces half the calcium in limestone. This hypothesis is reinforced by the fact that there is almost no young dolostone. Most dolostones are ancient rocks in which there was ample time for magnesium to replace calcium. Dolomite is less prone to being dissolved by acidic rainwater than is calcite, and therefore often forms prominent cliff faces, such as those at the Niagara Escarpment in southern Ontario.

Chert

Chert is a name used for a number of hard rocks made of microcrystalline silica (SiO_2), including *flint*, whose dark colour results from the organic matter within it; *jasper*, a red variety coloured by iron oxide; and banded *agate*. Chert deposits are commonly found in one of two situations: as irregularly shaped nodules in limestone/dolostone (Figure 6.14A) and as tabular layers of rock (Figure 6.14B). The silica composing many chert nodules may have been deposited inorganically by direct precipitation from water, sometimes developing

A

B

Figure 6.14 **A.** Chert commonly forms beds and blob-shaped nodules. This chert nodule in dolostone near Hamilton, Ontario, contains a fossil sponge, the silica-rich skeleton of which acted as a "seed" for dissolved silica to precipitate around (penny for scale). **B.** Banded iron formation from northern Ontario, showing alternating bands of magnetite/hematite (purple) and iron-bearing chert (red); quarter for scale. (Photo **A** by Denis Tetreault; photo **B** by Grant Young) around a fossil nucleus. However, most layers of chert originated primarily as biochemical sediment. Some marine organisms, such as diatoms and radiolarians, produce glasslike silica skeletons. These tiny organisms are able to extract silica even though seawater contains only tiny quantities. It is from their remains that most chert beds are believed to originate. Some bedded cherts, however, occur together with lava flows and layers of volcanic ash. In these cases, silica was derived from the decomposition of the volcanic ash and not from biochemical sources. Note that when a hand specimen of chert is being examined, there are few reliable criteria by which the mode of origin (inorganic versus biochemical) can be determined. Chert is also found interbedded with iron-rich deposits in *banded iron formation*, indicating there was more dissolved silica in the sea during Precambrian times than today (Figure 6.14B).

Like glass, most chert has a conchoidal fracture. Its hardness, ease of chipping, and ability to hold a sharp edge made chert a favourite of First Nations peoples for fashioning points for spears and arrows.

Evaporites

Very often, evaporation is the mechanism triggering deposition of chemical precipitates in places like salt flats, playa lakes, and lagoons (Figure 6.2). Minerals commonly precipitated in this fashion include halite (sodium chloride, NaCl), the chief component of rock salt, and gypsum (hydrous calcium sulphate, $CaSO_4 \cdot 2H_2O$), the main ingredient of *rock gypsum*. Both have significant importance. Halite is familiar to everyone as the common salt used in cooking and seasoning foods. In Canada, rock salt is used widely for de-icing roads during the winter months. Of course, it has many other uses and has been considered important enough that people have sought, traded, and fought over it for much of human history. Gypsum is the basic ingredient of plaster of Paris and is used most extensively in the construction industry for drywall and interior plaster (see Chapter 20).

In the geologic past, many areas that are now dry land were basins submerged under shallow arms of a sea that had only narrow connections to the open ocean (Figure 6.2). Under these conditions, seawater continually moved into the bay to replace water lost by evaporation. Eventually the waters of the bay became saturated and salt deposition began. Such deposits are called **evaporites**.

When a body of seawater evaporates, the minerals that precipitate do so in a sequence that is determined by their solubility. Less soluble minerals precipitate first and more soluble minerals precipitate later, as salinity increases. For example, gypsum

Figure 6.15 Salt flats develop in saline lakes of central British Columbia and the Canadian Prairies, as shown in this example in Saskatchewan. (Photo by John Conway)

precipitates when about two-thirds to three-quarters of the seawater has evaporated, and halite settles out when nine-tenths of the water has been removed. During the last stages of this process, potassium and magnesium salts precipitate. One of these last-formed salts, the mineral sylvite, is mined as a significant source of potassium (potash) for fertilizer.

On a smaller scale, evaporite deposits can be seen in such places as the Great Salt Lake of Utah and in saline lakes in Canada (Figure 6.15). Following rains or snowmelt, streams flow into an enclosed basin. As the water evaporates, **salt flats** form when dissolved materials are precipitated as a white crust on the ground.

COAL: AN ORGANIC SEDIMENTARY ROCK

Coal is made of organic matter. Under a magnifying glass it often reveals fossil remnants of leaves, bark, and wood that have been chemically altered but are still identifiable. This supports the conclusion that coal is the end product of large amounts of plant material buried for millions of years (Figure 6.16).

Coal formation requires large quantities of plant remains to accumulate in a swamp (Figures 6.17 and 6.2). Stagnant swamp water is oxygen-deficient, so complete decay (oxidation) of the plant material is not possible. Instead, the plants are attacked by certain bacteria, which partly decompose the organic material and liberate oxygen and hydrogen. As these elements escape, the percentage of carbon gradually increases. The bacteria are not able to finish the job of

SWAMP ENVIRONMENT

Figure 6.16 Successive stages in the formation of coal. (Photos by E. J. Tarbuck)

more sediment on top of the developing coal, the water and volatiles are pressed out and the proportion of *fixed carbon* (the remaining solid combustible material) increases. The greater the carbon content, the greater is the coal's energy ranking as a fuel. Deeper burial transforms lignite into a harder, more compacted black rock called *bituminous* coal. Compared with the peat from which it formed, a bed of bituminous coal may be only one tenth as thick. Canada is a major producer of bituminous coal; the largest deposits occur in the Maritimes, Alberta, and British Columbia.

Lignite and bituminous coals are sedimentary rocks. However, when sedimentary layers are subjected to the folding and deformation associated with mountain building, the heat and pressure cause a further loss of volatiles and water, thus increasing the concentration of fixed carbon. This metamorphoses bituminous coal into *anthracite*, a very hard, shiny black metamorphic rock. Canadian occurrences of anthracite are in the mountainous regions of northern British Columbia and Yukon. Although anthracite is a clean-burning fuel, it is not widespread (although it is more common in the U.S. Appalachians) and is more expensive to extract than the relatively flat-lying layers of bituminous coal.

Coal is a major energy resource. Its role as a fuel and some of the problems associated with burning coal are discussed in Chapter 20.

CLASSIFICATION OF SEDIMENTARY ROCKS

The classification scheme in Figure 6.18 divides sedimentary rocks into two major groups: detrital and chemical. The main criterion for subdividing the detrital rocks is particle size, whereas the primary basis for distinguishing among different rocks in the chemical group is their mineral composition.

As is the case with many classifications, the categories presented in Figure 6.18 are more rigid than in nature. In reality, many of the sedimentary rocks classified into the chemical group also contain at least small quantities of detrital sediment. Many limestones, for example, contain varying amounts of mud or sand, giving them a "sandy" or "shaley" quality. Conversely, because practically all detrital rocks are cemented with material that was originally dissolved in water, they too are far from being pure.

As was the case with the igneous rocks examined in Chapter 3, texture is also a part of sedimentary rock classification. There are two major textures used in the classification of sedimentary rocks: clastic and nonclastic. The term **clastic** is taken from the Greek *klastos*, meaning "broken." Rocks that

decomposition because they run out of oxygen and/or are destroyed by acids liberated from the plants.

The partial decomposition of plant remains in an oxygen-poor swamp creates a layer of *peat*, a soft brown material in which plant structures are still easily recognized. With shallow burial, peat slowly changes to *lignite*, a soft brown coal. Lignite is actively mined in Saskatchewan but also occurs in Alberta and Manitoba. Burial increases the temperature of sediments as well as the pressure on them.

The higher temperatures bring about chemical reactions within the plant materials and yield water and organic gases (volatiles). As the load increases from

Figure 6.17   Because stagnant swamp water does not allow plants to completely decay, large quantities of plant material can accumulate in a swamp.
(Copyright © Pavo Real/Alamy)

Detrital Sedimentary Rocks		
Clastic Texture Particle Size	Sediment Name	Rock Name
Coarse (over 2 mm)	Gravel (Rounded particles)	Conglomerate
Coarse (over 2 mm)	Gravel (Angular particles)	Breccia
Medium (1/16 to 2 mm)	Sand (If abundant feldspar is present the rock is called Arkose) •	Sandstone
Fine (1/256 to 1/16 mm)	Silt	Siltstone
Very fine (less than 1/256 mm)	Clay	Shale or mudstone

Chemical Sedimentary Rocks			
Composition	Texture	Rock Name	
Calcite, CaCO$_3$	Visible, similar-sized shells (and/or other skeletal components)	Coquina	Organic Limestone
Calcite, CaCO$_3$	Visible, variously sized shells (and/or other skeletal components) and calcareous mud	Fossiliferous Limestone	Organic Limestone
Calcite, CaCO$_3$	Microscopic skeletal components	Chalk	Organic Limestone
Calcite, CaCO$_3$	Crystalline, may be banded and/or porous	Inorganic Limestone (e.g., Travertine)	
Dolomite, CaMg(CO$_3$)$_2$	Variable (but commonly crystalline or laminated)	Dolostone	
Quartz, SiO$_2$	Very fine crystalline	Chert	
Gypsum CaSO$_4$ • 2H$_2$O	Fine to coarse crystalline	Rock Gypsum	
Halite, NaCl	Fine to coarse crystalline	Rock Salt	

Figure 6.18   Identification of sedimentary rocks. Sedimentary rocks are divided into two main groups, detrital and chemical, based on their source of sediment. The main criterion for naming detrital sedimentary rocks is particle size, whereas the primary criterion for naming chemical sedimentary rocks is their mineral composition. Note that the term "organic" in the chemical sedimentary rock category refers to the role of biological processes in the precipitation of minerals. This is distinct from the organic *content* of organic sedimentary rocks such as coal (altered, carbon-rich remains of once-living plant tissue).

A

Close up

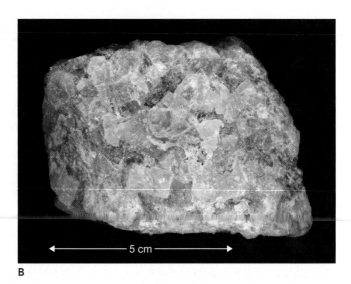

B

Figure 6.19   A. Rock salt, the substance that made Goderich, Ontario, famous, is said to have a nonclastic texture because it is composed of intergrown crystals. **B.** A similar crystalline texture is seen in this sample of potash from Saskatchewan. (Photo **A** by E. J. Tarbuck; photo **B** by C. Tsujita)

display a clastic texture consist of discrete fragments and particles that are cemented and compacted together. Although cement is present in the spaces between particles, these openings are rarely filled completely. Figure 6.18 shows that *all* detrital rocks have a clastic texture. The table also shows that some chemical sedimentary rocks exhibit this texture, too. For example, coquina, the limestone composed of shells and shell fragments, is obviously as clastic as a conglomerate or sandstone. To emphasize the biologic origin of their clasts, the term **bioclastic** is commonly applied to rocks dominated by such skeletal remains.

Some chemical sedimentary rocks have a **nonclastic** texture (also called crystalline texture) in which the minerals form a pattern of interlocking crystals. The crystals may be microscopically small (as in chert) or large enough to be visible without magnification (as with rock salt). Common examples of rocks with nonclastic textures are those deposited when seawater evaporates (Figure 6.19). The materials that make up many other nonclastic rocks may actually have originated as detrital deposits. In these instances, the particles probably consisted of shell fragments and other hard parts rich in calcium carbonate or silica. The clastic nature of the grains was subsequently obliterated or obscured when they became lithified into limestone or chert.

Nonclastic rocks consist of intergrown crystals, and some may resemble igneous rocks, which are also crystalline. The two rock types are usually easy to distinguish because the minerals contained in nonclastic sedimentary rocks are quite unlike those found in most igneous rocks. For example, rock salt, gypsum, and some forms of limestone consist of intergrown crystals, but the minerals within these rocks (halite, gypsum, and calcite) are soluble, seldom associated with igneous rocks, and scratch easily.

SEDIMENTARY STRUCTURES

Sediments exhibit a variety of structures. Some, such as graded beds, are created as currents decrease and allow sediment particles to settle and accumulate. Others form after the sediment is deposited; mud cracks, for example, are produced when mud that was formerly wet shrinks as it dries. When present, sedimentary structures provide additional information that can be useful in the interpretation of Earth history and in the search for natural resources (see Chapter 20).

Sedimentary rocks form as layer upon layer of sediment accumulates in various depositional environments. These layers, called **strata**, or **beds**, are probably *the single most common and characteristic feature of sedimentary rocks*. Each stratum is unique. It may be coarse sandstone, a fossil-rich limestone, a black shale, and so on. When you look at Figure 6.20 or look back through this chapter at the title page photo, Figure 6.5, and Figure 6.14B, you see many such layers, each different from the others. The variations in texture, composition, and

Figure 6.20 These Cretaceous strata exposed near Drumheller, Alberta, illustrate the characteristic layering of sedimentary rocks. The dark-coloured beds are composed of organic-rich mudstone, whereas the light-coloured beds are composed of siltstone and sandstone. (Photo by S. R. Hicock/Pearson Education)

thickness reflect the different conditions under which each layer was deposited.

The thickness of beds ranges from microscopically thin to tens of metres thick. Separating the strata are **bedding planes**, flat surfaces along which rocks tend to separate or break. Changes in the grain size or in the composition of the sediment being deposited can create bedding planes. Pauses in deposition can also lead to layering because chances are slight that newly deposited material will be exactly the same as previously deposited sediment. Generally, each bedding plane marks the end of one episode of short-distance transport.

Because most sediments accumulate as particles that settle from a fluid, most strata are originally deposited as horizontal layers. There are circumstances, however, when sediments do not accumulate in horizontal beds. Sometimes when a bed of sedimentary rock is examined, we see layers within it that are inclined to the horizontal. When this occurs, it is called **cross-bedding** and is most characteristic of sand dunes, river deltas, and certain stream channel deposits (Figure 6.21).

Graded beds represent another special type of bedding. In this case the particles within a single

A

B

Figure 6.21 **A.** The cut-away section of this sand dune shows cross-bedding. **B.** The cross-bedding of this sandstone indicates it was once a sand dune (see Chapter 18).
(Photo **A** by John S. Shelton; photo **B** by Robert Harding/Glow Images)

A

B

Figure 6.22 **A. Graded beds.** Each layer grades from coarse at its base to fine at the top. **B.** A graded bed in a Proterozoic turbidite deposit of northern Ontario. Note how the grain size decreases upward, from granules at the base of the bed to fine sand at the top.
(Photo by Grant Young)

suspension during a storm then settle out after the storm passes.

Other features found in sedimentary rocks also give clues to past environments. For example, a conglomerate may have been bed load in a high-energy stream (Figure 6.23). Wet mud is observed to dry and shrink on exposure to air, forming **mud cracks** (Figure 6.24). **Ripple marks** are small waves of sand that develop on the surface of a sediment layer by the action of moving water or air (Figure 6.25). The ridges form at right angles to the direction of motion. If the ripple marks were formed by air or water moving in essentially one direction, their form will be asymmetrical. These *current ripple marks* will have steeper sides in the down-current direction and more gradual slopes on the up-current side. Ripple marks produced by a stream flowing across a sandy channel or by wind blowing over a sand dune are two common examples of current ripples. When present in solid rock, they can be used to determine the direction of movement of ancient wind or water currents. Other ripple marks have a symmetrical form. These features, called *oscillation ripple marks*, result from the back-and-forth movement of surface waves in a shallow near-shore environment.

The significance of storms in the deposition of sediment in the sea has become apparent in the past couple of decades. Storms are capable of eroding, transporting, and depositing large volumes of sediment in a very short time, only hours to days.

sedimentary layer gradually change from coarse at the bottom to fine at the top (Figure 6.22). Graded beds are most characteristic of rapid deposition from water containing sediment of varying sizes. When a current experiences a rapid energy loss, the largest (heaviest) particles settle first, followed by successively smaller (lighter) grains. The deposition of a graded bed is most commonly associated with a turbidity current (Figure 6.2), a mass of sediment-choked water that is denser than clear water and that moves downslope along the bottom of a lake or ocean.* Graded beds can also be produced when sediment particles are thrown into

*More on these currents and graded beds can be found in the section "Submarine Canyons and Turbidity Currents" in Chapter 11.

Figure 6.23 In a turbulent stream channel, only large/heavy particles settle out. Finer sediments remain suspended and continue their downstream journey. This energetic river (photographed at low flow to see the boulders) is in the Coast Mountains of British Columbia.
(Photo by S. R. Hicock)

This contrasts greatly with the small volumes of sediment that are generally observed during calm water intervals. A common type of sedimentary structure found in sandy storm deposits is **hummocky cross-stratification**, characterized by low-angle laminations that define wavelike undulations up to 1 metre long in cross-section (Figure 6.26A). This type of structure is probably formed by large storm waves in the shallow marine environment.

Erosion and sorting of sediment on the sea floor by storms can also form concentrations of pebbles, shells, and other coarse-grained debris on areas of the sea floor that are otherwise dominated by fine-grained sediment (Figure 6.26B).

A

B

Figure 6.24 **A.** Mud cracks developed on a modern riverbank. This example is from the Thames River, London, Ontario. **B.** Mud cracks preserved in mudstone.
(Photo **A** courtesy of R. W. Hodder; photo **B** by Gary Yeowell/ Stone)

A

B

Figure 6.25 A. Underwater photo of ripple marks in sand on a shallow seafloor. **B.** Ripple marks preserved in Proterozoic sandstone.
(Photo **A** by Dudarev Mikhail/Shutterstock; photo **B** by Guy Plint)

A

B

Figure 6.26 A. Hummocky cross-stratification, as seen in this Cretaceous sandstone, is a sedimentary structure believed to reflect wave and current action generated by storms. Smallest increments of scale bar are in centimetres. **B.** Storms can also concentrate coarse-grained material, such as shell debris, while washing away much of the mud they were once buried in. Note that the lowermost shell-rich horizon in this photograph marks the base of a limestone bed containing hummocky cross-stratification.
(Photo **A** by Guy Plint; photo **B** by Jisuo Jin)

FOSSILS: EVIDENCE OF PAST LIFE

Fossils, the remains or traces of prehistoric life, are important inclusions in sediment and sedimentary rocks (Figure 6.27). Fossils can provide information on sedimentary environments, such as water salinity, temperature, turbidity, depth, and sediment softness/firmness, that may not otherwise be obvious in the physical characteristics of the host rocks. Further, fossils are important time indicators and play a key role in correlating rocks of similar ages among different areas of the world. Fossils can be loosely classified into two categories: *body fossils*, which preserve evidence of the tissues of an organism, and *trace fossils*, which preserve evidence of an organism's activities.

Only a tiny fraction of the organisms that lived during the geologic past have left evidence of their tissues as body fossils. Normally, the remains of an animal or a plant are totally destroyed. Under what circumstances are they preserved?

The preservation of any organic remains requires their isolation from scavengers and microbes that consume and disturb dead tissue and from the physical and chemical agents that assist in the breakdown of mineralized tissues. This means that fossil preservation is more likely to occur when the remains are rapidly entombed, or better yet, when rapid entombment is accompanied by the suppression of scavenging and decomposition. Such conditions were apparently met in the soft-tissue preservation of organisms in amber (fossil resin; Figure 6.27A), tar, and permafrost. However, these cases are exceptional. More commonly, the remains of dead organisms are buried in sediment, where scavengers and microbes degrade the remains to some degree.

Very rarely, the combination of rapid burial of remains and severely low oxygen levels that slow down the decomposition process allow soft tissues to be preserved. These remarkable circumstances were responsible for the soft tissue preservation observed in the famous Cambrian strata of the Burgess Shale in Yoho National Park, British Columbia (see Box 6.2). It is believed that the Burgess Shale organisms were rapidly buried by sediment slumps at the foot of a large submarine escarpment, a deep-water site with little or no oxygen to support decomposition. The Burgess Shale fossils are preserved as a result of both *carbonization*, the preservation of tissue as a carbon film upon the loss of volatile tissue components, and precipitation of clay or mica minerals on the tissue surfaces. The fossil assemblage of the Burgess Shale is extremely important because it provides a fairly faithful snapshot of the communities (dominated by soft-bodied organisms) that existed shortly after the initial explosive diversification of life at the beginning of the Paleozoic Era.

Soft tissue can also be represented in the fossil record by *imprints* despite not being preserved itself (Figure 6.27B). This type of preservation is typical in Precambrian fossils, which lacked hard

A   B

Figure 6.27   **A.** The soft tissues of this insect are beautifully preserved in amber. **B.** Imprints of spindle- and frond-shaped soft-bodied Ediacaran organisms from Mistaken Point, in the province of Newfoundland and Labrador.
(Photo **A** by Colin Keates © Dorling Kindersley; photo **B** by C. Tsujita)

BOX
6.2

CANADIAN PROFILE
The Burgess Shale: Yoho National Park, British Columbia

by Matt Devereux*

The fossil record can be rich with the remains of durable skeletal materials, such as shell, bone, teeth, and wood. Only in extremely rare circumstances are the softest tissues, like skin, muscle, and gut, ever preserved; consequently, there are very few localities in the world where soft tissue remains are found. The best known of these is the Middle Cambrian (515-million-year-old) Burgess Shale of Yoho National Park in British Columbia (Figure 6.B).

A prominent American scientist by the name of Charles Doolittle Walcott discovered the Burgess Shale in 1909. In seven summer collecting seasons between 1909 and 1924, he managed to excavate more than 60 000 specimens representing more than 100 different animals. These fossils now reside at the Smithsonian Institution in Washington, DC. More recent excavations, led by Desmond Collins of the Royal Ontario Museum, were just as successful, and many new species have been identified since Walcott's time.

Additional fossils have come from a few hundred cubic metres of shale excavated from a mountain ridge within walking distance of the town of Field, British Columbia (Figure 6.B). The shales were originally deposited as fine mud along the base of an ancient underwater cliff near the continental margin of ancient North America. This cliff has been traced over a distance of some 20 kilometres south of Walcott's quarry, along which other fossil localities have been identified. Though new and important discoveries have been made, none yet rival the original discovery of the Burgess Shale.

The incredibly well-preserved fossils give us a glimpse of life as it was shortly after the "big bang" of animal evolution known as the Cambrian Explosion (Figure 6.C). Some of the

Figure 6.B The Burgess Shale is exposed near the town of Field in Yoho National Park in British Columbia.

Figure 6.C A reconstruction of what the sea floor may have looked like in the Middle Cambrian, based on fossil remains preserved in the Burgess Shale. (Photo by Publiphoto/Science Source)

animals were probably ancestors of modern sea life, but a significant proportion are so strange that they continue to baffle scientists almost a century after their initial discovery. For example, one animal called

Opabinia had five eyes on the top of its head and a long snout ending in a claw. Another animal, *Wiwaxia*, looks like a computer mouse armed with blade-like spines. Many animals reveal delicate appendages and others have even been found with their last meal still visible in their gut cavities (Figure 6.D). More remarkable still, components of some of the gut remains are still identifiable (Figure 6.E).

Geologist and paleontologist Matt Devereux studied the Burgess Shale fauna as part of his graduate research at the University of Western Ontario. Used by permission.

Figure 6.D The delicate remains of a wide variety of lightly skeletonized organisms are preserved in exquisite detail in the Burgess Shale. Examples shown here are **A.** *Wiwaxia*; **B.** *Marrella*; and **C.** *Canadia*.
(Photo **DA** and **DC** reprinted with permission of the Royal Ontario Museum and Parks Canada © ROM2007_9581_1–J. B. Caron; photo **DB** reprinted with permission of the Royal Ontario Museum and Parks Canada © ROM2006_8107_38–Brian Boyle)

Figure 6.E An example of exceptional preservation of soft tissues in the Middle Cambrian Burgess Shale animal *Ottoia*. The animal's gut, containing partly digested food, is represented by the dark-coloured, U-shaped band that follows the length of the animal's body.
(Photo by Matt Devereux)

skeletons. Were it not for this type of preservation, the existence of complex life before the Paleozoic would be known only from the tracks and trails of a select few organisms and chemical traces of biologic activity.

Hard parts (e.g., shells, bones, and teeth) have a much higher preservation potential than soft tissue because of their physical and chemical durability. Therefore, these parts represent the vast majority of body fossils in the geologic record. If the hard parts are physically and chemically stable in their host sediments, they can be preserved unaltered from their original state. For example, shells composed of calcite or silica are commonly preserved without

Figure 6.28 Petrified dinosaur bone from southern Alberta. Pores that were once occupied by blood vessels have been infilled with *siderite* (iron carbonate) that precipitated from the porewaters of the surrounding sediment.
(Photo by Denis Tetreault)

Figure 6.29 Fossil coral replaced by silica (Manitoulin Island, Ontario). Note that the calcite matrix has dissolved away, leaving only the silicified (silica-replaced) fossil. (Photo by Denis Tetreault)

significant changes in their composition. However, hard parts composed of less stable materials (e.g., calcium carbonate in the form of aragonite) may re-crystallize or be completely dissolved away. Even hard parts have varying degrees of preservational quality.

The preservation of hard parts can follow a number of pathways, depending on the processes they are subjected to both before and after burial. In some cases, fossilization merely involves the filling of pores in the hard parts by minerals that are precipitated from sediment porewaters. This simple addition of minerals to the original remains is called *petrifaction*, or *permineralization*, and is a common mode of preservation observed in highly porous remains, such as bone and wood (Figure 6.28).

Alternatively, the original minerals in the hard parts may undergo *replacement*, a process that involves the substitution of original material by a different substance. The process of replacement is poorly understood but appears to operate at a molecular level and can faithfully preserve even the most delicate structures. It is not uncommon to find originally calcareous fossil remains replaced by silica (Figure 6.29) or pyrite. Cases in which both hard and soft tissues have been replaced by phosphate are also known.

Body fossils can also be preserved by virtue of the moulding properties of their surrounding sediments (Figure 6.30). For example, a buried bivalved organism with its valves clamped shut will leave an *external mould* in the sediment surrounding it. If soft sediment is able to fill the empty space between the valves, it will form an *internal mould*, preserving internal features of the shell, such as muscle scars. If the shell completely dissolves away, an internal mould, an external mould, and an empty space where the original shell existed are observed. If the empty space is later filled by minerals, a *cast*, or replica of the external form of the original shell, will be produced within the external mould (Figure 6.31).

Trace fossils do not represent the actual remains of organisms but rather record their activities. Such traces include footprints (Figure 6.32A), burrows, borings, trails, fossil excrement (Figure 6.32B), and gastroliths ("gizzard stones" of dinosaurs). As in body fossils, the preservation of trace fossils in sediment requires isolation from agents of disturbance that would otherwise obscure the evidence left by the organism. Burrows are commonly preserved because they automatically reside within the sediment and are therefore protected from surface processes. The trace in question is either formed within the sediment or, if produced on the surface, is rapidly buried to avoid being obscured by potential agents of disturbance.

A   B

Figure 6.30 A. Internal moulds of brachiopod shells, surrounded by empty spaces where the shells were dissolved. Internal moulds represent moulds of the interior surface of a fossilized object. Each of these particular shells contained a vertical plate that supported a feeding apparatus. This has been dissolved away to leave a V-shaped slit in each specimen. **B.** An external mould of a bivalve (clam) shell, showing external ribs and growth lines that adorned the outer surface of the shell.
(Photos by Denis Tetreault)

Figure 6.31 Cast of the stem of a fossil horsetail plant from sandstone of Joggins, Nova Scotia. The space once occupied by wood was filled in with sediment and produced a replica of the original exterior surface of the stem.
(Photo by Denis Tetreault)

A

B

Figure 6.32 A. Footprint of an ancient amphibian from Nova Scotia. **B.** Coprolite (fossil excrement), from Cretaceous rocks of Saskatchewan, possibly produced by a small dinosaur. The coprolite is approximately 15 centimetres long.
(Photos by Denis Tetreault)

CHAPTER SUMMARY

- Sedimentary rock consists of *sediment* that has lithified into rock mainly by *compaction* and *cementation*. Sedimentary rocks are of two main types: detrital and chemical.

- *Lithification* is part of *diagenesis*, the physical, chemical, and biologic changes that occur to sediments as they turn into rock. Compaction reduces *pore space* and expels fluids from sediments. Cementation occurs when soluble calcite, silica, and iron oxide join sediment particles. Some chemical rocks (e.g., evaporites) initially form as intergrown crystals.

- *Sedimentary environments* are places where sediment accumulates and include continental, transitional, and marine. Sediment contains clues about how and where it formed so sedimentary rocks are used to interpret Earth's history and to find useful resources.

- *Detrital sedimentary rocks* range from fine to coarse in this order: mudrocks, sandstone, and conglomerate or breccia.

- Precipitation of chemical sediments occurs by inorganic (evaporation) or organic (biochemical) processes. Limestone is made of calcite and forms either way. Inorganic limestones include travertine (dripstone in caves) and oolitic limestone. Other *chemical sedimentary rocks* are dolostone, chert, and evaporites.

- Distinct from the two main types of sedimentary rock (detrital and chemical), are *organic sedimentary rocks* such as coal.

- All detrital rocks have a *clastic* texture of discrete particles. Some chemical rocks, like *evaporites*, have a *nonclastic* texture of interlocking crystals.

- Sedimentary structures include *strata (beds)*, *crossbedding*, *mud cracks*, *ripple marks*, and *fossils*, which provide clues to ancient environments.

REVIEW QUESTIONS

1. How does a sedimentary rock differ from an igneous rock in terms of how it is formed? Does volcanic ash fit the necessary criteria to be considered a sedimentary rock as well as an igneous rock? Discuss.

2. What are the main processes involved in diagenesis?

3. How are chemical sedimentary rocks different from detrital sedimentary rocks in terms of how their constituents are deposited?

4. Explain how sedimentary facies relate to sedimentary environments.

5. Describe the manner in which most dolostone is believed to have formed.

6. Describe three types of limestone that could be considered to be "organic" or "biochemical" in origin.

7. Explain why coal differs from other sedimentary rocks and the conditions required for its formation. (Some argue that coal shouldn't be considered rock at all.)

8. How might the transportation history of a detrital sediment be reflected in the degree of sorting and the roundness of its constituent sedimentary particles?

9. How are sedimentary structures useful in the interpretation of ancient sedimentary environments represented in sedimentary rocks?

10. Describe how sedimentation rate and the abundance or scarcity of oxygen in a given sedimentary environment might influence the likelihood of an organism's dead remains to survive as fossils.

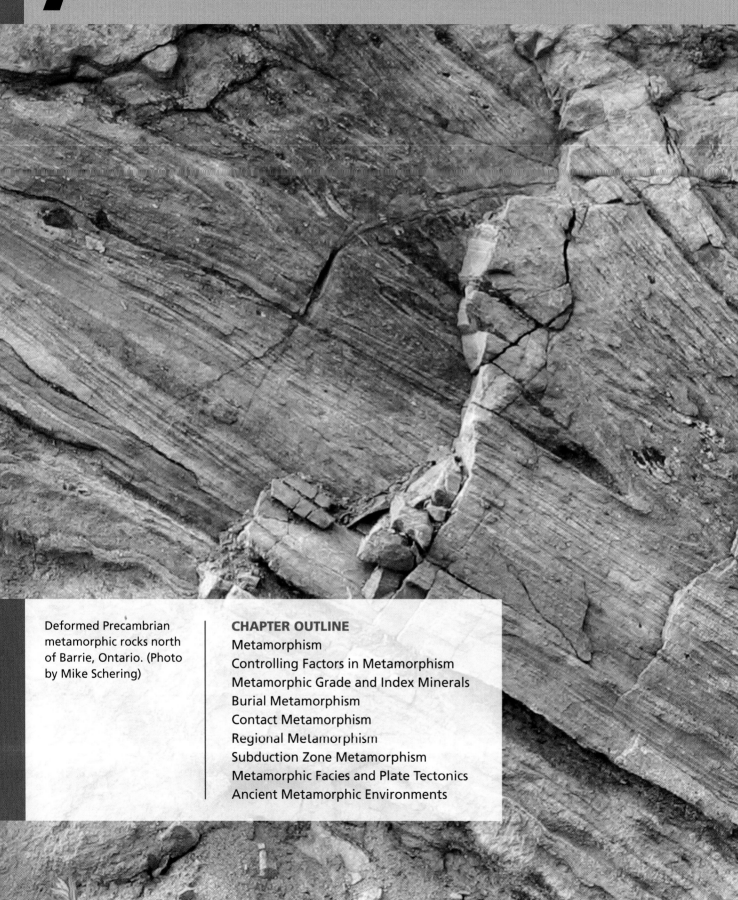

7 METAMORPHISM AND METAMORPHIC ROCKS

Deformed Precambrian metamorphic rocks north of Barrie, Ontario. (Photo by Mike Schering)

As we have seen in the previous chapters, igneous and sedimentary processes are relatively straightforward. Igneous rocks result from the intrusion or extrusion of magma generated within Earth, whereas sedimentary rocks result from deposition of particles derived from existing rock or by the precipitation of minerals from a solution. Metamorphism, however, involves some very complex physical and chemical processes that can affect existing rocks through heat, changes in pressure, the flow of fluids deep below Earth's surface, or a combination of these factors.

The conditions and time scales involved in metamorphism are difficult to comprehend. To begin to appreciate the dynamics of metamorphism we need only consider the belt of metamorphic rocks (Grenville Province in Figure 7.1A) that stretches from the northern Georgian Bay area of Ontario, through the northern St. Lawrence Region of Quebec, and into Newfoundland and Labrador. Around 1 billion years ago, these rocks lay several kilometres below the surface and were subjected to temperatures in excess of 800°C. This is because these very rocks occupied the roots of a mountain chain that may have risen as high as the present-day Himalayas. Incredibly, the intense deformation (Figure 7.1B) and radical mineral changes in these rocks occurred entirely while the rock was solid.

Metamorphism occurs under extreme conditions, and almost always deep below Earth's surface, so we cannot directly observe active metamorphic processes. Because of this, our understanding of metamorphic processes is largely built on observations of ancient metamorphic rocks and experiments conducted in special high-temperature/high-pressure laboratories.

METAMORPHISM

The term **metamorphism**, meaning to "change form," collectively refers to the changes that take place *when a rock is subjected to temperatures or pressures markedly different from those in which it originally formed.* These changes happen in a solid state, although hot fluids migrating through the rock may play a key role in the process. Physical and chemical characteristics of the rock change in order to establish equilibrium with the new temperature/pressure conditions it encounters.

The type and degree of change in the transformation of an existing **parent rock** to a metamorphic rock depends on the type and intensity of individual or combined metamorphic processes involved. On one hand, lightly metamorphosed slate can be difficult to distinguish from its shale parent rock. On the

B

Figure 7.1 **A.** Metamorphic rocks of the Grenville Province were formed in the roots of a Precambrian mountain chain that formed 1 billion years ago and may have risen as high as the Himalayas. Most of these metamorphic rocks are now covered with a thick pile of younger sedimentary rocks. **B.** Folded Precambrian metamorphic rocks of the Grenville Province at Parry Sound, Ontario.
(Photo by W. R. Church)

Ungava orogen

Hearne-Rae craton

Trans-Hudson orogen

Superior craton

Penokean orogen

Grenville Province

Appalachians

Age in billions of years
> 2.5
1.9–1.8
1.8–1.7
1.7–1.6
1.2–1.0
< 1.0

1000 km

A

Figure 7.2 Deformed metamorphic rocks exposed in southern Greenland.
(Photo by Carl Ozyer)

Composition of the Parent Rock

All metamorphic rocks originate from existing parent rocks. Even though elements can be redistributed between minerals, and some elements or volatiles, such as water, may leak in or out during metamorphism, the chemical composition of a metamorphic rock is usually inherited largely from its parent. For example, the metamorphism of a mafic igneous rock will result in the formation of a metamorphic rock that is relatively rich in iron- and magnesium-bearing minerals, whereas the metamorphism of a felsic igneous rock will result in a metamorphic rock that is depleted in such minerals but rich in feldspar and quartz. Likewise, clay minerals contained in shale can re-crystallize to form micas, and the calcite in marble is derived from a limestone parent. It is only in extreme cases of element loss or gain because of fluid migration that a metamorphic rock becomes substantially different in composition from its parent rock.

Heat as a Metamorphic Agent

Heat is one of the most important agents of metamorphism. Not only does heat drive the basic chemical reactions that transform minerals into new forms, it also influences the mobility and reactivity of chemically active fluids. The heating of parent rocks can occur in two ways. First, heat given off by an intrusive igneous body can locally bake the rocks surrounding it. Second, rocks can be cooked by Earth's internal heat (geothermal gradient) if they are brought to great depths below the surface, as in a subduction zone (Figure 7.3).

Keep in mind that different minerals are stable at different temperatures and therefore do not all change at the same time. For example, when temperatures exceed 200°C, clay minerals become unstable and start changing into micas. Conversely, such minerals as quartz remain stable at these temperatures and can remain so in environments with much higher temperatures.

other hand, metamorphism can be so severe that all of the distinguishing characteristics of the parent rock, including its original mineral content, become unrecognizable (Figure 7.2).

CONTROLLING FACTORS IN METAMORPHISM

The overall chemical composition of a metamorphic rock largely reflects that of its parent rock, but the **texture** and *specific mineral makeup* of the rock depend on the particular physical processes involved in the metamorphic transformation. The main factors controlling metamorphism are heat, pressure, and chemically active fluids. In this section, we will examine the significance of these fundamental factors.

Pressure as a Metamorphic Agent

Whereas the primary role of heat in metamorphism is to change the distribution of chemical components within a rock, pressure is primarily responsible for changing the physical characteristics of the rock. Pressure does, however, also influence the temperature at which certain minerals are stable and therefore plays a role in dictating the distribution of elements within a metamorphic rock. When discussing the deformation of rocks, the term *stress* is sometimes substituted for *pressure*.

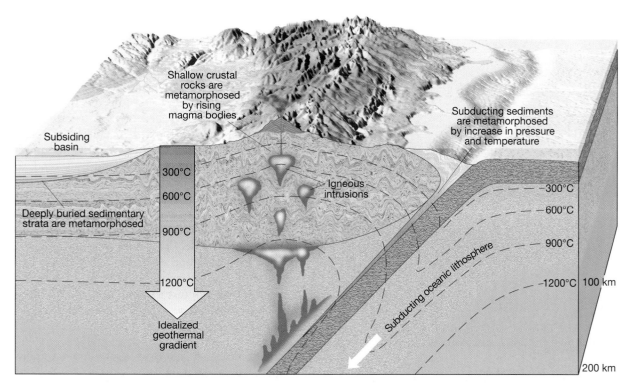

Figure 7.3 Illustration of the geothermal gradient and its role in metamorphism. Notice how the geothermal gradient is lowered by the subduction of comparatively cool oceanic lithosphere. By contrast, thermal heating is evident where magma intrudes the upper crust.

CONFINING PRESSURE (UNIFORM STRESS)

Confining pressure, also called **uniform stress**, involves the squeezing of a rock in all directions, "confining" the material into the smallest possible volume with no change in shape. Water pressure is a familiar form of confining pressure that increases with water depth under the weight of the overlying water mass. When you dive into deep water, you can feel the increasing water pressure in your ears, but your body is certainly not pressed flat. This is because the pressure is not only transmitted through the water from above but is also applied from all directions. In the same way, a rock below Earth's surface experiences uniform pressure from all directions under the weight of the overlying rock column (Figure 7.4A). Accordingly, confining pressure increases with increasing depth of burial. At great depths, confining pressure can force mineral grains to crowd together and crystal arrangements to become more compact. Because no internal deformation is involved, these simple changes form metamorphic rocks that are harder and denser and contain new minerals but are otherwise similar in appearance to their parent rocks (Figure 7.5A).

DIRECTED PRESSURE (DIFFERENTIAL STRESS)

Directed pressure, also called **differential stress**, refers to the unequal application of pressure, resulting in the distortion of a body (Figure 7.4B). Within Earth, directed pressure is largely associated with the horizontal shortening and stretching of Earth's crust caused by plate tectonic activity.

Three basic types of directed pressure are recognized. Perhaps the most obvious type is compressional stress that is characterized by a "pushing together" motion and results in crustal shortening (Figure 7.4B). Tensional stress involves a "pulling apart" motion that results in crustal stretching. Finally, in shear stress, forces are parallel but are directed in opposite directions, causing layers of material to slide parallel to one another like cards in a deck.

In surface environments where temperatures are comparatively low, rocks are *brittle* and tend to fracture when subjected to directed pressure. Continued deformation under such conditions grinds and pulverizes the mineral grains into small fragments. By contrast, in higher temperature environments, rocks are ductile. When rocks exhibit *ductile* behaviour, their mineral grains tend to flatten and elongate when subjected to directed pressure (see Figure 7.6A), and the rock tends to respond to directed pressure by flowing (rather than fracturing). The vast majority of metamorphic rocks affected by

Figure 7.4 The effects of pressure on the texture of metamorphic rocks. **A.** If solely affected by confining pressure (uniform stress), metamorphic rocks retain features of their parent rock, such as sedimentary beds. **B.** Directed pressure (differential stress) causes rocks to crumple in the plane of least stress, resulting in the deformation of sedimentary beds and/or other features inherited from the parent rock.

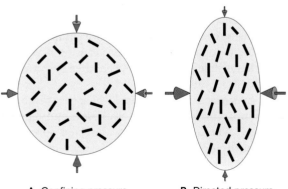

Figure 7.5 **A.** Confining pressure (uniform stress) acts to push mineral grains from all directions, allowing them to remain in their original orientation. **B.** Directed pressure (differential stress) causes grains to become preferentially aligned toward the plane of least stress.

directed pressure show evidence of ductile deformation (see Figure 7.6D).

The results of directed pressure and ductile deformation are clearly manifested in the spectacular folds and other structures found in many metamorphic rocks (Figure 7.2). However, on a much smaller (microscopic) scale, directed pressure also greatly affects the texture of metamorphic rocks. Under directed pressure, platy (sheet-like to tablet-shaped) and elongate grains of minerals tend to become aligned so that they are oriented parallel to the direction of minimum stress (Figure 7.5B). You can probably imagine what the internal texture of a pile of leaves would look like if you and all your friends sat on the pile. In the same way, the preferred orientation of platy and elongate mineral grains in a metamorphic rock affected by directed pressure is a layered or banded texture that is, quite fittingly, called **foliation** (*folium* = leaf). Three main factors influence the development of foliation:

1. Rotation of platy and/or elongate mineral grains into a new orientation

2. Changing the shape of equidimensional grains into elongate shapes that are aligned in a preferred orientation

3. Re-crystallization of minerals to form new grains growing in the direction of preferred orientation

The rotation of existing mineral grains is the easiest of these mechanisms to envision. Figure 7.5B illustrates the mechanics by which platy/elongate minerals are rotated. The new alignment is parallel to the direction of least stress and perpendicular to the direction of maximum stress. Although physical rotation of platy minerals contributes to the development of foliation under low to moderate stress conditions, other mechanisms dominate in more extreme environments.

Grain elongation, another factor that can impart a foliated appearance to a rock, results from internal deformation along planes within the crystal structure of mineral grains (Figure 7.6B). This type of elongation is well illustrated by the rock metaconglomerate. In this rock type, the drastic change in the shape of the pebbles is the net result of internal deformation within constituent mineral crystals of the pebbles (Figure 7.7).

Re-crystallization involves the creation of new mineral grains from old ones. In some cases, mineral components can be dissolved, transported to a different site, and re-precipitated on other mineral grains. In others, re-crystallization involves the mass transfer of mineral material from highly stressed to less stressed areas on individual mineral grains (Figure 7.6C).

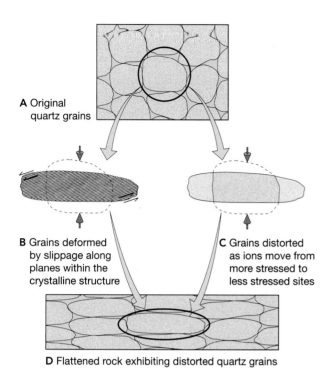

A Original quartz grains

B Grains deformed by slippage along planes within the crystalline structure

C Grains distorted as ions move from more stressed to less stressed sites

D Flattened rock exhibiting distorted quartz grains

Figure 7.6 Development of preferred orientations of such minerals as quartz, calcite, and olivine. **A.** Ductile deformation leading to the flattening and elongation of these roughly equidimensional mineral grains can occur in one of two ways. **B.** The first mechanism is a solid-state plastic flow that involves intracrystalline gliding of individual units within each grain. **C.** The second mechanism involves dissolving material from areas of high stress and depositing that material in locations of low stress. **D.** Both mechanisms change the shape of the grains, but the volume and composition of each grain remains essentially unchanged.

In both cases, crystal growth is focused in the direction of least stress, resulting in the preferred orientation of mineral grains. As discussed further in the next section, these mechanisms are greatly aided by chemically active fluids.

Figure 7.7 Metaconglomerate, also called stretched-pebble conglomerate. These once nearly spherical pebbles have been heated and flattened into elongate structures. (Photo by E. J. Tarbuck)

Chemically Active Fluids

At depth, hot water is released into surrounding rocks when a magma body cools and solidifies. Also, clay minerals, micas, and amphiboles are hydrated (contain water in their crystalline structures). Elevated temperatures and pressures cause these minerals to dehydrate, expelling hot, cation-laden water. Resulting chemically active fluids transport ions from one site in the crystal structure to another, facilitating re-crytallization. Hot fluids can also transport ions over large distances.

If rocks that surround a pluton are chemically different from fluids expelled from the pluton, there will likely be an exchange between the fluids and the host rocks, thereby changing the chemical composition of the rocks. This process is called *metasomatism*. One example of metasomatism is the formation of the mineral wollastonite ($CaSiO_2$) from calcite ($CaCO_3$), the primary ingredient in limestone. When a silica-rich hydrothermal solution invades limestone, calcite reacts with silica (SiO_2) to make wollastonite, and CO_2 is driven off.

METAMORPHIC GRADE AND INDEX MINERALS

Now that we have considered the various factors that influence the formation of metamorphic rocks, we can take a closer look at environments below Earth's surface, where most metamorphism takes place.

Metamorphic rocks are often described in terms of their **metamorphic grade**, or the intensity of metamorphism they have experienced. In general, an increase in metamorphic grade is indicated by the sequential appearance of minerals that are stable at progressively higher temperatures and, in some cases, progressively higher pressures. In some metamorphic rocks, texture can also be used as an indicator of grade.

As determined in laboratory studies, some metamorphic minerals form, and remain stable, within relatively narrow, well-defined ranges of temperature and pressure. Some of these minerals are used as **index minerals** to define the grade of a metamorphic rock (Figure 7.8). For example, the mineral *chlorite* begins to form at relatively low temperatures, cooler than 200°C. Thus, rocks that contain chlorite are referred to as *low grade*. At the opposite end of the spectrum, the mineral *sillimanite* forms only in extreme environments where temperatures exceed 600°C; and rocks containing sillimanite are considered *high grade*. *Intermediate grade* metamorphic rocks record conditions between these opposite ends of the spectrum and can contain metamorphic minerals such as biotite and garnet.

Figure 7.8   Index minerals provide information on the temperature and pressure conditions experienced by a rock during metamorphism. The parent rock in this case is shale. This diagram shows the temperature ranges in which selected index minerals are stable. Note that the stabilities of andalusite, kyanite, and sillimanite are sensitive to both temperature and pressure, making them useful index minerals for metamorphic rocks affected by both factors.

The formation of some metamorphic minerals depends on a combination of temperature and pressure conditions. Among such minerals are *andalusite*, *kyanite*, and *sillimanite* (Figure 7.8). These three polymorphs have the same chemical composition (Al_2SiO_5), but each is distinguished by a unique set of mineral properties, including crystal form. Because they have well-defined fields of stability with respect to both temperature and pressure, they are particularly useful as index minerals for some metamorphic rocks.

Figure 7.9   Basic types of metamorphism associated with changes in temperature and pressure. Note that true metamorphism occurs at temperatures higher than those experienced by sedimentary rocks during diagenesis. Metamorphic grade reflects the intensity of metamorphism experienced by a rock. In addition to the higher temperatures indicated by index minerals, increasing metamorphic grade is also recorded by an increase in the degree of foliation development if directed pressure is involved.

Because metamorphism may or may not involve significant changes in pressure as a rock is heated, and some rocks may not contain pressure-sensitive index minerals, it is important to consider the texture of a metamorphic rock when interpreting its conditions of formation (Figure 7.9). In rocks that have been heated without significant increases in directed pressure, increasing metamorphic grade is simply indicated by the appearance of higher temperature index minerals. In such cases, the more or less uniform pressure conditions allow platy and elongate mineral grains to remain randomly oriented regardless of the degree of heating, and the rock will retain a **nonfoliated** appearance. However, the increasing metamorphic grade of a rock subjected to significant increases in both temperature and directed pressure is reflected by the appearance of higher-temperature minerals, as well as increased grain size of the constituent minerals and the progressive development of foliation.

The basic spectrum of metamorphic conditions dictated by temperature and pressure changes are those classified in the categories of burial, contact, regional, and subduction zone metamorphism. The relative importance of these factors for each basic type of metamorphism is illustrated in Figure 7.9.

BURIAL METAMORPHISM

Burial metamorphism involves the mild alteration of rock (usually sedimentary, but sometimes volcanic) by an increase in temperature and confining pressure and can essentially be viewed as a step beyond sediment diagenesis (Figure 7.9). Such conditions are met in the deepest areas of sedimentary basins, ocean trenches, and passive margins where geothermal heat is sufficient to re-crystallize minerals in sedimentary parent rocks to form low-grade metamorphic minerals, such as *zeolites* (from hydration of silicates) and chlorite (altered from clay; Figure 7.10). As a result of increased confining pressure and minimal directed pressure, rocks become denser but are not distorted. They therefore resemble rocks affected by low-temperature contact metamorphism. The effects of this type of metamorphism can be so mild that such features as bedding and grain size variations are preserved.

The specific depth required for burial metamorphism varies according to differences in geothermal gradient from place to place. On average, low-grade metamorphism usually begins at depths of about 8 kilometres, where temperatures reach up to 200°C. However, burial metamorphism can occur closer to the surface in areas with steeper geothermal gradients.

Figure 7.10   Sample of volcanic tuff from South Island, New Zealand, subjected to burial metamorphism. Because this rock has been affected by confining pressure only, the individual grains of the rock (including shards of volcanic glass and grains of feldspar) have retained their original shape. However, metamorphic minerals, such as zeolites and chlorite (imparting a greenish colour), are present in the ground mass. The width of the image is approximately 5 millimetres.
(Photo by David Dillon)

CONTACT METAMORPHISM

Contact metamorphism (also known as *thermal metamorphism*) occurs when rocks immediately surrounding an igneous body are cooked and therefore altered from their original state. The altered rocks define a zone called an **aureole** (*aureolus* = golden halo; Figure 7.11). Although small intrusions, such as dykes and sills, typically form aureoles only a few centimetres thick, large intrusions, such as batholiths, can produce aureoles that extend outward for several kilometres.

Although contact metamorphism is not entirely restricted to shallow crustal depths, it is most easily recognized when it has occurred near the surface. Here, the temperature contrast between the intrusion and the host rock is greatest and confining pressure is low.

Metamorphic rocks produced by contact metamorphism are characteristically nonfoliated because contact metamorphism involves the simple baking of a parent rock in the absence of directed pressure. Resulting random crystal orientation is most obvious in metamorphic rocks that contain many platy or elongate mineral crystals. Parent rocks that produce such minerals when metamorphosed include sedimentary mudrocks, such as shale, and mafic igneous rocks, such as basalt. Heating can both transform clay minerals of shale into platy

A Emplacement of igneous body and metamorphism

B Crystallization of pluton

Roof pendant

C Exposed pluton and metamorphic cap rock after uplift and erosion

Figure 7.11   Sierra Nevada, near Bishop, California. Contact metamorphism (**A**) produces a zone of alteration called an aureole around an intrusive igneous body (**B**). In the photo (**C**), the dark layer, called a roof pendant, consists of metamorphosed host rock adjacent to the upper part of the light-coloured igneous pluton. The term *roof pendant* implies that the rock was once the roof of a magma chamber. **Inset:** Close-up view of the igneous pluton and dark hornfels resulting from the metamorphism of the host rock.
(Photo **C** by John S. Shelton)

micas and encourage ferromagnesian components of basalt to form elongate crystals of amphibole. In both cases, a dark-coloured, nonfoliated, and rather homogeneous-looking rock is produced called *horn-fels*. In some cases, large grains of metamorphic minerals, called *porphyroblasts*, impart a spotted appearance or **porphyroblastic texture** to the rock (Figure 7.12). A distinguishing feature of this texture is that neither the porphyroblasts nor platy/elongate crystals within the surrounding matrix exhibit preferred orientation.

Metamorphic grade decreases away from the igneous intrusion that acted as a heat source. Thus, a zone of high metamorphic grade containing garnet and sillimanite would be expected to lie well within a metamorphic aureole near the central intrusion, whereas a zone of low metamorphic grade containing chlorite would be expected to occur near the outer edge of the aureole (Figure 7.13).

Not all parent rocks contain the mineral components to produce platy and elongate minerals, and therefore a number of other nonfoliated metamorphic

Figure 7.12 Hornfels is a metamorphic rock produced by contact metamorphism. The hornfels has a spotted appearance because of the presence of large crystals (porphyroblasts) of the mineral *cordierite*. This hornfels was produced when a mud-rich parent rock was baked by heat released from a felsic intrusive body (preserved as a light-coloured igneous rock at the bottom of the photograph). Scale bar: 1 centimetre. (Photo by W. R. Church)

rock types can result from contact metamorphism. Two common rocks besides hornfels produced during contact metamorphism are *quartzite* (Figure 7.14A) and *marble* (Figure 7.14B), which result from contact metamorphism of quartz sandstone and limestone, respectively. At the same time, we emphasize that

although quartzite and marble are commonly associated with contact metamorphism, they are not diagnostic of this type of metamorphism.

REGIONAL METAMORPHISM

The majority of metamorphic rocks observed on Earth can be attributed to **regional metamorphism**. This type of metamorphism occurs over a wide area and is closely tied to the increased pressures and temperatures associated with convergent plate boundaries. During convergence, large segments of Earth's crust are squeezed in a horizontal direction, imposing substantial directed pressure (Figure 7.15). As the rocks are deformed, the crust is shortened and thickened, like a rumpled carpet. This thickening causes crust above sea level to be pushed up to form mountains and crust below sea level to be forced downward to form the "roots" of the mountains, where the most intense metamorphic activity occurs as confining pressures increase. In addition, rocks are subjected to elevated temperatures that accompany both deep burial and the emplacement of magma from the mantle.

The intensity of regional metamorphism becomes greatest when continents collide. The cores of many mountain ranges resulting from continental collision consist of folded and faulted metamorphic rocks, commonly intermixed with intruded igneous rocks. As these deformed rock masses are uplifted, erosion removes the overlying material to expose the igneous and metamorphic rocks that compose the central core of the mountain range.

As with contact metamorphism, the rocks that best display the effects of regional metamorphism are those containing lots of platy or elongate mineral

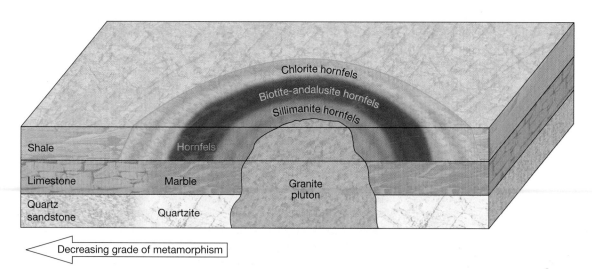

Figure 7.13 Metamorphic grade within a metamorphic aureole decreases away from the intrusive body, as indicated by the distribution of temperature-sensitive index minerals (see Figure 7.8).

Figure 7.14 **A.** Quartzite is a nonfoliated metamorphic rock formed from quartz sandstone. The photomicrograph shows the interlocking quartz grains typical of quartzite. **B.** Marble, a crystalline rock formed by the metamorphism of limestone. Photomicrograph shows interlocking calcite crystals using cross-polarized light. (Photos by E. J. Tarbuck)

Figure 7.15 Regional metamorphism occurs where rocks are squeezed between two converging lithospheric plates during mountain building.

grains, whose orientations provide clues to the nature of pressure applied. The increased intensity of directed pressure that accompanies increasing temperature and confining pressure causes platy and elongate minerals to attain a preferred orientation. Thus foliated rocks are characteristic of regional metamorphism. The metamorphism of shale is emphasized in this section because it is widespread and contains the necessary chemical ingredients to produce the platy and elongate mineral crystals that best define foliation.

In regional metamorphism, metamorphic index minerals and texture change systematically with both increasing temperatures and pressures, whereas temperature is the main factor influencing metamorphic grade in contact metamorphism.

Regional Metamorphism of Shale

In this section, we track the transformation of shale into the metamorphic rock types *slate* (Figure 7.16A), *phyllite* (Figure 7.16B), *schist* (Figure 7.16C), and *gneiss* (Figure 7.16D) with increasing temperature and pressure. The relative depths at which these rock types might be formed within an active mountain belt are illustrated in Figure 7.16.

SLATE Slate is a very fine-grained foliated rock primarily composed of mica flakes that are too small to be seen with the unaided eye (Figure 7.16A). It is typically produced by the low-grade metamorphism of clay-rich mudrocks, such as shale, but in rare instances it can also form from volcanic ash.

Slate looks similar to shale but is much harder and commonly has a slight sheen. Slate can be readily distinguished from sedimentary mudrock, such as shale, by its lack of an earthy smell when rubbed and the ringing sound it produces when struck by a fingernail or other hard object. Shale, in contrast, usually has an earthy smell because of its volatile content and produces a dull thud when struck because the platy minerals are not held together as tightly. Because of the preferred orientation of platy minerals in the direction of weakest stress, slate develops **rock cleavage** (also known as *slaty* cleavage; Figure 7.17), which allows it to be broken into very thin, flat slabs (Figure 7.18). Rock cleavage must not be confused with bedding, which you will recall is a sedimentary feature. Bedding, along with most other

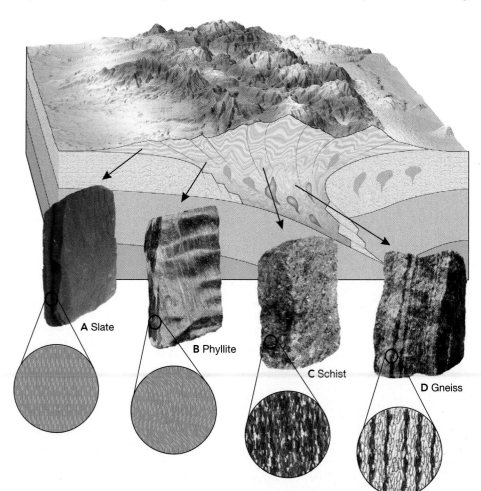

A Slate

B Phyllite

C Schist

D Gneiss

Figure 7.16 Rocks produced from the regional metamorphism of shale. Low-grade metamorphism produces slate (**A**) and phyllite (**B**). Medium-grade metamorphism produces schist (**C**), and high-grade metamorphism produces gneiss (**D**). Note the progressive alignment and increased grain size of platy and elongate minerals with increasing temperature and directed pressure associated with mountain building. (Photos **A** and **C** by C. Tsujita; photo **B** by E. J. Tarbuck; photo **D** by C. Tsujita/Pearson Education)

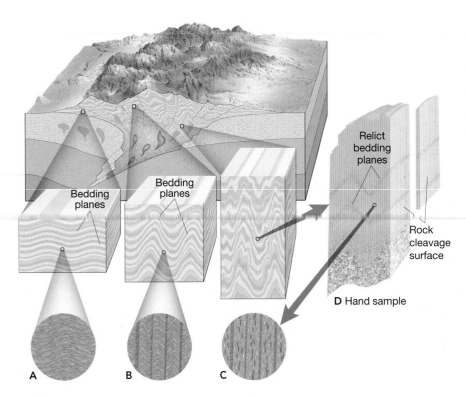

Figure 7.17 Development of one type of rock cleavage. As shale is strongly folded (**A**, **B**) and metamorphosed to form slate, the developing mica flakes are bent into microfolds. **C**. Further metamorphism results in the re-crystallization of mica grains along the limbs of these folds to enhance the foliation. **D**. Hand sample of slate illustrates rock cleavage and its orientation to relict bedding surfaces.

sedimentary features, is commonly obliterated when platy minerals align themselves in response to directed stress. The resulting planes of rock cleavage almost never coincide with bedding (Figure 7.17). Rock cleavage is also not to be confused with mineral cleavage, which passes *within*, rather than *between*, individual mineral crystals.

The colour of slate is dependent on the specific minerals it contains. Black (carbonaceous) slate

contains organic material, red slate contains iron oxide, and green slate usually contains chlorite.

PHYLLITE Phyllite is a low-grade metamorphic rock produced at slightly higher temperatures and pressures than slate. Its constituent platy minerals are larger than those of slate, giving it a glossy sheen, but are still too small to be seen by the unaided eye. Phyllite also exhibits rock cleavage, but the cleavage surfaces

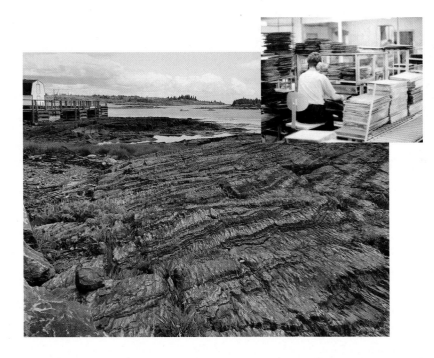

Figure 7.18 Slaty cleavage is exhibited in this exposure of metamorphic rocks at Blue Rocks, Nova Scotia. Note that the direction of cleavage (which extends from the upper left corner to lower right corner of the photo) developed perpendicular to the sedimentary layers of the parent rock (turbidite beds) that alternated from clay-rich (preserved as diffuse dark stripes) to sand-rich (preserved as lighter, quartz-rich stripes). **Inset photo:** The parallel alignment of platy minerals in this rock allows slate to be split into thin, flat plates. This worker at Hurley Slateworks Company (Brittania Cove, Newfoundland) is trimming plates of slate for use as roof tiles. (**Main photo** courtesy of Diane Johnston; **inset photo** courtesy of Dr. W. Lawson Dickson/Newfoundland and Labrador Department of Natural Resources)

commonly have a slightly wavy appearance, which reflects the higher degree of directed pressure it has experienced relative to slate (Figure 7.16B). Phyllite is commonly either grey, indicating a high muscovite content, or green, indicating the presence of chlorite.

SCHIST Schist is a medium- to coarse-grained metamorphic rock dominated by platy mica minerals (biotite and muscovite) large enough to be seen by the unaided eye (Figure 7.16C) and represents a medium metamorphic grade, one step higher than phyllite. These platy minerals have an obvious preferred orientation that defines a distinctive schistose foliation or **schistosity** in this rock type. In addition to platy minerals, schists contain smaller amounts of blocky and tabular minerals, such as feldspar, and can also contain elongate grains of minerals, such as amphibole.

The term *schist* refers to the texture of the rock. To indicate the composition, names of constituent minerals are used. For example, schists composed primarily of muscovite and biotite are called mica schists. Depending on the intensity of metamorphism and composition of their parent rocks, mica schists commonly contain accessory minerals, some of which are unique to metamorphic rocks. Common metamorphic minerals include garnet, *staurolite*, and sillimanite, in which case the rock is called garnet-mica-schist, staurolite-mica schist, and so on. In addition to schistosity, some schists show striking examples of porphyroblastic texture, in which mica grains appear to be wrapped around large crystals of minerals, such as garnet.

GNEISS Gneiss is the term applied to medium- to coarse-grained banded metamorphic rocks in which granular and elongate (as opposed to platy) minerals predominate. It is of high metamorphic grade. The most common minerals in gneiss are quartz, potassium feldspar, and sodium-rich plagioclase feldspar. Most gneisses contain lesser amounts of biotite, amphibole, and muscovite that develop a preferred orientation. Some gneisses will split along layers of platy minerals, but most break into irregular pieces.

During high-grade metamorphism, the light and dark components separate into layers, giving gneisses their characteristic banded or layered appearance, called **gneissic texture** or *gneissosity*.

Thus, most gneisses consist of alternating bands of white or pink feldspar-rich zones and layers of dark ferromagnesian minerals (Figures 7.2 and 7.16D). These banded gneisses commonly show evidence of deformation (Figure 7.2).

Gneiss forms from the high-grade metamorphism of shale and represents the highest grade reached by such rocks during regional metamorphism before the onset of melting. Like schists, gneisses can also include large crystals of metamorphic minerals, such as garnet and staurolite. Gneisses can also form by the regional metamorphism of granite or its aphanitic equivalent, rhyolite. In addition to gneissosity, some gneisses exhibit a porphyroblastic texture, with large eye-shaped porphyroblasts of quartz, feldspar, or garnet.

Regional Metamorphism of Basalt

Unlike shale, which is primarily composed of hydrous clay minerals, basalt is predominantly composed of anhydrous minerals, such as plagioclase feldspar and the ferromagnesian minerals olivine and pyroxene. A basalt parent rock therefore produces different mineral assemblages, and hence different types of metamorphic rocks, than a shaly parent rock when subjected to conditions of regional metamorphism (Figure 7.19). In particular, the metamorphic rocks derived from basalt have a higher

A   B   C

Figure 7.19 Rocks produced from the regional metamorphism of basalt. **A.** Greenschist representing low-grade metamorphism. **B.** Amphibolite representing medium-grade metamorphism. **C.** Granulite representing high-grade metamorphism. (Photos by C. Tsujita)

abundance of minerals containing iron and magnesium than those derived from mudrocks. It is only at low metamorphic grades that platy mineral grains are sufficiently abundant to produce obvious foliation. At medium to high metamorphic grades, the foliation in basalt-derived metamorphic rocks tends to be less pronounced than in mudrock-derived metamorphic rocks because the foliation is defined by the preferred orientation of elongate crystals of ferromagnesian minerals, rather than platy crystals of mica.

GREENSCHIST At low grades of metamorphism, ferromagnesian minerals, such as olivine and pyroxene, contained in the parent basalt are hydrated to form minerals such as chlorite. Chlorite imparts both a phyllite-like foliation and a green colour to the rock. This type of rock, called greenschist (Figure 7.19A), is of equivalent metamorphic grade to slate and phyllite.

AMPHIBOLITE When subjected to higher temperatures and pressures, chlorite and associated hydrated minerals lose water and are converted to amphiboles. The resulting rock, called *amphibolite* (Figure 7.19B), is of equivalent metamorphic grade to the schist produced from a shale parent. The preferred orientation of needle-like amphibole crystals produces a foliation that is less distinct than in greenschist.

GRANULITE At even higher temperatures and pressures, the amphibole minerals contained in amphibolite are further dehydrated to produce pyroxenes and garnets. The high-grade metamorphic rock thus produced, called *granulite* (Figure 7.19C), is equivalent to gneiss produced from mudrock parents but has a very coarse-grained granular texture. The constituent mineral crystals, including those of pyroxene, are typically blocky in shape. Because of the low degree of elongation in the mineral crystals, little preferred orientation of grains is apparent.

The Upper Limit of Regional Metamorphism

In the extreme environments in regional metamorphism, rocks begin to partially melt and pass into a transition zone between metamorphism and the igneous realm. In such environments, part of the rock remains solid and can be considered as part of the metamorphic process, but part of it is melted to form magma. Rocks called **migmatites** represent this somewhat ambiguous state and include both metamorphic and igneous components. They are generally included in metamorphic rocks because they represent the very last possible step a metamorphic rock can take in its passage through conditions of progressively higher temperature and pressure. Recall from our discussion of igneous rocks that different minerals melt at different temperatures. Light-coloured silicates, such as quartz and potassium feldspar, have the lowest melting temperatures and begin to melt first, whereas the mafic silicates, such as amphibole and biotite, remain solid. When the partially melted rock cools, the light bands have an igneous appearance, whereas the dark bands consist of solid metamorphic components. The igneous bands commonly form tortuous folds and sometimes contain angular fragments of the dark components (Figure 7.20).

Figure 7.20 Migmatite texture. The lighter-coloured parts are igneous rock composed of quartz, feldspar, and biotite, while the dark foliated pieces have a metamorphic origin. (Photo by Zbynek Burival/Shutterstock)

Figure 7.21   Rocks produced by subduction zone metamorphism. **A.** Blueschist, representing low-temperature, high-pressure conditions (note the blue-coloured amphibole, called glaucophane). **B.** Eclogite, representing high-temperature, high-pressure conditions of the mantle. Note the pink grains of garnet and green grains of pyroxene. (Photos by C. Tsujita)

Regional Metamorphism and Nonfoliated Rocks

The fact that many rocks produced by regional metamorphism are foliated does not mean that all of them show this texture, because some parent rocks lack the necessary elements to produce the platy or elongate mineral grains that define foliation in metamorphic rocks. Such minerals as quartz and calcite occur in various shapes and therefore do not define a foliation as readily as do such minerals as micas. As in contact metamorphism, regional metamorphism transforms quartz sandstone to quartzite, and limestone to marble. As a result of the lack of platy and elongate minerals, pure quartzites (Figure 7.14A) and marbles (Figure 7.14B) produced by regional metamorphism can look identical to ones produced by contact metamorphism, at least to the unaided eye. However, in some cases impurities, such as clay in the host rocks, produce some faint banding in regionally metamorphosed rocks that are otherwise homogeneous in appearance.

SUBDUCTION ZONE METAMORPHISM

Subduction zone metamorphism is technically a form of regional metamorphism but is discussed here in a separate category because of the special

conditions involved. Metamorphism in the region of a subducted slab is characterized by very high pressures and relatively low temperatures (Figures 7.3 and 7.9). Rocks lying on both sides of the plate boundary are affected. Because a subducted oceanic slab is cold and is a poor heat conductor, rocks on the top of the subducted slab and on the underside of the overlying plate encounter a large increase in pressure at a rapid rate but remain relatively cool. Under these conditions, a peculiar, sodium-rich, blue-coloured amphibole forms, called *glaucophane*. Because of the preferred orientation of elongate glaucophane grains, the rock exhibits foliation and is called *blueschist* (Figure 7.21A). Continued subduction drags rocks into the mantle, where the blueschist is further transformed into a rock called *eclogite*, characterized by pyroxene and garnet (Figure 7.21B).

Other localized types of metamorphism also occur, such as the reaction of rocks with hot fluids of igneous activity, and the pulverizing of rocks along faults and through the impact of asteroids and comets. Box 7.1 explains the latter.

METAMORPHIC FACIES AND PLATE TECTONICS

A **metamorphic facies** is defined by a distinctive assemblage of minerals that can be used to designate a particular set of metamorphic environmental

BOX
7.1

UNDERSTANDING EARTH
Impact Metamorphism

It is now clear that comets and aster-oids have collided with Earth far more frequently than previously thought, based on more than 100 giant impact structures called astroblemes (*astro* = star, *blema* = wound from a projec-tile) that have been found worldwide. The Barringer Crater in Arizona bears the familiar bowl-like shape that we generally associated with impact cra-ters (Figure 7.A). Many astroblemes also exist in Canada, and include the Manicouagan Crater in Quebec, the Sudbury Basin in Ontario, and the Eagle Butte structure in Alberta.

When high-velocity projectiles (comets, asteroids) hit Earth's surface, pressures reach millions of atmospheres and temperatures exceed 2000°C momentarily. The result is pulverized, shattered, and melted rock. Where impact craters are relatively fresh, shock-melted ejecta and rock frag-ments ring the impact site. Although most material is deposited close to its source, some ejecta can travel great distances. One example is tektites (*tektos* = molten), beads of silica-rich glass up to a few centimetres in size resulting from rapid quenching of blobs of the molten ejecta. These can fall hundreds of kilometres away from the impact site.

Shock metamorphism produces some distinctive deformation features. At the microscopic end of the scale are shock lamellae, linear features devel-oped because of small-scale partial melting. Shock lamellae are recog-nized relatively easily in such minerals as quartz that do not have planar cleavage or fracture planes that the shock lamellae could otherwise be confused with. On the large scale of deformation features are *shatter cones*. These are nested cone-like structures that emanate from the point of impact and can be compared with the small-scale patterns produced in glass when a rock damages the windshield of a car. The presence of these structures in rocks surrounding the Sudbury Basin provides evidence

Figure 7.A   Barringer Crater, located west of Winslow, Arizona. (Photo by Michael Collier)

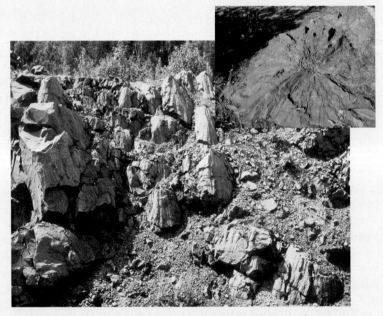

Figure 7.B   Upward-pointing shatter cones made in Precambrian greywacke, near Sudbury, Ontario. **Inset:** Close-up view of a single shatter cone cross-section. (**Main** photo by Grant Young; **inset** photo by S. R. Hicock)

suggesting it represents the site of a large meteorite impact that occurred during the Precambrian (Figure 7.B). Because the Sudbury Basin has been deformed, the orientations of shatter

cones vary from place to place, but it is assumed that before this deformation, the pointed ends of all the shatter cones were consistently oriented toward the site of impact.

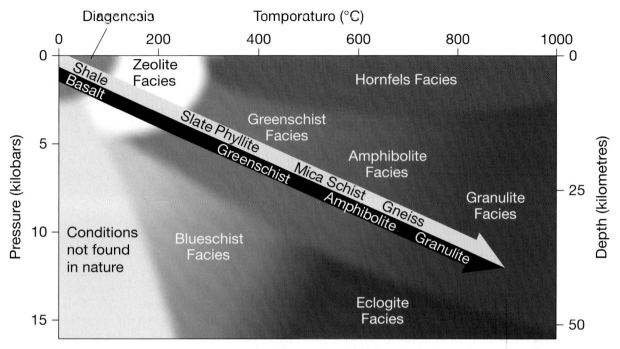

Figure 7.22 Metamorphic facies and corresponding temperature and pressure conditions. Note the equivalent metamorphic rocks produced from regional metamorphism of shale and basalt parent rocks.

conditions recorded in the rocks (Figure 7.22). One advantage of this scheme is that rocks produced by different types of metamorphism can be interpreted within a single, unified context.

The names of metamorphic facies refer to metamorphic rocks derived specifically from a basaltic parent rock. This is because Pentti Eskola, the geologist who proposed the metamorphic facies scheme in 1915, concentrated on the metamorphism of basalts, and his basic terminology, although now slightly modified, has stuck ever since. The names of Eskola's facies serve as convenient labels for a particular combination of temperature and pressure values. In other words, even if a non-basaltic parent rock produces indicator minerals other than what a basalt would produce under a given set of metamorphic conditions, the names of Eskola's facies are used for the purpose of denoting the temperature and pressure ranges embodied by the metamorphic rock.

Figure 7.23 The association of metamorphic facies with plate tectonic environments.

Comparison of Figure 7.22 and Figure 7.9 illustrates the usefulness of the metamorphic facies concept in the interpretation of metamorphic environments. Figure 7.23 shows how facies fit into the context of plate tectonics. The *hornfels facies*, not surprisingly, is associated with the high temperatures and low pressures involved in contact metamorphism. The *zeolite facies* reflects very low-grade metamorphism involving low heat and low pressure and is generally associated with burial metamorphism and the very lowest grade of regional metamorphism. The increasing temperatures and pressures associated with regional metamorphism are recorded by the *greenschist-amphibolite-granulite facies* sequence. Subduction zone metamorphism is characterized by the *blueschist facies*, representing relatively low temperatures but high pressures. Finally, rocks of the *eclogite facies* are diagnostic of very high temperatures and pressures encountered by a deeply subducted slab of oceanic lithosphere.

ANCIENT METAMORPHIC ENVIRONMENTS

In addition to the linear belts of metamorphic rocks that are found along the axes of most mountain belts,

even larger expanses of metamorphic rocks exist within the stable continental interiors (Figure 7.24). These relatively flat expanses of metamorphic rocks and associated igneous rocks are called **shields**. One such region, the Canadian Shield, has very little topographic expression and forms the bedrock over much of Canada. Radiometric dating of rocks in the Canadian Shield indicates that it is composed of rocks that range in age from 1.8 billion to over 4 billion years. Rocks near Great Bear Lake in the Northwest Territories yielded radiometric dates of 4.03 billion years, and rocks in northwest Quebec of 4.28 billion years, currently the oldest known rocks in the world (Figure 7.25).

Because shields are ancient and their rock structure is similar to that found in the cores of younger, deformed mountainous terrains, they are assumed to be remnants of much earlier periods of mountain building (Figure 7.24). This evidence strongly supports the generally accepted view that Earth has been a dynamic planet throughout most of its history. Studies of these vast areas of metamorphism in the context of the plate tectonic model have given geologists new insights into the problem of discerning just how the continents came to exist. We will consider this topic further in Chapter 13.

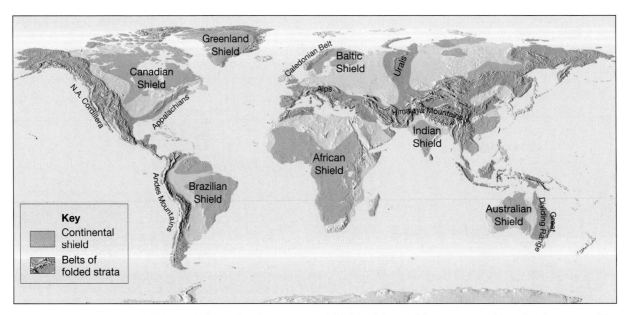

Figure 7.24 Occurrences of metamorphic rocks. The continental shields of the world are composed largely of metamorphic rocks and associated igneous intrusions. In addition, the deformed portions of many mountain belts are also metamorphic. The remaining area shown in this map is the stable continental interior, which generally consists of undeformed sedimentary beds that overlie metamorphic and igneous basement rocks that are buried extensions of the shields.

Figure 7.25 Ancient metamorphic and igneous rocks on the shore of northwest Quebec. These rocks are part of the Canadian Shield and are among the most ancient on Earth. **Inset:** Close-up sample of the Nuwuagittuq greenstone belt, determined by radiometric dating to be 4.28 billion years old, currently the oldest known rocks in the world. (Photos by Jonathan O'Neil)

CHAPTER SUMMARY

- *Metamorphism* transforms rocks into metamorphic rocks without melting—by heat, pressure (stress), and fluids. Heat drives chemical reactions. Pressure includes *confining* (uniform in all directions) and *directed* (uneven). Fluids enhance chemical reactions. At depth rocks are warm and ductile and deform by flowing.

- *Metamorphic grade* is indicated by index minerals that reflect temperature and pressure conditions.

- *Nonfoliated* texture (e.g., in marble) is mainly temperature controlled. *Foliation* of rocks (e.g., *schistosity*) is mainly controlled by directed pressure during mountain building.

- Metamorphism of shale produces *slate, phyllite, schist,* and then *gneiss* with increasing grade; basalt produces *greenschist, amphibolite,* and then *granulite.*

- *Metamorphic facies* reflect the temperature and pressure conditions of rock transformation in three main settings: *contact metamorphism* (high temperatures), *regional metamorphism* (high temperatures/pressures), and *subduction zone metamorphism* (high pressures).

MasteringGeology   www.masteringgeology.com

Looking for additional review and test prep materials? Visit the Study Area in MasteringGeology to enhance your understanding of this chapter's content by accessing a variety of resources, including

Self-Study Quizzes, Geoscience Animations, GEODe Tutorials, RSS feeds, flashcards, weblinks, self-study quizzes, and an optional Pearson eText.

REVIEW QUESTIONS

1. Why is heat such an important agent of metamorphism?

2. How is confining pressure (uniform stress) different from directed pressure (differential stress)?

3. What role do chemically active fluids play in metamorphism?

4. Describe the difference between burial metamorphism, contact metamorphism, and regional metamorphism.

5. With which type of plate boundary is regional metamorphism associated?

6. What is foliation and how does it differ from sedimentary bedding?

7. Starting with shale as a parent rock, name the main types of metamorphic rocks (and their corresponding types of foliation) that form sequentially in regional metamorphism with increasing grade (i.e., increasing temperature and pressure).

8. Repeat question 7, beginning with a parent rock of basalt rather than shale.

9. Describe the concept of metamorphic facies. Why are metamorphic facies useful in the interpretation of metamorphic conditions that rocks have experienced?

GEOLOGIC TIME

8

Carbonate rocks at Chute Vauréal, Anticosti Island, Quebec, preserve a record of geologic processes that operated hundreds of millions of years ago, during the Ordovician Period. (Photo by Jisuo Jin)

In the late eighteenth century, James Hutton recognized the immensity of Earth history and the importance of time as a component in all geologic processes. In the nineteenth century, Sir Charles Lyell and others effectively demonstrated that Earth had experienced many episodes of mountain building and erosion, which must have required great spans of geologic time. Although these pioneering scientists understood that Earth was very old, they had no way of knowing its true age. Was it tens of millions, hundreds of millions, or even billions of years old? A geologic time scale was developed that showed the sequence of events based on relative dating principles. What are these principles? What part do fossils play? With the discovery of radioactivity and radiometric dating techniques, geologists now can assign fairly accurate dates to many of the events in Earth history. What is radioactivity? Why is it a good clock for dating the geologic past?

GEOLOGY NEEDS A TIME SCALE

Like the pages in a long and complicated history book, rocks record the geologic events (Figure 8.1)

Figure 8.1 The history of this large boulder illustrates the immensity of geologic time. The boulder is composed of metamorphic rock that once lay several kilometres below Earth's surface in the roots of a great Precambrian mountain chain. Uplift and erosion over hundreds of millions of years exposed the rock at the surface. During the last Ice Age, the boulder was dislodged from the bedrock surface and transported to a site near its present location. It now lies on this rocky beach, near Port Severn, Ontario, where it is being slowly broken down by physical and chemical weathering.
(Photo by Mike Schering)

and changing life forms of the past. The book, however, is not complete. Many pages, especially in the early chapters, are missing. Others are tattered, torn, or smudged. Yet enough of the book remains to allow much of the story to be deciphered, much like the rock record.

Interpreting Earth history is a prime goal of the science of geology. Like a sleuth, the geologist must interpret the clues found preserved in the rocks. By studying rocks, especially sedimentary rocks, and the features they contain, geologists can unravel the complexities of the past.

Geologic events by themselves, however, have little meaning until they are put into a time perspective. Studying history, whether it is that of humans or dinosaurs, requires a clock. Among geology's major contributions to science are the *geologic time scale* and the discovery that Earth history is exceedingly long.

RELATIVE DATING: KEY PRINCIPLES

Geologic Time

The geologists who developed the geologic time scale revolutionized the way people think about time and perceive our planet. They learned that Earth is much older than anyone had previously imagined and that its surface and interior have been changed over and over again by the same geologic processes that operate today.

During the late nineteenth and early twentieth centuries, attempts were made to determine Earth's age. Although some of the methods appeared promising at the time, none of these early efforts proved to be reliable. What these scientists were seeking was a **numeric date**. Such dates specify the actual number of years that have passed since an event occurred. Today our understanding of radioactivity allows us to accurately determine numeric dates for rocks that represent important events in Earth's distant past. We will study radioactivity later in this chapter. Before the discovery of radioactivity, geologists had no reliable method of numeric dating and had to rely solely on relative dating.

Relative dating means that rocks are placed in their proper *sequence of formation*—which ones formed first, second, third, and so on. Relative dating cannot tell us how long ago something took place, only that it followed one event and preceded another. The relative dating techniques that were developed are valuable and still widely used. Numeric dating methods did not replace these techniques; they simply supplemented them. To establish a relative time scale, a few basic principles or rules had to be discovered and applied. Although they may seem obvious to us today, they were major breakthroughs in thinking at the time, and their discovery was an important scientific achievement.

Law of Superposition

Nicolaus Steno, a Danish anatomist, geologist, and priest (1638–1686), is credited with being the first to recognize a sequence of historical events in an outcrop of sedimentary rock layers. Working in the mountains of western Italy, Steno applied a very simple rule that has come to be the most basic principle of relative dating—**the law of superposition** (*super* = above, *positum* = to place). The law simply states that in an undeformed sequence of sedimentary rocks, each bed is older than the one above and younger than the one below. Although it may seem obvious that a rock layer could not be deposited with nothing beneath it for support, it was not until 1669 that Steno clearly stated this principle.

This rule also applies to other surface-deposited materials, such as lava flows and beds of ash from volcanic eruptions. Applying the law of superposition to the beds exposed in the upper portion of the Grand Canyon (Figure 8.2), we can easily place the layers in their proper order. Among those that are pictured, the sedimentary rocks in the Supai

Group are the oldest, followed in order by the Hermit Shale, Coconino Sandstone, Toroweap Formation, and Kaibab Limestone.

Principle of Original Horizontality

Steno is also credited with recognizing the importance of another basic principle, called the **principle of original horizontality**. Simply stated, it means that layers of sediment are generally deposited in a horizontal position. Thus, if we observe rock layers that are flat, it means they have not been disturbed and still have their *original* horizontality. The layers in the Chute Vauréal illustrate this in the chapter-opening photo, as do those of the Grand Canyon (Figure 8.2). But if the layers are folded or inclined at a steep angle, they must have been moved into that position by crustal disturbances some time after their deposition (Figure 8.3).

Principle of Cross-Cutting Relations

When a fault cuts through other rocks, or when magma intrudes and crystallizes, we can assume that the fault or intrusion is younger than the rocks affected. For example, in Figure 8.4, the faults and dykes clearly must have occurred after the sedimentary layers were deposited.

A

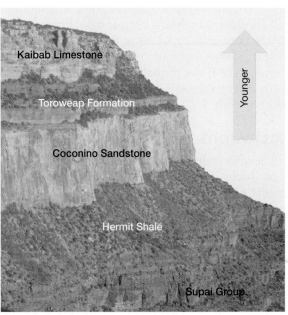

B

Figure 8.2 Applying the law of superposition to these layers exposed in the upper portion of the Grand Canyon, the Supai Group is the oldest, and the Kaibab Limestone is the youngest. (Photo by E. J. Tarbuck)

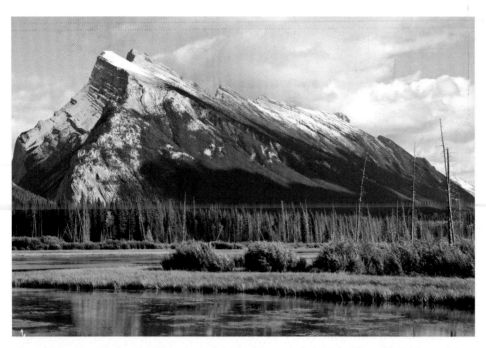

Figure 8.3 Most layers of sediment are deposited in a nearly horizontal position. Thus, when we see rock layers that are inclined, we can assume that they must have been moved into that position by crustal disturbances after their deposition. Mount Rundle, Alberta. (Photo by Henry Lien/Shutterstock)

This is the principle of **cross-cutting relations**. By applying the cross-cutting principle, you can see that fault A occurred *after* the sandstone layer was deposited because it "broke" the layer. Likewise, fault A occurred *before* the conglomerate was laid down, because that layer is unbroken.

We can also state that dyke B and its associated sill are older than dyke A because dyke A cuts the sill. In the same manner, we know that the batholith was emplaced after movement occurred along fault B but before dyke B was formed. This is true because the batholith cuts across fault B, while dyke B cuts across the batholith.

Inclusions

Sometimes inclusions can aid the relative dating process. **Inclusions** (*includere* = to enclose) are fragments of one rock unit that have been enclosed within another. The basic principle is logical and straightforward. The rock mass adjacent to the one containing the inclusions must have been there first to provide the rock fragments. Therefore, the rock mass containing inclusions is the younger of the two. Figure 8.5 provides an example: The inclusions of intrusive igneous rock in the adjacent sedimentary layer indicate that the sedimentary layer was deposited on top of a weathered igneous mass rather than being intruded from below by magma that later crystallized.

Unconformities

When we observe layers of rock that have been deposited essentially without interruption, we call them **conformable**. Particular sites exhibit conformable beds representing certain spans of geologic time. However, no place on Earth has a complete set of conformable strata.

Throughout Earth history, the deposition of sediment has been interrupted over and over again. All such breaks in the rock record are termed unconformities. An **unconformity** is a gap in the record produced by erosion and/or non-deposition. In the former case, uplift and erosion are followed by subsidence and renewed sedimentation. Unconformities are important features because they represent significant geologic events in Earth history. Moreover, their recognition helps us identify what intervals of time are not represented by strata and thus are missing from the geologic record.

The rocks exposed in the Grand Canyon of the Colorado River represent a tremendous span of geologic history. The canyon's colourful strata record a long history of sedimentation in a variety of environments: advancing seas, rivers, and deltas, tidal flats, and sand dunes. But the record is not continuous. Unconformities represent vast amounts of time that have not been recorded in the canyon's layers. Figure 8.6 is a geologic cross-section of the Grand Canyon. Refer to it as you read about the

Conglomerate

Shale

Sandstone

Batholith

Sill

Fault A

Dyke B

Dyke A

Fault B

Figure 8.4 Cross-cutting relations represent one principle used in relative dating. An intrusive rock body is younger than the rocks it intrudes. A fault is younger than the rock layers it cuts.

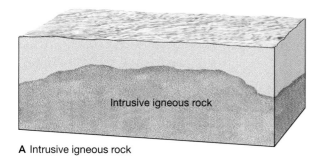

Intrusive igneous rock

A Intrusive igneous rock

B Exposure, weathering, and erosion of intrusive igneous rock

Sedimentary layers

Inclusions of igneous rock

Nonconformity

C Deposition of sedimentary layers

Figure 8.5 These three diagrams illustrate one way that inclusions can form, and a type of unconformity termed a *nonconformity*. In the third diagram we know the igneous rock must be older because pieces of it are included in the overlying sedimentary bed. A nonconformity occurs when older intrusive igneous rocks are in contact with younger sedimentary layers. The photo shows an inclusion of dark igneous rock in a lighter-coloured and younger host rock. (Photo © Jonathan Larsen/Diadem Images/Alamy)

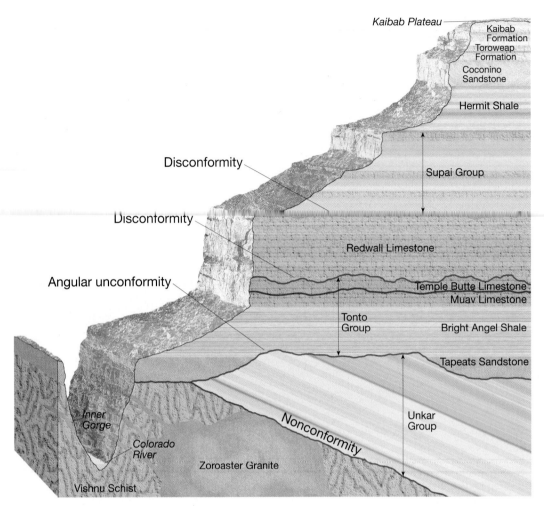

Figure 8.6 This cross-section through the Grand Canyon illustrates the three basic types of unconformities. An angular unconformity can be seen between the tilted Precambrian Unkar Group and the Cambrian Tapeats Sandstone. Two disconformities are marked, above and below the Redwall Limestone. A nonconformity occurs between the igneous and metamorphic rocks of the Inner Gorge and the sedimentary strata of the Unkar Group.

three basic types of unconformities: angular unconformities, disconformities, and nonconformities.

ANGULAR UNCONFORMITY Perhaps the most easily recognized unconformity is an **angular unconformity**. It consists of tilted or folded sedimentary rocks that are overlain by younger, more flat-lying strata. An angular unconformity indicates that during the pause in deposition, a period of deformation (folding or tilting) and erosion occurred (Figure 8.7).

When James Hutton* studied an angular unconformity in Scotland more than 200 years ago, it was clear to him that it represented a major episode of geologic activity as well as an immense time span implied by such relationships.

DISCONFORMITY When contrasted with angular unconformities, **disconformities** are more common but usually far less conspicuous because the strata on either side are essentially parallel. Many disconformities are difficult to identify because the rocks above and below are similar and they show little evidence of erosion. Such a break commonly resembles an ordinary bedding plane but can represent a significant gap in the rock record. Other disconformities are easier to identify because the ancient erosion surface is cut deeply into the older rocks below.

NONCONFORMITY The third basic type of unconformity is a **nonconformity**. Here the break separates older metamorphic or intrusive igneous rocks from younger sedimentary strata (Figures 8.5 and 8.6). Just as angular unconformities and disconformities imply crustal movements, so too do nonconformities. Intrusive igneous masses and metamorphic

_____

*This pioneering geologist is discussed in the section on the birth of modern geology in Chapter 1.

Sea level

5
4
3
2
1

A Deposition

5
4
3
2
1

B Folding and uplifting

5
4
3
2
1

C Erosion

6 (Angular
unconformity)

Sea level

9
8
7
6
5
4
3
2
1

D Subsidence and renewed deposition

E

Figure 8.7 Formation of an angular unconformity. An angular unconformity represents an extended span during which deformation and erosion occurred. Part E shows an angular unconformity (subsequently tilted) at Siccar Point, Scotland, that was first described by James Hutton more than 200 years ago.
(Photo by A. P. Trujillo/APT Photos)

rocks originate far below the surface. Thus, for a nonconformity to develop, an episode of uplift and the erosion of overlying rocks must occur. Once exposed at the surface, the igneous or metamorphic rocks are subjected to weathering and erosion before subsidence and the renewal of sedimentation.

CORRELATION OF ROCK LAYERS

To develop a geologic time scale that is applicable to the entire Earth, rocks of similar age in different regions must be matched up. Such a task is referred to as **correlation**.

Correlation by Physical Criteria

Within a limited area, correlating rocks of one locality with those of another can be done simply by walking along the outcrop. However, this may not be possible when the rocks are mostly concealed by soil and vegetation. Correlation over short distances is often achieved by noting the position of a bed in a sequence of strata. Or a layer may be identified in another location if it is composed of distinctive or uncommon minerals.

By correlating the rocks from one place to another, a more comprehensive view of the geologic history of a region is possible. Figure 8.8, for example, shows the correlation of strata at three sites on the Colorado Plateau in southern Utah and northern Arizona. No single locale exhibits the entire sequence, but correlation reveals a more complete picture of the sedimentary rock record.

Many geologic studies involve relatively small areas. Although they are important in their own right, their full value is realized only when they are correlated with other regions. Although the methods just described are sufficient to trace a rock formation over relatively short distances, they are not adequate for matching up rocks that are separated by great distances. When correlation between widely separated areas or between continents is the objective, geologists must rely on fossils.

Fossils and Correlation

The existence of fossils (Chapter 6) had been known for centuries, yet it was not until the late eighteenth and early nineteenth centuries that their significance as geologic tools was made evident. During this time an English engineer and canal builder, William Smith, discovered that each rock formation in the canals he worked on contained fossils unlike those in the beds either above or below. Further, he noted

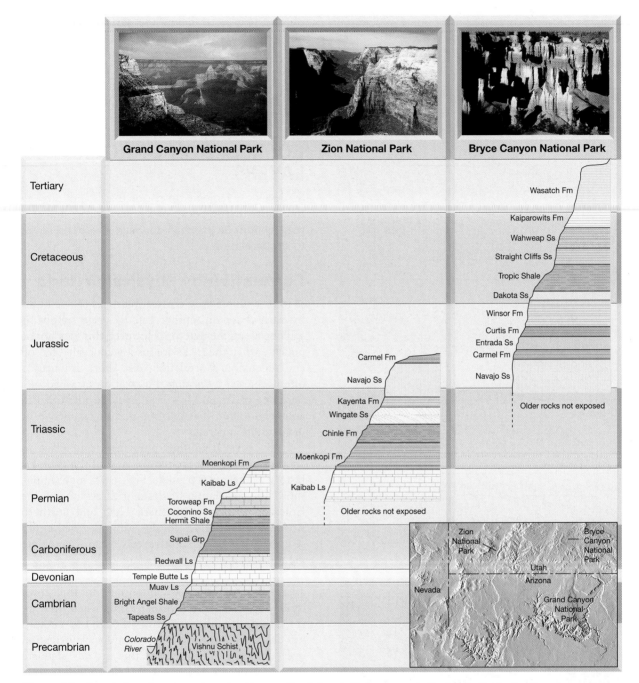

Figure 8.8 Correlation of strata at three locations on the Colorado Plateau reveals the total extent of sedimentary rocks in the region.
(After U.S. Geological Survey; **photos** by E. J. Tarbuck)

that sedimentary strata in widely separated areas could be identified—and correlated—by their distinctive fossil content.

Based on Smith's and others' classic observations, one of the most important and basic principles in historical geology was formulated: *Fossil organisms succeed one another in a definite and determinable order, and therefore any time interval can be recognized by its fossil content*. This has come to be known as the **principle of fossil succession**. In other words, when fossils are arranged according to their age, they do not present a random or haphazard picture. Instead they document the evolution of life through time.

For example, an Age of Trilobites is recognized quite early in the fossil record. Then, in succession,

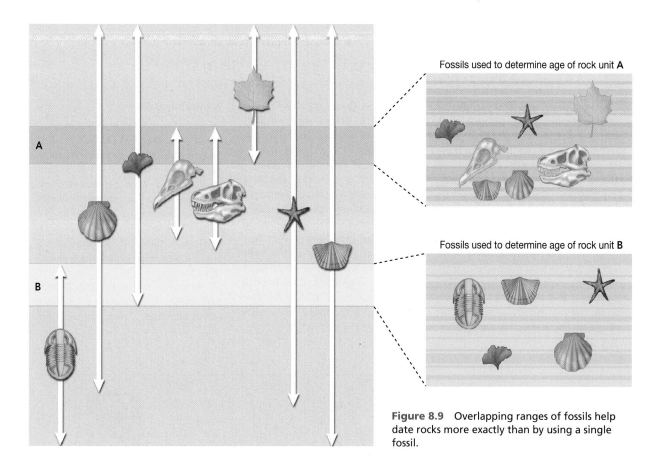

Fossils used to determine age of rock unit **A**

Fossils used to determine age of rock unit **B**

Figure 8.9 Overlapping ranges of fossils help date rocks more exactly than by using a single fossil.

paleontologists recognize an Age of Fishes, an Age of Coal Swamps (best fossils found at Joggins, Nova Scotia), an Age of Reptiles, and an Age of Mammals. These ages pertain to groups that were especially plentiful and characteristic during particular episodes. Within each of the ages are many subdivisions that are based, for example, on certain species of trilobites and certain types of fish, reptiles, and so on. This same succession of dominant organisms, never out of order, is found on every continent.

When fossils were found to be time indicators, they became the most useful means of correlating rocks of similar age in different regions, especially **index fossils**. These fossils are widespread geographically and are limited to a short span of geologic time, so their presence provides an important method of matching rocks of the same age (see Box 8.1). However, rock formations do not always contain a specific index fossil. In such situations, groups of fossils are used to establish the age of the bed. Figure 8.9 illustrates how an assemblage of fossils can be used to date rocks more precisely than could be accomplished by the use of any one of the fossils.

Fossils are also important environmental indicators (see Box 8.1). Although much can be deduced about past environments from characteristics of sedimentary rocks, a close examination of their fossils can provide more information. For example, when the remains of certain clam shells are found in limestone, the geologist assumes that the region was once covered by a shallow sea. Also, by using what we know of living organisms, we can conclude that fossil animals with thick shells capable of withstanding pounding and surging waves inhabited shorelines. Conversely, animals with thin, delicate shells probably indicate deep, calm offshore waters. Hence, by looking closely at the types of fossils, the approximate position of an ancient shoreline can be identified.

Fossils can also be used to indicate the former temperature of the water. Certain kinds of present-day corals must live in warm and shallow tropical seas, like those around Florida and the Bahamas. When similar types of coral are found in ancient limestones, they indicate the marine environment that must have existed when they were alive. These examples illustrate how fossils can help unravel the complex story of Earth history.

BOX
8.1

UNDERSTANDING EARTH
Index Fossils and Ecology of Organisms

At a very basic level, the degree to which the remains of marine organisms are distributed over the globe depends on the life habits of their owners. For example, an organism that lives in well-sorted sand in shallow water would probably be restricted to a very narrow geographic zone near the coastline, whereas an organism that lives its entire life in the plankton of marine surface waters would be able to drift over wide expanses of the sea. Furthermore, the shell of an organism living in a beach environment pounded by waves would be less likely to be preserved than that of an organism whose remains settle on a quiet, muddy sea floor. An added practical advantage of many of these latter forms is that they are microscopic in size and therefore many individuals can be extracted from a relatively small sample of rock. Consistent with these factors, most of the index fossils that form the basis of global correlations represent the remains of drifting or swimming organisms that lived in the water column (Figure 8.A). Some particularly important index fossils are described next.

Planktonic Drifters

Foraminifera are amoeba-like animals, most of which construct a calcium carbonate shell. Small (less than 1 millimetre) planktonic forms are important Mesozoic and Cenozoic index fossils. Bottom-dwelling forms of foraminifera range from the Paleozoic to the present and are also important index fossils, particularly in Paleozoic strata, but are less widespread than planktonic forms.

Coccoliths are very tiny (0.002–0.02 millimetres) plates of calcium carbonate that cover single-celled,

Figure 8.A Some important index fossils of the Phanerozoic Eon, life habits of organisms whose remains are represented, and their time ranges. Among planktonic drifters are foraminifera, coccoliths, acritarchs, dinoflagellates, graptolites, and chitinozoans. Among the swimming organisms are conodonts, graptolites, and ammonoids. Two types of bottom-dwelling organisms that are extensively used as index fossils are trilobites and flatclams.
(Photo of coccoliths on algal spore by Jeremy Young; foraminifera photos reproduced with permission of the Geological Association of Canada (GAC) from *Cretaceous Rocks and Their Foraminifera in the Manitoba Escarpment,* by D. H. McNeil and W. G. E. Caldwell, GAC Special Paper 21(1981); graptolite by Alfred Lenz; chitinozoan courtesy of U.S. Geological Survey; acritarch by Andrew MacRae; dinoflagellate by Graham Williams; conodonts reproduced with the permission of Natural Resources Canada 2013, courtesy of the Geological Survey of Canada (Photo 203349 by Godfrey Nowlan); ammonoid and flatclams by C. Tsujita; trilobite by Denis Tetreault)

planktonic algae called coccolitho phores. They are important index fossils of the mid to late Mesozoic and the Cenozoic.

Organic-walled cysts of planktonic algae known as *acritarchs* and *dinoflagellates* are commonly used in relative dating. Acritarchs range from the Proterozoic to the present day but are primarily used in pre-Mesozoic strata. Dinoflagellates are extensively used as index fossils for strata of Cretaceous age to the present. Cysts are bodies that represent the resting stage of otherwise planktonic organisms.

Chitinozoans are tiny (0.05–0.4 millimetres) flask-shaped fossils of unknown biologic affinity that are important early Ordovician to late Devonian index fossils.

Swimmers

Conodonts are microscopic (0.2–5 millimetres) tooth-like objects that were elements of the feeding apparatus of small eel-like animals that were active swimmers. They are important index fossils for the Paleozoic and early Mesozoic (Triassic).

Graptolites are extinct colonial animals that formed long, saw-blade-shaped forms that were passive floaters, now useful in the relative dating of Ordovician to Silurian strata.

Ammonoids are extinct but were related to squids and octopuses and were probably active swimmers. Their calcareous shells are important index fossils for the late Paleozoic and the Mesozoic.

During the Phanerozoic Eon, at times the stagnation of bottom water in deep areas of sedimentary basins prevented organisms from living there. During these times the remains of most bottom-dwelling organisms tend to have a patchy distribution on a global scale and are therefore unsuitable for correlation. Even so, a few organisms had high tolerance for low-oxygen conditions and are used as index fossils for regional correlations. Some of these are described next.

Bottom Dwellers

Trilobites are extinct but distantly related to present-day crabs, shrimps, lobsters, insects, spiders, scorpions, and barnacles. Their calcium carbonate skeletons are used as index fossils primarily in Cambrian to Devonian strata.

Bivalves (also called clams) constructed a bivalved shell of calcium carbonate. A group of them called "flatclams" are especially useful: Scallop-like flatclams are index fossils in Triassic strata, whereas oyster-like forms are important in Cretaceous strata.

DATING WITH RADIOACTIVITY

In addition to establishing relative ages by using the principles above, it is also possible to obtain reliable numeric dates for events in the geologic past. For example, we know that Earth is about 4.6 billion years old and that the dinosaurs became extinct about 66 million years ago. Dates that are expressed in millions and billions of years truly stretch our imagination, because our personal clocks involve time measured in hours, weeks, and years. Nevertheless, the vast expanse of geologic time is a reality, and it is radiometric dating that allows us to measure it.

Radioactivity

Recall from Chapter 2 that each atom has a nucleus containing protons and neutrons and that the nucleus is surrounded by electrons. Electrons have a negative electrical charge, and protons have a positive charge. A neutron is actually a proton and an electron combined, so it has no charge (it is neutral or balanced in charge).

The forces that bind protons and neutrons together in the nucleus are usually strong. However, in some isotopes, the nuclei are unstable because the forces binding protons and neutrons together are not strong enough. The nuclei of such isotopes spontaneously break apart and emit energy, resulting in the property we call radioactivity. The process involving the breakdown of a radioactive isotope is called radioactive decay.

An unstable radioactive isotope is referred to as the *parent*, and the isotopes resulting from the decay of the parent are termed the *daughter products*. Figure 8.10 provides an example of radioactive decay. When the radioactive parent uranium-238 (its mass number) decays, it follows a number of steps before finally becoming the stable daughter product lead-206. Thus radioactivity can provide a reliable means of calculating the ages of rocks and minerals that contain particular radioactive isotopes.

The procedure is called **radiometric dating**. Radiometric dating is reliable because the rates of decay for many isotopes have been precisely measured and do not vary under the physical conditions that exist in Earth's crust. Therefore, each radioactive isotope used for dating has been decaying at a fixed rate since the formation of the rocks in which it occurs, and the products of decay have been accumulating at a corresponding rate. For example, when uranium is incorporated into a mineral that crystallizes from magma, there is virtually no lead (the stable daughter product) from previous decay. The

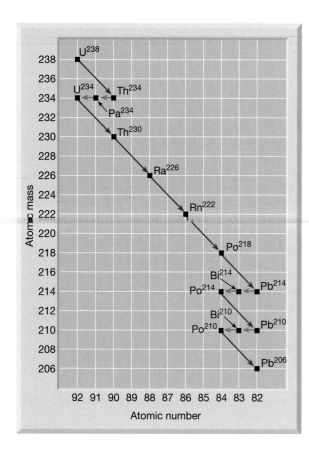

Figure 8.10 The most common isotope of uranium (U-238) is an example of a radioactive decay series. Before the stable end product (Pb-206) is reached, many different isotopes are produced as intermediate steps.

radiometric clock starts at this point. As the uranium in this newly formed mineral disintegrates, atoms of the daughter product are trapped, and measurable amounts of lead eventually accumulate.

Half-Life

The time required for half of the nuclei in a sample to decay is called the **half-life** of the isotope. Half-life is a common way of expressing the rate of radioactive disintegration. Figure 8.11 illustrates what occurs when a radioactive parent decays directly into its stable daughter product. When the quantities of parent and daughter are equal (ratio 1:1), we know that one half-life has transpired. When one-quarter of the original parent atoms remain, and three-quarters of them have decayed to the daughter product, the parent/daughter ratio is 1:3 and we know that two half-lives have passed. After three half-lives, the ratio of parent atoms to daughter atoms is 1:7 (one parent atom for every seven daughter atoms).

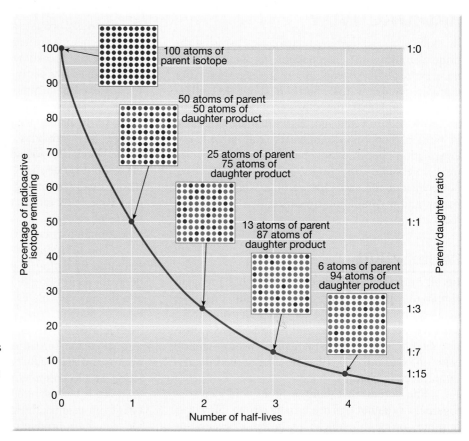

Figure 8.11 The radioactive-decay curve shows change that is exponential. Half of the radioactive parent remains after one half-life. After a second half-life one-quarter of the parent remains, and so forth.

If the half life of a radioactive isotope is known and the parent/daughter ratio can be determined, the age of the sample can be calculated. For example, assume that the half-life of a hypothetical unstable isotope is 1 million years and the parent/daughter ratio in a sample is 1:15. Such a ratio indicates that four half-lives have passed and that the sample must be 4 million years old.

TABLE 8.1 Isotopes Frequently Used in Radiometric Dating

Radioactive Parent	Stable Daughter Product	Currently Accepted Half-Life Values
Uranium-238	Lead-206	4.5 billion years
Uranium-235	Lead-207	704 million years
Thorium-232	Lead-208	14.0 billion years
Rubidium-87	Strontium-87	48.8 billion years
Potassium-40	Argon-40	1.3 billion years

Radiometric Dating

Notice that the *percentage* of radioactive atoms that decay during one half-life is always the same: 50 percent. However, the *actual number* of atoms that decay with the passing of each half-life continually decreases. Thus, as the percentage of radioactive parent atoms declines, the proportion of stable daughter atoms rises, with the increase in daughter atoms just matching the drop in parent atoms. This fact is the key to radiometric dating.

Of the many radioactive isotopes that exist in nature, five have proved particularly useful in providing radiometric ages for ancient rocks (Table 8.1). Rubidium-87, thorium-232, and the two isotopes of uranium are used only for dating rocks that are millions of years old, but potassium-40 is more versatile. Canadians are leading the way in using cosmic ray–generated isotopes to date exposed rock surfaces and to reconstruct landscape evolution (see Box 8.2).

BOX
8.2

CANADIAN PROFILE
Dating Earth's Surface with Terrestrial Cosmogenic Nuclides

John Gosse*

Earth is continuously bombarded by radiation that originates from outside our solar system. Fortunately, the geomagnetic field deflects much of the radiation, but even at the equator where the field is strongest some of the highest energy particles can still penetrate. When the cosmic particles, or rays, enter the atmosphere, they interact with the nuclei of nitrogen and oxygen and create a secondary flux of radiation. The secondary particles include neutrinos, electrons, muons, pions, neutrons, protons, and heavier particles called nuclides, which are nuclei of atoms without electrons. The secondary particles may have enough energy to continue to interact with matter deeper in the atmosphere and even in the lithosphere, biosphere, and hydrosphere. For instance, carbon-14 is produced cosmogenically in the atmosphere.

Figure 8.B A former lake that filled this basin in north central Baffin Island was rapidly drained about 8000 years ago after glacier ice that dammed the lake melted. The exposure age on emerged shorelines and delta indicate when glacial retreat occurred and when the lake drained.
(Photo courtesy of Dr. John C. Gosse)

Figure 8.C Exposure dates of 15 900 years on large erratic boulders near Peggy's Cove, Nova Scotia, record when the last ice sheet margin retreated from the continental shelf and onto land.
(Photo © Bill Brooks/Alamy)

Figure 8.D By exposure dating stream-polished surfaces down the wall of Granite Gorge of the Grand Canyon, researchers can determine how fast the Colorado River incised the Grand Canyon.
(Photo courtesy of Laura Crossey)

Cosmic-ray-produced (cosmogenic) beryllium-10 is a terrestrial cosmogenic nuclide (TCN) that is produced in quartz when an energetic secondary neutron destroys the nucleus of a silicon-28 atom or an oxygen-16 nucleus. Although many cosmogenic nuclides are so unstable that they decay quickly, many are stable (He_3, Ne_{21}, Ar_{38}) or have a long enough half-life that they are useful for geologic dating (Be_{10} $t_{1/2}$ = 1.4 Ma, Al_{26} $t_{1/2}$ = 0.7 Ma, Cl_{36} $t_{1/2}$ = 0.3 Ma, C_{14} $t_{1/2}$ = 5.7 ka).

The average energy of secondary cosmic radiation decreases with depth so in rock and sediments in the upper few metres of Earth's surface, the concentration of TCN also decreases with depth. The rate that these TCN are produced in rocks depends on how thick the atmosphere is above the sample (cosmic ray flux to mountain tops or airplanes is greater than the flux at sea level). For example, at sea level Be^{10} is produced at the rate of five Be^{10} atoms per gram of quartz per year. Consider that our tans get darker with longer exposure to solar rays. Similarly, the TCN concentration (atoms per gram) in minerals increases with time with greater exposure to cosmic rays. Because there are so few TCN atoms among the 1024 atoms of a gram of a mineral, TCNs are usually measured by using high precision instruments. By measuring the concentrations of these rare nuclides we can calculate the time since a rock surface was exposed at Earth's surface. For a stable TCN,

Time = Concentration/Production rate

The cosmic clock begins as soon as the rock is exposed, so the technique is useful for dating lavas, fault scarps, emerged beaches and deltas (Figure 8.B), deglaciated landforms and erratic boulders (Figure 8.C), alluvial fans, stream terraces, stream-eroded canyon walls (Figure 8.D), and landslides. Surfaces as young as decades, and as old as tens of millions of years, have been measured in the Dry Valleys of Antarctica and hyper-arid deserts where erosion has not removed much of the cosmic ray exposure record. The technique is useful for helping determine the recurrence intervals of volcanic eruptions, earthquake faulting, flooding, and landsliding, and the influence of climate change on global glacial ice volumes.

John Gosse is a professor in the department of Earth Sciences (and Canada Research Chair in Earth System Evolution) at Dalhousie University. Used by permission.

POTASSIUM-ARGON Although the half-life of potassium-40 is 1.3 billion years, analytical techniques make possible the detection of tiny amounts of its stable daughter product, argon-40, in some rocks that are younger than 100 000 years. Another important reason for its frequent use is that potassium is an abundant constituent of many common minerals, particularly micas and feldspars.

Although potassium (K) has three natural isotopes, K^{39}, K^{40}, and K^{41}, only K^{40} is radioactive.

When K^{40} decays, it does so in two ways. About 11 percent changes to argon-40 (Ar^{40}). The remaining 89 percent of K^{40} decays to calcium-40 (Ca^{40}). The decay of K^{40} to Ca^{40}, however, is not useful for radiometric dating, because the Ca^{40} produced by radioactive disintegration cannot be distinguished from calcium that may have been present when the rock formed.

The potassium-argon clock begins when potassium-bearing minerals crystallize from magma or form within a metamorphic rock. At this point the new minerals will contain K^{40} but will be free of Ar^{40}, because this element is an inert gas that does not chemically combine with other elements. As time passes, the K^{40} steadily decays. The Ar^{40} produced by this process remains trapped within the mineral's crystal lattice. Because no Ar^{40} was present when the mineral formed, all of the daughter atoms trapped in the mineral must have come from the decay of K^{40}. To determine a sample's age, the K^{40}/Ar^{40} ratio is measured precisely and the known half-life for K^{40} applied.

SOURCES OF ERROR It is important to realize that an accurate radiometric date can be obtained only if the mineral remained a closed system during the entire period since it formed. This means there was neither the addition nor loss of parent or daughter isotopes from the mineral, which is not always the case. In fact, an important limitation of the potassium-argon method arises from the fact that argon is a gas and it can leak from minerals, throwing off measurements. Indeed, losses can be significant if the rock is subjected to relatively high temperatures. Of course, a reduction in the amount of Ar^{40} leads to an underestimation of the rock's age. Sometimes temperatures are high enough for a sufficiently long interval that all argon escapes. When this happens, the potassium-argon clock is reset and dating the sample will give only the time of thermal resetting, not the true age of the rock. For other radiometric clocks, a loss of daughter atoms can occur if the rock has been subjected to weathering or leaching. To avoid such a problem, one simple safeguard is to use only fresh, un-weathered material and not samples that may have been chemically altered.

Dating with Carbon-14

To date geologically recent events, radioactive carbon-14 is used in **radiocarbon dating**. Because the half-life of carbon-14 is only 5730 years, it can only be used for dating events from recorded history and to about 50 000 years.

Carbon-14 is continuously produced in the upper atmosphere during cosmic ray bombardment. It quickly becomes incorporated into carbon dioxide, which circulates in the atmosphere and is absorbed by living matter. Thus all organisms contain a small amount of carbon-14, including you.

As long as an organism is alive, the decaying radiocarbon is continually replaced and the proportions of carbon-14 and carbon-12 remain constant. Carbon-12 is the stable and most common isotope of carbon. However, when any plant or animal dies, the amount of carbon-14 gradually decreases as it decays to nitrogen-14. By comparing the proportions of carbon-14 and carbon-12 in a sample, radiocarbon dates can be determined. Although carbon-14 is only useful in dating the last small fraction of geologic time, it is also a valuable tool for anthropologists, archaeologists, and historians.

THE GEOLOGIC TIME SCALE
Geologic Time

Geologists have divided the whole of geologic history into units of various magnitudes. Together, they compose the **geologic time scale** of Earth history (Figure 8.12). The major units of the time scale were delineated during the nineteenth century, principally by workers in Western Europe and Great Britain. Because radiometric dating was unavailable at that time, the entire time scale was created by using methods of relative dating. It was only in the twentieth century that radiometric methods permitted numeric dates to be added.

Structure of the Time Scale

The geologic time scale subdivides the 4.6-billion-year history of Earth into many different units and provides a meaningful time frame within which the events of the geologic past are arranged. As shown in Figure 8.12, **eons** represent the greatest expanses of time. The eon that began about 541 million years ago is the **Phanerozoic**, a term derived from Greek words meaning *visible life*. It is an appropriate description because the rocks and deposits of the Phanerozoic eon contain abundant fossils that document major evolutionary trends.

The Phanerozoic Eon is divided into **eras**. The three eras within the Phanerozoic are the **Paleozoic** (*palaios* = ancient, *zoe* = life), the **Mesozoic** (*meso* = middle, *zoe* = life), and the **Cenozoic** (*ceno* = recent,

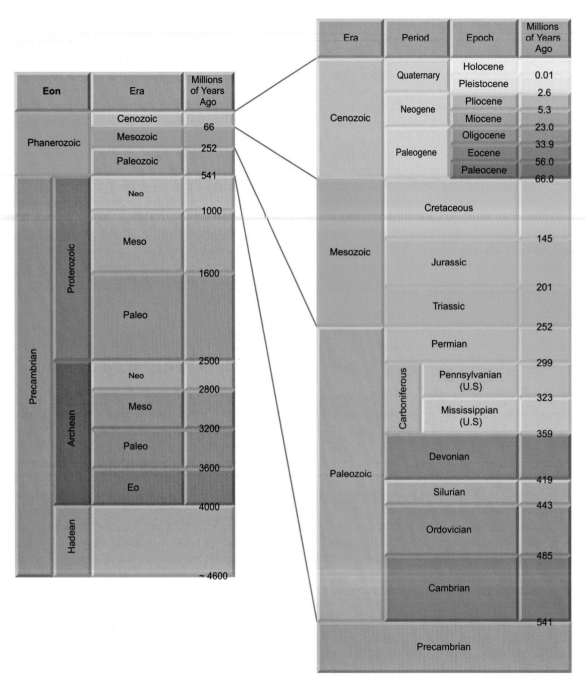

Figure 8.12 The geologic time scale. The numeric ages were added long after the time scale had been established by using relative dating techniques.
(Data from International Commission of Stratigraphy's Geologic Time Scale, 2012)

zoe = life). As the names imply, the eras are bounded by profound worldwide changes in life forms (see Box 8.3).

Each era is subdivided into time units known as **periods.** The Paleozoic has six, the Mesozoic three, and the Cenozoic two. Each of these periods is characterized by a somewhat less profound change in life forms as compared with the eras. The eras and periods of the Phanerozoic, with brief explanations of each, are presented in Table 8.2.

Finally, each of the periods is divided into still smaller units called **epochs.** As you can see in Figure 8.12, seven epochs have been named for the periods of the Cenozoic. The epochs of other periods usually are termed *paleo, meso,* and *neo.*

BOX
8.3

EARTH AS A SYSTEM
Demise of the Dinosaurs

The boundaries between divisions on the geologic time scale represent times of significant geologic and biologic change. Of special interest is the boundary between the Mesozoic Era ("middle life") and Cenozoic Era ("recent life"), about 66 million years ago (Figure 8.E). Around this time, more than half of all plant and animal species died out in a *mass extinction*. This boundary (Figure 8.12) marks the end of the era in which dinosaurs (Figure 8.F) and other reptiles dominated the landscape and the beginning of the era when mammals become very important.

The extinction of the dinosaurs is generally attributed to this group's inability to adapt to some radical change in environmental conditions. What event could have triggered the rapid extinction of the dinosaurs—one of the most successful groups of land animals ever to have lived?

The most strongly supported hypothesis proposes that about 66 million years ago, a large meteorite approximately 10 kilometres in diameter collided with Earth (Figure 8.G). The speed at impact was about 90 000 kilometres per hour! The force of the impact vaporized the meteorite and trillions of tonnes of Earth's crust. Huge quantities of dust and other metamorphosed debris were blasted high into the atmosphere. For a year or two the encircling dust cloud greatly restricted the sunlight reaching Earth's surface. With insufficient sunlight for photosynthesis, delicate food chains most likely would have collapsed. Large plant-eating dinosaurs would have been affected more adversely than smaller life forms because of the tremendous volume of vegetation they consumed. Next would have come the demise of large carnivores. When the sunlight returned, more than half of the species on Earth, including numerous marine organisms, had become extinct.

Figure 8.E   A coal seam (visible as a black layer) in the uppermost Frenchman Formation near Eastend, Saskatchewan, marks the boundary between the uppermost Cretaceous strata and lowermost Paleogene strata at this site. Canada's most famous *Tyrannosaurus rex*, affectionately named "Scotty," was found 28.3 metres below this level. (Image courtesy of the Royal Saskatchewan Museum)

Figure 8.F   Dinosaurs dominated the North American landscape through much of the Mesozoic Era. *Tyrannosaurus* was one of the last meat-eating dinosaurs to have roamed North America just before the great mass extinction that occurred at the end of the Cretaceous Period. (Photo by Sabena Jane Blackbird/Alamy)

This period of mass extinction appears to have affected all land animals larger than dogs. Supporters of the catastrophic-event scenario suggest that small, rat-like mammals were able to survive a breakdown in their food chains lasting perhaps several months. Large dinosaurs, they contend, could not survive this event. The loss of these large reptiles opened a habitat for the small mammals that remained. This new habitat, along with evolutionary opportunities, led to the development of the large mammals that occupy our modern world.

What evidence points to such a catastrophic collision 66 million years ago? Primarily, a thin layer of sediment nearly 1 centimetre thick marks the boundary between Cretaceous and Paleogene strata worldwide. This sediment contains a high level of the element *iridium*, rare in Earth's crust but found in high proportions in stony meteorites. Could this layer be the scattered remains of the meteorite that was responsible for the environmental changes that led to the demise of many reptile groups?

Despite its growing support, some scientists disagree with the impact hypothesis. They suggest instead that huge volcanic eruptions led to the breakdown in the food chain. To support their hypothesis, they cite enormous outpourings of lavas in the Deccan Plateau of northern India about 66 million years ago.

Whatever caused the end-Cretaceous extinction, we now have a greater appreciation of the role of catastrophic events in shaping the history of our planet and the life that occupies it. Could a catastrophic event having similar results occur today? This possibility may explain why an event that occurred 66 million years ago has captured the interest of so many.

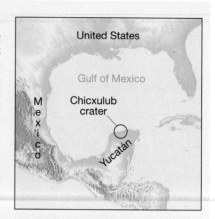

Figure 8.G Chicxulub crater is a giant impact crater that formed about 66 million years ago and has since been filled with sediments. About 180 kilometres in diameter, Chicxulub crater is regarded by some researchers as the impact site of the meteorite that resulted in the demise of the dinosaurs.

TABLE **8.2** Major Divisions of Geologic Time

Cenozoic Era (Age of Recent Life)	Quaternary Period	From the Latin word *quaternarius*, relating to the number four. This term is a remnant of a much older time scale scheme, in which the Quaternary was the youngest of four main divisions (the others being the Primary, Secondary and Tertiary)
	Neogene Period*	From the Greek words *neo* (new) and *genes* (born)
	Paleogene Period*	From the Greek words *palaios* (ancient) and *genes* (born)
Mesozoic Era (Age of Middle Life)	Cretaceous Period	Derived from Greek word for chalk (*kreta*) and first applied to extensive deposits that form white cliffs along the English Channel (see Figure 6.13); extinction of the dinosaurs at the end of this period
	Jurassic Period	Named for the Jura Mountains, located between France and Switzerland, where rocks of this age were first studied; age of dinosaurs
	Triassic Period	Taken from the word *trias* in recognition of the threefold character of these rocks in Europe; dinosaurs first appeared
Paleozoic Era (Age of Ancient Life)	Permian Period	Named after the province of Perm, Russia, where these rocks were first studied
	Carboniferous Period**	The literal meaning of this term is "carbon-bearing" and refers to the extensive coal measures of Western Europe that are of this age
	Devonian Period	Named after Devonshire County, England, where these rocks were first studied
	Silurian Period Ordovician Period	Named after Celtic tribes, the Silures and the Ordovices, that lived in Wales during the Roman Conquest
	Cambrian Period	Taken from Roman name for Wales (Cambria), where rocks containing the earliest evidence of complex forms of life were first studied
Precambrian		The time between the birth of the planet and the appearance of skeletonized forms of life; about 88 percent of Earth's estimated 4.6 billion years fall into this span

Source: Data from U.S. Geological Survey and the International Commission of Stratigraphy

*According to the International Commission of Stratigraphy, the term *Tertiary*, which is still widely used, is no longer considered a period of the Cenozoic internationally; many geologists remain opposed to this controversial ruling.

**In North America, the Carboniferous Period is divided into the Mississippian and Pennsylvanian subperiods (Figure 8.12). The names of these subperiods (formerly considered periods in the United States) refer to the extensive exposures of rocks representing this interval of time in the Mississippi River Valley and the state of Pennsylvania, respectively.

Precambrian Time

Notice that the detail of the geologic time scale does not begin until about 541 million years ago, the date for the beginning of the Cambrian Period. The nearly 4 billion years before the Cambrian are divided into three eons, the **Hadean** (*Hades* = mythological subterranean world of departed spirits), the **Archean** (*archaios* = ancient), and the **Proterozoic** (*proteros* = before, *zoe* = life). It is also common for this vast expanse of time to simply be referred to as the **Precambrian**. Although it represents about 88 percent of Earth history, the Precambrian is not divided into nearly as many smaller time units as the Phanerozoic Eon because Precambrian history is not known in great enough detail.

The quantity of information geologists have deciphered about Earth's past is somewhat analogous to the detail of human history. The further back we go, the less is known. Certainly more data and information exist about the past 10 years than for the first decade of the twentieth century; the events of the nineteenth century have been documented much better than the events of the first century BCE; and so on. So it is with Earth history. The more recent past has the freshest, least disturbed, and more observable record. The further back in time geologists go, the more fragmented the record and clues become.

Other reasons help explain our lack of a detailed time scale for this vast segment of Earth history:

1. The first abundant fossil evidence does not appear in the geologic record until the beginning of the Cambrian Period. Before the Cambrian, simple life forms, such as algae, bacteria, fungi, and worms, predominated. All of these organisms lack hard parts, an important condition favouring preservation. For this reason, only a meagre Precambrian fossil record exists. Many exposures of Precambrian rocks have been studied in some detail, but correlation is often difficult when fossils are lacking.

2. Because Precambrian rocks are very old, most have been subjected to a great many changes. Much of the Precambrian rock record is composed of highly distorted metamorphic rocks. This makes the interpretation of past environments difficult, because many of the clues present in the original sedimentary rocks have been destroyed.

Radiometric dating has provided a partial solution to the troublesome task of dating and correlating Precambrian rocks. But untangling the complex Precambrian record still remains a daunting task.

DIFFICULTIES IN DATING THE GEOLOGIC TIME SCALE

Although reasonably accurate numeric dates have been worked out for the periods of the geologic time scale (Figure 8.12), the task has not been easy: The main reason is that not all rocks can be dated by radiometric methods. Recall that for a radiometric date to be useful, all the minerals in the rock must have formed at about the same time. For this reason, radioactive isotopes can be used to determine when minerals in an igneous rock crystallized and when pressure and heat created new minerals in a metamorphic rock.

However, samples of sedimentary rock can only rarely be dated directly by radiometric means. Although a detrital sedimentary rock can include particles that contain radioactive isotopes, the rock's age cannot be accurately determined because the grains composing the rock are not the same age as the rock in which they occur. Rather, the sediments have been weathered from rocks of diverse ages. To date sedimentary rocks, the strata are commonly related to datable igneous masses, as in Figure 8.13. This shows the necessity of combining laboratory dating methods with field observations of rocks.

Radiometric dates obtained from metamorphic rocks can also be difficult to interpret, because the age of a particular mineral in a metamorphic rock does not necessarily represent the time when the rock initially formed. Instead, the date might indicate any one of a number of subsequent metamorphic phases in which the clock may have been reset.

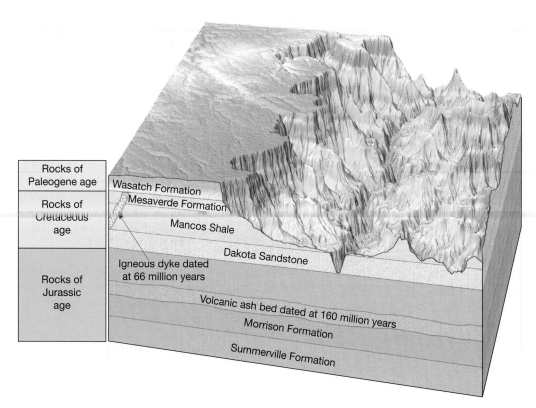

Figure 8.13 Numeric dates for sedimentary layers are usually determined by examining their relationship to igneous rocks. Thus the Morrison and Summerville formations, dated as Jurassic on the basis of their fossils, must be older than 16 million years; the Mesaverde Formation, older than 66 million years; and the Wasatch Formation, younger than 66 million years. (U.S. Geological Survey)

CHAPTER SUMMARY

- Earth history is put in sequence with *relative ages* (older or younger) and *numeric dates* (time in years). Relative dating uses *superposition* (youngest on top), *original horizontality*, *cross-cutting relations* (younger rocks cut older), and *inclusions* (rock containing inclusion is younger).

- *Unconformities* are gaps in the rock record: *angular unconformity* (flat rocks over tilted), *disconformities* (parallel strata), and *nonconformities* (sedimentary on older igneous/metamorphic rocks).

- *Correlation* matches rocks in different areas based on fossil succession (*index fossils*) and physical rock features.

- *Parent radioactive isotopes* decay to stable *daughter products*. *Half-life* is how long the parent decays until only half of it remains; with parent/daughter ratio, it is used to calculate the age of a rock.

- The *geologic time scale* presents the oldest event at the bottom and youngest at the top. It is divided into eons: Hadean, Archean, Proterozoic, Phanerozoic. The Phanerozoic Eon is subdivided into eras: Paleozoic, Mesozoic, Cenozoic. Geologists assign ages to undatable sedimentary rocks by relating them to datable igneous bodies.

REVIEW QUESTIONS

1. Distinguish between numeric and relative dating.

2. What is the law of superposition? How are cross-cutting relations used in relative dating?

3. If sedimentary layers (beds) are steeply inclined in an exposure (outcrop) of rock, what principle allows you to assume that the beds were tilted after they were deposited?

4. Consider an outcrop in which a mass of granite is observed to be in direct contact with a layer of sandstone. Using a principle described in this chapter, explain how you can determine whether the sandstone was deposited on top of the granite, or whether the granite was intruded from below after the sandstone was deposited.

5. Distinguish among angular unconformity, disconformity, and nonconformity.

6. What is meant by the term *correlation*, and why are fossils such powerful tools in correlating strata over great distances?

7. Why is radiometric dating the most reliable method of dating the geologic past in an absolute sense (i.e., on the basis of years)?

8. How are epochs, periods, eras, and eons related to one another within the subdivided framework of the geologic time scale?

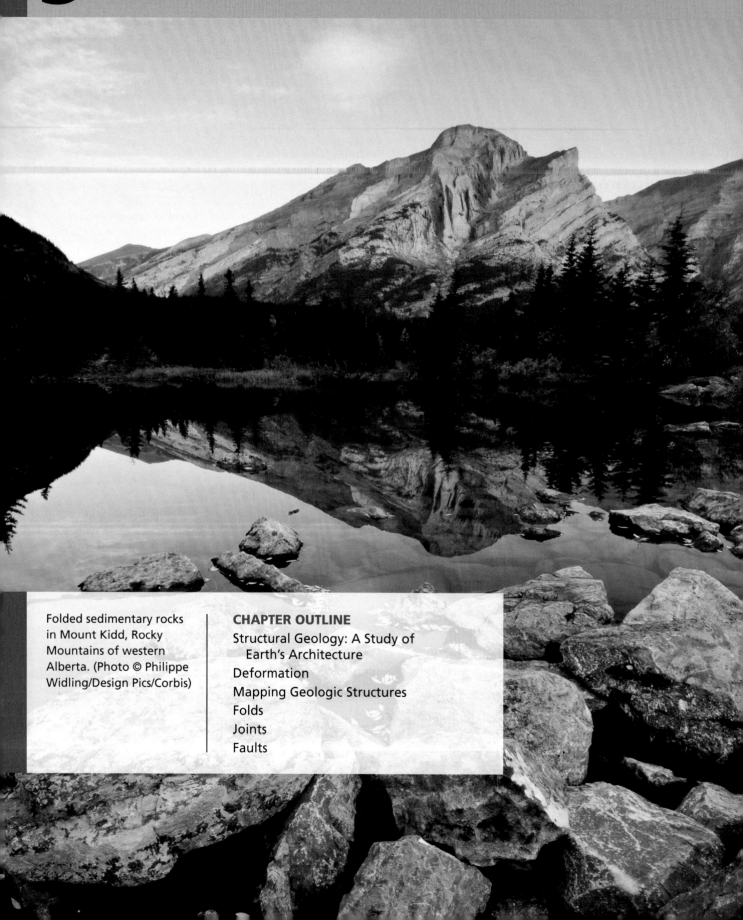

9

CRUSTAL DEFORMATION

Folded sedimentary rocks in Mount Kidd, Rocky Mountains of western Alberta. (Photo © Philippe Widling/Design Pics/Corbis)

CHAPTER OUTLINE

Tectonic forces deform rocks in the crust. Evidence demonstrating the operation of enormous forces within Earth includes thousands of kilometres of rock layers that are bent, contorted, overturned, and sometimes riddled with fractures (Figure 9.1). In the Canadian Rockies, for example, some rock units have been thrust for dozens of kilometres over other layers. On a smaller scale, crustal movements of a few metres occur along faults during major earthquakes. In addition, rifting (spreading) and extension of the crust produce elongate depressions; over long spans of geologic time, they create ocean basins.

STRUCTURAL GEOLOGY: A STUDY OF EARTH'S ARCHITECTURE

The results of tectonic activity are strikingly apparent in Earth's major mountain belts (see chapter opening photo). Here, rocks containing fossils of marine organisms can be found thousands of metres above sea level, and massive rock units show evidence of having been intensely fractured and folded, as though they were made of putty. Even in the stable interiors of the continents, rocks reveal a history of deformation that shows they have been uplifted from much deeper levels in the crust.

Structural geologists study the architecture of Earth's crust and the influence of deformation on that architecture. By studying the orientations of faults and folds, as well as small-scale features of deformed rocks, structural geologists can often reconstruct the original geologic setting and the nature of the forces that generated these rock structures. In this way, the complex events of Earth's geologic history are revealed.

An understanding of rock structures is not only important in deciphering Earth's history, but it is also basic to our economic well-being. For example, many occurrences of oil and natural gas are associated with geologic structures that act to trap these fluids in valuable "reservoirs" (see Chapter 20).

Furthermore, rock fractures are sites of hydrothermal mineralization, which means they can be

Figure 9.1   Uplifted and folded sedimentary strata in the Kananaskis area of Alberta. These layers of rock, originally deposited in horizontal beds, have been folded as a result of the collision between the North American and Juan de Fuca lithospheric plates.
(Photo by S.R. Hicock)

sites of metallic ore deposits. Moreover, the orientation of fracture surfaces, which represent zones of weakness in rocks, must be considered when selecting sites for major construction projects, such as bridges, hydroelectric dams, and nuclear power plants. In short, a working knowledge of rock structures is essential to our modern way of life.

In this chapter we will examine the forces that deform rock, as well as the structures that result. The basic geologic structures associated with deformation are folds, joints, faults, and foliation (including rock cleavage). Because rock cleavage and foliation were examined in Chapter 7, this chapter will be devoted to the remaining rock structures and the tectonic forces that produce them.

DEFORMATION

Every body of rock, no matter how strong, has a limit beyond which it will fracture or flow. **Deformation** (*de* = out, *forma* = form) is a general term that refers to all changes in the original form (like that in Figure 9.2A) or size of a rock body. Deformation can also produce changes in the location and orientation of rock. Most crustal deformation occurs along or near plate margins. Recall from Chapter 1 that the lithosphere consists of large segments (plates) that move relative to one another. Plate motions and the interactions along plate boundaries generate tectonic forces that cause rock units to deform.

Force, Stress, and Strain

Force is any influence that tends to put stationary objects in motion or change the motions of moving bodies. From everyday experience, you know that if a door is stuck (stationary), you apply force to open it (put it in motion).

To describe the forces that deform rocks, structural geologists use the term **stress**—the amount of force applied to a given area. The magnitude of stress is not simply a function of the amount of force applied; it also relates to the area on which the force acts. For example, if you are walking barefoot on a hard, flat surface, the force (weight) of your body is distributed across your entire foot, so the stress acting on any one point of your foot is low. However, if you step on a small pointed rock (ouch!), the stress concentration at a single point on your foot will be high. Thus, you can think of stress as a measure of how concentrated the force is. As discussed in Chapter 7, stress can be applied uniformly from all directions (uniform stress) or non-uniformly (differential stress from directed pressure).

Whereas stress is the force applied to a given area, **strain** is the visible result of that force. *Strained bodies do not retain their original configuration during deformation.* Figure 9.1 illustrates the strain (deformation) exhibited by rock units near Canmore, Alberta.

Types of Stress

When stress is applied unequally from different directions, it is termed **differential stress**. Differential stress that shortens a rock body is known as **compressional** (*com* = together, *premere* = to press) **stress**. Compressional stresses associated with plate collisions tend to shorten and thicken Earth's crust by folding and faulting (Figure 9.2B). Recall from our discussion of metamorphic rocks that compressional stress is more concentrated at places where mineral grains are in contact, causing mineral matter to migrate from areas of high stress to areas of low stress (see Figure 7.6). As a result, the mineral grains (and the rock unit) tend to shorten in the direction parallel to maximum stress and elongate perpendicular to the direction of greatest stress.

When stress tends to elongate or pull apart a rock unit, it is known as **tensional** (*tendere* = to stretch) **stress** (Figure 9.2C). Where plates are being rifted apart (divergent plate boundaries), tensional stresses tend to lengthen those rock bodies located in the upper crust by displacement along faults. At depth, however, displacement is accomplished by a type of puttylike flow.

Differential stress can also cause rock to **shear** (Figure 9.2D). Shearing is similar to the slippage that occurs between individual playing cards when the top of the deck is moved relative to the bottom (Figure 9.3). In near-surface environments, shearing often occurs on closely spaced parallel surfaces of weakness, such as bedding planes, foliation, and microfaults. Further, at transform fault boundaries, shearing stresses produce large-scale offsets along major fault zones. By contrast, at great depths where temperatures and confining pressures are high, shearing is accomplished by solid-state flow.

How Rocks Deform

When rocks are subjected to stresses greater than their own strength, they begin to deform, usually by flowing (folding) or fracturing (faulting) (Figure 9.4). It is easy to visualize how rocks break, because we normally think of them as being brittle. But how can rock units be *bent* into intricate folds without being broken during the process? To answer this question, structural geologists

A Undeformed strata (rock body)

CUBE
OF
ROCK

B Horizontal compressional stress causes rock bodies
to shorten horizontally and thicken vertically.

COMPRESSION

C Horizontal tensional stress causes rock bodies
to lengthen horizontally and thin vertically.

TENSION

D Shear stress causes displacements
along fault zones or by ductile flow.

SHEAR

Figure 9.2   Deformation of Earth's crust caused by tectonic forces and associated
stresses resulting from the movement of lithospheric plates. **A.** Strata before
deformation. **B.** Compressional stresses associated with plate collisions tend to shorten
and thicken Earth's crust by folding and faulting. **C.** Tensional stresses at divergent plate
boundaries tend to lengthen rock bodies by displacement along faults in the upper
crust and ductile flow at depth. **D.** Shear stresses at transform plate boundaries tend to
produce offsets along fault zones.

The right side of the diagram illustrates the deformation (strain) of a cube of
rock in response to the differential stresses illustrated in corresponding diagrams to
the left.

A Deck of playing cards

B Shearing occurs when hand pushes top of deck

Figure 9.3 Illustration of shearing and the resulting deformation (strain). **A.** An ordinary deck of playing cards with a circle embossed on its side. **B.** By sliding the top of the deck relative to the bottom, we can illustrate the type of shearing that commonly occurs along closely spaced planes of weakness in rocks. Notice that the circle becomes an ellipse, which can be used to measure the amount and type of strain. Additional displacement (shearing) of the cards would result in further strain and would be indicated by a change in the shape of the ellipse.

performed laboratory experiments in which rocks were subjected to differential stress under conditions that simulated those existing at various depths within the crust (Figure 9.5).

Although each rock type deforms somewhat differently, the general characteristics of rock deformation were determined from these experiments. When stress is gradually applied, rocks first respond by deforming elastically. Changes that result from *elastic deformation* are recoverable; that is, like a rubber band, the rock will return to nearly its original size and shape when the stress is removed.

TEMPERATURE AND CONFINING PRESSURE Rocks near the surface, where temperatures and confining pressures are low, tend to behave like a brittle solid and fracture once their strength is exceeded. This type of deformation is called **brittle** (*bryttian* = to shatter) **failure** or **brittle deformation**. From our everyday experience, we know that glass objects, wooden pencils, china plates, and even our bones exhibit brittle failure once their strength is surpassed. By contrast, at depth, where temperatures and confining pressures are high, rocks exhibit *ductile* behaviour. **Ductile deformation** is a type of solid-state flow that produces a change in the size and shape of an object without fracturing. Ordinary objects that display ductile behaviour include modelling clay, beeswax, caramel candy, and most metals. Ductile deformation of a rock—strongly aided by high temperature and high confining pressure—is somewhat similar to the deformation of a penny flattened by a train (Figure 9.5). One way this type of solid-state flow is accomplished within a rock is by gradual slippage and recrystallization along planes of weakness within the crystal lattice of mineral grains (see Figure 7.6B).

Figure 9.4 Deformed sedimentary strata in the Rocky Mountains of northern British Columbia. (Photo © Eye Ubiquitous/Alamy)

Figure 9.5 Ductile deformation of pennies flattened by a train.
(Photo by A. Houben/Shutterstock

Figure 9.6 Folded gneiss in Ontario exhibiting the results of ductile behaviour. These rocks were deformed at great depth and were subsequently exposed at the surface. (Photo © Bill Brooks/Alamy)

This microscopic form of gradual solid-state flow involves slippage that disrupts the crystal lattice and immediate re-crystallization that repairs the structure. Rocks that display evidence of ductile flow usually were deformed at great depth and can exhibit contorted folds that give the impression that the strength of the rock was akin to soft putty (Figure 9.6).

ROCK TYPE Crystalline rocks composed of minerals that have strong internal molecular bonds tend to fail by brittle fracture. By contrast, sedimentary rocks that are weakly cemented, or metamorphic rocks that contain zones of weakness, such as foliation, are more susceptible to ductile flow. Rocks that are weak and thus most likely to behave in a ductile manner when subjected to differential stress include rock salt, gypsum, and shale. Limestone, schist, and marble are of intermediate strength. Rock salt is so weak that it deforms under small amounts of differential stress and rises like stone pillars through beds of sediment that lie in and around the Gulf of Mexico, and off the east coast of Canada (see Chapter 20).

Perhaps the weakest naturally occurring solid to exhibit ductile flow on a large scale is glacial ice. By comparison, quartzite, granite, and basalt are strong and brittle. In a near-surface environment, strong, brittle rocks will fail by fracturing when subjected to stresses that exceed their strength.

TIME One key factor that researchers are unable to duplicate in the laboratory is how rocks respond to small amounts of stress applied over long spans of *geologic time*. However, everyday experience reveals that marble benches sag under their own weight over a hundred years or so, and wooden bookshelves can bend after being loaded with books for a relatively short time. Thus forces that are unable to deform rock when initially applied may cause rock to flow if the stress is maintained over an extended time.

The processes by which rocks deform occur along a continuum that ranges from pure brittle fracture at one end to ductile flow at the other. In fact the elegant folds and flow patterns we see in deformed rocks are generally achieved by the combined effect of distortion, sliding, and rotation of the individual grains that make up a rock. Finally, this distortion and reorganization of mineral grains takes place in rock that is essentially solid.

MAPPING GEOLOGIC STRUCTURES

The processes of deformation generate features at many different scales. At one extreme are Earth's major mountain systems. At the other extreme, highly localized stresses create minor fractures in bedrock. All of these phenomena are referred to as **rock structures**. Before beginning our discussion of rock structures, let us examine the way geologists describe and map them.

When conducting a study of a region, a geologist identifies and describes the dominant structures. A structure is commonly so large that only a small portion is visible from any particular vantage point. In many situations, most of the bedrock is concealed by vegetation or by recent sedimentation. Consequently, the reconstruction must be done by using data gathered from a limited number of outcrops. Despite such difficulties, a number of mapping techniques enable geologists to reconstruct the orientation and shape of the existing structures. In recent years this work has been aided by advances in aerial photography, satellite and GIS (geographic information system) imagery, and the extensive development of the global positioning system (GPS)

for many geologic applications. In addition, seismic reflection profiling (see Box 10.4) and drill holes provide data on the composition and structure of rocks that lie at depth.

Geologic mapping is most easily accomplished where sedimentary strata are exposed. This is because sediments are usually deposited in horizontal layers. If the sedimentary rock layers are still horizontal, this tells geologists that the area is probably undisturbed structurally. But if strata are inclined, bent, or broken, this indicates deformation occurred following deposition.

Strike and Dip

Geologists use measurements called strike and dip to help determine the orientation or attitude of a rock layer, joint, or fault surface (Figure 9.7). By knowing the strike and dip of rocks at the surface, geologists can predict the nature and structure of rock units

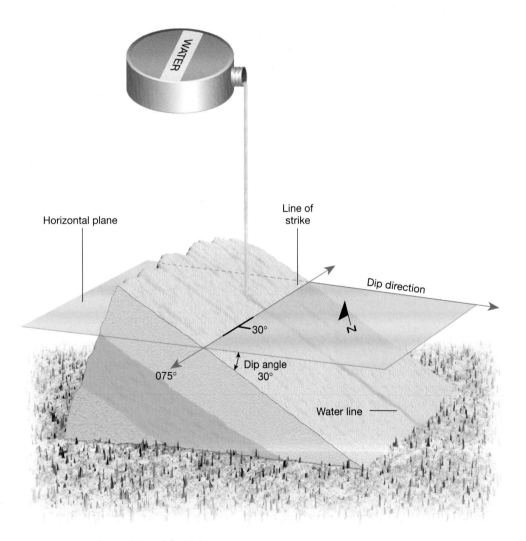

Figure 9.7 Strike and dip of a rock layer.

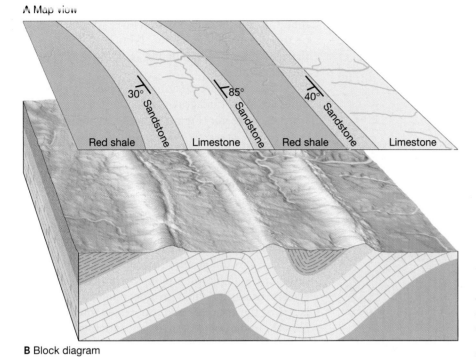

A Map view

Red shale   Sandstone   Limestone   Sandstone   Red shale   Sandstone   Limestone

30°   85°   40°

B Block diagram

Figure 9.8 By establishing the strike and dip of outcropping sedimentary beds on a map (**A**) geologists can infer the orientation of the structure below ground (**B**).

and faults that are hidden beneath the surface, beyond their view.

Strike is the compass direction of the line produced by the intersection of an inclined rock layer or fault with a horizontal plane (Figure 9.7). The strike, or compass bearing, is generally expressed in azimuth form, as a three-digit angle clockwise from north. For example, 010° means the line of strike is 10° clockwise from north. The strike of the rock units illustrated in Figure 9.7 is approximately 075°.

Dip is the angle of inclination of the surface of a rock unit or fault measured from a horizontal plane. In Figure 9.7 the dip angle of the rock layer is 30°. A good way to visualize dip is to imagine that water will always run down the rock surface parallel to the dip direction, which will always be at a 90° angle to the strike.

In the field, geologists measure the strike and dip of sedimentary rocks at as many outcrops as practical. These data are then plotted on a topographic map or an aerial photograph, along with a colour-coded description of the rock. From the orientation of the strata, an inferred orientation and shape of the structure can be established, as shown in Figure 9.8. By using this information, the geologist can reconstruct the pre-erosional structures and begin to interpret the region's geologic history.

FOLDS

During mountain building, flat-lying sedimentary and volcanic rocks are often bent into a series of wavelike undulations called **folds**. Folds in sedimentary strata are much like those that would form if you were to hold the ends of a sheet of paper and then push them together. Some folds are broad flexures in which rock units hundreds of metres thick have been slightly warped. Others are very tight microscopic structures found in metamorphic rocks. However, most folds result from compressional stresses that shorten and thicken the crust. Occasionally, folds are found singly, but most often they occur as a series of undulations.

Figure 9.9 shows the parts of a fold. The two sides are called *limbs*. A line drawn along the crest of the fold is termed the *axis* of the fold. In some folds, as in Figure 9.9A, the axis is horizontal, or parallel to the surface. However, in more complex folding, the fold axis is often inclined at an angle known as the *plunge* (Figure 9.9B). Further, the *axial plane* is an imaginary surface that divides a fold as symmetrically as possible.

Types of Folds

The two most common types of folds are called anticlines and synclines (Figure 9.10). An **anticline** is most commonly formed by the up-folding, or

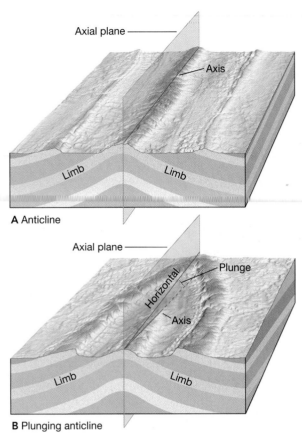

A Anticline

B Plunging anticline

Figure 9.9 Idealized sketches illustrating the features associated with symmetrical folds. The axis of the fold in **A** is horizontal, whereas the axis of the fold in **B** is plunging.

arching, of rock layers (Figure 9.9).* Anticlines are sometimes spectacularly displayed where highways

---

*By strict definition, an anticline is a structure in which the oldest strata are found in the centre of the structure. This most typically occurs when strata are up-folded. Further, a syncline is strictly defined as a structure in which the youngest strata are found in the centre. This occurs most commonly when strata are down-folded.

have been cut through deformed strata. Commonly found in association with anticlines are down-folds, or troughs, called **synclines**. Notice in Figure 9.11 that the limb of an anticline is also a limb of the adjacent syncline.

Basic folds are described as *symmetric* when the limbs are mirror images of each other and *asymmetric* when they are not (Figure 9.11). An asymmetric fold is said to be *overturned* if one limb is tilted beyond the vertical (see Figure 9.10). An overturned fold can also lie on its side so that the axial plane of the fold would actually be horizontal. These *recumbent* folds are common in mountainous regions, such as the Alps of Europe.

The ends of folds die out much like the wrinkles in cloth. Some folds plunge as the axis of the fold descends into the ground (Figure 9.12). Figure 9.13 shows an example of a plunging anticline and the pattern produced when erosion removes the upper layers of the structure and exposes its interior. Note that the outcrop pattern of an anticline points in the direction it is plunging, whereas the opposite is true for a syncline. The topography that results when erosional forces attack folded sedimentary strata is schematically illustrated in Figures 9.10 and 9.12.

Although we have separated our discussion of folds and faults, in the real world, folds are generally intimately coupled with faults. Examples of this close association are broad regional features called monoclines. Particularly prominent features of the Colorado Plateau, **monoclines** (*mono* = one, *kleinen* = incline) are large, step-like folds in otherwise horizontal sedimentary strata (Figure 9.14). These folds appear to be the result of the reactivation of steeply dipping fault zones located in basement rocks beneath the plateau. As large blocks of basement rock were displaced upward along ancient faults, the comparatively ductile sedimentary strata above responded by folding. On the Colorado Plateau,

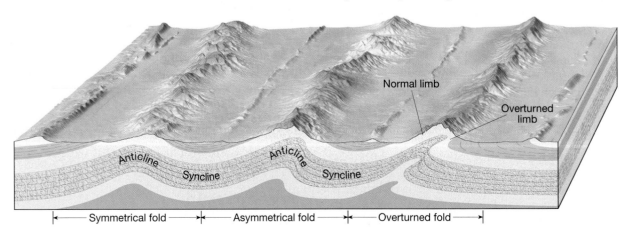

Figure 9.10 Block diagram of principal types of folded strata. The up-folded, or arched, structures are anticlines. The down-folds, or troughs, are synclines. Notice that the limb of an anticline is also the limb of the adjacent syncline.

Figure 9.11
Syncline (left) and
anticline (right) share
a common limb.
(Photo by
E. J. Tarbuck)

monoclines display a narrow zone of steeply inclined beds that flatten out to form the uppermost layers of large elevated areas, including the San Rafael Swell (Figure 9.14). Displacement along these reactivated faults commonly exceeds 1 kilometre.

Domes and Basins

Broad up-warps in basement rock can deform the overlying cover of sedimentary strata and generate large folds. When this up-warping produces a

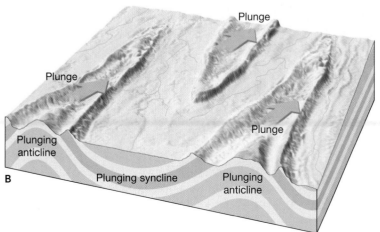

Figure 9.12   Plunging folds. **A.** Idealized view of plunging folds in which a horizontal surface has been added. **B.** View of plunging folds as they might appear after extensive erosion. Notice that in a plunging anticline the outcrop pattern "points" in the direction of the plunge, while the opposite is true of plunging synclines.

Figure 9.13 Sheep Mountain, a doubly plunging anticline. Note that erosion has cut the flanking sedimentary beds into low ridges that make Vs pointing in the directions of plunge.
(Photo by John S. Shelton)

circular or elongate structure, the feature is called a **dome** (Figure 9.15A). Down-warped structures having a similar shape are termed **basins** (Figure 9.15B).

The Black Hills area of western South Dakota is a large structural dome thought to be caused by up-warping. Here erosion has stripped away the highest portions of the up-warped sedimentary beds, exposing older igneous and metamorphic rocks in the centre (Figure 9.16). Remnants of these once continuous sedimentary layers surround, and dip away from, the central crystalline core of this structure.

Domes can also be formed by the intrusion of magma (laccoliths), as shown in Figure 3.27B. In addition, the upward migration of salt formations can produce domes that are common in the Gulf of Mexico.

Several large basins exist in North America. The Michigan (Figure 9.17) and Williston basins have very gently sloping beds similar to saucers. These basins are thought to be the result of lithospheric thinning or plume activity that caused the crust to subside (see Figure 13.16). A few structural basins may have been the result of giant asteroid impacts (e.g., Sudbury, Ontario, and Manicouagan, Quebec).

Because large basins contain sedimentary beds sloping at such low angles, they are usually identified by the age of the rocks composing them. The youngest rocks are found near the centre, and the oldest rocks are at the flanks. This is just the opposite order of a dome, such as the Black Hills, where the oldest rocks form the core.

Figure 9.14 Monocline. **A.** The San Rafael monocline, Utah. **B.** Monocline consisting of bent sedimentary beds that were deformed by faulting in the bedrock below.
(Photo A © SCPhotos/Alamy)

Figure 9.15 Gentle up-warping and down-warping of crustal rocks produce domes (**A**) and basins (**B**). Erosion of these structures results in an outcrop pattern that is roughly circular or elliptical.

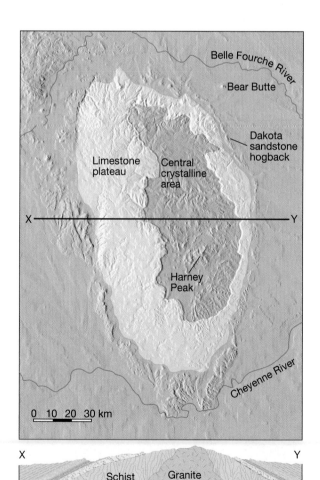

Figure 9.16 The Black Hills of South Dakota, a large dome with resistant igneous and metamorphic rocks exposed in the core. The lower figure shows the cross-section between X and Y.

JOINTS

Among the most common rock structures resulting from brittle deformation are fractures called **joints** along which no appreciable displacement has occurred. Although some joints have a random orientation, most occur in roughly parallel groups (see Figure 5.6).

Chapter 4 introduced *columnar joints* that form when igneous rocks cool and develop shrinkage fractures that produce elongate, pillar-like columns (Figures 3.30 and 9.18). Also recall that sheeting produces a pattern of gently curved joints that develop more or less parallel to the surface of large exposed igneous bodies, such as batholiths (e.g., Figures 5.4 and 5.5).

Most joints are produced when rocks in the outermost crust are deformed. Here tensional and shearing stresses cause the rock to fail by brittle fracture. For example, when folding occurs, rocks situated at the axes of the folds are elongated and pulled apart to produce tensional joints. Extensive joint patterns can also develop in response to relatively subtle, and often barely perceptible, regional up-warping and down-warping of the crust.

Many rocks are broken by two or even three sets of intersecting joints that slice the rock into numerous regularly shaped blocks where chemical weathering can occur. In many areas groundwater movement and dissolution are controlled by the joint pattern (Figure 9.19). Moreover, a system of joints can influence the direction that stream

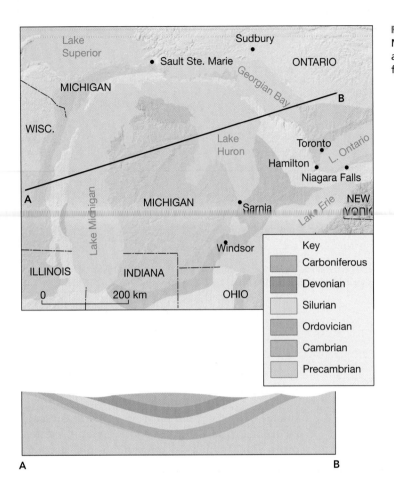

Figure 9.17   The bedrock geology of the Michigan Basin. Notice that the youngest rocks are centrally located, while the oldest beds flank this structure.

courses follow (see Chapter 15). Furthermore, some of the world's largest and most important mineral deposits were emplaced along joint systems. Hydrothermal solutions (mineralizing fluids) can migrate into fractured host rocks and precipitate economically important amounts of copper, silver, gold, zinc, lead, and uranium (see Chapter 20).

Further, highly jointed rocks present a risk to the construction of engineering projects, including highways and dams. On June 5, 1976, 14 lives were lost and nearly US$1 billion in property damage

Figure 9.18   This felsic igneous intrusion exposed on the Baie Verte Peninsula of Newfoundland and Labrador exhibits columnar joints.
(Photo courtesy of R. W. Hodder)

Figure 9.19   These Silurian dolostones exposed in a road cut south of Meaford, Ontario, have broken along joints to produce sheer vertical surfaces.
(Photo by C. Tsujita)

occurred when the Teton Dam in Idaho failed. This earthen dam was constructed of very erodible clays and silts and was situated on highly fractured volcanic rocks. Although attempts were made to fill the voids in the jointed rock, water gradually penetrated the subsurface fractures and undermined the dam's foundation. Eventually, the moving water cut a tunnel into the clays and silts. Within minutes the dam failed, sending a 20-metre-high wall of water down the Teton and Snake rivers.

FAULTS

Faults are fractures in the crust along which displacement has taken place. Occasionally, small faults can be recognized in road cuts where sedimentary beds have been offset a few metres, as shown in Figure 9.20. Faults of this scale usually occur as single discrete breaks. By contrast, large faults, like the San Andreas Fault in California, have displacements of hundreds of kilometres and consist of many interconnecting fault surfaces (see Box 9.1). These *fault zones* can be several kilometres wide and are often easier to identify from high-altitude photographs than at ground level.

Sudden movements along faults cause most earthquakes (see Chapter 10). However, many faults are inactive remnants of past deformation. Along active faults, rock is often broken and pulverized as crustal blocks on opposite sides of a fault slip past one another. The loosely coherent, clayey material that results from this activity is called *fault gouge*. On some fault surfaces the rocks become highly polished and striated, or grooved, as the crustal blocks slide past one another. These polished, streaked, and striated surfaces with tiny straight parallel ridges, called *slickensides* (*slicken* = smooth), provide geologists with evidence for the direction of the most recent displacement along the fault. Geologists classify faults by these relative movements, which can be predominantly horizontal, vertical, or oblique.

Dip-Slip Faults

Faults in which the movement is primarily parallel to the dip (or inclination) of the fault surface are called **dip-slip faults.** Up and down displacements along dip-slip faults can produce long, low cliffs called **fault scarps** (*scarpe* = a slope). Fault scarps (e.g., Figure 9.21) are produced by displacements that generate earthquakes.

It is common practice to call the rock surface immediately above the fault the *hanging wall* and the rock surface below it, the *footwall* (Figure 9.22). This

Figure 9.20 Faulting caused the displacement of these sedimentary beds. Beds on the left side of the fault have moved downward relative to those on the right side. (Photo by Dr. Morley Read/Shutterstock)

nomenclature arose from miners who excavated tunnels along fault zones containing ore deposits. The miners would walk on the rocks below the mineralized fault zone (the footwall) and hang their lanterns on the rocks above (the hanging wall).

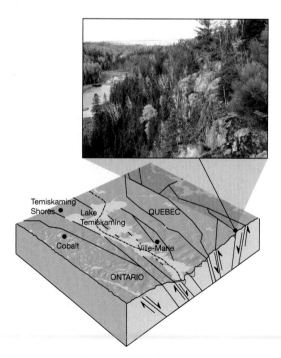

Figure 9.21 This sheer cliff represents the footwall of a normal dip-slip fault associated with a failed rift called the Lake Temiskaming Structural Zone. This ancient rift valley was formed in the latest Proterozoic to earliest Paleozoic time when the Iapetus Ocean—the precursor to the Atlantic Ocean—was being formed. (Photo by S. R. Hicock)

PEOPLE AND THE ENVIRONMENT
The San Andreas Fault System

The San Andreas, the best-known and largest fault system in North America, first attracted wide attention after the great 1906 San Francisco earthquake and fire. Following this devastating event, geologic studies demonstrated that a displacement of as much as 5 metres along the fault had accompanied the earthquake. It is now known that this dramatic event is just one of many thousands of earthquakes that have accompanied repeated movements along the San Andreas throughout its 29-million-year history.

Where is the San Andreas fault system located? As shown in Figure 9.A, it trends in a northwesterly direction for nearly 1300 kilometres through much of western California. At its southern end, the San Andreas connects with a spreading centre located

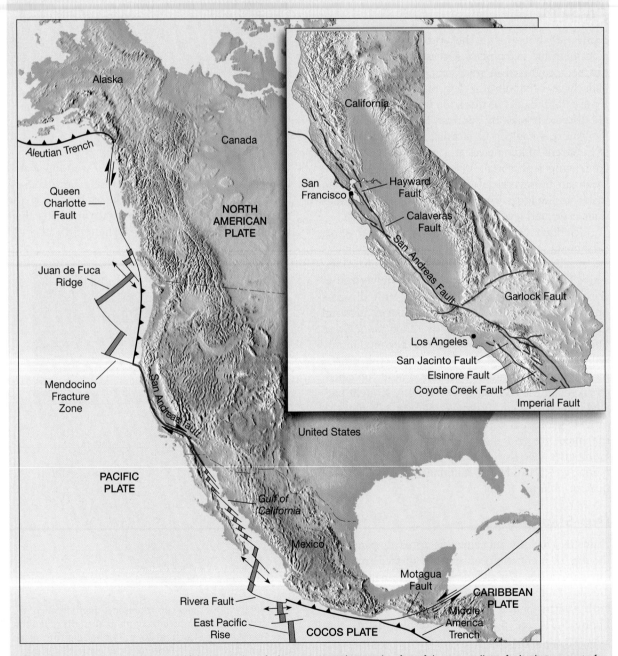

Figure 9.A Map showing the extent of the San Andreas fault system. **Inset** shows only a few of the many splinter faults that are part of this great fault system.

TABLE 9.A   Major Earthquakes on the San Andreas Fault System

Date	Location	Magnitude	Remarks
1812	Wrightwood, CA	7.0	Church of San Juan Capistrano collapsed, killing 40 worshippers
1812	Santa Barbara channel	7.0	Churches and other buildings wrecked in and around Santa Barbara
1838	San Francisco peninsula	7.0	At one time thought to have been comparable with the great earthquake of 1906
1857	Fort Tejon, CA	8.25	One of the greatest U.S. earthquakes; occurred near Los Angeles, then a city of 4000
1868	Hayward, CA	7.0	Rupture of the Hayward Fault caused extensive damage in San Francisco Bay area
1906	San Francisco, CA	8.25	The great San Francisco earthquake; as much as 80 percent of the damage caused by fire
1940	Imperial Valley	7.1	Displacement on the newly discovered Imperial Fault
1952	Kern County	7.7	Rupture of the White Wolf Fault; largest earthquake in California since 1906; did US$60 million in damage and killed 12 people
1971	San Fernando Valley	6.5	US$500 million in damage and 58 lives lost
1989	Santa Cruz Mountains	7.1	Loma Prieta earthquake; US$6 billion dollars in damage, 62 lives lost, and 3757 people injured
1994	Northridge (Los Angeles area)	6.9	More than US$15 billion in damage, 51 lives lost, and more than 5000 injured

in the Gulf of California. In the north, the fault enters the Pacific Ocean at Point Arena, where it is thought to continue its northwesterly trend, eventually joining the Mendocino Fracture Zone. In the central section, the San Andreas is relatively simple and straight. However, at its two extremities, several branches spread from the main trace, so that in some areas the fault zone is tens of kilometres in width.

Over much of its extent, a linear trough reveals the presence of the San Andreas Fault. When the system is viewed from the air, linear scars, offset stream channels, and elongate ponds mark the trace in a striking manner. On the ground, however, surface expressions of the faults are much more difficult to detect. Some of the most distinctive landforms include long, straight escarpments, narrow ridges, and sag ponds formed by the settling of blocks within the fault zone. Further, many stream channels characteristically bend sharply to the right where they cross the fault (Figure 9.B).

With the formulation of the theory of plate tectonics, geologists began to realize the significance of this great fault system. The San Andreas Fault is a transform boundary separating two lithospheric plates that move very slowly. The Pacific plate, located to the west, moves northwestward relative to the North American plate, causing earthquakes along the fault (Table 9.A).

The San Andreas is undoubtedly the most studied of any fault system in the world. Although many questions remain unanswered, geologists have learned that each fault segment exhibits somewhat different behaviour. Some portions of the San Andreas exhibit a slow creep with little noticeable seismic activity. Other segments regularly slip, producing small earthquakes, while still other segments seem to store elastic energy for hundreds of years and rupture in great earthquakes. This knowledge is useful when assigning earthquake hazard potential to a given segment of the fault zone.

Because of the great length and complexity of the San Andreas Fault, it is more appropriately referred to as a "fault system." This major fault system consists primarily of the San Andreas Fault and several major branches, including the Hayward and Calaveras

Figure 9.B Aerial view showing offset stream channels across the San Andreas Fault on the Carrizo Plain in California. (Photo © Aurora Photos/Alamy)

faults of central California and the San Jacinto and Elsinore faults of southern California (see Figure 9.A). These major segments, plus a vast number of smaller faults that include the Imperial Fault, San Fernando Fault, and the Santa Monica Fault, collectively accommodate the relative motion between the North American and Pacific plates.

Blocks on opposite sides of the San Andreas Fault move horizontally in opposite directions, such that if a person stood on one side of the fault, the block on the opposite side would appear to move to the right when slippage occurred. This type of displacement is known as **right-lateral strike-slip** by geologists (see Figure 9.B).

Ever since the great San Francisco earthquake of 1906, when as much as five metres of displacement occurred, geologists have attempted to establish the cumulative displacement along this fault over its 29-million-year history. By matching rock units across the fault, geologists have determined that the total accumulated displacement from earthquakes and creep exceeds 560 kilometres, for an average rate of just less than 2 centimetres per year.

Two major types of dip-slip faults are **normal faults** and **reverse faults**. In addition, when a reverse fault has an angle of dip of less than 45°, it is called a **thrust fault**.

NORMAL FAULTS Dip-slip faults are classified as normal faults when the hanging wall block moves down relative to the footwall block (Figure 9.23). Most normal faults have steep dips of about 60° and tend to flatten out with depth. Because of the downward motion of the hanging wall, normal faults accommodate lengthening, or extension, and thinning of the crust.

Normal faulting is prevalent at spreading centres where plate divergence occurs. Here, a central block called a **graben** (*graben* = ditch) is bounded by normal faults and drops as the plates separate (Figure 9.24). These grabens produce an elongate valley bounded by relatively uplifted structures called **horsts**. The Rift Valley of East Africa is made up of several large grabens, above which tilted horsts produce a linear mountainous topography. This valley, nearly 6000 kilometres long, contains the excavation sites of some of the earliest human fossils. Examples of inactive rift valleys include the Rhine Valley in Germany and the Triassic-age grabens of the eastern United States. Even larger inactive normal fault systems are the rifted continental margins, such as along the east coasts of the Americas and the west coasts of Europe and Africa.

Normal faults represent tensional stresses that pull the crust apart. This "pulling apart" can be accomplished either by uplifting that causes the surfaces to stretch and break (see Chapter 13) or by diverging horizontal forces.

REVERSE AND THRUST FAULTS Reverse faults and thrust faults (dip <45°) are dip-slip faults where the hanging wall block moves up relative to the footwall block (Figure 9.25). Because the hanging wall block moves up and over the footwall block, reverse and thrust faults accommodate shortening of the crust.

Most high-angle reverse faults are small and accommodate local displacements in regions dominated by other types of faulting. Thrust faults exhibit displacement ranging from millimetres to tens of kilometres.

Thrust faulting is most pronounced in subduction zones and other convergent boundaries where plates are colliding and compressional forces dominate. In these settings, crustal blocks are displaced *toward* one another, resulting in crustal thickening and shortening.

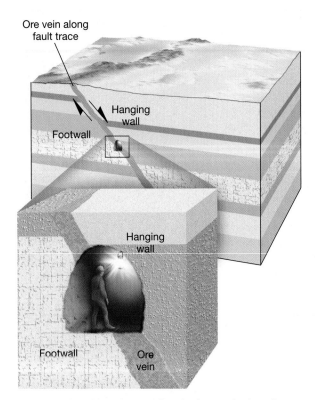

Figure 9.22 The rock immediately above a fault surface is the *hanging wall*, and that below is called the *footwall*. These names came from miners who excavated ore along fault zones. The miners hung their lanterns on the rocks above the fault trace (hanging wall) and walked on the rocks below the fault trace (footwall).

Figure 9.23 Block diagrams illustrating a normal fault. **A.** Rock strata before faulting. **B.** The relative movement of displaced blocks. Displacement can continue in a fault-block mountain range over millions of years and consist of many widely spaced episodes of faulting. **C.** How erosion might alter the up-faulted block. **D.** Eventually the period of deformation ends and erosion becomes the dominant geologic process.

In mountainous regions, such as the Alps, Northern Rockies, Himalayas, and Appalachians, thrust faults have displaced strata as far as 50 kilometres over adjacent rock units. The result of this large-scale movement is that older strata end up overlying younger rocks. A classic site of thrust faulting occurs in the Crowsnest Pass of Alberta (Figure 9.26). Here, mountain peaks that provide the area's majestic scenery have been carved from Paleozoic rocks that were displaced over much younger Cretaceous strata. At the eastern edge of the Crowsnest Pass is an outlying peak called Crowsnest Mountain. This structure is an isolated remnant of the thrust sheet that was severed by the erosional forces of glacial ice and running water. An isolated block, such as Crowsnest Mountain, is called a **klippe** (*klippe* = cliff) (Figure 9.27).

Strike-Slip Faults

Faults in which the dominant displacement is horizontal and parallel to the strike of the fault surface are called **strike-slip faults**. Many strike-slip faults produce a linear trace that is visible

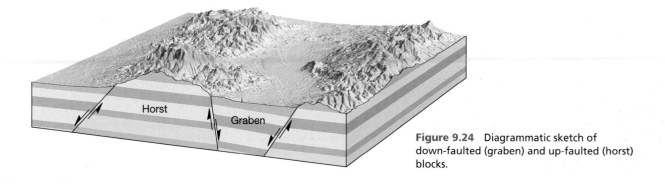

Figure 9.24 Diagrammatic sketch of down-faulted (graben) and up-faulted (horst) blocks.

Figure 9.25   Block diagram showing the relative movement along a reverse fault.

over a great distance (Figure 9.28). Rather than a single fracture, large strike-slip faults consist of a zone of roughly parallel fractures, up to several kilometres wide. The most recent movement, however, is often along a strand only a few metres wide, which may offset features, such as stream channels (Figures 9.29 and 9.B). Furthermore, crushed and broken rocks produced during faulting are more easily eroded, often producing linear valleys or troughs that mark the locations of strike-slip faults.

The earliest scientific records of strike-slip faulting were made following surface ruptures that produced large earthquakes. One of the most noteworthy of these was the great San Francisco earthquake of 1906. During this strong earthquake, structures such as fences that were built across the San Andreas Fault were displaced by as much as 4.7 metres. Because the movement along the San Andreas causes the crustal block on the opposite side of the fault to move to the right as you face the fault, it is called a *right-lateral* strike-slip fault. The Great Glen Fault in Scotland is a well-known example of a *left-lateral* strike-slip fault, which exhibits the opposite sense of displacement. The total displacement along the Great Glen Fault is estimated to exceed 100 kilometres. Also associated with this fault trace are numerous lakes, including Loch Ness, the home of the legendary monster.

Many major strike-slip faults cut through the lithosphere and accommodate motion between two large lithospheric plates. In Chapter 1 you

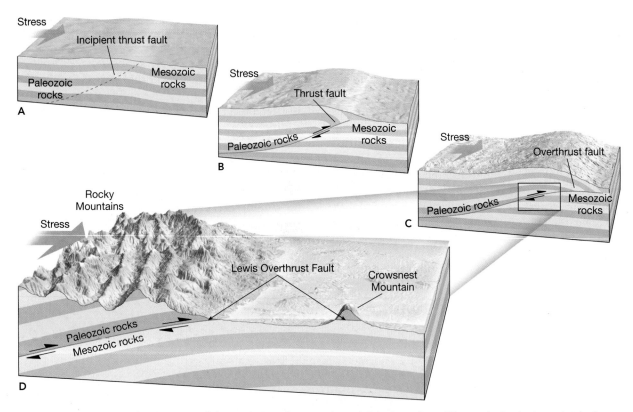

Figure 9.26   Idealized development of the Lewis Overthrust Fault near Crowsnest Pass, Alberta. **A.** Geologic setting before deformation. **B, C.** Large-scale movement along a thrust fault displaced Paleozoic rock over Mesozoic strata in the region of the Crowsnest Pass. **D.** Erosion by glacial ice and running water sculpted the thrust sheet into a majestic landscape and isolated remnants of the thrust sheet, such as Crowsnest Mountain.

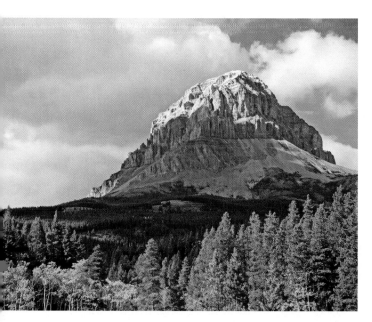

Figure 9.27 Crowsnest Mountain in the Crowsnest Pass area of southwest Alberta is a klippe.
(Photo © Kris Butler/Alamy)

Figure 9.28 Aerial view of strike-slip (right-lateral) fault in Southern Nevada.
(Photo by Marli Miller)

learned that this special kind of strike-slip fault is called a **transform** (*trans* = across, *forma* = form) **fault**. Numerous transform faults cut the oceanic lithosphere and link spreading oceanic ridges. Others accommodate displacement between continental plates that move horizontally with respect to each other. One of the best-known transform faults is California's San Andreas Fault (Box 9.1). This plate-bounding fault can be traced for about 950 kilometres from the Gulf of California to a point along the Pacific Coast north of San Francisco, where it continues out to sea. This movement has accommodated the northward displacement of southwest California and the Baja Peninsula of Mexico in relation to the remainder of North America. The nature of these important structures will be discussed in more detail in Chapter 12.

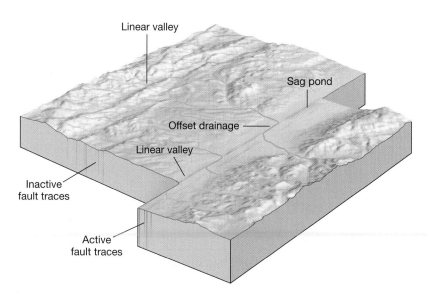

Linear valley

Sag pond

Offset drainage

Linear valley

Inactive
fault traces

Active
fault traces

Figure 9.29 Block diagram illustrating the features associated with strike-slip faults. Note how stream channels have been offset by fault movement. The faults in this diagram are right-lateral strike-slip faults.
(Based on R. L. Wesson and others)

CHAPTER SUMMARY

- Rocks *deform* under confining pressure (from all directions) or *differential stress* (*compressional* that squeezes or *tensional* that stretches). *Strain* is the result of stress.
- Rocks deform elastically (no damage if stress removed) then by ductile flow or fracture beyond their elastic limit. Strained rocks tend to undergo *brittle failure* near the surface and *ductile deformation* at depth.
- Rock strata or fault surfaces are measured using *strike* (azimuth of horizontal line on the surface) and *dip* (inclination of surface).
- Geologic structures include *folds* (formed due to buckling under compressional stress), *joints* (parallel fractures in rock without

displacement), and *faults* (fractures in rock with displacement).
- There are two main categories of faults: *dip-slip* (up and down) and *strike-slip* (sideways). Dip-slip faults are further classified as either normal (hanging wall moves down in response to tension) or reverse (hanging wall moves up in response to compression).
- Broad up-warping and down-warping of the crust form *domes* and *basins*, respectively.
- Large *thrust faults* are low-angle *reverse faults* where plates collide, forming mountain belts. The San Andreas is a famous right-lateral strike-slip (also *transform*) fault.

MasteringGeology   www.masteringgeology.com

Looking for additional review and test prep materials? Visit the Study Area in MasteringGeology to enhance your understanding of this chapter's content by accessing a variety of resources, including

Self-Study Quizzes, Geoscience Animations, GEODe Tutorials, RSS feeds, flashcards, weblinks, self-study quizzes, and an optional Pearson eText.

REVIEW QUESTIONS

1. How are stress and strain related to force?
2. Describe the difference between compressional and tensional stresses.
3. How is brittle deformation different from ductile deformation?
4. Compare and contrast anticlines with synclines, domes with basins, and anticlines with domes.
5. How are joints different from faults?
6. What two measurements are used to establish the orientation of deformed strata? Distinguish between them.

7. At which of the three types of plate boundaries do the following types of faulting predominate: 1) normal faulting; 2) reverse faulting; 3) strike-slip faulting?
8. List three factors that determine how rocks will behave when exposed to stresses that exceed their strength. Briefly explain the role of each.
9. What are thrust faults and under what circumstances do they form?

EARTHQUAKES AND EARTH'S INTERIOR   10

An earthquake-generated tsunami crashes into the northeast coast of Honshu, Japan in March, 2011. (Photo by Sadatsugu Tomizawa/Getty Images)

"It just kept going. We had lamps in the house fall over. The chandelier in the kitchen was swaying. You could barely stand. I've never been more scared in my life!"* Thus recalled the fire chief of Masset on Graham Island following the second strongest earthquake ever recorded in Canada. The magnitude 7.7 quake in 2012 was surpassed only by the magnitude 8.1 event of 1949 in the same area (see Figure 10.A in Box 10.1). Fortunately the 2012 quake caused no deaths or major damage in this sparsely populated part of the country, but it was felt as far away as Yukon and Alberta. The only significant casualties were the popular hot spring pools that dried up on Hotspring Island (Figure 10.1). Ninety-four aftershocks greater than magnitude 4 continued for nine days after the main event.

Sirens issued a tsunami warning, and people were evacuated from their homes as far away as Hawaii, but the warning was soon called off. The earthquake generated only small waves, because strike-slip movement (rather than dip-slip; see Chapter 9) dominates along the Queen Charlotte fault that separates the Pacific and North American plates (Figure 10.A). Tsunami are generated by *vertical* movement of the sea floor, which pushes sea water toward the surface to become a big wave.

Earthquakes and associated phenomena, such as tsunami and landslides, are tangible reminders that Earth is a highly dynamic system, both above and below its surface. Each year, more than a thousand earthquakes occur in Canada alone, although the majority of these produce vibrations that are simply too weak to be felt by humans and can be detected only by sensitive instruments.

Occasionally, media reports alert us to particularly strong earthquake events. The most severe earthquake disasters in recent times have included

*Stephen Grosse, interviewed in CBC News, "6.3-magnitude aftershock hits near B.C.'s Haida Gwaii" Oct 28, 2012.

those centred in Izmit, Turkey (August 17, 1999, with more than 17 000 deaths); Gujarat, India (January 26, 2001, with more than 20 000 deaths); the Bam region of Iran (December 26, 2003, with more than 25 000 deaths); Sumatra, Indonesia (December 26, 2004, with 230 000 deaths, many by tsunami); Haiti (January 12, 2010, with 100 000 deaths); and Japan (March 11, 2011, 15 700 deaths). Disasters like these are difficult for most Canadians to comprehend; indeed, many Canadians have never even *felt* an earthquake in their lifetime. The events that occurred in the Indian Ocean, Haiti, and Japan are particularly significant in that they changed the consciousness of millions of people worldwide. Victims were reported in at least eight countries bordering the Indian Ocean after the 2004 event. In a sense, these disasters were truly felt by the global community. Before the 2004 disaster, few people had heard the term *tsunami*; by the next day, it had become a household word. It was a strong reminder that earthquake hazards can extend far beyond the area in which an earthquake itself is generated. These events were also wake-up calls to the many nations that, having not experienced an earthquake for some time, had become complacent about preparing for such a disaster.

Ancient stories of the Aboriginal peoples of Vancouver Island, historical documents from Japan, computer-modelling methods, and a variety of geologic evidence indicate that an earthquake of similar magnitude to the Sumatra-Andaman earthquake occurred in 1700. Canada is not immune to tsunami: A rare Atlantic tsunami associated with the 1929 Grand Banks, Newfoundland and Labrador, earthquake was responsible for about 27 deaths—historically, the largest number of deaths attributed to a single Canadian earthquake. Thus, the question is not "will another earthquake occur in Canada?" but, rather, "when will the next big earthquake happen—and where?" Answering this question will require

Figure 10.1 Before (**A**) and after (**B**) views of hotsprings on Hotspring Island in Gwaii Haanas National Park. The 2012 earthquake cut off the groundwater source of these pools and two others. (Photo **A** by Mark Sundstrom, photo **B** by Parks Canada)

knowledge of past earthquake events and the study of current earthquake activity.

In this chapter, we examine what earthquakes are, how they are produced, the damage they cause, and how they are studied. We also explore the positive side of earthquakes—how the behaviour of seismic waves has been used to deduce the structure of Earth's interior.

WHAT IS AN EARTHQUAKE?

An **earthquake** is the vibration of Earth produced by the rapid release of energy. Most often, earthquakes are caused by slippage along faults in Earth's crust. The energy released radiates in all directions from its source—the **hypocentre** (also called the *focus*)—in the form of seismic waves. These waves are analogous to those produced when a stone is dropped into a calm pond (Figure 10.2), however an earthquake generates seismic waves that radiate throughout Earth. Even though the energy dissipates rapidly with increasing distance from the hypocentre, sensitive instruments located around the world record the event. The **epicentre** (*epi* = upon, *centr* = a point) is the location on the surface directly above the hypocentre.

Earthquakes and Faults

The tremendous energy released by atomic explosions or by volcanic eruptions can produce earthquakes, but these events are relatively weak and infrequent. In addition to vertical crustal displacements involving uplift and subsidence, offsets in

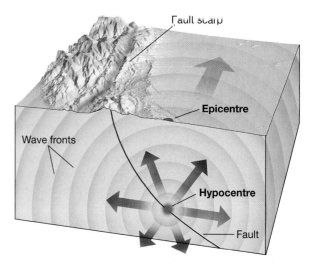

Figure 10.2 Earthquake hypocentre and epicentre. The hypocentre is the place within Earth at which the initial displacement occurs. The epicentre is the surface location directly above the hypocentre.

fence lines, roads, and other structures indicate that horizontal movement also occurs (Figure 10.3). The latter movements are usually associated with faults (Chapter 9) that produce destructive earthquakes.

Most of the motion along faults can be satisfactorily explained by plate tectonic theory (Chapter 1). Mobile plates of lithosphere interact with neighbouring plates, straining and deforming the rocks at their margins. In fact, it is along the faults associated with plate boundaries that most earthquakes occur. Furthermore, earthquakes are repetitive: As soon as one is over, the continuous motion of the plates resumes, adding stress to the rocks until they fail again.

Figure 10.3 This fence was offset 2.5 metres during the 1906 San Francisco earthquake.
(Photo by G. K. Gilbert, U.S. Geological Survey)

Elastic Rebound

The actual mechanism of earthquake generation eluded geologists until H. F. Reid of Johns Hopkins University conducted a study following the great 1906 San Francisco earthquake. The earthquake was accompanied by horizontal surface displacements of several metres along the northern portion of the San Andreas Fault. This 1300-kilometre fault zone extends northwest–southeast through southern California and separates two great sections of Earth's crust: the North American plate and the Pacific plate. Field investigations determined that during the 1906 quake, the Pacific plate lurched as much as 9.7 metres northward past the adjacent North American plate.

The mechanism for earthquake formation that Reid deduced from this information is illustrated in Figure 10.4. In part A you see an existing fault. In part B, tectonic forces slowly deform (bend) crustal rocks on both sides of the fault and build up elastic energy, much like a wooden stick does if bent. Eventually, the frictional resistance holding the rocks together is overcome. As slippage occurs at the weakest point (the hypocentre), displacement exerts stress farther along the fault, where additional slippage occurs (Figure 10.4C) until most of the built-up stress is released (Figure 10.4D). This slippage allows the deformed rock to "snap back." The vibrations we know as an earthquake occur as the rock elastically returns to its original shape. The springing back of the rock was termed **elastic rebound** by Reid because the rock behaves elastically, much like a stretched rubber band does when it is released. After release, stress builds up again along the fault as the earthquake cycle continues.

In summary, most earthquakes are produced by the rapid release of elastic energy stored in rock that has been subjected to great stress. Once the strength of the rock is exceeded, it suddenly ruptures, causing the vibrations of an earthquake. Earthquakes most commonly occur along existing faults whenever the frictional forces on the fault surfaces are overcome.

Foreshocks and Aftershocks

The intense vibrations of the 1906 San Francisco earthquake lasted about 40 seconds. Although most of the displacement along the fault occurred in this rather short span, additional movements along this and other nearby faults lasted for several days following the main quake. The adjustments that follow a major earthquake often generate smaller earthquakes called **aftershocks**. Although these aftershocks are usually much weaker than the main

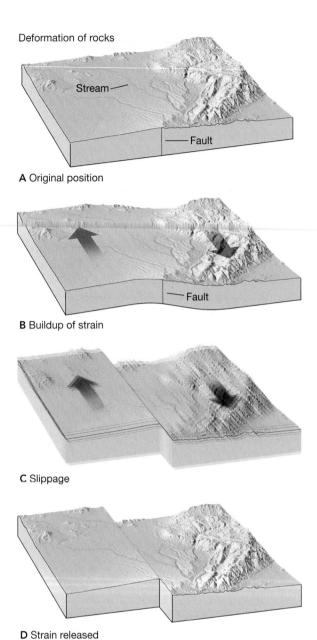

A Original position

B Buildup of strain

C Slippage

D Strain released

Figure 10.4 Elastic rebound. As rock is deformed, it bends, storing elastic energy. Once strained beyond its breaking point, the rock fails (breaks), releasing the stored-up energy as earthquake waves.

earthquake, they can sometimes destroy already badly weakened structures. This occurred during a 1988 earthquake in Armenia and the 2010 Haitian quake. A large aftershock collapsed many structures that had been weakened by the main tremor.

In addition, small earthquakes called **foreshocks** often precede a major earthquake by days or, in some cases, by as much as several years. Monitoring of these foreshocks has been used as a means of predicting forthcoming major earthquakes, with mixed success.

SEISMOLOGY

The study of earthquake waves, **seismology** (*seismos* = shake, *ology* = the study of) dates back to attempts by the Chinese almost 2000 years ago to determine the direction from which these waves originated. They used a large hollow jar containing a suspended mass (similar to a clock pendulum) connected in some fashion to the jaws of several large dragon figurines that encircled the container (Figure 10.5). The jaws of each dragon held a metal ball. When earthquake waves reached the instrument, the relative motion between the suspended mass and the jar would dislodge some of the metal balls into the waiting mouths of frog figurines directly below.

The Chinese were probably aware that the first strong ground motion from an earthquake is directional, and when it is strong enough, all poorly supported items will topple over in the same direction. Apparently they used this fact, plus the position of the dislodged balls, to detect the direction to an earthquake's source. However, the complex motion of seismic waves makes it unlikely that the actual direction to source was determined accurately.

In principle, modern **seismographs** (*seismos* = shake, *graph* = write), instruments that record seismic waves, are not unlike the device used by the early Chinese. Seismographs have a mass freely suspended from a support that is attached to the ground (Figure 10.6). When the vibration from a distant

Figure 10.5 Ancient Chinese seismograph. During an Earth tremor, the dragons located in the direction of the main vibrations would each drop a ball into the mouth of the frog below it.
(Photo by James E. Patterson)

Figure 10.6 Principle of the seismograph. The inertia of the suspended mass tends to keep it motionless, while the recording drum, which is anchored to bedrock, vibrates in response to seismic waves. Thus the stationary mass provides a reference point from which to measure the amount of displacement occurring as the seismic wave passes through the ground. **A.** Seismograph designed to record horizontal movement. **B.** Seismograph designed to record vertical ground motion.

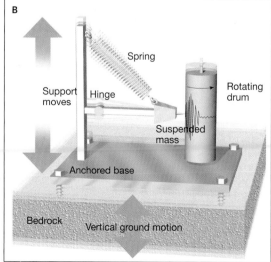

earthquake reaches the instrument, the **inertia*** (*iners* = idle) of the mass keeps it relatively stationary while Earth and the support move. The movement of Earth in relation to the stationary mass is recorded on a rotating drum, magnetic tape, or digital device.

**Inertia: Simply stated, objects at rest tend to stay at rest, and objects in motion tend to remain in motion, unless acted on by an outside force. You probably have experienced this phenomenon when an automobile you were in stopped quickly and your body continued to move forward.*

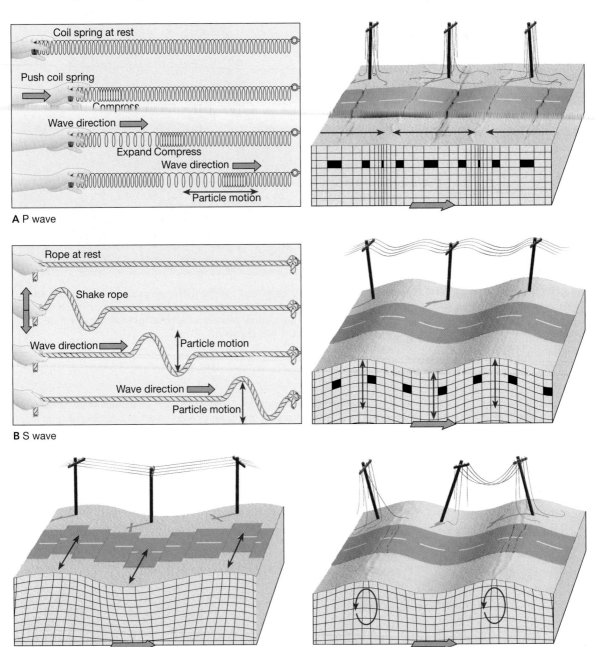

Figure 10.7 Basic types of seismic waves and their characteristic motion. (Note that during a typical earthquake, ground shaking consists of a combination of various kinds of seismic waves that have complex movements in three dimensions.) **A.** As illustrated by a coil spring, P waves are compressional waves that alternately compress and expand the material through which they pass. The back-and-forth motion produced as compressional waves travel along the surface can cause the ground to buckle and fracture, and they can cause power lines to break. **B.** S waves cause material to oscillate at right angles to the direction of wave motion. Because S waves can travel in any plane, they produce up-and-down and sideways shaking of the ground. **C.** One type of surface wave is essentially the same as that of an S wave that exhibits only horizontal motion. This kind of surface wave moves the ground from side to side and can be particularly damaging to the foundations of buildings. **D.** Another type of surface wave travels along Earth's surface, much like rolling ocean waves. The arrows show the elliptical movement of rock as the wave passes.

The records obtained from seismographs, called **seismograms** (*seismos* = shake, *gramma* = what is written), provide a great deal of information concerning the behaviour of seismic waves. Seismic waves are energy forms that radiate out in all directions from the focus. The propagation (transmission) of this energy can be compared to the shaking of gelatin in a bowl that results as some is spooned out. Whereas the gelatin will have one mode of vibration, seismograms reveal that two main groups of seismic waves are generated by the slippage of a rock mass. The wave types that travel through Earth's interior are called **body waves**. The types that travel along the outer part of Earth are called **surface waves**. Body waves are further divided into two types, called **primary waves**, or **P waves**, and **secondary waves**, or **S waves**, based on their movements through matter.

P waves are "push–pull" waves—they push (compress) and pull (expand) rocks in the direction the wave is travelling (Figure 10.7A). Imagine holding someone by the shoulders and shaking that person. This push–pull movement is how P waves move through Earth. Solids, liquids, and gases resist a change in volume when compressed and will elastically spring back once the force is removed. Therefore, P waves, which are compressional waves, can travel through all these materials.

Conversely, S waves "shake" the particles at right angles to their direction of travel. This can be illustrated by fastening one end of a rope and shaking the other end, as shown in Figure 10.7B. Unlike P waves, which temporarily change the *volume* of intervening material by alternately compressing and expanding it, S waves temporarily change the *shape* of the material that transmits them. Because fluids (gases and liquids) do not respond elastically to changes in shape, they will not transmit S waves.

The motion of surface waves is somewhat more complex (Figure 10.7C). As surface waves travel along the ground, they cause the ground and anything resting on it to move, much as ocean swells toss a ship. In addition to their up-and-down motion, surface waves have a side-to-side motion similar to an S wave oriented in a horizontal plane. This latter motion is particularly damaging to the foundations of structures.

By observing a "typical" seismic record, as shown in Figure 10.8, you can see major differences among these seismic waves: P waves are the fastest and arrive at the recording station first, then S waves, and then surface waves. In solid materials, P waves travel 1.7 times as fast as S waves, and S waves travel 1.1 times as fast as surface waves. For example, through granite P waves travel about 6 kilometres per second; and S waves, about 3.6 kilometres per second.

A system was developed for locating earthquake epicentres by using seismograms from earthquakes whose epicentres could be easily pinpointed from physical evidence. From these seismograms, travel-time graphs were constructed (Figure 10.9). The first travel-time graphs were greatly improved when seismograms became available from nuclear explosions, because the precise location and time of detonation were known.

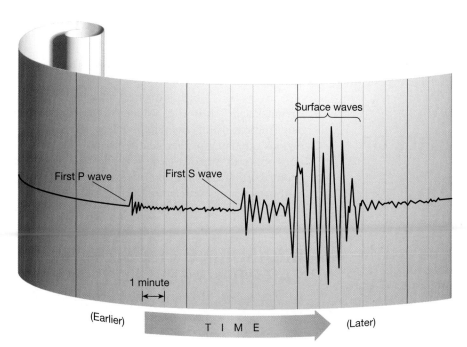

Figure 10.8 Typical seismogram. Note the time interval (about 5 minutes) between the arrival of the first P wave and the arrival of the first S wave.

Surface waves

First P wave

First S wave

1 minute

(Earlier)　T I M E　(Later)

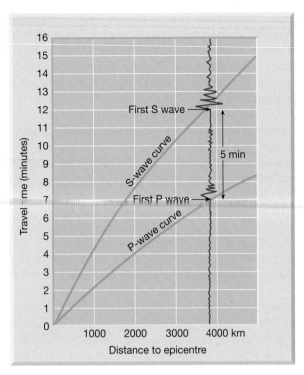

Figure 10.9 A travel-time graph is used to determine the distance to the epicentre. The difference in arrival times of the first P and S waves in the example is 5 minutes. Thus, the epicentre is roughly 3800 kilometres away.

In addition to velocity differences, also notice in Figure 10.8 that the height or, more correctly, the amplitude of these wave types varies. The S waves tend to have a slightly greater amplitude than the P waves, while the surface waves, which cause the greatest destruction, tend to exhibit an even greater amplitude. Because surface waves are confined to a narrow region near the surface and are not spread throughout Earth as P and S waves are, they retain their maximum amplitude longer. Surface waves also have longer periods (time intervals between crests); therefore, they are commonly referred to as **long waves**, or **L waves**.

LOCATING THE SOURCE OF AN EARTHQUAKE

The difference in velocities of P and S waves provides a method for locating the epicentre. The principle used is analogous to a race between two vehicles, one faster than the other. The P wave always wins the race, arriving ahead of the S wave. But the greater the length of the race, the greater will be the difference in the arrival times at the finish line (the seismic station). Therefore, the greater the interval measured on a seismogram between the arrival of the first P wave and the first S wave,

the greater the distance to the earthquake source. By using the sample seismogram in Figure 10.8 and the travel-time curves in Figure 10.9, we can determine the distance separating the recording station from the earthquake in two steps: (1) Determine the time interval between the arrival of the first P wave and the first S wave, and (2) find on the travel-time graph the equivalent time spread between the P and S wave curves. From this information, we can determine that this earthquake occurred 3800 kilometres from the recording instrument.

Now we know the *distance*, but what about *direction?* As shown in Figure 10.10, the precise location can be found using triangulation when the distance is known from three or more different seismic stations. On a globe, we draw a circle around each seismic station, representing its epicentre distance. The point at which the three circles intersect is the epicentre of the quake.

Earthquake Belts

About 95 percent of the energy released by earthquakes originates in a few relatively narrow zones that wind around the globe (Figure 10.11). The greatest energy is released, and seismic activity occurs, along a path around the outer edge of the Pacific Ocean known as the *circum-Pacific belt*, including Japan, the Philippines, Chile, and numerous volcanic island chains, as exemplified by the Aleutian Islands.

Another major concentration of strong seismic activity extends through the mountainous regions that flank the Mediterranean Sea and continues through Iran and on past the Himalayan complex. Figure 10.11 indicates that yet another continuous belt extends for thousands of kilometres through the world's oceans. This zone coincides with the oceanic ridge system, an area of frequent but weaker seismic activity.

Areas of North America included in the circum-Pacific belt lie adjacent to California's San Andreas Fault and along the western coastal regions extending to the Aleutian Islands. Other sections of North America are regarded as regions where strong earthquakes are likely to occur. In Canada earthquakes are concentrated in British Columbia but do occur elsewhere (Box 10.1).

MEASURING THE SIZE OF EARTHQUAKES

Historically, seismologists have employed a variety of methods to obtain two fundamentally different measures that describe the size of an earthquake:

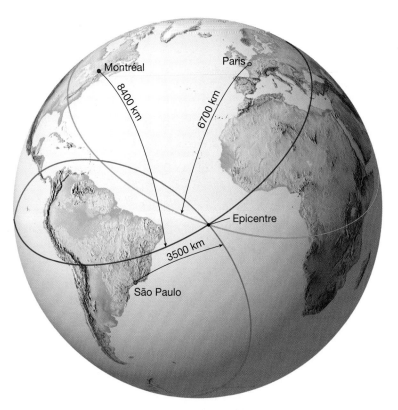

intensity and magnitude. The first to be used was **intensity**—a measure of the degree of earthquake shaking at a given locale based on the amount of damage. With the development of seismographs, it was possible to obtain a quantitative measure of an earthquake based on seismic records rather than uncertain personal estimates of damage. The measurement that was developed, called **magnitude**, relies on calculations that use data provided by seismic records (and other techniques) to estimate the amount of energy released at the source of the earthquake.

Both intensity and magnitude provide useful, although quite different, information about

Figure 10.11 Distribution of the 14 229 earthquakes with magnitudes of at least 5 between 1980 and 1990. (Data from National Geophysical Data Center/NOAA)

CANADIAN PROFILE
Earthquakes in Canada

David Eaton*

On August 22, 1949, residents of Haida Gwaii (at that time called the Queen Charlotte Islands) were jolted by Canada's largest measured earthquake. With a magnitude of 8.1, this offshore tremor ranks as one of the great earthquakes of the twentieth century, well recorded around the globe. The earthquake knocked cows off their feet and caused an oil tank at Cumshewa Inlet to collapse. Even 300 kilometres away in Terrace, British Columbia, the ground shaking was so intense that standing on the street was described as "like being on the heaving deck of a ship at sea." Fortunately, the sparse population of the region meant that casualties and property damage were light in comparison with other earthquakes of similar magnitude, such as the 1946 Vancouver Island earthquake (Figure 10.12B).

The 1949 earthquake ruptured a major segment of the Queen Charlotte fault system, an active right-lateral transform fault along Canada's west coast (Figure 10.A). Across the fault, the Pacific plate is creeping slowly northward relative to North America, in a manner analogous to lithospheric movement along the San Andreas Fault system in California. Friction across the fault resists this motion, causing stress to accumulate during aseismic intervals. The sudden release of stored energy during an earthquake (elastic rebound) starts the earthquake cycle once again.

In southwest British Columbia, a different plate-tectonic setting exists, more akin to Japan than California (Figure 10.A). From southern Vancouver Island to northern California, the oceanic Juan de Fuca plate is subducting beneath the North American plate within a system known as the Cascadia subduction zone. Although large earthquakes have taken place, such as the widely felt Nisqually earthquake near Seattle, Washington, on February 28, 2001, the Cascadia subduction zone

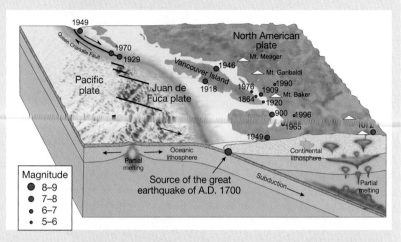

Figure 10.A   Configuration of lithospheric plates and locations of significant earthquakes that have been recorded in British Columbia. (Based on Turner, R. J. W., Clague, J. J., Groulx, B. J. 1998: Geoscape Vancouver, living with our geological landscape; Geological Survey of Canada, Open File 3309.)

Figure 10.B   The distribution and magnitudes of earthquakes in Canada since 1980. (Reproduced with the permission of Natural Resources Canada, 2010, and courtesy of Earthquake Canada)

is unusual because no large historical earthquake has occurred along the dipping plate boundary. (The Nisqually earthquake took place within the oceanic slab as it broke apart during descent into the mantle.) There is now compelling scientific evidence, however, that a so-called megathrust earthquake took place with an estimated magnitude of 9.0 along the plate boundary on January 26, 1700, before settlement of the region by Europeans.

The timing of this earthquake is known from the oral traditions of the Cowichan people of Vancouver Island, from the study of tree rings in remnant stumps of drowned forests in estuaries along the Oregon and Washington coast, and from meticulous Japanese written records of a devastating tsunami. By using computer simulations, scientists have demonstrated that the tsunami must have originated near the west coast of North America.

The giant Cascadia earthquake of 1700 was not a unique event. Studies of shoreline sediments from Oregon to Vancouver Island reveal a cyclic pattern of sudden downdrop of the coast, followed by a slow rebound in elevation. In the past 6000 years, 13 such great earthquakes have been documented. We are presently in the midst of a long span of episodic stress buildup between megathrust earthquake events, producing coastal uplift and a squeezing of Vancouver Island that is measurable by using modern survey techniques. The next offshore megathrust earthquake will happen, perhaps hundreds of years in the future, and residents of southwest British Columbia and adjacent areas need to be ready for it.

The tectonically active west coast is not the only part of Canada that experiences earthquakes. Figure 10.B shows a map of earthquakes in Canada since 1980, catalogued as part of the National Earthquake Hazards Program of the Geological Survey of

Figure 10.C On June 23, 2010, tremors from a magnitude 5.0 earthquake centred near Val-des-Bois, Quebec (approximately 60 km north of Ottawa), were felt over much of eastern and southern Ontario and northeastern United States. Minor damage to buildings and roads was experienced within tens of kilometres of the epicentre. This bridge, located a few kilometres south of Val-des-Bois, collapsed as a direct result of the earthquake. (Photo by Jean Levac/The Ottawa Citizen)

Canada. In western Canada, zones of earthquake activity are found in the Rocky Mountains of southwest Alberta and the Mackenzie Mountains of the Northwest Territories, where earthquakes of magnitudes up to 6.6 have been recorded. These bands of seismicity are thought to be the result of transmission of plate boundary stresses from convergent margins (Cascadia and Alaska), far into the North American plate.

Although very far from any active plate boundary, parts of eastern Canada also experience moderate earthquakes, such as the magnitude 5.9 Saguenay earthquake on November 25, 1988, and more the recent magnitude 5.0 Val-des-Bois earthquake on June 23, 2010 (Figure 10.C). The seismicity of eastern

Canada is mainly concentrated along the Ottawa and St. Lawrence River valleys, and in the Appalachians of Quebec and New Brunswick. Like intraplate earthquakes in the United States, including the New Madrid earthquake sequence in 1811–1812, the cause of these earthquakes is not well understood. The zones of seismicity appear to be associated with the locations of ancient rifted margins or failed rift zones, which may rupture (reactivate) in response to the slow movement of North America away from the spreading mid-Atlantic ridge.

David Eaton is a professor in the Department of Earth Sciences at the University of Calgary.

earthquake strength. Consequently, both measures are still used to describe the relative sizes of earthquakes.

Intensity Scales

At one time historical records provided the only accounts of the severity of earthquake shaking and destruction. The use of these descriptions—compiled without any standards for reporting—made accurate comparisons of earthquake sizes difficult. To standardize the study of earthquake severity, early earthquake investigators developed various intensity scales that considered damage done

to buildings, descriptions of the event, and secondary effects—landslides and the extent of ground rupture. By 1902, Giuseppe Mercalli had developed a relatively reliable intensity scale, which in a modified form is still used today. The **Modified Mercalli Intensity Scale** (Table 10.1) was developed by using California buildings as its standard, but it is appropriate for use throughout most of the United States and Canada to estimate the strength of an earthquake (see Figure 10.12). For example, if some well-built wooden structures and most masonry buildings are destroyed by an earthquake, that earthquake would be assigned an intensity of X on the Mercalli scale (Table 10.1).

TABLE **10.1**   Modified Mercalli Intensity Scale

I	Not felt except by a very few under especially favourable circumstances.
II	Felt by a few persons at rest, especially on upper floors of buildings.
III	Felt quite noticeably indoors, especially on upper floors of buildings.
IV	During the day, felt indoors by many, outdoors by few. Sensation like heavy truck striking building.
V	Felt by most people, many awakened. Disturbances of trees, poles, and other tall objects sometimes noticed.
VI	Felt by all; many frightened and run outdoors. Some heavy furniture moved; few instances of fallen plaster or damaged chimneys. Damage slight.
VII	Everybody runs outdoors. Damage negligible in buildings of good design and construction; slight to moderate in well-built ordinary structures; considerable in poorly built or badly designed structures.
VIII	Damage slight in specially designed structures; considerable in ordinary substantial buildings with partial collapse; great in poorly built structures (fall of chimneys, factory stacks, columns, monuments, walls).
IX	Damage considerable in specially designed structures. Buildings shifted off foundations. Ground cracked conspicuously.
X	Some well-built wooden structures destroyed. Most masonry and frame structures destroyed. Ground badly cracked.
XI	Few, if any (masonry) structures remain standing. Bridges destroyed. Broad fissures in ground.
XII	Waves seen on ground surfaces. Objects thrown upward into air. Damage total.

Sources: Giuseppe Mercalli, 1884 and 1906; Adolfo Cancani, 1902; August Heinrich Sieberg; Harry O. Wood and Frank Neumann, in Bulletin of the Seismological Society of America, vol. 21, no. 4, December 1931.

Despite their usefulness, particularly in regions without seismographs, intensity scales have severe drawbacks: They are based on destruction by earthquakes that depend not only on the severity of ground shaking but also on population density, building design, and the nature of surface materials. In British Columbia, for example, the 1946 Vancouver Island earthquake caused more property damage (Figure 10.12B) than the much stronger earthquake that occurred west of the Queen Charlotte Islands in 1949, largely because it affected a more densely populated area. Haiti (2010) experienced intensity of VII-IX on the Mercalli scale.

A

B

Figure 10.12   **A.** Modified Mercalli Intensity map showing intensity of shaking associated with an earthquake (magnitude 7.3) that occurred at 10:15 a.m. on June 23, 1946. The epicentre was in central Vancouver Island, near the communities of Courtenay and Campbell River. **B.** Damage to a school in Courtenay, British Columbia, resulting from the 1946 earthquake.
(Reproduced with the permission of Natural Resources Canada 2013, courtesy of Earthquakes Canada. Photos reproduced with the permission of Natural Resources Canada 2013, courtesy of the Geological Survey of Canada)

Magnitude Scales

To compare earthquakes across the globe, a measure was needed that does not rely on parameters that vary considerably from one part of the world to another. Consequently the Richter scale was developed.

RICHTER MAGNITUDE In 1935, Charles Richter of the California Institute of Technology developed the first magnitude scale by using seismic records to estimate the relative sizes of earthquakes. As shown in Figure 10.13, the **Richter scale** is based on the amplitude of the largest seismic wave (P, S, or surface wave) recorded on a seismogram. Because seismic waves weaken as the distance between the earthquake epicentre and the seismograph increases (in a manner similar to light), Richter developed a method that accounted for the decrease in wave amplitude with increased distance. Theoretically, as long as the same, or equivalent, instruments were used, monitoring stations at various locations would obtain the same Richter magnitude for every recorded earthquake. In practice, however, different recording stations often obtained slightly different Richter magnitudes for the same earthquake—a consequence of the variations in rock types through which the waves travelled.

Although the Richter scale has no upper limit, the largest magnitude recorded was 8.9. These great shocks released an amount of energy that is roughly equivalent to the detonation of 1 billion tonnes of TNT. Conversely, earthquakes with a Richter magnitude of less than 2.0 are not felt by humans. Earthquakes vary enormously in strength, and great earthquakes produce wave amplitudes that are thousands of times larger than those generated by weak tremors. To accommodate this wide variation, Richter used a *logarithmic scale* to express magnitude, where a *tenfold* increase in wave amplitude corresponds to an increase of 1 on the magnitude scale. Thus, the amount of ground shaking for a magnitude 5 earthquake is 10 times greater than that produced by a magnitude 4 earthquake.

In addition, each unit of Richter magnitude equates to roughly a *32-fold energy increase*. Thus, an earthquake with a magnitude of 6.5 releases 32 times as much energy as one with a magnitude of 5.5, and

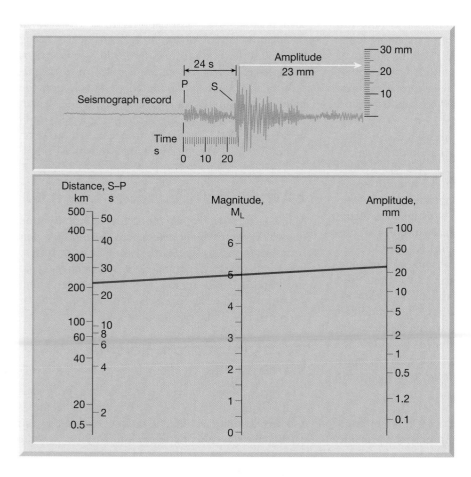

Figure 10.13 Illustration showing how the Richter magnitude of an earthquake can be determined graphically by using a seismograph record from a Wood-Anderson instrument. First, measure the height (amplitude) of the largest wave on the seismogram (23 millimetres) and then the distance to the hypocentre by using the time interval between S and P waves (24 seconds). Next, draw a line between the distance scale (left) and the wave amplitude scale (right). By doing this, you obtain the Richter magnitude (M_L) of 5. (Data from California Institute of Technology)

TABLE 10.2   Earthquake Magnitude and Energy Equivalence

Earthquake Magnitude (M_L)	Energy Released (millions of ergs)	Approximate Energy Equivalence
0	630 000	0.5 kilograms of explosives
1	20 000 000	
2	630 000 000	Energy of lightning bolt
3	20 000 000 000	
4	630 000 000 000	450 kilograms of explosives
5	20 000 000 000 000	
6	630 000 000 000 000	1946 Bikini atomic bomb test
		1994 Northridge earthquake
7	20 000 000 000 000 000	2010 Haiti earthquake
8	630 000 000 000 000 000	1906 San Francisco earthquake
		1980 Eruption of Mount St. Helens
9	20 000 000 000 000 000 000	1964 Alaskan earthquake
		1960 Chilean earthquake
10	630 000 000 000 000 000 000	Annual U.S. energy consumption

Source: U.S. Geological Survey.
Note: For each unit increase in magnitude, the energy released increases 31.6 times.

roughly 1000 times as much energy as one with a magnitude of 4.5 (Table 10.2). A major earthquake with a magnitude of 8.5 releases millions of times as much energy as the smallest earthquakes felt by humans.

OTHER MAGNITUDE SCALES Richter's original goal was modest in that he only attempted to rank the earthquakes of southern California (shallow-focus earthquakes) into groups of large, medium, and small magnitude. Hence, Richter magnitude was designed to study nearby (or local) earthquakes and is denoted by the symbol (M_L)—where M is for *magnitude* and L is for *local*.

The convenience of describing the size of an earthquake by a single number that could be calculated quickly from seismograms makes the Richter scale a powerful tool. Further, unlike intensity scales that could only be applied to populated areas of the globe, Richter magnitudes could be assigned to earthquakes in more remote regions and even to events that occurred in the ocean basins. As a result, the method devised by Richter was adapted to a number of different seismographs located throughout the world. In time, seismologists modified Richter's work and developed new magnitude scales. These modified scales were initially calibrated to be equivalent to the Richter scale and have contributed to efforts to measure the size of earthquakes. However, despite their usefulness, none of these scales is adequate for describing very large earthquakes.

MOMENT MAGNITUDE Seismologists now employ a more precise measure called **moment magnitude** (M_W). Moment magnitude is calculated by using a combination of factors that include the average amount of displacement along the fault, the area of the rupture surface, and the shear strength of the faulted rock.

Because moment magnitude estimates the total energy released, it is better for measuring very large earthquakes. Thus seismologists have recalculated the magnitudes of older, strong earthquakes using the M_W scale. For example, the 1906 San Francisco earthquake, which had an M_L surface-wave magnitude of 8.3, would be demoted to M_W 7.9 on the moment magnitude scale, whereas the 1964 Alaskan earthquake with an M_L 8.3 Richter magnitude would be increased to M_W 9.2. The strongest earthquake on record is the 1960 Chilean earthquake with M_W 9.5.

EARTHQUAKE DESTRUCTION

Many factors determine the degree of destruction that will accompany an earthquake. The most obvious is the magnitude of the earthquake and its proximity to a populated area. Fortunately, most earthquakes are small and occur in remote regions. However, about 20 major earthquakes are reported annually, one or two of which can be catastrophic.

Destruction from Seismic Vibrations

The 1964 Alaskan earthquake provided geologists with new insights into the role of ground shaking as a destructive force. As the energy released by an earthquake travels along Earth's surface, it causes the

Figure 10.14 Damage caused to the five-storey J. C. Penney Co. building, Anchorage, Alaska. Very little structural damage was incurred by the adjacent building. (Courtesy of NOAA)

ground to vibrate in a complex manner by moving up and down as well as from side to side. The amount of structural damage attributable to the vibrations depends on several factors, including (1) the intensity of the vibrations, (2) the duration of the vibrations, (3) the nature of the material on which the structure rests, and (4) the design of the structure.

All of the multi-storey structures in Anchorage were damaged by the vibrations. The more flexible wood-frame residential buildings fared best. However, many homes were destroyed when the ground failed. A striking example of how construction variations affect earthquake damage is shown in Figure 10.14. You can see that the steel-frame building on the left withstood the vibrations, whereas the poorly designed J. C. Penney building was badly damaged. Engineers have learned that non-reinforced masonry buildings are the most serious safety threat in earthquakes.

Most large structures in Anchorage were damaged due to the long duration of this earthquake, even though they were built according to the earthquake building standards of the day. Most quakes consist of tremors that last less than a minute. The Alaska quake was a notable exception: It reverberated for three to four minutes.

AMPLIFICATION OF SEISMIC WAVES Although each part of the region near the epicentre will experience about the same intensity of ground shaking, the destruction can vary considerably because soft sediments amplify vibrations more than solid bedrock. Thus, buildings in Anchorage suffered heavy damage because they were built on unconsolidated sediments. By contrast, most of the nearby town of Whittier, although much closer to the epicentre, sits on granite and suffered less damage.

LIQUEFACTION In areas where unconsolidated materials are saturated with water, earthquake vibrations can generate a phenomenon known as **liquefaction** (*liqueo* = to be fluid, *facio* = to make). Under these conditions, what had been a stable soil turns into a mobile fluid that is not capable of supporting buildings or other structures (Figure 10.15). As a result, underground objects, such as storage tanks

Figure 10.15 Effects of liquefaction. This tilted building rests on unconsolidated sediment that behaved like quicksand during the 1985 Mexican earthquake. (Photo by James L. Beck)

Figure 10.16 These "mud volcanoes" were produced by the Loma Prieta earthquake of 1989 in California. They formed when fountains of sand and water shot from the ground, an indication that liquefaction had occurred. (Photo by Richard Hilton)

and sewer lines, can literally float to the surface of their newly liquefied environment. Buildings and other structures can settle and collapse. During the 1989 Loma Prieta earthquake in California, foundations failed and geysers of sand and water shot from the ground, indicating that liquefaction had occurred (Figure 10.16). During the 2011 Japan earthquake, liquefaction caused buidings to sink a couple of metres.

Tsunami

Most deaths associated with the 1964 Alaskan and 2004 Sumatran earthquakes were caused by *tsunami** (*tsu* = harbour, *nami* = waves), or seismic sea waves. Before the catastrophic tsunami of December 26, 2004, in Indonesia, and the Japanese one of March 11, 2011 (Box 10.2), these destructive waves were commonly called tidal waves by the media. However, that name is incorrect; the waves are generated by earthquakes, not the tidal effect of the Moon or Sun.

Most tsunami result from vertical displacement along a fault that lifts a large slab of sea floor (Figure 10.17). Once created, a tsunami resembles the ripples formed when a pebble is dropped into a

*Seismic sea waves were given the name *tsunami* by the Japanese, who have suffered a great deal from them. The term *tsunami* is now used worldwide.

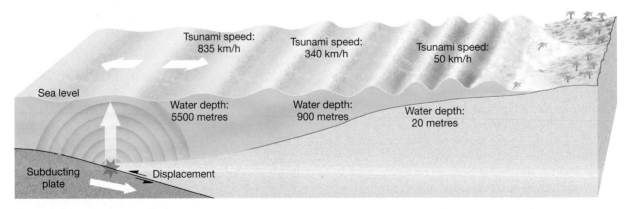

Figure 10.17 Schematic drawing of a tsunami generated by displacement of the ocean floor. The speed of a wave correlates with ocean depth. As shown, waves moving in deep water advance at speeds in excess of 800 kilometres per hour. Speed gradually slows to 50 kilometres per hour at depths of 20 metres. Decreasing depth slows the movement of the wave. As waves slow in shallow water, they grow in height until they topple and rush onto shore with tremendous force. The size and spacing of these swells are not to scale.

UNDERSTANDING EARTH
2011 Japan Tsunami

On March 11, 2011, a magnitude 9.0 (M_W) earthquake occurred 373 kilometres northeast of Tokyo (Figure 10.D), the strongest ever recorded in Japan. The resulting tsunami slammed into the east coast of Honshu (Japan's most populous island; Figure 10.E) and reached a runup height of almost 38 metres. It swept cars, boats, and burning buildings inland toward factories, fields, and cluttered highways. Stranded survivors cried for help as they frantically searched for relatives. There was no electricity or water for people in shelters.

The tsunami also damaged property in Hawaii, California, the Galapagos Islands, and Peru. Together the earthquake and tsunami claimed more than 15 700 human lives, left more than 130 000 homeless, and caused US$309 billion in damage to buildings, roads, bridges, railways, and nuclear reactors, as well as electrical, water, gas, and communications services. The tsunami was generated as the ocean floor was suddenly thrust up about seven metres near the epicentre, located near the Japan Trench, where the Pacific plate subducts beneath the Eurasian plate. Japan's recovery was slowed by over 100 powerful aftershocks, which followed the main event for months. On October 26, 2013, the same area was jolted by a 7.3 M_W quake that generated a small tsunami causing little damage.

Figure 10.D Wave heights of the tsunami generated by the 2011 Japan earthquake. The tsunami reached its greatest height (black) along the east shore of Honshu, near the epicentre, but also reached the Hawaiian Islands and the Americas. (Image courtesy of the National Oceanic and Atmospheric Administration)

Figure 10.E The east shore of Honshu, hit by a tsunami in 2011. (Sadatsugu Tomizawa/Getty Images)

pond, except tsunami advance across the ocean at amazing speeds of about 800 kilometres per hour. However, a tsunami in the open ocean can pass undetected because its height is usually less than 1 metre and the distance between wave crests ranges from 100 to 700 kilometres. On entering shallower coastal waters, these destructive waves are slowed down and the water begins to pile up to heights that can exceed 30 metres (Figure 10.17). As the crest of a tsunami approaches the shore, it appears as a rapid

PEOPLE AND THE ENVIRONMENT
Tsunami Warning System

In 1946 a large tsunami struck the Hawaiian Islands without warning. A wave more than 15 metres high left several coastal villages in shambles. This destruction motivated the U.S. Coast Guard to establish a tsunami warning system for coastal areas of the Pacific that includes 26 countries. From seismic observatories throughout the region, large earthquakes are reported to the Pacific Tsunami Warning Center in Honolulu, Hawaii. Scientists at the Center use tidal gauges and sea buoys to determine whether a tsunami has been formed after a quake. Within an hour a warning is issued. Although tsunami travel very rapidly, there is sufficient time to evacuate all but the region nearest the epicentre (Figure 10.F). For example, a tsunami generated near the Aleutian Islands would take 5 hours to reach Hawaii, and one generated near the coast of Chile would travel 15 hours before reaching Hawaii.

Figure 10.F Tsunami travel times to Honolulu, Hawaii, from selected locations throughout the Pacific.
(Data from NOAA)

rise in sea level, with a turbulent and chaotic surface. Tsunami can be very destructive (see Boxes 10.2 and 10.3). Canadian examples include the 1929 tsunami that killed 27 people and damaged 40 villages along the Burin Peninsula of southern Newfoundland and Labrador, and the 1964 tsunami (generated by the great Alaskan earthquake) that caused extensive damage to Port Alberni on Vancouver Island (Figure 10.18). The Burin tsunami was triggered by a magnitude 7.2 earthquake (epicentre 250 kilometres south of the south shore of Newfoundland) that caused a turbidity current of 200 cubic kilometres to rush down the continental slope of the Grand Banks, rupturing 12 transatlantic cables. The wave rose to 27 metres and reached the coasts of South Carolina and Portugal.

The first warning of an approaching tsunami is a rapid withdrawal of water from beaches. Coastal residents need to heed this warning and move to higher ground because about 5 to 30 minutes later,

the retreat of water is followed by a surge capable of extending several kilometres inland. In a successive fashion, each surge is followed by rapid oceanward retreat of the sea.

Landslides and Ground Subsidence

In the 1964 Alaskan earthquake, the greatest damage to structures was from landslides and ground subsidence triggered by the vibrations. At Valdez and Seward, the violent shaking caused deltaic materials to experience liquefaction; the subsequent slumping carried both waterfronts away. Because of the threat of recurrence, the entire town of Valdez was relocated about seven kilometres away on more stable ground. In Valdez, 31 people on a dock died when it slid into the sea.

Most of the damage in the city of Anchorage was also attributed to landslides. Many homes were

Figure 10.18 Damage to buildings associated with the tsunami that hit Port Alberni, British Columbia, in 1964.
(Photo by Charles Tebby/Alberni Valley Museum)

destroyed in Turnagain Heights when a layer of clay lost its strength and more than 80 hectares of land slid toward the ocean (Figure 10.19). A portion of this spectacular landslide (Earthquake Park) was left in its natural condition as a reminder of this destructive event. Downtown Anchorage was also disrupted as sections of the main business district dropped by as much as three metres.

Fire

During the 1906 earthquake in San Francisco many non-reinforced brick buildings were extensively damaged by vibrations. However, the greatest destruction was to large wooden structures by fires when gas and electrical lines were severed. The fires raged out of control for three days and devastated more than 500 blocks of the city. The problem was compounded by the initial ground shaking, which broke the city's water lines into hundreds of unconnected pieces. Although only a few deaths were attributed to the San Francisco fire, such is not always the case. A 1923 earthquake in Japan triggered an estimated 250 fires causing 100 000 deaths, devastated the city of Yokohama, and destroyed more than half the homes in Tokyo.

CAN EARTHQUAKES BE PREDICTED?

The earthquake that shook Northridge, California, on January 17, 1994, was brief (about 40 seconds) and only of moderate rating (M_W 6.7), but it killed 57 people and caused about US$40 billion in damage. The amount of devastation caused by the earthquake was high because the area is densely populated and highly developed. Seismologists warn that earthquakes of comparable or greater strength will occur along the San Andreas Fault.

Short-Range Predictions

We currently do not have an *absolutely* reliable method for making short-range earthquake predictions. However, substantial efforts to achieve this objective are being put forth in Japan, the United States, China, and Russia—countries where earthquake risks are high. This research has concentrated on monitoring possible *precursors*—phenomena that precede and thus provide a warning of a forthcoming earthquake. In California, for example, seismologists are measuring uplift, subsidence, and strain in the

Figure 10.19 Turnagain Heights slide caused by the 1964 Alaskan earthquake. **A.** Vibrations from the earthquake caused cracks to appear near the edge of the bluff. **B.** Within seconds blocks of land began to slide toward the sea on a weak layer of clay. In less than five minutes, as much as 200 metres of the Turnagain Heights bluff area had been destroyed. **C.** Photo of a small portion of the Turnagain Heights slide.
(Photo **C** courtesy of U.S. Geological Survey)

rocks near active faults. Some Japanese and Chinese scientists are studying anomalous animal behaviour that may precede a quake. Other researchers are monitoring changes in groundwater levels, while still others are trying to predict earthquakes based on increase in frequency of foreshocks.

Long-Range Forecasts

In contrast to short-range predictions within hours or days, long-range forecasts give the probability of a certain magnitude earthquake occurring on a time scale of 30 to 100 years or more. Long-range forecasts assume that earthquakes are repetitive or cyclic, like the weather: As soon as one earthquake is over, the continuing motions of Earth's plates begin to build stress in the rocks again until they fail once more. This has led seismologists to study historic records of earthquakes, looking for patterns to determine the probability of recurrence.

With this concept in mind, seismologists plotted the distribution of rupture zones associated with great earthquakes around the world. The maps revealed that individual rupture zones tend to occur adjacent to one

another without appreciable overlap, thereby tracing out a plate boundary. Because plates move at known rates, the researchers predicted that over one or two centuries, major earthquakes would occur along each segment of the plate boundary.

When researchers studied historical records, they discovered that some zones had not produced a great earthquake in more than a century. These quiet zones, called **seismic gaps**, were identified as probable sites for major earthquakes in the next few decades (Figure 10.20).

Another method of long-term forecasting, known as *paleoseismology* (*palaios* = ancient, *seismos* = shake, *ology* = the study of), has been implemented. One technique involves studying layered deposits that were offset by prehistoric seismic disturbances. Researchers recently discovered strong evidence that very powerful earthquakes (magnitude of 8 or larger) have repeatedly struck the Pacific Northwest over the past several thousand years. The most recent event occurred about 300 years ago. As a result of these findings, public officials have taken steps to strengthen some of the region's existing dams, bridges, and water systems.

In summary, it appears that the best prospects for making useful earthquake predictions involve

Figure 10.20 Map showing epicentres of large shallow earthquakes recorded from 1929 to 2012 along the northwest coast of British Columbia and the fault ruptures with which they were associated. The seismic gap located immediately west of southern Haida Gwaii was almost closed by the 2012 earthquake and denotes the most likely location for the next large earthquake along the Queen Charlotte Fault.
(Courtesy of Tricouni Press Ltd. with modifications)

forecasting magnitudes and locations on time scales of years or perhaps even decades. These forecasts are important because they provide information used to develop earthquake building standards and to assist in land-use planning.

PROBING EARTH'S INTERIOR

Wells drilled into the crust in search of oil, gas, and other natural resources have generally been confined to the upper 7 kilometres—only a small fraction of Earth's 6370-kilometre radius. Even the deepest well has penetrated to a depth of only 12.3 kilometres.

Fortunately, geologists have learned a great deal about Earth's composition and structure through computer modelling, high-pressure laboratory experiments, and samples of the solar system (meteorites) that collide with Earth. In addition, many clues to the physical conditions inside our planet have been acquired through the study of seismic waves generated by earthquakes and nuclear explosions. As seismic waves pass through Earth, they carry information to the surface about the materials through which they were transmitted. Hence, when carefully analyzed, seismic records provide an image of materials below the surface. The Canadian LITHOPROBE project, for example, has yielded exciting insights on the deep lithosphere from the processing of seismic data (see Box 10.4).

Much of our knowledge of Earth's interior comes from the study of earthquake waves that penetrate Earth and emerge at some distant point. The technique involves accurately measuring the

---

BOX 10.4

CANADIAN PROFILE
Lithoprobe: Probing the Depths of Canada

David Eaton*

Unlike the oceanic crust, continents preserve a record of Earth's early history, including how ancient mountains formed and how the continents grew and developed over time. Geoscientists are faced with a daunting challenge, however: to reconstruct this tectonic record from fragmentary evidence provided by rocks exposed at the surface. Canada's LITHOPROBE project, which commenced in 1984, is

a bold multi-institutional endeavour to unravel the tectonic evolution of North America with a focus on the critical third dimension of geology: depth. With collaboration by more than 900 scientists working in academia, government agencies, and the petroleum and mining industries, LITHOPROBE has involved a significant segment of Canada's Earth science community in a coordinated research effort. The research program was divided into a series of transects that

collectively span the evolution of the North American continent in time (about 4 billion years) and space.

To achieve adequate resolution of geologic features down to the base of the crust (approximately 40 kilometres) and the upper mantle, LITHOPROBE research has been spearheaded by multichannel seismic-reflection (MSR) profiling. Adapted from the petroleum industry, where it is used extensively for exploration of the top 10 kilometres

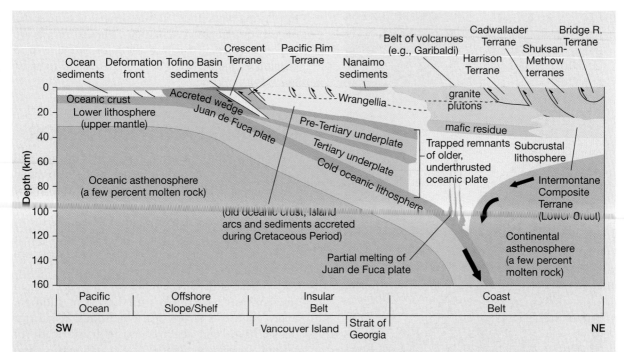

Figure 10.G Part of the Canadian LITHOPROBE project involved the study of the lithospheric structure of western Canada. Among the exciting discoveries was the detection of lithospheric fragments (underplates) that remain lodged under the west coast region and have contributed to the growth of mountain roots.
(Modified from image courtesy of R. M. Clowes. Used by permission.)

of sedimentary basins, this technique makes use of P waves, usually generated mechanically by using vibroseis trucks, to record faint echoes produced at buried geologic contacts, faults, and shear zones. Much like medical imaging techniques, the seismic data are processed by computer to enhance the seismic reflections, producing cross-sectional images that can be compared with geologic data to reveal the underlying anatomy of the lithosphere. Specialists in all areas of geology, geophysics, and geochemistry have collaborated on major geotectonic problems by using techniques that include basic mapping, precise geochronology, electromagnetic studies, seismic refraction, and paleomagnetism.

LITHOPROBE's pilot study on Vancouver Island demonstrated that MSR profiling methods can be used to map layers near the top of the descending Juan de Fuca slab (Figure 10.G). It showed slabs of lithosphere welded to the continental lithosphere of western British Columbia as *underplates*. Results from this modern subduction system (Cascadia) have provided a template for understanding ancient subduction systems. Furthermore, subduction "scars" have been detected in the mantle beneath Archean rocks of the Superior craton in Quebec and the Proterozoic Great Bear Arc in the Northwest Territories. These results establish that the subduction occurred in some areas in the late Archean and support the concept

that subducted slabs can be accreted to the base of continental plates as part of the process of formation of deep lithospheric roots.

LITHOPROBE's main research focused on ancient shield and platform regions where North America is known to have grown via a series of mountain-building events. LITHOPROBE profiles have allowed geoscientists to trace structural contacts down to the base of the crust (Moho). This work has led to the discovery of previously unrecognized mountain belts that lie buried beneath undeformed sedimentary rocks.

For further information visit **www.lithoprobe.ca**.

David Eaton is a professor in the Department of Earth Sciences at the University of Calgary.

time required for P and S waves to travel from an earthquake or nuclear explosion to a seismic station. Because the time required for P and S waves to travel through Earth depends on the properties of the materials encountered, seismologists search for variations in travel times that cannot be accounted for simply by differences in the distances travelled.

These variations correspond to changes in the properties of the materials encountered.

One major problem is that to obtain accurate travel times, seismologists must establish the exact location and time of an earthquake. This is commonly a difficult task because most earthquakes occur in remote areas. By contrast, the time and location of a nuclear test explosion is always known precisely. Despite the limitations of studying seismic waves generated by earthquakes, seismologists in the first half of the twentieth century were able to use them to determine the major layers of Earth. It was not until the early 1960s, when nuclear testing was in its heyday and networks consisting of hundreds of sensitive seismographs were deployed, that the finer structures of Earth's interior were established with certainty.

The Nature of Seismic Waves

To examine Earth's composition and structure, we must first study some of the basic properties of wave transmission, or *propagation*. Seismic energy travels out from its source in all directions as waves. The paths taken by these waves as *rays* (lines drawn perpendicular to the wave front) are shown in Figure 10.21. Significant characteristics of seismic waves include the following:

- The velocity of seismic waves depends on the density and elasticity of the intervening material. Seismic waves travel most rapidly in rigid materials that elastically spring back to their original shapes when the stress caused by a seismic wave is removed. For instance, crystalline rock transmits seismic waves more rapidly than does a layer of unconsolidated mud.

- Within a given layer, the speed of seismic waves generally increases with depth because pressure increases and squeezes the rock into a more compact elastic material.

- Compressional waves (P waves) are able to propagate through liquids as well as solids because when compressed, these materials behave elastically.

- Shear waves (S waves) cannot propagate through liquids because, unlike solids, liquids have no shear strength. When liquids are subjected to forces that act to change their shapes, they simply flow.

- In all materials, P waves travel faster than S waves.

- When seismic waves pass from one material to another, the path of the wave is refracted (bent).* In addition, some of the energy is reflected from the discontinuity (the boundary between the two dissimilar materials). This is similar to what happens to light when it passes from air into water.

Thus seismic waves speed up or slow down and can be refracted (bent) or reflected when they cross discontinuities. These measurable changes in seismic wave motions enable seismologists to probe Earth's interior.

---

*Refraction occurs provided that the ray is not travelling perpendicular to the boundary.

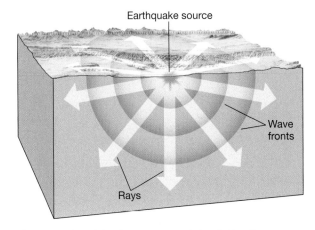

Figure 10.21   Seismic energy travels in all directions from an earthquake source (hypocentre). The energy can be portrayed as expanding wave fronts or as rays drawn perpendicular to the wave fronts.

Seismic Waves and Earth's Structure

If Earth were a perfectly homogeneous body, seismic waves would spread through it in all directions, travelling in a straight line at a constant speed. Instead, seismic waves reaching seismographs located farther from an earthquake travel at faster average speeds than those recorded at locations closer to the event. This general increase in speed with depth is a consequence of increased pressure, which enhances the elastic properties of deeply buried rock. As a result, the paths of seismic rays through Earth are refracted as shown in Figure 10.22.

As more sensitive seismographs were developed, it became apparent that abrupt velocity changes

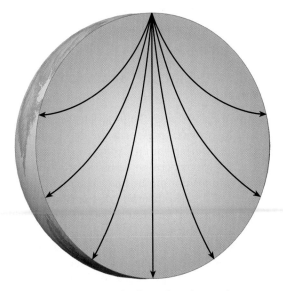

Figure 10.22   Wave paths through a planet where velocity increases with depth.

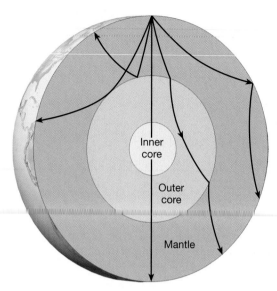

Figure 10.23 A few of the many possible paths that seismic rays take through Earth.

also occur at particular depths. Because these discontinuities were detected worldwide, seismologists concluded that Earth must be composed of distinct shells that have varying compositions or mechanical properties (Figure 10.23; see also Figure 1.17).

DISCOVERING EARTH'S MAJOR BOUNDARIES

From global seismic data seismologists have developed a detailed image of Earth's interior (Figure 1.17). This model is continually being fine-tuned as more data become available, new seismic techniques are employed, and laboratory studies determine the properties of various Earth materials under the extreme environments found deep in Earth.

The Crust–Mantle Boundary (the Moho)

In 1909 a pioneering Yugoslavian seismologist, Andrija Mohorovičić, presented the first convincing evidence for layering within Earth. The boundary he discovered separates crustal materials from rocks of different composition in the underlying mantle, and it was named the **Mohorovičić discontinuity** in his honour. The name for this boundary was quickly shortened to **Moho.**

By carefully examining the seismograms of shallow earthquakes, Mohorovičić found that seismic stations located more than 200 kilometres from an earthquake obtained appreciably faster average travel velocities for P waves than did stations located nearer the quake (Figure 10.24). In particular, P waves that reached the closest stations first had velocities that averaged about 6 kilometres per second. By contrast, the seismic energy recorded at more distant stations travelled at speeds that approached 8 kilometres per second. From these data, Mohorovičić concluded that below 50 kilometres, a layer exists with properties markedly different from those of Earth's crust.

Figure 10.24 illustrates how Mohorovičić reached this important conclusion. Notice that the first wave to reach the seismograph located 100 kilometres from the epicentre travelled the shortest route directly through the crust. However, at the seismograph located 300 kilometres from the epicentre, the first P wave to arrive travelled through the mantle, a zone of higher velocity. Thus, although this wave travelled a greater distance, it reached the recording instrument sooner than did the rays taking the more direct route. This is because a large portion of its journey was through a region having a composition where seismic waves travel more rapidly. This principle is analogous to a driver taking a bypass route around a large city during rush hour. Although this alternative route is longer, it may be faster.

The Core–Mantle Boundary

A few years later, in 1914, the location of another major boundary was established by German seismologist Beno Gutenberg.* This discovery was based primarily on the observation that P waves diminish and eventually die out completely about 100° from an earthquake (Figure 10.25). Then, about 140° away, the P waves reappear, but about two minutes later than would be expected based on the distance travelled. This belt, where direct seismic waves are absent, is about 40° wide and has been named the **P-wave shadow zone**** (Figure 10.25).

Gutenberg realized that the P-wave shadow zone could be explained if Earth contained a core that was composed of material unlike the overlying mantle. The core, which Gutenberg calculated to be located at a depth of 2900 kilometres, must somehow hinder the transmission of P waves, similar to the way in which light rays are blocked by an object that casts a shadow. However, rather than actually stopping the P waves, the shadow zone is produced

---

*The core–mantle boundary had been predicted by R. D. Oldham in 1906, but his arguments for a central core did not receive wide acceptance.

**As more sensitive instruments were developed, weak and delayed P waves that enter this zone via reflection were detected.

A Time 1—Slower shallow waves arrive at seismic station 1 first.

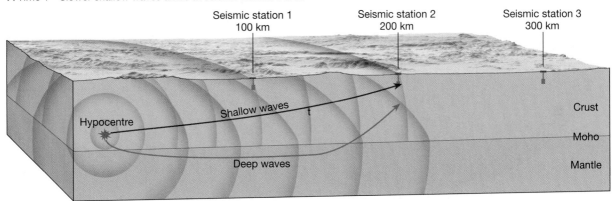

B Time 2—Slower shallow waves arrive at seismic station 2 first.

C Time 3—Faster deeper waves arrive at seismic station 3 first.

Figure 10.24   Idealized paths of seismic waves travelling from an earthquake hypocentre to three seismic stations. In parts **A** and **B**, you can see that the two nearest recording stations receive the slower waves first because the waves travelled a shorter distance. However, as shown in part **C**, beyond 200 kilometres, the first waves received passed through the mantle, which is a zone of higher velocity.

by bending (refracting) of the P waves, which enter the core, as shown in Figure 10.25.

It was further determined that S waves do not travel through the core. This fact led geologists to conclude that at least a portion of this region is liquid. This conclusion was further supported by the observation that P-wave velocities suddenly drop dramatically as they enter the core. Because melting reduces the elasticity of rock, this evidence

pointed to the existence of a liquid layer below the rocky mantle.

Discovery of the Inner Core

In 1936 the last major subdivision of Earth's interior was predicted by Inge Lehmann, a Danish seismologist. Lehmann discovered a new region of seismic reflection and refraction within the core: a

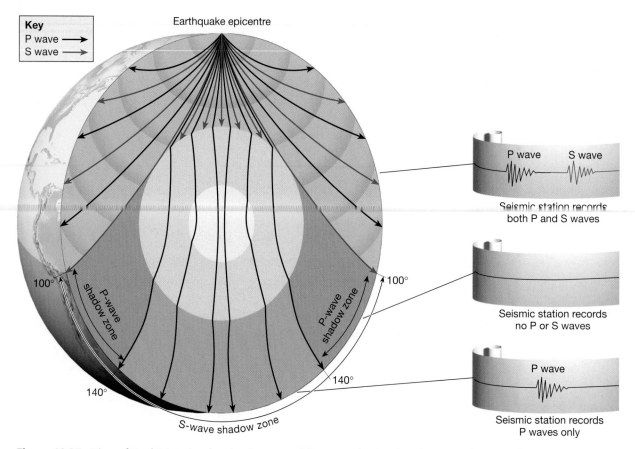

Figure 10.25 View of Earth's interior showing P-wave and S-wave paths. Any location more than 100° from the earthquake epicentre will not receive direct S waves because the outer core will not transmit them. Although P waves are also absent beyond 100°, they are recorded beyond 140° because of refraction.

core within a core. The size of the **inner core** was not precisely established until the early 1960s, when underground nuclear tests were conducted in Nevada. Because the exact location and time of the explosions were known, echoes from seismic waves that bounced off the inner core revealed its size.

From these data, the inner core was found to have a radius of about 1200 kilometres. Furthermore, P waves passing through the inner core have appreciably faster average velocities than do those penetrating only the outer core. The apparent increase in the elasticity of the inner core is evidence that this innermost region is solid.

CHAPTER SUMMARY

- *Earthquakes* occur when crustal rocks rupture at the *hypocentre*, below the *epicentre* on Earth's surface. Rupture generates *seismic waves* and occurs by *elastic rebound* to release built-up stress along a fault. *Foreshocks* often precede a major earthquake and *aftershocks* follow it.

- Seismic waves include *body* (through Earth) and *surface* (around Earth). Body waves include faster

primary or *P waves* that travel through rock along a direct path and *secondary* or *S waves* that shake rock at right angles to travel direction.

- *Epicentres* are located using travel times of P and S waves and triangulating distances from three or more seismic stations. Most epicentres occur along the circum-Pacific belt and the oceanic ridge system.

- The *Modified Mercalli Intensity Scale* is based on damage to buildings. Magnitude estimates of energy released use the *Richter scale* by comparing largest wave amplitude with distance to the epicentre. Each higher integer means 32 times more energy was released.
- Structural damage depends on wave amplitude, duration of vibrations, substrate (geology), and structural design. Secondary effects of quakes include *tsunami*, landslides, subsidence, and fire.

- While short-range predictions are not yet possible, earthquake-prone regions with *seismic gaps* (overdue) are well known. P and S waves travel faster in solid elastic materials, slower in weaker layers, and are reflected and refracted (bent) at material boundaries. This tells us that Earth's layers are crust, mantle, outer liquid, and inner solid core.

MasteringGeology
www.masteringgeology.com

Looking for additional review and test prep materials? Visit the Study Area in MasteringGeology to enhance your understanding of this chapter's content by accessing a variety of resources, including

Self-Study Quizzes, Geoscience Animations, GEODe Tutorials, RSS feeds, flashcards, weblinks, self-study quizzes, and an optional Pearson eText.

REVIEW QUESTIONS

1. What is an earthquake? Under what circumstances do earthquakes occur?
2. How are faults, hypocentres, and epicentres related?
3. Explain what is meant by elastic rebound.
4. Describe the principle of a seismograph.
5. List the major differences between P (primary), S (secondary), and L (surface or long) waves. Which of these seismic wave types causes the greatest destruction?
6. Each increase of 1 on the Richter scale corresponds to a _____ -fold increase in wave amplitude and a _____ -fold increase in energy release.

7. In addition to seismic vibrations, what other factors contribute to the destruction associated with earthquakes?
8. What is a tsunami? How is one generated?
9. Explain how the following boundaries within Earth's interior were discovered:
   a. The crust-mantle boundary (Mohorovičić discontinuity or Moho)
   b. The core-mantle boundary
   c. The inner core–outer core boundary
10. What types of information are useful in making short-range predictions versus long-range forecasts of future earthquake activity?

11 THE OCEAN FLOOR

Colourful coral and other marine animals cling to a vertical submarine cliff in the deep ocean waters off the coast of Nova Scotia. (Photo by Dale Sanders/ Masterfile)

CHAPTER OUTLINE

Mapping the Ocean Floor
Continental Margins
Features of the Deep-Ocean Basin
Coral Reefs and Atolls
Sea-floor Sediments
Mid-Ocean Ridges

Because rock deformation and earthquakes often occur near lithospheric plate boundaries, and plate boundaries are commonly found offshore, we will now look at the topography and materials that compose the ocean floor. This information will prepare you to examine evidence for plate tectonics from the ocean floor in the next chapter, including magnetic, earthquake, and sedimentary data. As you will see in Chapter 12, that evidence convinced many scientists of the validity of the theory of plate tectonics.

If all water were drained from the ocean basins, we would see a great diversity of features, including linear chains of volcanoes, deep canyons, rift valleys, and large submarine plateaus. The scenery would be nearly as varied as that on the continents.

An understanding of the ocean floor's varied topography did not unfold until the historic three-year voyage of the H. M. S. *Challenger* (Figure 11.1). From December 1872 to May 1876, the *Challenger* expedition made the first study of the global ocean. The 127 500-kilometre trip took the ship and its crew of scientists to every ocean except the Arctic. They sampled the depth of the water by laboriously lowering a weighted line overboard. Not many years later, the knowledge gained by the *Challenger* was expanded with the laying of transatlantic cables.

MAPPING THE OCEAN FLOOR

In the 1920s a technological breakthrough occurred with the invention of electronic depth-sounding equipment (**echo sounder**). (The echo sounder is also referred to as *sonar*, an acronym for *so*und *navi*gation *a*nd *r*anging.) The echo sounder works by transmitting sound waves toward the ocean bottom (Figure 11.2A). A sensitive receiver intercepts the echo reflected from the bottom, and a clock precisely measures the time interval to fractions of a second.

By knowing the velocity of sound waves in water (about 1500 metres per second) and the time required for the energy pulse to reach the ocean floor and return, depth can be established. The depths determined from continuous monitoring of these echoes are plotted, creating a profile of the ocean floor. By laboriously combining profiles from several adjacent traverses, a chart of the sea floor is produced. Although much more complete and detailed than anything available before, these charts show only the largest topographic features of the ocean floor (see Figure 11.7).

In the past few decades, researchers have designed even more sophisticated echo sounders to map the ocean floor. In contrast to simple echo sounders, *multibeam sonar* employs an array of sound sources and listening devices. Thus, rather than obtaining the depth of a single point every few seconds, this technique obtains a profile of a narrow strip of sea floor (Figure 11.2B). These profiles are recorded every few seconds as the research vessel advances, building a continuous swath of relatively detailed coverage. (A ship will map a section of sea floor by travelling in a back-and-forth pattern like someone would use when mowing a lawn.)

Despite their greater efficiency and enhanced detail, research vessels equipped with multibeam sonar travel at a mere 10 to 20 kilometres per hour. It would take 100 vessels outfitted with this equipment hundreds of years to map the entire sea floor. Another technological breakthrough that has led to an enhanced understanding of the sea floor involves measuring the shape of the surface of the global ocean from space. After compensating for waves, tides, currents, and atmospheric effects, it was discovered that the water's surface is not perfectly flat; gravity attracts water toward regions where massive sea floor features occur. Therefore, mountains and ridges

Figure 11.1 The H. M. S. *Challenger*. (From C. W. Thompson and Sir John Murray, *Report on the Scientific Results of the Voyage of the H. M. S.* Challenger, Vol. 1. Great Britain: Challenger Office, 1895, Plate 1, Library of Congress)

Figure 11.2   Echo sounders. **A.** An echo sounder determines the water depth by measuring the time interval required for an acoustic wave to travel from a ship to the sea floor and back. The speed of sound in water is 1500 metres per second. Therefore, depth = 1/2(1500 m/s × echo travel time). **B.** Modern multibeam sonar obtains a profile of a narrow swath of sea floor every few seconds.

produce elevated areas on the ocean surface, and, conversely, canyons and trenches cause slight depressions. Satellites equipped with *radar altimeters* are able to measure these subtle differences by bouncing microwaves off the sea surface (Figure 11.3). These devices can measure variations as small as a few centimetres. Cross-checked with traditional sonar depth measurements, the data are used to produce ocean-floor maps, such as Figure 11.7.

Oceanographers studying the topography of the ocean floor have delineated three major units: continental margins, deep-ocean basins, and mid-ocean ridges. The map in Figure 11.4 outlines these areas for the North Atlantic, and the profile at the bottom illustrates the varied topography. Such profiles usually have their vertical dimension exaggerated many times—40 times in this case—to make topographic features more conspicuous. Because of this, the slopes shown in the sea-floor profile appear to be *much* steeper than they actually are.

CONTINENTAL MARGINS

Two main types of **continental margins** have been identified: passive and active. Passive margins are found along most of the coastal areas that surround the Atlantic Ocean, including the east coasts of North and South America, as well as the coastal areas of western Europe and Africa. Passive margins are *not* associated with plate boundaries and therefore

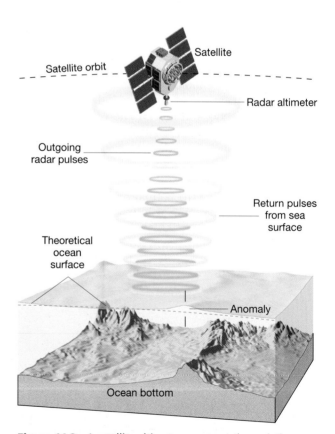

Figure 11.3   A satellite altimeter measures the variation in sea surface elevation, which is caused by gravitational attraction and mimics the shape of the sea floor. The sea surface anomaly is the difference between the measured and theoretical ocean surface.

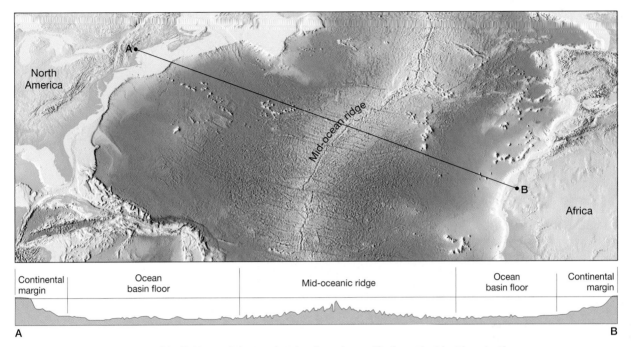

Continental margin	Ocean basin floor	Mid-oceanic ridge	Ocean basin floor	Continental margin

A   B

Figure 11.4 Major topographic divisions of the North Atlantic and a profile from the Maritimes to the coast of North Africa.

experience very little volcanism and few earthquakes. Here, weathered materials that eroded from the adjacent land mass accumulate to form a thick, broad wedge of relatively undisturbed sediments.

By contrast, **active continental margins** occur where oceanic lithosphere is being subducted beneath the edge of a continent. The result is a relatively narrow margin, consisting of highly deformed sediments that were scraped from the descending lithospheric slab. Active continental margins are common around the Pacific Rim, where they parallel deep oceanic trenches.

Passive Continental Margins

The features composing a **passive continental margin** include the continental shelf, the continental slope, and the continental rise (Figure 11.5).

CONTINENTAL SHELF The **continental shelf** is a gently sloping submerged surface extending from the shoreline toward the deep-ocean basin. Because it is underlain by continental crust, it is clearly a flooded extension of the continents. Almost nonexistent along some continents, the continental shelf may extend seaward as far as 1500 kilometres along others. On average, the shelf is about 80 kilometres wide at a depth of 130 metres deep at the seaward edge, and its inclination, one-tenth of a degree. The slope is so slight that it would appear to an observer to be a horizontal surface.

Although continental shelves represent only 7.5 percent of the total ocean area, they have economic, biologic, and political significance because they contain important mineral deposits, including large reservoirs of petroleum and natural gas, and huge sand and gravel deposits. The waters above the continental shelf contain many important fishing grounds that are significant sources of food.

Although the continental shelf is relatively featureless, some areas are mantled by extensive glacial deposits and are thus quite rugged. The most profound features are long valleys extending from the coastline into deeper waters. Many of these valleys are the seaward extensions of river valleys on the adjacent land mass. Such valleys appear to have been excavated during the Pleistocene Epoch (the last Ice Age).

During that time great quantities of water were contained in vast ice sheets on the continents, which caused sea level to drop by 100 metres or more, exposing large areas of the continental shelves. Rivers extended their courses, and land-dwelling plants and animals inhabited the newly exposed portions of the continents. Dredging off the east coast of North America has produced the remains of numerous land dwellers, including mammoths, mastodons, and horses, adding to the evidence that portions of the continental shelves were once above sea level.

Most continental shelves (e.g., east coast of Canada) consist of shallow-water sediments several kilometres thick that are interbedded with limestones that formed during earlier periods of coral reef building, a process that occurs only in shallow water. Such evidence led researchers to conclude that these thick

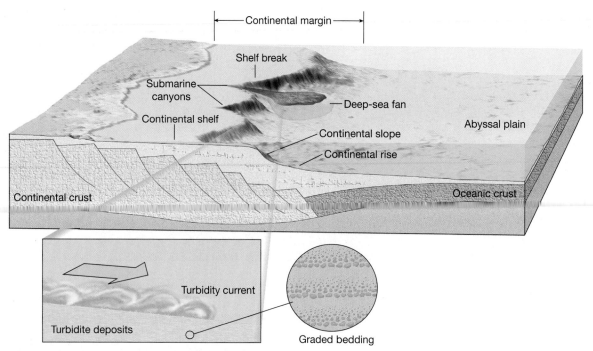

Figure 11.5   Schematic diagram depicting the major features of a passive continental margin. Note that the slopes shown for the continental shelf and continental slope are greatly exaggerated. The continental shelf has an average slope of 1/10 of 1 degree, while the continental slope has an average slope of about 5 degrees. Erosion of the continental margin, enlargement of submarine canyons, and deposition of detrital sediment in the deep sea are accomplished by downslope-flowing turbidity currents. These sediment-laden, high-density currents lose momentum as they reach the relatively flat abyssal plain, and deposit their loads as turbidites characterized by graded bedding. Over time, the accumulation of turbidites focused near the mouths of submarine canyons produce lobe-shaped sediment bodies called deep-sea fans.

accumulations of sediment are produced along a gradually subsiding continental margin.

CONTINENTAL SLOPE   Marking the seaward edge of the continental shelf is the **continental slope**, a relatively steep structure that marks the boundary between continental crust and oceanic crust (Figure 11.5). As you will learn in Chapter 12, this boundary represents the original rift after a continent split apart (the last major splitting was the breakup of the supercontinent Pangaea) and thus the true edge of a continent. The continental slope averages 5 degrees (in places may increase to 25 degrees) and only 20 kilometres wide.

CONTINENTAL RISE   The continental slope merges into the **continental rise** where the slope drops to about one third of a degree. The rise may extend for hundreds of kilometres into the deep-ocean basin.

The continental rise consists of a thick accumulation of sediment that moved downslope from the continental shelf to the deep-ocean floor. The sediments are delivered to the base of the continental slope by turbidity currents that follow submarine canyons (Figure 11.5), where they deposit sediment that forms a **deep-sea fan**. As fans from adjacent submarine canyons grow, they coalesce to produce the

continuous apron of sediment at the base of the continental slope that we call the continental rise.

Submarine Canyons and Turbidity Currents

Deep, steep-sided valleys known as **submarine canyons** are cut into the continental slope and may extend across the entire continental rise to the deep-ocean basin (Figure 11.5). Although some of the canyons appear to be the seaward extensions of river valleys, such as the Amazon River, others are not directly associated with existing river systems. Furthermore, because these canyons extend to depths far below the lowest level of the sea during the Ice Age, we cannot attribute their formation to stream erosion. These features must be created by some process that operates far below the ocean surface.

Most available information favours the view that submarine canyons have been eroded, at least in part, by turbidity currents (Figure 11.5). **Turbidity currents** are downslope movements of dense, sediment-laden water. They are created when sand and mud on the continental shelf and slope are dislodged, perhaps by an earthquake, and are thrown into suspension. Because such mud-choked water is denser than normal seawater, it flows downslope, eroding and entraining more sediment. These muddy torrents are thought to be the major factor in the growth of most submarine canyons.

Narrow continental margins (e.g., California to British Columbia coast) are dissected by numerous submarine canyons. Here, headward erosion has extended many of these canyons landward into shallow water, where longshore currents are active. As a result, sediments carried to the coasts by rivers are transported along the shore until they reach a submarine canyon. This steady supply of sediment collects until it becomes unstable and moves as a massive underwater landslide (turbidity current) to the deep-ocean floor.

Turbidity currents eventually lose momentum and come to rest along the floor of the ocean basin (Figure 11.5). As these currents slow, the suspended sediments begin to settle out. First, the coarser, heavier sand is dropped, followed by successively finer deposits of silt and then clay. Consequently, these deposits, called **turbidites**, are characterized by a decrease in sediment grain size from bottom to top, producing **graded bedding** (Figure 11.5). Thus turbidity currents are an important mechanism of sediment transport in the ocean (Box 11.1).

Active Continental Margins

Along some coasts a narrow continental slope descends abruptly into a deep-ocean trench located between the continent and ocean basin. Thus, the landward wall of the trench and the continental slope are essentially the same feature.

Active continental margins are located primarily around the Pacific Ocean in areas where the leading edge of a continent is overrunning oceanic lithosphere (Figure 11.6). Here sediments from the ocean floor and pieces of oceanic crust are scraped from the descending oceanic plate and plastered against the edge of the overriding continent. This chaotic accumulation of deformed sediment and scraps of oceanic crust is called an **accretionary** (*ad* = toward, *crescere* – grow) **wedge**. Prolonged subduction, along with the accretion of sediments on the landward side of the trench, can produce a large accumulation of sediments along a continental margin. For example, a large accretionary wedge is found along the northern coast of Japan's Honshu Island, and pieces of an ancient wedge compose part of Newfoundland and Labrador.

Some subduction zones have little or no accumulation of sediments, indicating that ocean sediments are being carried into the mantle with the subducting plate.

FEATURES OF THE DEEP-OCEAN BASIN

Between the continental margin and the oceanic ridge system lies the **deep-ocean basin** (Box 11.2). The size of this region—almost 30 percent of Earth's surface—is roughly comparable to the percentage of the surface that projects above sea level as land. Here we find deep-ocean trenches, abyssal plains, and seamounts.

Deep-Ocean Trenches

Deep-ocean trenches are long, relatively narrow features that form the deepest parts of the ocean (Table 11.1). Most trenches are located in the Pacific Ocean (Figure 11.7). The Challenger Deep, in the Mariana Trench, is almost 11 000 metres below sea level.

Trenches are sites where moving lithospheric plates plunge back into the mantle and earthquakes and volcanoes are created as one plate descends beneath another. Thus, trenches commonly parallel volcanic arcs along plate boundaries. The release of volatiles (mainly water) from a descending plate triggers melting in the wedge of asthenosphere above it. This buoyant material slowly migrates upward and gives rise to volcanic activity at the surface.

Figure 11.6 Active continental margin. Here sediments from the ocean floor are scraped from the descending plate and added to the continental crust as an accretionary wedge.

BOX 11.1

Grand Banks Earthquake and Turbidity Current

On November 18, 1929, an earthquake measuring 7.2 M_L on the Richter scale occurred at about 5:00 p.m. on the Laurentian Slope near the eastern edge of the Grand Banks. The quake was felt throughout the Atlantic provinces but produced only minor damage. At 7:30 p.m., however, a tsunami hit the Atlantic coast, causing great devastation, particularly in the Burin Peninsula of Newfoundland and Labrador, where 27 people drowned and boats and buildings were destroyed.

The earthquake occurred at a time when long-distance communication was limited to the telegraph, a system that required extensive cable systems. Based on the timing of telegraph communication breaks, it was realized that a number of cables were severed at the precise time of the earthquake, near the epicentre. More difficult to explain was the sequence of cable breaks southeast of the epicentre (Figure 11.A-A); the last, and most distant cable, hundreds of kilometres away, was cut more than 13 hours after the earthquake. It was not until the 1950s, when a lobe-shaped deposit (see Figure 11.A-B) of graded gravel and sand up to 1 metre thick was discovered on the deep-ocean floor, that the reason for the successive cable breaks was realized: the instantaneous cable breaks occurred because of slumping near the epicentre, and the later successive cable breaks resulted from the downslope movement of a turbidity current that deposited the sand (see Figure 11.A-C)

The timing of the cable breaks in the deep sea provided the first indication of how fast turbidity currents can flow. It is estimated that the speed of the Grand Banks turbidity current reached 20 metres per second on the steepest part of the continental slope, slowing to 11 metres per second on the abyssal plain. The total area of deposition from this single event is estimated to be up to 250 000 square kilometres.

Figure 11.A The interpretation of submarine mass-wasting processes based on telegraph cable breaks that occurred during and after the Grand Banks earthquake of 1929. **A.** The locations of the submarine telegraph cables (solid yellow lines), sections of cable breakage (dashed white lines), and length of time elapsed between the earthquake event and the breakage of the cables are indicated. Orange dots represent points of "instantaneous" cable breakage that occurred at the same time as the earthquake. Yellow dots indicate points of cable breakage that occurred after the earthquake. **B.** Location of the area of slumping interpreted to have occurred during the earthquake (as indicated by instantaneous cable breaks), and the distribution of the turbidite deposited after the earthquake. **C.** A schematic cross-section of the transect X-Y in part A, showing the relative locations of cable breaks due to slumping versus those associated with the passage of a turbidity current. (Source: Based on Heezen, B.C. and Ewing, M., 1952, "Turbidity currents and submarine slumps, and the 1929 Grand Banks Earthquake," American Journal of Science, v. 250, p. 849–873)

GEOLOGY AND POPULAR MEDIA
Many Days After Tomorrow . . .

Not only does sea level drop during glaciations but the world's oceanic thermohaline circulation system (global conveyor belt in Figure 11.B) slows down and can even stop. This is the correct (but highly exaggerated) premise of the 2004 disaster film *The Day After Tomorrow*, in which Earth enters the next Ice Age as climatologist Jack Hall (portrayed by Dennis Quaid) rallies to save the world. Today as warm surface water flows into the North Atlantic, it gives off heat as it cools (like a refrigerator) and evaporates, thereby becoming more saline and dense. Just south of Greenland the dense cold water descends to the floor of the deep-ocean basin, where

it becomes North Atlantic deep water that travels south toward Antarctica. According to scientific studies of ice cores and deep sea sediments, a major cold spell occurred in the northern hemisphere about 11 000 years ago that was likely caused by large glacial lakes draining cold fresh water into the North Atlantic, reducing salinity (density), temporarily shutting down movement of the oceanic conveyor belt, and inducing regional cooling. However, the timing of this conveyor shutdown is science fiction: It took at least decades to accomplish in the past, not one week as depicted in the movie. Also, the instant deep-freeze of New York City was due to

rapid downdraft cooling of air in a huge hurricane, whereas in reality air gets warmer as it descends. Furthermore, hurricanes form over warm ocean water (not over land) and no storm could occupy an entire continent as shown in the film. Finally, the giant wave that flooded New York in the film could not be generated by a storm (storms cause gradual, smaller rises in water level) and it looked more like an earthquake-induced tsunami that would be unlikely on a passive continental margin like the eastern seaboard. Thus, while the basic principle of regional cooling is correct, the details in this film are pure Hollywood.

Figure 11.B The global ocean conveyor belt (thermohaline circulation system) is driven by changes in ocean water density linked to water temperature and salinity. This circulation system is partly responsible for large-scale heat transfer from the tropics to polar regions.

TABLE **11.1** Dimensions of Some Deep-Ocean Trenches

Trench	Depth (km)	Average Width (km)	Length (km)
Aleutian	7.7	50	3700
Central America	6.7	40	2800
Japan	8.4	100	800
Java	7.5	80	4500
Kurile–Kamchatka	10.5	120	2200
Mariana	11.0	70	2550
Peru–Chile	8.1	100	5900
Philippine	10.5	60	1400
Puerto Rico	8.4	120	1550
South Sandwich	8.4	90	1450
Tonga	10.8	55	1400

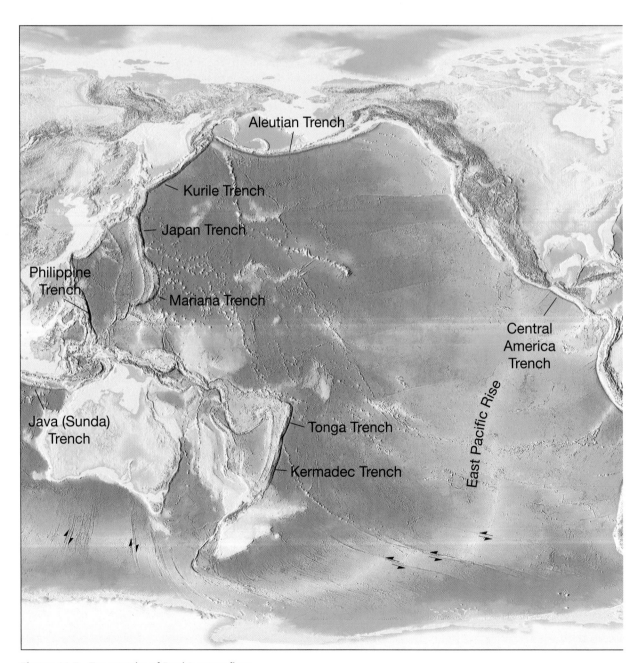

Figure 11.7 Topography of Earth's ocean floor.

Abyssal Plains

Abyssal (*a* = without, *byssus* = bottom) **plains** are incredibly flat features and likely the most level places on Earth. For example, the abyssal plain found off the coast of Argentina has less than 3 metres of relief over a distance exceeding 1300 kilometres (Figure 11.7, dark area off southeast coast of South America). The monotonous topography of abyssal plains will occasionally be interrupted by the protruding summit of a partially buried volcanic peak.

Using seismic profilers (instruments whose signals penetrate far below the ocean floor) researchers have determined that abyssal plains owe their relatively featureless topography to thick accumulations of primarily turbidite sediments that have buried an otherwise rugged ocean floor.

Abyssal plains are found in all the oceans. However, because the Atlantic Ocean has fewer trenches to act as traps for the sediments carried down the continental slope, it has more extensive abyssal plains than does the Pacific.

Seamounts

Dotting the ocean floors are isolated volcanic peaks called **seamounts**. These features may rise hundreds of metres above the surrounding topography. Although these broad conical peaks have been discovered in all the oceans (e.g., Flemish Cap in the north

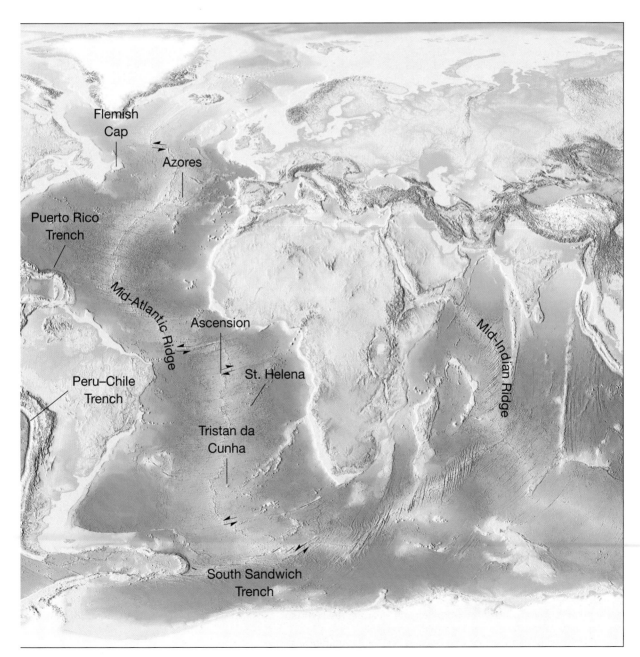

Atlantic, which is 560 kilometres east of St. John's; shown in Figure 11.7), the greatest number have been identified in the Pacific.

Many of these undersea volcanoes form near oceanic ridges, regions of sea-floor spreading. If a volcano grows rapidly, it may emerge as an island. Examples of volcanic islands in the Atlantic include the Azores, Ascension, Tristan da Cunha, and St. Helena.

Although they exist as islands, some of these volcanoes are eroded to near sea level by running water and wave action. Over millions of years the islands gradually sink as the moving plate slowly carries them from the oceanic ridge area. These submerged flat-topped seamounts are called **tablemounts** or **guyots.*** In other instances, guyots may be

———

The term guyot is named after Princeton University's first geology professor. It is pronounced "GEE-oh" with a hard g as in give.

remnants of eroded volcanic islands that were formed away from the ridge crest, possibly by hot-spot activity. Here subsidence occurs after the volcanic activity ceases and the sea floor cools and contracts.

CORAL REEFS AND ATOLLS

Coral reefs are among the most picturesque features found in the ocean. They are constructed primarily from the calcareous (calcite-rich) skeletal remains of corals that are cemented by secretions of corals and certain algae. Reef-building corals grow best in warm, clear sunlit waters. The limiting depth of active reef growth is only about 45 metres.

In 1831 naturalist Charles Darwin set out aboard the British ship H. M. S. *Beagle* on its famous five-year expedition that circumnavigated the globe. During the voyage he developed a hypothesis on the formation of coral islands, called **atolls**. As Figure 11.8E illustrates,

D Barrier reef

E Atoll

Figure 11.8   Formation of a coral atoll because of the gradual sinking of oceanic crust and upward growth of the coral reef. **A.** Fringing reef forms around volcanic island. **B.** As the volcanic island sinks, the fringing reef gradually becomes a barrier reef. **C.** Eventually, the volcano is completely submerged and an atoll remains. **D.** Aerial view of Bora Bora with surrounding barrier reef. **E.** Aerial view of Tetiaroa Atoll in the Pacific. The light blue waters of the relatively shallow lagoon contrast with the dark blue of the deep ocean surrounding the atoll. (Photo **D** © Hemis/Alamy; photo **E** by Douglas Peebles Photography/Alamy) atolls consist of a nearly continuous ring of coral reef surrounding a central lagoon. Darwin's hypothesis was that coral reefs form on the flanks of sinking volcanic islands. As the island slowly sinks on moving oceanic crust (sea-floor spreading), the corals continue to build the reef complex upward (Figure 11.8). Darwin's proposal was confirmed after World War II when the United States drilled into two atolls (Eniwetok and Bikini), which became sites for testing atomic bombs. Drilling revealed that volcanic rock did indeed underlie the thick coral reef structure.

SEA-FLOOR SEDIMENTS

Except for a few areas, such as near the crests of mid-ocean ridges, the ocean floor is mantled with sediment. Part of this material has been deposited by turbidity currents, and the rest has slowly settled to the bottom from above. On average, the thickness of this carpet of debris varies from 500 to 1000 metres on the relatively flat areas of the ocean floor distant from land, but can exceed 9 kilometres in some trenches.

Although deposits of sand-sized particles of sediment are found on the deep-ocean floor, mud is the most common sediment covering this region. Mud also dominates on the continental shelf and slopes; however, the sediments in these areas are coarser overall because of greater quantities of sand.

Sampling has revealed that sand deposits are most prevalent as beach deposits along the shore. In some cases, though, coarse sediment, which we normally expect to be deposited near the shore, occurs in irregular patches at greater depths near the seaward limits of the continental shelves. Some sand may have been deposited by strong localized currents capable of moving coarse sediment far from shore; however, much of it appears to be the result of sand deposition on ancient beaches. Such beaches formed during the Ice Age, when sea level was much lower than today.

Types of Sea-floor Sediments

The vast majority of sediments that cover Earth's ocean floors consist of materials categorized as: (1) **terrigenous** (*terra* = Earth, *generare* = to produce) and (2) **biogenous** (*bio* = life, *generare* = to produce). Although each category is discussed separately below, it is important to remember that all sea-floor sediments are mixtures of these components to a greater or lesser extent.

TERRIGENOUS SEDIMENTS Terrigenous sediment consists primarily of mineral grains that were weathered and eroded from continental rocks, and then transported to the ocean. The sand-sized particles settle near shore. However, because the very smallest particles take years to settle to the ocean floor, they may be carried for thousands of kilometres by ocean currents. Virtually every part of the ocean receives some terrigenous sediment although the rate of accumulation can be exceedingly slow; in ocean floor areas distant from shore, a one-centimetre layer can take as long as 5000 to 50 000 years to form. In contrast, on the continental margins near the mouths of large rivers, terrigenous sediment accumulates rapidly. In the Gulf of Mexico, for example, the sediment carried by the Mississippi River has settled in a water depth of many kilometres.

Because fine particles remain suspended in the water for a very long time, ample opportunity exists for chemical reactions to occur. Because of this, the colours of the deep-sea sediments are often red or brown. This results when iron in the particles or in the water reacts with dissolved oxygen in the water and produces a coating of iron oxide (rust).

BIOGENOUS SEDIMENTS Biogenous sediment consists of shells and skeletons of planktonic marine microorganisms that live in the sunlit surface waters of the oceans (Figure 11.9). When these organisms die, their remains rain down and accumulate on the sea floor.

The most common biogenous type of sediment in the world's oceans is called *calcareous* ($CaCO_3$) *ooze*. This type of sediment is produced by a multitude of planktonic micro-organisms, such as foraminifera (Figure 11.9) and coccolithophores (see Box 8.1) with calcareous shells, inhabiting warm surface waters. After death, their calcareous hard parts accumulate on the sea floor to form ooze, which, as its name implies, has the consistency of thick, soupy mud. However, when calcareous hard

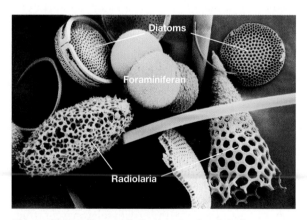

Figure 11.9 Microscopic hard parts of radiolaria (siliceous) and foraminifera (calcareous) are examples of biogenous sediments. This photomicrograph has been enlarged hundreds of times.
(Photo courtesy of Biophoto Associates/Science Source)

parts slowly sink through a cool layer of water, they begin to dissolve. This results because cold seawater is rich in carbon dioxide and is thus more acidic than warm water. In seawater deeper than about 4500 metres, calcareous shells will completely dissolve before they reach the bottom. Consequently, calcareous ooze does not accumulate in the deep-ocean basins.

Other biogenous sediments include *siliceous* (SiO_2) *oozes* and deposits of phosphate-rich materials. The former are composed primarily of opaline skeletons (single-celled algae called diatoms) and protozoans called radiolarians (Figure 11.9), whereas the latter are derived from the bones, teeth, and scales of fish and other marine organisms. Unlike calcareous shells, siliceous material is less soluble with water depth and does accumulate in deep-ocean basins.

OTHER OCEAN FLOOR MATERIALS Although less important volumetrically than the terrigenous and biogenous sediment components discussed above, there are other materials of interest that are known to occur on deep ocean floors. Among these are **manganese nodules** (Figure 11.10), rounded blackish lumps composed of a complex mixture of metal (primarily iron and manganese hydroxides) that form very slowly on the floors of the ocean basins. Also occurring on ocean floors are *sulphide deposits* associated with volcanic activity in rift zones (e.g., at mid-ocean ridges); aspects of the formation and economic significance of ancient examples of such deposits are discussed in detail in Chapter 20.

MID-OCEAN RIDGES

Our knowledge of **mid-ocean ridges** comes from soundings taken of the ocean floor, core samples obtained from deep-sea drilling, visual inspection by using deep-diving submersibles (Figure 11.11), and even first-hand inspection of slices of ocean floor that have been shoved up onto dry land (e.g., in Newfoundland and Labrador). The ocean-ridge system is characterized by an elevated position, extensive faulting, and numerous volcanic structures that have developed on the newly formed crust (Figure 11.12).

The interconnected ocean-ridge system is the longest topographic feature on Earth's surface, exceeding 70 000 kilometres. Representing 20 percent of Earth's surface, the ocean-ridge system winds through all major oceans in a manner similar to the seam on a baseball (see Figure 11.7). The term *ridge* may be misleading, as these features are not narrow but have widths of from 1000 to 4000 kilometres

Figure 11.10 Manganese nodules collected from the sea floor.
(Photo by John Cancalosi/Alamy)

and, in places, can occupy as much as half the total area of the ocean floor. An examination of Figure 11.7 shows that the ridge system is broken into segments that are offset by large transform faults. Farther along the axis of some segments are deep down-faulted structures called **rift valleys**.

Although ocean ridges stand two to three kilometres above the floors of adjacent deep-ocean basins, they are much different from mountains found on the continents. Rather than consisting of thick sequences of folded and faulted sedimentary rocks, ocean ridges consist of layer on layer of basaltic rocks that have been faulted and uplifted. Approaching the ridge crest, the topography begins to exhibit greater local relief as volcanic structures and faulted valleys become more prominent. The most rugged topography is found on those ridges that exhibit large rift valleys.

Partly because of its accessibility to both American and European scientists, the Mid-Atlantic Ridge has been studied more thoroughly than other ridges systems (see Figure 11.7). The Mid-Atlantic Ridge is a broad submerged structure standing up to 2500 metres above the adjacent ocean basin floor.

In a few places, such as Iceland, the ridge has actually grown above sea level. Throughout most of its length, however, this divergent plate boundary lies 2500 metres below sea level. Another prominent feature of the Mid-Atlantic Ridge is its deep linear rift valley extending along the ridge axis. In places this rift valley is deeper than the Grand Canyon of the Colorado River and two or three times as wide. The name *rift valley* has been applied to this feature because it is so strikingly similar to continental rift valleys, such as the East African Rift Valley.

Figure 11.11 The deep-diving submersible *Alvin* is 7.6 metres long, weighs 16 tons, has a cruising speed of 1 knot, and can reach depths up to 4000 metres. A pilot and two scientific observers are along during a normal 6 to 10 hour dive.
(Photo by Rod Catanach KRT/ Newscom)

Sea-floor Spreading

Sea-floor spreading (see Chapter 1) occurs along relatively narrow zones, called **rift zones**, located at the crests of ocean ridges (see Box 11.3). As plates move apart, magma wells up into the newly created fractures and generates new slivers of oceanic lithosphere (Figure 11.12). This continually operating process generates new lithosphere that moves away from the ridge crest in a conveyor-belt fashion.

Active rift zones are characterized by frequent, but generally weak, earthquakes and a rate of heat flow that is greater than most other crustal segments. Here vertical displacement of large slabs of oceanic crust caused by faulting and the growth of volcanic piles contributes to the characteristically rugged topography of the oceanic ridge system. Further, the rocks along the ridge axis appear very fresh and are nearly devoid of sediment. Away from the ridge axis the topography becomes more subdued, and the thickness of the sediments and the depth of the water increase. Gradually the ridge system grades into the flat, sediment-laden abyssal plains of the deep-ocean basin.

Figure 11.12 A photograph taken from the *Alvin* during project FAMOUS shows lava extrusions in the rift valley of the Mid-Atlantic Ridge. Large toothpaste-like extrusions, such as this one, are common features. A mechanical arm is sampling an adjacent blister-like extrusion.
(Photo courtesy of Woods Hole Oceanographic Institution)

Richard Léveillé*

Sitting in a computer-filled, darkened room, a group of geologists, biologists, and chemists peer intently at video monitors showing astonishing imagery of giant smoke-billowing, chimney-like rock formations and an abundance of bizarre animals. Is this a scene from Hollywood's latest sci-fi blockbuster? No, it's a typical scene from a research vessel located 250 kilometres southwest of Vancouver Island. The images are being relayed to the ship by the Canadian remotely controlled vehicle *ROPOS* (*Remotely Operated Platform for Ocean Science*), which is busy working more than two kilometres below the surface along the Juan de Fuca Ridge. This seafloor mountain chain is actively being created by the rifting and pulling apart of the Pacific and Juan de Fuca lithospheric plates and the production of new oceanic crust by upwelling magma.

Along ridges such as the Juan de Fuca, cold seawater is entrained several hundreds of metres into the highly fractured basaltic crust, where it is then heated at depth by magmatic sources. Along the way, the heated water strips metals and elements, such as sulphur, from the surrounding rocks. This heated fluid tends to rise upward because of convection, following conduits and fractures that are concentrated along the ridges. When it reaches the surface of the crust, the temperature of the fluid can be more than 400°C, but it does not boil because of the extremely high pressures caused by the water column above the vents. When this hydrothermal fluid comes into contact with the much colder seawater, minerals rapidly precipitate and form a shimmering smoke-like cloud, which gives *black smokers* their name (Figure 11.C). Some minerals immediately solidify and contribute to the formation of spectacular chimney-like structures, which can be as tall as a 15-storey building, and are appropriately given names like *Godzilla* and *Inferno*. In some cases, these chimneys and related deposits contain

Figure 11.C   A black smoker spewing hot, mineral-rich water along the East Pacific Rise. As heated solutions meet cold seawater, sulphides of copper, iron, and zinc precipitate immediately, forming mounds of minerals around these vents. (Photo by Dudley Foster, Woods Hole Oceanographic Institute)

concentrated amounts of iron, copper, zinc, lead, silver, and even gold.

The Juan de Fuca vents are also remarkable for the biology that they support. In these environments, completely devoid of sunlight, microorganisms take advantage of the mineral-rich hydrothermal fluid to perform what is known as chemosynthesis. The microbial communities, in turn, support larger, more complex animals, such as fish, crabs, worms, mussels, and clams. Some species at these vents are not found anywhere else on Earth. The most famous of these, and perhaps most unusual, is a particular type of tubeworm (Figure 11.D). With their white chitinous tubes and bright red plumes, these conspicuous creatures contain bacteria growing in their *trophosome*, an internal organ designed for harvesting bacteria. These *symbiotic* bacteria rely on the tubeworm to provide them with a suitable habitat and, in return, they provide carbon-based building blocks to the tubeworms.

Figure 11.D   Large tubeworms are among the organisms found in the extreme environment of mid-ocean ridges where sunlight is nonexistent. These organisms derive nourishment and energy from processes associated with hydrothermal vents. (Photo by Alfred F. Giddings)

Richard Léveillé is a research scientist at the Canadian Space Agency and l'Université du Québec à Montréal.

BOX
11.3   CANADIAN PROFILE
Deep-Sea Hydrothermal Vents in Canada's Backyard

A ridge system is elevated because newly created oceanic crust is hot, and occupies more volume than cooler rocks of the deep-ocean basin. As the young lithosphere travels away from the spreading centre, it gradually cools and contracts. This thermal contraction accounts, in part, for the greater ocean depths that exist away from the ridge. It takes about 80 million years before cooling and contraction cease completely. By this time, rock that was once part of an elevated ocean-ridge system is located in the deep-ocean basin, where it is mantled by thick accumulations of sediment.

During sea-floor spreading, new material is equally added to the two diverging plates; hence, we would expect new ocean floor to grow symmetrically on each side of a centrally located ridge crest. Indeed, the ridge systems of the Atlantic and Indian oceans are located near the middle of these water bodies and as a consequence are named mid-ocean ridges. However, the East Pacific Rise is situated far from the centre of the Pacific Ocean. Despite uniform spreading along the East Pacific Rise, much of the Pacific Basin that once lay east of this spreading centre has been overridden by the westward migration of the North American plate.

Structure of the Oceanic Crust

Geologists have been able to examine the structure of the ocean floor first-hand in Newfoundland and Labrador, Cyprus, and California, where slivers of oceanic crust have been thrust high above sea level. These outcrops reveal that the ocean floor consists of three distinct layers (Figure 11.13A). The upper layer is mainly basaltic **pillow lavas;** the middle layer comprises interconnected dykes called **sheeted dykes;** and the lower layer is made up of gabbro, the coarse-grained equivalent of basalt that crystallized at depth. This sequence of rocks is called an **ophiolite complex** (Figures 11.13 and 11.14). From studies of various ophiolite complexes and related data, geologists have pieced together a scenario for the formation of the ocean floor.

The magma that migrates upward to create new ocean floor originates from partially melted peridotite in the asthenosphere. In the region of the

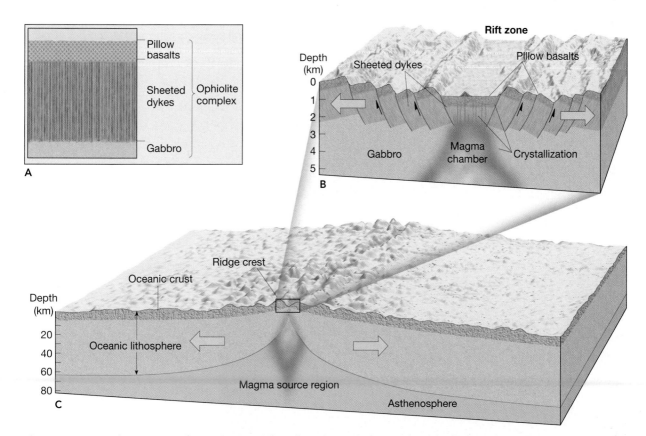

Figure 11.13   **A.** The structure of oceanic crust is thought to be equivalent to the ophiolite complexes that have been discovered elevated above sea level in such places as California and Newfoundland and Labrador. **B.** The formation of the three units of an ophiolite complex in the rift zone of an oceanic ridge. **C.** Diagram illustrating the site where new ocean crust is generated.

rift zone, this magma source may lie more than 40 kilometres below the sea floor. Being molten and less dense than the surrounding solid rock, the magma gradually moves upward and enters large reservoirs located only a few kilometres below the ridge crest (Figure 11.13B). As the ocean floor moves apart, numerous fractures develop in the crust, permitting this magma to migrate to the surface (Figure 11.13C). (Eventually magma in these vertical fractures will crystallize, generating the zone of sheeted dykes.)

During each eruptive phase, the initial lava flows are quite fluid and spread over the rift zone in broad, thin sheets. As new flows are added to the ocean floor, each is cut by fractures that allow additional lava to migrate upward and form overlying layers. Later in each eruptive cycle, as the magma in the shallow reservoir cools and thickens, shorter flows with a more characteristic pillow form occur (Figure 11.14A and 4.5D). Depending on the rate of flow, the thick pillow lavas may build into volcano-sized mounds. These mounds will eventually be cut off from their supply of magma and be carried away from the ridge crest by sea-floor spreading.

The magma that remains in the subterranean chamber will crystallize at depth to generate thick units of coarse-grained gabbro. This lowest rock unit forms as crystallization takes place along the walls and floor of the magma chamber. In this manner the processes at work along a ridge system generate the sequence of rocks found in an ophiolite complex (Figure 11.14B).

A

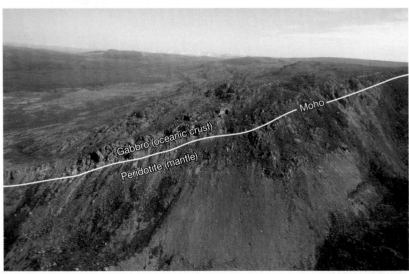

B

Figure 11.14   A. Ancient pillow lava at Trinity Bay on the island of Newfoundland. **B.** A rare glimpse of the Moho provided by the deepest levels of an ophiolite complex exposed in Table Mountain, Gros Morne National Park, Newfoundland and Labrador. The uppermost mantle and lower crust are represented by peridotite and gabbro, respectively.
(Photo **A** reproduced with the permission of Natural Resources Canada 2013, courtesy of the Geological Survey of Canada (Photo 152518 by Catherine Hickson); photo **B** by W. R. Church)

CHAPTER SUMMARY

- *Passive continental margins* have a gently sloping *continental shelf* and a steeper *continental slope* that, in turn, merge into a gradually sloping *continental rise*.

- *Turbidity currents* transport sediment from the continental shelf down the continental slope via *submarine canyons*. Emerging from the mouths of submarine canyons, turbidity currents rapidly decelerate as they encounter the decrease in gradient at the base of the continental slope, causing their sediment to settle out as *turbidites* with *graded bedding* in lobe-shaped *deep-sea fans*.

- The gradual slope of *continental rise* is maintained by the ongoing out-building of an apron of coalesced deep-sea fans at the base of the continental slope.

- *Active continental margins* have an *accretionary wedge* and deep-ocean *trench*. *Deep ocean basins* include deep-ocean trenches, flat *abyssal plains* covered with fine sediment, and volcanic *seamounts*.

- *Coral reefs* form in warm, sunlit waters and atolls consist of a ring of coral attached to a sinking submarine volcano.

- Sediments that accumulate in ocean basins consist largely of mineral-rich *terrigenous* and skeletal *biogenous* components.

- *Mid-ocean ridges* form an almost continuous submarine mountain range with a *rift zone* where magma creates new slivers of oceanic crust by seafloor spreading. The structure of oceanic crust is known from rock sequences called *ophiolite complexes* within which basaltic *pillow lavas* are observed to overlie *sheeted dykes* that, in turn, extend to *gabbro* below.

MasteringGeology

www.masteringgeology.com

Looking for additional review and test prep materials? Visit the Study Area in MasteringGeology to enhance your understanding of this chapter's content by accessing a variety of resources, including

Self-Study Quizzes, Geoscience Animations, GEODe Tutorials, RSS feeds, flashcards, weblinks, self-study quizzes, and an optional Pearson eText.

REVIEW QUESTIONS

1. Name the three major features of a continental margin, and describe the distinguishing characteristics of each.

2. Describe the main distinguishing characteristic of a turbidite and how this reflects the manner in which turbidites are deposited.

3. Explain how the velocity of the turbidity current triggered by the 1929 Grand Banks earthquake was calculated.

4. How does an active continental margin differ from a passive continental margin?

5. Describe two main types of sediment found in the deep sea, explaining how they differ in terms of the materials they contain and the manner in which they are deposited.

6. What is an atoll and how do Charles Darwin fit into our current understanding of how these features form?

7. What is the primary reason that the oceanic ridge system is elevated relative to other areas of the ocean floor?

8. How have studies on ophiolites contributed to our current knowledge of the structure of the crust underlying the oceans?

12 PLATE TECTONICS: THE FRAMEWORK FOR MODERN GEOLOGY

Aerial photo showing fault scarps and fissures in the eastern flank of the Dabbahu segment of the Red Sea rift in Ethiopia, where the Arabian and African plates are in the process of splitting apart. Recent magma intrusion, earthquake activity, vertical displacement along normal faults, and at least four fissure eruption events between 2005 and 2010 provide an exciting glimpse of plate tectonic processes in action. (Photo by C. J. Ebinger/University of Rochester)

CONTINENTAL DRIFT AND PALEOMAGNETISM

In Chapter 1 we saw the early evidence that continents broke away from a former supercontinent called *Pangaea*. The evidence included the fit of continents, matching fossils and mountain chains now separated by ocean basins, and ancient glaciated rocks of the same age in many parts of the southern hemisphere. Recall that Alfred Wegener proposed a crude hypothesis of continental drift to account for the evidence; this hypothesis was effectively rejected in the first half of the twentieth century. Between the time of Wegener's death in 1930 and the early 1950s, very little new information became known about the continental drift hypothesis. For example, not much was known about the ocean floor (Chapter 11), which represents more than 70 percent of Earth's surface. This relatively unexplored area held the key to unravelling many secrets of our planet, especially rock magnetism.

Paleomagnetism

In many respects Earth's magnetic field is like that produced by a simple bar magnet. Invisible lines of force pass through Earth and extend from one pole to the other (Figure 12.1). A compass needle, itself a small magnet free to move about, aligns with these lines of force and thus points toward the magnetic poles.

The technique used to study ancient magnetic fields relies on the fact that certain rocks contain minerals that serve as "fossil compasses." These

Figure 12.1   Earth's magnetic field consists of lines of force much like those a giant bar magnet would produce if placed through the centre of Earth.

iron-rich minerals, such as magnetite, are abundant in lava flows of basaltic composition. As the lava cools, these minerals become magnetized in the direction parallel to the existing magnetic lines of force. Once the minerals cool and solidify, the magnetism they possess retains this direction. In this regard, they behave much like a compass needle: They point toward the existing magnetic poles at the time of their cooling. Then, if the rock is moved or if the magnetic pole changes position, the rock magnetism will in most instances retain its original alignment. Rocks that formed thousands or millions of years ago and recorded the location of the magnetic poles at that time are said to possess fossil magnetism, or **paleomagnetism**. Born and educated in Britain, and later joining the Geological Survey of Canada as a geophysicist, Edward A. (Ted) Irving studied the paleomagnetism of ancient rocks to provide the first physical evidence for continental drift.

Apparent Polar Wandering

About the same time as Irving, in the 1950s S. K. Runcorn and his associates conducted a study by using rocks from European localities that led to an unexpected discovery: The magnetic alignment in the iron-rich minerals in lava flows of different ages varied widely. A plot of the apparent position of the magnetic north pole revealed that during the past 500 million years, the position of the pole has gradually wandered from a location in the Pacific Ocean northward to its present location in the Canadian Arctic (Figure 12.2). This was strong evidence that either the magnetic poles had migrated through time, an idea known as *polar wandering*, or that the lava flows moved—in other words, the continents had drifted.

Although the magnetic poles are known to move slightly in an erratic path around the geographic poles (Earth's rotation axis), studies of paleomagnetism from numerous locations show that the positions of the magnetic poles, averaged over thousands of years, correspond closely to the positions of the geographic poles. Therefore, the more acceptable explanation for the apparent polar wandering paths was provided by Wegener's hypothesis. If the magnetic poles remain stationary, their *apparent movement* is produced by continental drift.

Further evidence for continental drift came a few years later when another polar-wandering curve was constructed for North America (Figure 12.2A). To nearly everyone's surprise, the curves for North America and Europe had similar paths, except that they diverged by about 30 degrees longitude. When these rocks solidified, could there have been two

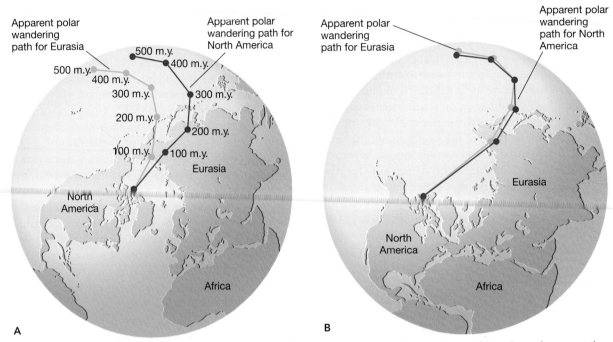

Figure 12.2 Simplified apparent polar-wandering paths as established from North American and Eurasian paleomagnetic data. **A.** The more westerly path determined from North American data was caused by the westward movement of North America by about 30 degrees from Eurasia. **B.** The positions of the wandering paths when the land masses are reassembled. (Note that *m.y.* stands for "million years ago.")

magnetic north poles that migrated parallel to each other? This is very unlikely. The differences in these migration paths, however, can be reconciled if the two presently separated continents are placed next to each other, as we now believe they were before opening of the Atlantic Ocean (Figure 12.2B). Then the two polar-wandering curves nearly overlap. This convinced some researchers that continental drift had indeed occurred. However, there was still the problem of identifying a mechanism, something that would allow continents to move closer together or farther apart while still connected by solid ocean floor. A new era had begun.

A SCIENTIFIC REVOLUTION BEGINS

During the 1950s and 1960s the ocean floor was mapped (Chapter 11) and the global oceanic ridge system discovered. The Mid-Atlantic Ridge was found to parallel the continental margins on both sides of the Atlantic (see Figure 11.7). Its central rift valley extends the length of the Mid-Atlantic Ridge and indicates that great tensional forces, high heat flow, and volcanism occur there.

Earthquake studies conducted near the deep-ocean trenches demonstrated that tectonic activity occurs at great depths beneath the ocean. Flat-topped seamounts hundreds of metres below sea level showed signs of formerly being islands that somehow became submerged. Furthermore, dredging and drilling of the oceanic crust did not bring up rock that was older than 180 million years. Could the ocean floor actually be a geologically young feature?

The Sea-floor Spreading Hypothesis

In the early 1960s, American geophysicist Harry Hess put these newly discovered facts together into a hypothesis that was later named *sea-floor spreading*. He proposed that the ocean ridges are located above zones of upwelling in the mantle (Figure 12.3). As rising material from the mantle spreads laterally, sea floor is carried in a conveyor-belt fashion away from the ridge crest. Here, tensional forces fracture the crust and provide pathways for magma to intrude and generate new slivers of oceanic crust. Thus, as the sea floor moves away from the ridge crest, newly formed crust replaces it.

Hess further proposed that the deep-ocean trenches, such as the Peru–Chile Trench, are sites at which ocean crust is drawn back into the planet. Here the older portions of the sea floor are gradually consumed as they descend into the mantle. Conclusive evidence to support his ideas came later from studying magnetism of the sea floor.

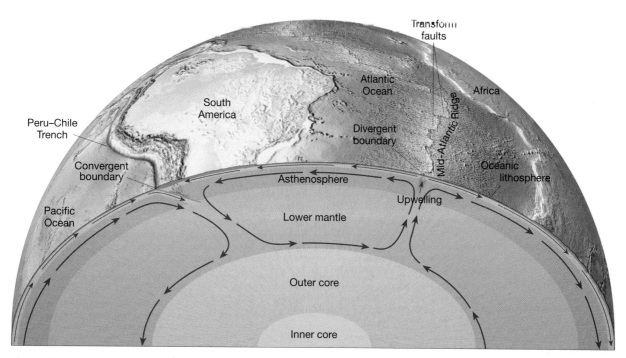

Figure 12.3 Sea-floor spreading. Harry Hess proposed that upwelling of mantle material along the mid-ocean ridge system created new sea floor. The convective motion of mantle material carries the sea floor in a conveyor-belt fashion to the deep-ocean trenches, where the sea floor descends into the mantle.

Geomagnetic Reversals

Geophysicists began to accept the fact that Earth's magnetic field periodically reverses polarity; that is, the north magnetic pole assumes a location near the south geographic pole, and vice versa (see Box 1.2). A rock solidifying during one of the episodes of reverse polarity will be magnetized with the polarity opposite that of rocks being formed today. When rocks exhibit the same magnetism as the present magnetic field, they are said to possess **normal polarity,** whereas rocks exhibiting the opposite magnetism are said to have **reversed polarity**.

Evidence for magnetic reversals was obtained from lavas and sediments from around the world, and researchers established a time scale for polarity reversals. In many areas volcanic activity has occurred sporadically for periods of millions of years, so the task was to measure the polarity of paleomagnetism in numerous lava flows of various ages (Figure 12.4). These data were used to determine the dates when the polarity of Earth's magnetic field changed (Figure 12.5). Researchers discovered alternating stripes of high- and low-intensity magnetism that trend roughly parallel to the ridge crest. This was accomplished by using very sensitive instruments called **magnetometers**, which were towed behind research vessels over segments of the ocean floor, as shown in Figure 12.6.

This relatively simple pattern of magnetic variation defied explanation until 1963, when Lawrence W. Morley of the Geological Survey of Canada, and British colleagues Fred Vine and D. H. Matthews, suggested that the stripes of high-intensity magnetism are regions where the paleomagnetism of the ocean crust exhibits normal polarity. Consequently, these rocks *enhance* (reinforce) the existing magnetic field (Figure 12.6A). Conversely, the low-intensity stripes are regions where the ocean crust is polarized in the reverse direction and therefore *weakens* the existing magnetic field. Morley, Vine, and Matthews reasoned that as magma solidifies along narrow rifts at the crest of an oceanic ridge, it is magnetized with the polarity of the existing magnetic field (Figure 12.7). Because of sea-floor spreading, this stripe of magnetized crust would gradually increase in width. When Earth's magnetic field reverses polarity, any newly formed sea floor (having the opposite polarity) would form in the middle of the old stripe. Gradually, the two parts of the old stripe are carried in opposite directions away from the ridge crest. Subsequent reversals would build a mirror-image pattern of normal and reverse stripes, as shown in Figure 12.7. A few years later a survey across the Mid-Atlantic Ridge just south of Iceland (Figure 12.6C) revealed a pattern of magnetic stripes exhibiting a remarkable degree of symmetry about the ridge axis (Figure 12.6B).

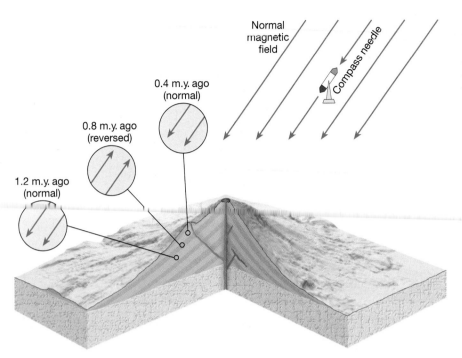

Figure 12.4 Schematic illustration of paleomagnetism preserved in lava flows of various ages. Such data as these from various locales were used to establish the time scale of polarity reversals shown in Figure 12.5.

The Last Piece of the Puzzle

The 1960s have been characterized as a period of chaos in the tectonics debate. Some geologists believed in sea-floor spreading and continental drift, whereas others held the theory that an expanding Earth could better account for the displacement occurring at the crests of oceanic ridges. According to the latter view, land masses once covered the entire surface of Earth, as shown in Figure 12.8. As Earth expanded, the continents split into their current configurations, while new sea floor "filled in" the space between them as they drifted apart (Figure 12.8). However, the expanding Earth theory is not valid because Earth's volume and diameter have remained essentially constant for billions of years, and because our planet has been gradually cooling.

Against this background entered J. Tuzo Wilson, a Canadian geophysicist who provided the piece needed to formulate the theory of plate tectonics. He suggested that large faults connected the global mobile belts into a continuous network that divides Earth's outer shell into several "rigid plates." In addition, Wilson described three types of plate margins and how solid blocks of Earth's outer shell moved relative to one another. At oceanic ridges, plates are moving apart, whereas along deep-ocean trenches, plates move together. Furthermore, along great faults—which he named *transform faults*—plates slide past one another. In a broad sense, Wilson had presented what would later be called the *theory of plate tectonics*.

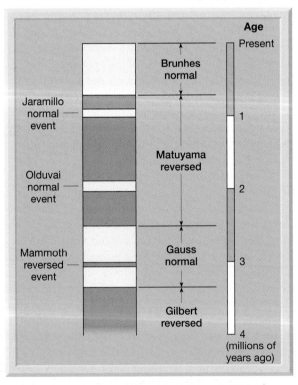

Figure 12.5 Time scale of Earth's magnetic field in the recent past. This time scale was developed by establishing the magnetic polarity for lava flows of known age. (Based on data from Allen Cox and G. B. Dalrymple)

A Magnetometer record showing symmetrical magnetic field across ridge

High intensity

Low intensity

Key
☐ Normal polarity
▨ Reverse polarity

Ridge crest

Iceland

Mid-Atlantic Ridge

B Research vessel towing magnetometer across ridge crest

C Location map

Figure 12.6 The ocean floor as a magnetic tape recorder. **A.** Schematic representation of magnetic intensities recorded as a magnetometer is towed across a segment of the Mid-Atlantic Ridge. **B.** Notice the symmetrical stripes of low- and high-intensity magnetism that parallel the ridge crest. Morley and colleagues suggested that the stripes of high-intensity magnetism occur where normally magnetized oceanic basalts enhance the existing magnetic field. Conversely, the low-intensity stripes are regions where the crust is polarized in the reverse direction, which weakens the existing magnetic field.

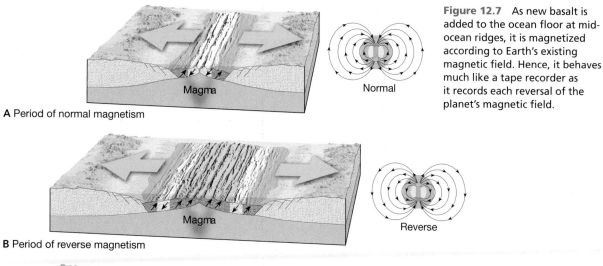

Figure 12.7 As new basalt is added to the ocean floor at mid-ocean ridges, it is magnetized according to Earth's existing magnetic field. Hence, it behaves much like a tape recorder as it records each reversal of the planet's magnetic field.

Magma

A Period of normal magnetism

Normal

Magma

B Period of reverse magnetism

Reverse

Magma

C Period of normal magnetism

Normal

Figure 12.8 An alternative hypothesis to continental drift was an expanding Earth. According to this view Earth was once only half its current diameter and covered by a layer of continents. As Earth expanded, the continents split into their current configurations, while new sea floor filled in the spaces as they drifted apart.

This theory provided a unified explanation for what seemed to be numerous unrelated observations from the fields of geology, paleontology, geophysics, and oceanography, among others.

By the end of the 1960s the concepts of continental drift and sea-floor spreading were united, Wegener had been vindicated, and the revolution in geology was nearing an end.

PLATE TECTONICS: THE NEW PARADIGM

Plate tectonics can be defined as the composite of a variety of ideas that explain the observed motion of Earth's lithosphere through the mechanisms of *subduction* and *sea-floor spreading*, which, in turn, generate Earth's major features, including continents and ocean basins. The implications of plate tectonics are so far-reaching that this theory has become the basis for viewing most geologic processes.

Earth's Major Plates

As introduced in Chapter 1, according to the plate tectonics model, the uppermost mantle, along with the overlying crust, behaves as a strong, rigid layer, known as the **lithosphere**. This outermost shell overlies a weaker region in the mantle known as the **asthenosphere**. Further, the lithosphere is broken into numerous segments, called *plates*, that are in motion and are continually changing in shape and size. As shown in Figure 1.16, and discussed in Chapter 1, the seven major lithospheric plates are the North American, South American, Pacific, African, Eurasian, Australian-Indian, and Antarctic plates. The largest is the Pacific plate, which is located mostly within the Pacific Ocean. Several of the large plates include an entire continent and a large area of sea floor, such as the South American plate. This is a major departure from Wegener's

continental drift hypothesis, which proposed that the continents moved through the ocean floor, not with it. Note also that none of the plates are defined entirely by the margins of a continent.

Intermediate-size plates include the Caribbean, Nazca, Philippine, Arabian, Cocos, and Scotia plates. More than a dozen smaller plates have been identified but are not shown in Figure 1.16. All major interactions among plates occur along or near their boundaries (divergent, convergent, and transform). These were introduced in Chapter 1 and will now be covered in detail.

DIVERGENT PLATE BOUNDARIES

Most **divergent plate boundaries** (also called *spreading centres*) are located along the crests of oceanic ridges and can be thought of as *constructive plate margins* because this is where new oceanic lithosphere is generated (Figure 12.9). Here, as the plates move away from the ridge axis, the fractures created are filled with molten rock that wells up from the hot mantle below. This magma cools to produce new slivers of sea floor. In a continuous manner, spreading and upwelling of magma adds oceanic lithosphere between the diverging plates. As you will see, divergent boundaries can also form on the continents (see Box 12.1).

Oceanic Ridges and Sea-Floor Spreading

Along well-developed divergent plate boundaries, the sea floor is elevated, forming the **oceanic ridge**. As we learned in Chapter 11, the interconnected ocean ridge system is the longest topographic feature on Earth, stands higher than the floor of adjacent ocean basins, winds through all major ocean basins in a manner similar to the seam on a baseball, is broken up into segments by transform faults, and has some segments with wide, down-faulted rift valleys.

Sea-floor spreading creates new sea floor along the oceanic ridge system. Typical rates of spreading average around 5 centimetres per year. Comparatively slow spreading rates of 2 centimetres per year are found in the North Atlantic, whereas spreading rates exceeding 15 centimetres per year have been measured along sections of the East Pacific Rise. These rates are rapid enough to form all of Earth's ocean basins within the past 200 million years. As mentioned earlier, little of the ocean floor that has been dated exceeds 180 million years in age.

BOX
12.1

UNDERSTANDING EARTH
The Breakup of a Supercontinent

A great deal of evidence has been gathered to support the notion that Alfred Wegener's supercontinent of Pangaea began to break apart about 180 million years ago, as he had originally suggested (Figure 12.A, part A). An important consequence of this continental rifting was the creation of a "new" ocean basin, the Atlantic. As you can see in Figure 12.A, part B, the rifting that eventually resulted in the Atlantic basin occurred over an extended time. The first rift developed between North America and Africa and generated great volumes of Jurassic-age basalts. These basalts are present as weathered flows (e.g., North Mountain, Nova Scotia) and

sills (e.g., Palisades Sill, New York) along the Eastern Seaboard of North America but primarily are buried beneath rocks that form the continental shelf. Radiometric dating of this material indicates that rifting began in various stages between 180 million and 165 million years ago. This span can be used as the birthdate for this section of the North Atlantic.

Rifting that formed the South Atlantic began about 130 million years ago near the tips of what are now Africa and South America. As this rift propagated northward, it gradually opened the South Atlantic (compare Figure 12.A, parts B and C). Continued rifting of the southern land mass of Gondwanaland sent

India on a northward journey. By the early Cenozoic, about 50 million years ago, Australia began to separate from Antarctica, and the South Atlantic had emerged as a full-fledged ocean (Figure 12.A, part D).

A modern map (Figure 12.A, part E) shows that India eventually collided with Asia, an event that began about 50 million years ago and created the Himalayas and the Tibetan Plateau. About the same time, the separation of Greenland from Eurasia completed the breakup of the northern land mass (Laurasia). Also, notice the recent formation of the Baja Peninsula along with the Gulf of California. This event began less than 10 million years ago.

Figure 12.A Several views of the breakup of Pangaea over 200 million years.

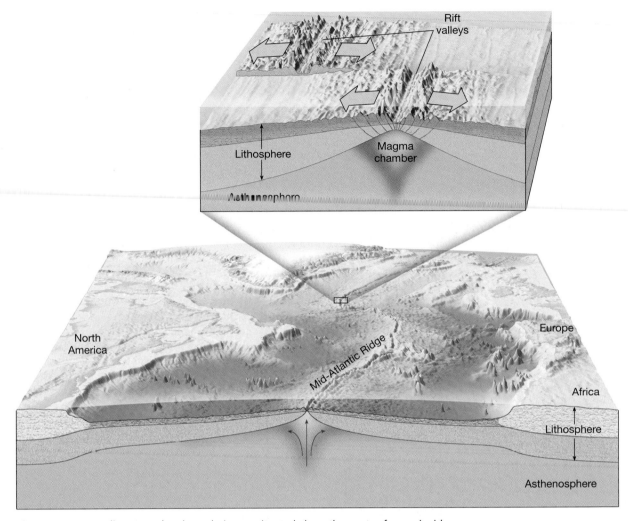

Figure 12.9 Most divergent plate boundaries are situated along the crests of oceanic ridges.

During sea-floor spreading, the magma that is injected into newly developed fractures forms dykes that tend to cool from their outer borders inward toward their centres. Injection and spreading rates exceed cooling rates so that continued spreading produces new fractures that split these young rocks roughly in half. New material is added about equally to the two diverging plates and new ocean floor grows symmetrically on each side of a centrally located ridge crest. As noted in Chapter 11, the ridge systems of the Atlantic and Indian oceans are located near the middle of these water bodies and as a consequence are called *mid-ocean ridges*. Conversely, the East Pacific Rise is situated far from the centre of the Pacific Ocean.

Continental Rifts

Spreading centres can also develop within a continent, in which case the land mass may split into two or more smaller segments, as Alfred Wegener had proposed for the breakup of Pangaea. Examples of active continental rifts include the East African Rift valleys, the Baikal Rift in southcentral Siberia, the Rhine Valley (Northwest Europe), the Rio Grande Rift, and the Basin and Range Province in western North America. Continental rifting occurs where opposing tectonic forces pull lithosphere apart. Mantle upwelling induces broad up-warping of the overlying lithosphere (Figure 12.10A), which is stretched, causing brittle crustal rocks to break into large slabs. As crust continues to get pulled apart, slabs sink and generate an elongated depression called a continental rift (Figure 12.10B).

The East African Rift valleys may represent the initial stage in the breakup of a continent, as described above, or they may be destined to become failed rift arms, such as the Niger arm in Figure 12.11A. Large shield volcanoes, such as Mount Kilimanjaro and Mount Kenya, exemplify

Figure 12.10 A. Rising magma up-warps the crust, causing numerous cracks in the rigid lithosphere. **B.** As the crust is pulled apart, large slabs of rock sink, generating a rift zone. **C.** Farther spreading generates a narrow sea. **D.** Eventually, an expansive ocean basin and ridge system are created.

the extensive volcanic activity that has accompanied continental rifting for over 20 million years (Figure 12.11B).

If rifting continues, the rift valley will lengthen and deepen, eventually extending out to the margin of the plate (Figure 12.10C). At this point the rift will become a narrow linear sea with an outlet to the ocean, similar to the Red Sea (Figure 12.11B). The Red Sea formed when the Arabian Peninsula rifted from Africa, an event that began about 30 million years ago and provides us with a view of how the Atlantic Ocean may have looked in its infancy. The

boundary between oceanic and continental crust (Figure 12.10D) represents the original rift or split of the former continent and becomes the true edge of the new continent. The surface expression of this crustal boundary is the *continental slope* discussed in Chapter 11.

Not all rift valleys develop into full-fledged spreading centres. Extending from Lake Superior to Kansas through central North America is a failed rift (Figure 12.12). This once active rift valley is filled with volcanic rocks that were extruded onto the crust more than a billion years ago.

Figure 12.11 **A.** Cracks produced by mantle-plume-related doming of the lithosphere tend to produce rift zones that meet at triple junctions. Where two of the three rift arms in a particular triple-junction zone meet rift arms of other triple-junction systems, they form a composite rift zone, along which spreading can continue and ultimately form an ocean basin. The arms that do not connect with others eventually stop spreading and therefore become failed rifts that simply become filled with sediment. Some of the major river systems follow the trends of ancient failed rifts. This diagram shows the rift arms that developed just before the opening of the Atlantic Ocean (~200 million years ago). **B.** East African rift valleys and associated features.

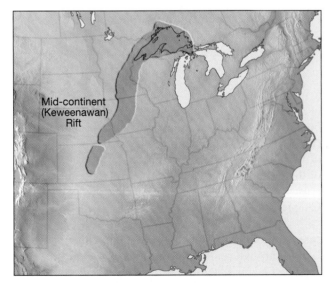

Figure 12.12 Map showing location of a failed rift extending from Lake Superior to Kansas.

CONVERGENT PLATE BOUNDARIES

Although new lithosphere is continually being added at the oceanic ridges, our planet is not growing larger—its total surface area and volume remain constant. To accommodate the newly created lithosphere, older portions of oceanic plates return to the mantle along **convergent plate boundaries**. (Because lithosphere is consumed or "destroyed" at convergent boundaries, they are also called *destructive plate margins*.) As two plates slowly converge, the leading edge of one is bent downward, allowing it to slide beneath the other along a *subduction zone*. The surface expression produced by the descending plate is an ocean *trench*, such as the Peru–Chile Trench (Figures 11.7, 12.13A). Trenches formed in this manner can be thousands of kilometres long, up to 11 kilometres deep, and up to 120 kilometres wide (see Table 11.1 and Figure 11.7).

Oceanic–Continental Convergence

Whenever the leading edge of a continental plate converges with an oceanic plate, the buoyant continental plate remains "floating," while the denser oceanic slab sinks into the asthenosphere (Figure 12.13A). As the oceanic slab descends, some of the sediments carried on the subducting plate and pieces of oceanic crust are scraped off and plastered against the edge of the overriding buoyant continental block. This chaotic mixture of deformed sediment and scraps of oceanic crust is called an *accretionary wedge*, as described in Chapter 11. In western Mexico, the Cocos plate is being subducted and at least half of the sediment carried on it is removed this way. As a result, this process adds to the buildup of sediment along continental margins.

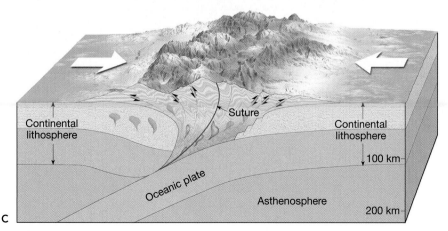

Figure 12.13 Zones of plate convergence. **A.** Oceanic–continental. **B.** Oceanic–oceanic. **C.** Continental–continental.

When a descending plate reaches a depth of about 100 kilometres, heat drives water and other volatile components from the subducted sediments into the overlying mantle (Figure 12.13A). These substances act as a flux does at a steel-making foundry, inducing partial melting of mantle rocks at reduced temperatures. The partial melting of mantle rock generates magmas that have a mafic or occasionally intermediate composition. The newly formed magma, being less dense than the rocks of the mantle, will rise buoyantly. Often the magma, being denser than continental rocks, will pool beneath the overlying continental crust, where it may melt some of the silica-enriched rocks. Eventually some of this silica-rich magma may migrate to the surface, where it can give rise to volcanic eruptions, some of which are explosive.

Such mountains as the Andes, which were produced, in part, by volcanic activity associated with the subduction of oceanic lithosphere, are called **continental volcanic arcs**. The Cascade Range of British Columbia, Washington, Oregon, and California consists of several well-known volcanic mountains, including Mount Baker, Mount St. Helens, Mount Rainier, and Mount Shasta (see Figure 4.17). The Cascade Range remains active, as the continuing activity of Mount St. Helens testifies.

Oceanic–Oceanic Convergence

When two oceanic slabs converge, one descends beneath the other, initiating volcanic activity in a manner similar to what occurs at an oceanic–continental boundary. But instead of forming on a continent, the volcanoes build upward from the ocean floor, ultimately forming an arc-shaped chain of volcanic islands called a **volcanic island arc** (Figure 12.13B). The islands themselves are spaced about 80 kilometres apart, built on submerged ridges of volcanic material a few hundred kilometres wide. The Japanese, Aleutian, Mariana, and Tonga islands are examples of volcanic island arcs. Island arcs such as these are generally located 100 to 300 kilometres from the trench axis. Located adjacent to the island arcs just mentioned are the Japan Trench, the Aleutian Trench, the Mariana Trench, and the Tonga Trench (see Figure 11.7). Most volcanic island arcs are located in the western Pacific.

Continental–Continental Convergence

As you saw earlier, when an oceanic plate is subducted beneath continental lithosphere, an Andean-type volcanic arc develops along the margin of the continent. However, if the subducting plate also

Figure 12.14 The collision of India and Asia about 50 million years ago produced the majestic Himalayas.

contains continental lithosphere, continued subduction eventually brings the two continents together. Whereas oceanic lithosphere is relatively dense and sinks into the asthenosphere, continental lithosphere is buoyant, which prevents it from being subducted to any great depth. The result is a collision between the two continental blocks (Figure 12.13C).

Such a collision occurred when the subcontinent of India rammed into Asia and produced the Himalayas—the most spectacular mountain range on Earth (Figure 12.14). During this collision, the continental crust buckled, fractured, and was generally shortened and thickened. In addition to the Himalayas, several other major mountain systems, including the Alps, Appalachians, and Urals, formed during continental collisions.

Before a continental collision, the land masses involved are separated by an ocean basin. As the continental blocks converge, the intervening sea floor is subducted beneath one of the plates. Subduction initiates partial melting in the overlying mantle rocks, which in turn results in the growth of a volcanic arc.

The volcanic arc always develops on the overriding plate. Eventually, as the intervening sea floor is consumed, these continental masses collide. This folds and deforms the accumulation of sediments along the continental margin as if they had been crushed in a gigantic vice. The result is the formation of a new mountain range composed of deformed and metamorphosed sedimentary rocks, and possibly slivers of oceanic crust and upper mantle.

TRANSFORM FAULT BOUNDARIES

The third type of plate boundary is the **transform fault boundary**, which is characterized by strike-slip faulting, where plates move past one another without the production or destruction of lithosphere (*conservative plate margins*). Transform faults were first identified where they join offset segments of an ocean ridge (see Figure 11.7).

As noted earlier, they were discovered in 1965 by J. Tuzo Wilson of the University of Toronto (Box 12.2),

BOX 12.2 CANADIAN PROFILE
John Tuzo Wilson: Canada's Champion of Plate Tectonics

Vic Tyrer*

In the 1960s J. Tuzo Wilson (Figure 12.B) was one of a group of Earth scientists who developed the theory of plate tectonics. His many contributions to the theory include an explanation for the opening and closing of ocean basins, now known as the Wilson Cycle (see Chapter 13). In 1965 he proposed the existence of transform faults to explain the numerous narrow fracture zones and earthquakes found in oceanic crust. His idea of magma plumes rising through Earth's crust and creating local hot spots explained intraplate volcanoes, such as the Hawaiian Island chain.

Born in Ottawa, J. Tuzo Wilson was the first graduate in geophysics from the University of Toronto in 1930. He went on to become an assistant geologist with the Geological Survey of Canada from 1936 to 1939. Following service in the Canadian Army, he became a professor of geophysics at the University of Toronto from 1946 to 1974.

Wilson was the director general of the Ontario Science Centre from 1974

to 1985, where he combined his scientific vision with his commitment to public education. He was as comfortable in the Science Centre's classrooms as he was in the boardroom, frequently capturing the imagination of young students and adults alike with hands-on demonstrations of plate tectonics by using his familiar "lighter and paper" explanation of the Hawaiian Islands.

Wilson gave his last public lecture at the Ontario Science Centre in February 1992. His lecture, "With Zest to Go, in Quest to Know," recounted his lifetime travels of more than three million kilometres and seven continents in his quest to understand and teach the inner workings of Earth.

On May 3, 2001, the Ontario Science Centre unveiled a tribute to its former director general in the form of a geodetic monument. Central to the monument is the sculpture's large iron spike. Visitors are asked to imagine that the spike has been driven into the Earth's core. The iron spike remains fixed, seemingly gouging a trough in

Figure 12.B John Tuzo Wilson, Canadian pioneer of plate tectonics. (Photo courtesy of the Ontario Science Centre)

the surrounding concrete plaza as the North American plate "drifts" westward a few centimetres per year. The trough marks a total of 2.3 metres of tectonic movement during Tuzo Wilson's lifetime (1908–1993).

Vic Tyrer was the Earth science programmer at the Ontario Science Centre from 1978 to 1999. Used by permission.

when he suggested that these large faults connect the globally active belts into a network of several rigid plates. Thus, Wilson was the first to suggest that Earth was made of individual plates, while at the same time identifying the faults along which relative motion between the plates is made possible.

Most transform faults join two segments of a mid-ocean ridge (Figure 12.15). Here, they are part of prominent linear breaks in the oceanic crust known as **fracture zones**, which include both the transform faults and their inactive extensions into the plate interior. These fracture zones are present approximately every 100 kilometres along the trend of a ridge axis. As shown in Figure 12.15, active transform faults lie only *between* the two offset ridge segments. Here, sea floor produced at one ridge axis

moves in the opposite direction from sea floor produced at an opposing ridge segment (sea-floor spreading). Thus, between the ridge segments these adjacent slabs of oceanic crust are slipping past each other along a transform fault. Beyond the ridge crests are the inactive zones, where the fractures produced by strike-slip faulting are preserved as linear topographic scars. These fracture zones tend to curve such that small segments roughly parallel the direction of plate motion at the time of their formation.

Although most transform faults are located within the ocean basins, a few cut through continental crust. Two examples are the earthquake-prone San Andreas Fault of California and the Alpine Fault of New Zealand.

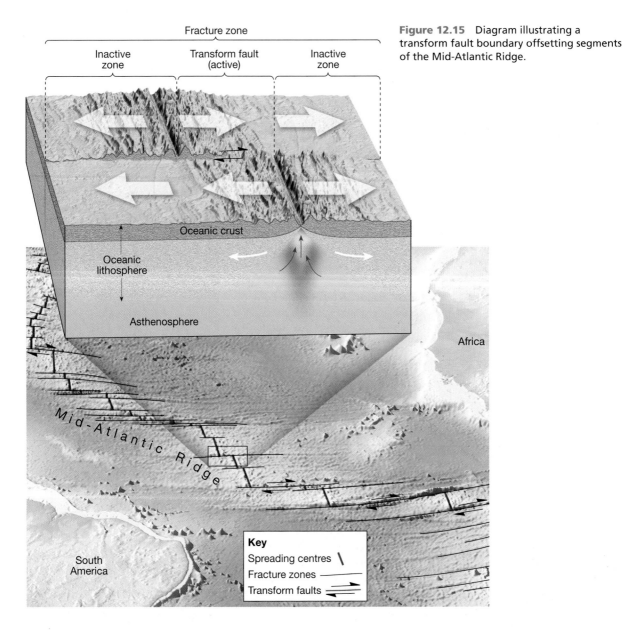

Figure 12.15 Diagram illustrating a transform fault boundary offsetting segments of the Mid-Atlantic Ridge.

TESTING THE PLATE TECTONICS MODEL

With the development of plate tectonics, Earth scientists began testing this model of how Earth works. We have already presented evidence supporting continental drift and sea-floor spreading; more evidence follows. Note that much of this evidence was not new; rather, new interpretations of existing data turned the tide of opinion.

Plate Tectonics and Earthquakes

By the late 1960s, seismologists demonstrated the close association between deep-hypocentre earthquakes and subduction zones, and the absence of deep-hypocentre earthquakes along the oceanic ridge system—observations that were consistent with the new model.

The significance of seismologic studies to the support and refinement of the model of plate tectonics is striking in the depth distribution of earthquake hypocentres at subduction zones. Deep-ocean trenches form at convergent plate boundaries where dense slabs of oceanic lithosphere sink into the mantle. In support of the model, the depths of earthquakes associated with the Japan Trench (Figure 12.16) increase toward mainland Asia, reflecting the westward subduction of oceanic lithosphere toward the west. A similar pattern of earthquake hypocentres occurs along the west margin of South America, where the Nazca plate is subducting under the South American plate.

Shallow-focus earthquakes are produced as the descending plate interacts with the overriding lithosphere. As the slab descends farther westward into the asthenosphere, deeper and deeper earthquakes are generated. Provided the subducting plate is rigid, earthquakes generated within it (due to internal faulting) provide a powerful method of tracking the plate's descent. The fact that very few earthquakes have been recorded at depths below 700 kilometres may reflect loss of the plate's rigidity due to heating.

Evidence from Ocean Drilling

Some of the most convincing evidence of sea-floor spreading has come from drilling directly into ocean-floor sediment. From 1968 until 1983, this was done by the Deep Sea Drilling Program and its drilling ship, the *Glomar Challenger*.

In each ocean basin, holes were drilled through the entire thickness of sediments to the mafic rock below. An important objective was to gather samples of sediment from just above the igneous crust as a means of dating the sea floor at each site.* Because sedimentation begins immediately after the oceanic crust forms, remains of micro-organisms found in the

---

*Radiometric dates of the ocean crust itself are unreliable because of the alteration of basalt by seawater.

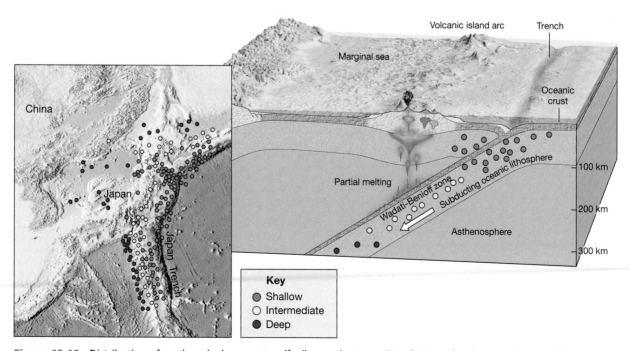

Figure 12.16 Distribution of earthquake hypocentres (foci) near the Japan Trench. Note that intermediate- and deep-hypocentre earthquakes occur only within the colder sinking slab of oceanic lithosphere. (Based on data from National Oceanic and Atmospheric Administration.)

Figure 12.17 The *JOIDES Resolution*, the drilling ship of the Ocean Drilling Program. This modern drilling ship has replaced the *Glomar Challenger* in the important work of sampling the floor of the world's oceans. (Photo courtesy of Ocean Drilling Program)

oldest sediments—those resting directly on the basalt—can be used to date the ocean floor at that site.

When the oldest sediment from each drill site was plotted against its distance from the ridge crest, the plot demonstrated that the age of the sediment increased with distance from the ridge. This finding agreed with the sea-floor-spreading hypothesis, which predicted that the youngest oceanic crust would be found at the ridge crest and that the oldest oceanic crust would be at the continental margins, where sediments have been accumulating on it longer.

Furthermore, drill cores from the *Glomar Challenger* revealed that sediments are almost entirely absent on the ridge crest and that the sediment thickens with increasing distance from the ridge. Because the ridge crest is younger than the areas farther away from it, this pattern of sediment distribution should be expected if the sea-floor-spreading hypothesis is correct.

The Ocean Drilling Program succeeded the Deep Sea Drilling Program and, like its predecessor, it was a major international effort. The more technologically advanced drilling ship, the *JOIDES Resolution*, now continues the work of the *Glomar Challenger*.* The *JOIDES Resolution* can drill in water up to 8200 metres deep and contains onboard

laboratories equipped with a large and varied array of seagoing scientific research equipment (Figure 12.17). The *JOIDES Resolution* is now part of a new international venture called the Integrated Ocean Drilling Program that also uses other research vessels, including the massive 210-metre-long *Chikyu* (meaning "planet Earth" in Japanese).

Hot Spots and Mantle Plumes

Mapping of seamounts in the Pacific Ocean revealed a chain of volcanic structures extending from the Hawaiian Islands to Midway Island and continuing northward toward the Aleutian Trench (Figure 12.18). Radiometric dating in this chain showed that the volcanoes increase in age with increasing distance from Hawaii. Hawaii has the youngest volcanoes in the chain and rose from the sea floor less than a million years ago, whereas Midway Island is 27 million years old and Suiko Seamount, near the Aleutian Trench, is 65 million years old (Figure 12.18).

Researchers agree that a rising plume of hot mantle rock is located beneath the island of Hawaii. Decompression melting of this hot rock occurs as it enters the low-pressure environment near the base of the lithosphere, generating on the surface a volcanic area known as a **hot spot**. As the Pacific plate moved over this hot spot, successive volcanic structures were built. The age of each volcano indicates the time when it was situated over the relatively stationary **mantle plume**.

---

*JOIDES stands for Joint Oceanographic Institutions for Deep Earth Sampling.

Figure 12.18   The chain of islands and seamounts that extends from Hawaii to the Aleutian Trench was generated as the Pacific plate moved over a mantle plume (hot spot). Radiometric dating of the Hawaiian Islands shows that the volcanic activity increases in age moving away from the "Big Island" of Hawaii.

This pattern is shown in Figure 12.18. Kauai is the oldest of the large islands in the Hawaiian chain. Five million years ago, when it was positioned over the hot spot, Kauai was the "Hawaii" or Big Island of its day (Figure 12.18). Evidence of Kauai's age can be seen by examining its well-developed red soils and extinct volcanoes, which have been eroded into jagged peaks and vast canyons. By contrast, the south slopes of the comparatively young island of Hawaii consist of fresh lava flows, and three of its volcanoes, Mauna Loa and Kilauea, and (submarine) Loihi, remain active.

Thus, as a part of the entire Hawaiian Island–Emperor Seamount chain, these volcanic structures were apparently formed by the same motion of the Pacific plate over fixed mantle plumes. Not only does this evidence support the fact that the plates do indeed move over Earth's mantle but the hot spot "tracks" also trace the direction of the plate motion. Notice in Figure 12.18, for example, that the

Hawaiian Island–Emperor Seamount chain bends. This particular bend in the track occurred about 45 million years ago, when the motion of the Pacific plate changed from nearly due north to northwest as new subduction zones formed. Similarly, hot spots found on the floor of the Atlantic have increased our understanding of the migration of land masses following the breakup of Pangaea.

The existence of mantle plumes and their association with hot spots is well documented. Most mantle plumes are considered long-lived structures that appear to maintain relatively fixed positions within the mantle. Research suggests that at least some mantle plumes originate at great depth, perhaps at the mantle–core boundary. Others, however, may have a much shallower origin. Of the 40 or so hot spots that have been identified, more than a dozen are located near spreading centres. For example, the mantle plume located beneath Iceland

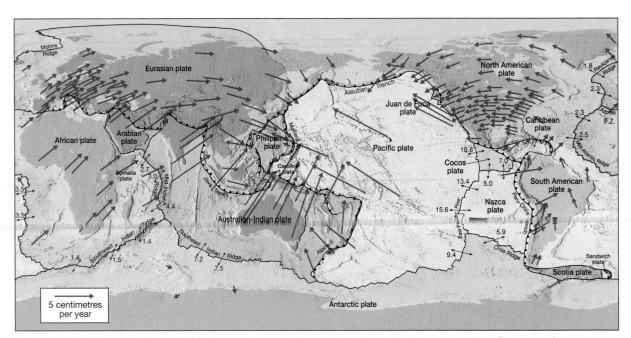

Figure 12.19 This map illustrates directions and rates of plate motion in centimetres per year. Sea-floor-spreading velocities (shown with black arrows and labels) are based on the spacing of dated magnetic stripes (anomalies). The red arrows show plate motion at selected locations based on GPS data (the length of each red arrow is proportional to the rate of motion). (Seafloor data from DeMets and others, GPS data from Jet Propulsion Laboratory.)

is responsible for the large accumulation of volcanic rocks built above sea level along the northern section of the Mid-Atlantic Ridge.

MEASURING PLATE MOTION

A number of methods have been employed to establish the direction and rate of plate motion. As noted earlier, hot spot tracks, like those of the Hawaiian Island–Emperor Seamount chain, trace the movement of the Pacific plate relative to the mantle below. By measuring the length of this volcanic chain and the time interval between the formation of an old structure (e.g., Suiko Seamount) and the youngest structure (e.g., Hawaii), we can calculate an average rate of plate motion. In this case the volcanic chain is roughly 6000 kilometres long and has formed over the past 65 million years—making the average rate of movement about 9 centimetres per year. The accuracy of this calculation hinges on the hot spot maintaining a fixed position in the mantle; recent evidence suggests that some hot spots may slowly migrate.

Recall that the magnetic stripes measured on the floor of the ocean (Figure 12.6B) also provide a method to work out plate velocities—at least as averaged over millions of years. By using paleomagnetism and other indirect techniques, researchers have been able to work out relative plate velocities, as shown on the map in Figure 12.19.

It is currently possible, with the use of modern technology, to directly measure the relative motion between plates. This is accomplished by repeatedly establishing the exact locations of, and hence the distance between, two observing stations situated on opposite sides of a plate boundary. Currently, a satellite positioning technique is used that employs GPS (*global positioning system*). You may be familiar with GPS, which uses two dozen satellites to accurately locate any individual who is equipped with a handheld receiver. By using two spaced receivers, signals obtained by these instruments can be used to calculate relative positions within a few millimetres. Techniques that use GPS receivers have been useful in establishing small-scale crustal movements such as those that occur across active faults.

THE DRIVING MECHANISM

The plate tectonics theory *describes* plate motion and the effects of this motion. Therefore, acceptance of this model does not rely on the mechanism that drives plate motion. This is fortunate, because the mechanism or combination of mechanisms responsible for driving plate tectonics remains controversial. Three main mechanisms (mantle drag, ridge sliding and slab pull) have been proposed to explain *how* plate motion might be achieved and are briefly summarized next.

Figure 12.20 Three main mechanisms have been proposed to explain the movement of lithospheric plates. In mantle drag, the plates move like conveyor belts atop convection currents operating in the asthenosphere (red). Ridge sliding involves gravitational sliding of oceanic lithosphere down the flanks of elevated oceanic ridges. In slab pull, older, dense oceanic lithosphere pulls the trailing portion of a plate as it sinks into a subduction zone.

Mantle Drag

Convective flow in the mantle is the primary mechanism for transporting heat away from Earth's interior to the surface, where it is eventually radiated to space. When mantle rock is heated, it decreases in density and rises toward the surface, whereas when it cools, it increases in density and sinks. It has been suggested that frictional forces set up between the tops of convection cells in the asthenosphere and the base of overlying oceanic lithospheric plates are sufficient to drag the plates along like conveyor belts (Figure 12.20). A point of controversy in this model is whether it could generate enough friction to allow mantle flow to drive plate movement. There is also disagreement about where mantle convection cells are—whether they are confined to the asthenosphere, if they occur in the asthenosphere and mesosphere, or if they circulate throughout the entire thickness of the mantle.

Ridge Sliding and Slab Pull

It has been realized recently that oceanic plates may play a direct role in their own movement. One possibility is that diverging oceanic plates move by **ridge sliding**, a mechanism by which oceanic plates slide downward and outward from the ridge crest under the influence of gravity. This mechanism is alternatively called ridge push, although this is a misnomer because there is no outward pressure from the ridge itself (Figure 12.20). Another proposal views plate movement resulting from old, cold, denser oceanic lithosphere sinking into underlying asthenosphere toward Earth's interior. This mechanism is called **slab pull** (Figure 12.20) and emphasizes the tugging effect of sinking as the leading edge of an oceanic plate descends down a subduction zone. At present, most scientists favour slab pull, although ridge push and/or convection may operate in tandem with slab pull as part of a more complex system of driving forces in plate tectonics.

CHAPTER SUMMARY

- *Paleomagnetic* studies have revealed that continents have wandered due to sea-floor spreading. New sea floor is generated at oceanic ridges, and old, dense sea floor is consumed at deep-ocean trenches.

- Earth's lithosphere is broken into seven main plates (and several smaller ones) that continually move and change configuration over time.

- *Divergent plate boundaries* occur where plates move away from one another—at oceanic ridges where new sea floor is created, or where continents split, creating new ocean basins.

- *Convergent plate boundaries* occur where plates move toward one another—oceanic–continental, where subduction of the oceanic plate forms a *continental volcanic arc*; oceanic–oceanic, where subduction forms a *volcanic island arc*; and continental–continental, where collision forms high mountains.

- *Transform fault boundaries* occur where plates slip past each other typically between two oceanic ridge segments.

- Plate tectonics theory is supported by many independent lines of evidence. These include apparent magnetic polar wandering paths; the global distribution of earthquakes, continental rifts, mid-ocean ridges, volcanic arcs, ocean trenches, and volcanic islands associated with *hot spot* tracks; the symmetrical pattern of magnetic intensities recorded in ocean floor rock; increasing sediment age/thickness away from ridges; and

direct measurement of plate motion in the present day via GPS and other technologies.

- Mechanisms that may play roles in driving the movement of lithospheric plates are *slab-pull* by the sinking of the cold, dense leading edge of a plate down a subduction zone; *ridge sliding* via gravitational sliding of oceanic plates down the sloping flanks of spreading ridges; and *mantle dragging*, the direct lateral dragging of a plate due to the frictional resistance of the base of a lithospheric plate and the mantle material convecting underneath it. Debate continues on the nature of mantle convection and its influence on plate motion.

MasteringGeology   www.masteringgeology.com

Looking for additional review and test prep materials? Visit the Study Area in MasteringGeology to enhance your understanding of this chapter's content by accessing a variety of resources, including

Self-Study Quizzes, Geoscience Animations, GEODe Tutorials, RSS feeds, flashcards, weblinks, self-study quizzes, and an optional Pearson eText.

REVIEW QUESTIONS

1. In Chapter 1, we examined evidence supporting Alfred Wegener's hypothesis of continental drift—an important precursor to the modern concept of plate tectonics. Explain how later paleomagnetic studies gave further support to Wegener's idea that continents have "drifted" over time.

2. What is meant by "sea-floor spreading"? Who is credited with formulating the initial concept of sea-floor spreading?

3. Describe how scientists Morley, Vine, and Matthews related magnetic reversals, recorded as alternating "stripes" of high- and low-magnetic intensity in oceanic crust, to the concept of sea-floor spreading.

4. At what type of plate boundary is lithosphere formed? At what type is it consumed? Why must

the formation (production) and consumption (destruction) of the lithosphere be occurring at about the same rate (on a global scale)?

5. Why can oceanic lithosphere be subducted while continental lithosphere cannot?

6. Canadian scientist J. Tuzo Wilson is credited with identifying one of the three basic types of plate boundaries. How does the boundary type discovered by Wilson fit into plate tectonics, and how does it differ from the other two?

7. Describe how the linear pattern of intraplate volcanic islands, such as in the Hawaiian Island Chain, can be explained by plate tectonics.

8. Describe the three main mechanisms that have been suggested to drive the movement of Earth's lithospheric plates.

MOUNTAIN BUILDING AND CONTINENTAL FRAMEWORKS

13

Mountains in Peter Lougheed Provincial Park, Alberta. (Photo by BGSmith/Shutterstock)

Few geologic features of Earth have captured people's attention as much as mountains. Throughout the ages, mountains have inspired legends, appeared as prominent motifs in works of art, influenced the placement of political boundaries, and challenged the physical abilities of those bold enough to climb them.

To geologists, mountains are extremely important features for different reasons. First, mountains expose spectacular sedimentary rock sequences that are the basis for interpreting the sequence of events in Earth's history. Second, igneous and metamorphic rocks forced upward to the surface during mountain building provide information on processes that occur so deep in Earth's crust that they cannot be observed directly. Third, mountains supply geologists with information that is critical to understanding large-scale tectonic processes.

In the context of the Earth system, mountains influence drainage patterns of rivers, supply sediment that is the parent material for soil in lowland regions, and, in some areas of the world, greatly influence regional climatic conditions.

The fact that mountains differ in shape, size, and arrangement reflects differences in the processes that produce them as well as in the character and duration of the processes that act to wear them down (Figure 13.1).

ISOSTASY: WHY EARTH ISN'T SMOOTH

Continents stand higher than ocean basins because of **isostasy**, the state of gravitational equilibrium achieved by the flotation of buoyant lithosphere on top of the more dense material of the asthenosphere. Recall that the lower density and greater thickness of continental crust relative to oceanic crust allows the upper surface of a continent to stand at a significantly greater elevation than the ocean floor. On a slightly smaller scale, isostasy also explains why

Figure 13.1 Comparison of two of Canada's mountain systems. **A.** The relatively youthful mountains in the Western Cordillera have high, sharp peaks. **B.** The much older mountains in the Appalachians, as seen here along the Cabot Trail of Cape Breton Island, Nova Scotia, have been worn down to rolling hills. (Photo **A** © Radius Images/Alamy; photo **B** © J. A. Kraulis/Masterfile)

Figure 13.2 This drawing illustrates how wooden blocks of different thicknesses float in water. In a similar manner, thick sections of crustal material float higher than do thinner crustal slabs.

regions within a continental land mass can vary considerably in elevation.

Perhaps the easiest way to grasp the concept of how isostasy affects continental topography is to envision a series of wooden blocks of different heights floating in water, as shown in Figure 13.2. Note that the thin wooden blocks float only slightly above the water line, whereas the thick blocks stand very high. In a very general sense, the same principle applies to elevation differences in continents; regions underlain by thick continental lithosphere stand higher than those underlain by thin continental lithosphere.

This simple model of isostasy is a good starting point for explaining why certain features of Earth stand lower or higher than others on a regional scale. However, because it is a rather static depiction of the lithosphere, it does not give us insights as to *how*, *where*, *or when such features are produced.* Moreover, it does not account for the smaller scale deviations in elevation (e.g., high-standing volcanoes in rift zones) that complicate the overall appearance of certain physiographic regions. To address these aspects, it is necessary to examine mountains in the context of their tectonic history. The name for the processes that collectively produce mountains is **orogenesis** (*oros* = mountains, *genesis* = to come into being).

MOUNTAINS AND PLATE TECTONIC ENVIRONMENTS

A **mountain** can be loosely defined as a landform with an obvious peak that rises significantly above the land surrounding it, generally 300 metres or more. When we consider mountains as part of the larger scale framework of continental features (Figure 13.3), it is clear that mountains tend to occur in linear patterns. They range in scale from small **mountain ranges**, consisting simply of a linked series of mountains, to regionally extensive **mountain belts** that can be extremely complex both in relief and in internal structure. These linear features are generally oriented parallel to plate boundaries, where stresses generated by plate movement are the most intense. Because of isostasy, the modifications of crustal thickness that take place in extensional or compressional tectonic environments are accompanied by dramatic changes in land elevation.

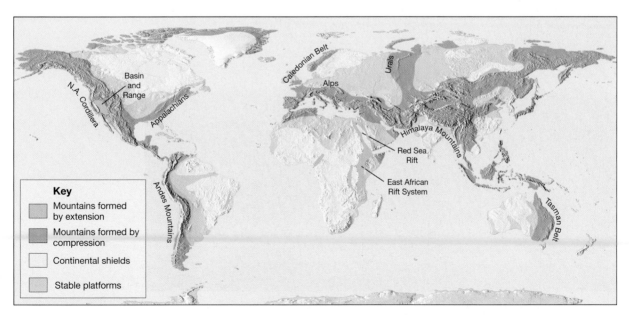

Figure 13.3 The basic framework of continents consists of mountains associated with extensional settings (rifts), compressional mountain belts, continental shields, and stable platforms.

In general, continental lithosphere subjected to extension is stretched and thinned, and it effectively collapses as fault-bounded blocks. In such cases, mountainous relief is primarily due to the rotation of sinking lithospheric blocks, as observed in the formation of rift valleys. In contrast, continental lithosphere that has been compressed, deformed, and thickened, as observed along convergent margins, stands very high, producing towering highlands.

Furthermore, mountains produced in convergent margins, despite being worn down, have left evidence of their existence as deformed belts within the ancient shields of continental land masses. These deformed belts, called *orogens*, indicate that large continents, such as North America, are the products of interactions with several crustal blocks. Before we explore this concept further, we will examine how various types of mountains fit into the plate tectonic scheme.

MOUNTAINS IN DIVERGENT MARGIN SETTINGS

Significant topographic relief is produced by tensional forces and the downward sliding and rotation of fault-bounded blocks. As discussed in Chapter 12 (see Figure 12.10), continental crust can be put into a state of tension when an ascending mantle plume pushes upward on the base of the lithosphere, causing it to dome upward. In the process, the lithosphere thins and cracks to form rift valleys. Margins

Figure 13.4   Linear mountains mark the tops of tilted fault blocks produced by crustal extension. Volcanoes are built by the extrusion of magma, adding to the rugged topography of rift regions.

of rift valleys begin to collapse, causing blocks of lithosphere to slide downward relative to one another along normal faults. The resulting rift margins on both sides of the valley have a step-like appearance, with the blocks near the axis of the valley lying at lower elevations than those at the outer edges of the valley (Figure 13.4). The spectacular relief observed in the East African Rift is largely the result of the downward sliding of such fault-bounded blocks (Figure 13.5).

Volcanism that accompanies the stretching and faulting of the crust contributes further to the high relief produced in continental rift margins. For example, Mount Kilimanjaro (5895 metres), located in Tanzania just adjacent to the Kenya border, was produced by volcanism that accompanied the formation of the East African Rift.

Figure 13.5   Mountainous terrain of Jebel Zabara along the Red Sea coast of Egypt. The highlands represent the exposed edges of tilted fault blocks of the Red Sea rift system. (Photo by W. R. Church)

Figure 13.6   Rifting can ultimately lead to the development of an ocean basin, bordered by passive continental margins. The step-like topography at the edges of continents inherited from the precursor rift valley is subdued by the accumulation of sediment on the resulting passive margins.

PASSIVE MARGINS: PRECURSORS TO CONVERGENT MARGINS

With continued divergence and volcanism, a continental rift valley can evolve into an oceanic spreading centre. The originally narrow valley is transformed into a narrow sea and may develop further into a full-fledged ocean. The opposing walls of a rift valley become continental margins that border the spreading ocean (Figure 13.6), with a staircase-like profile from their rift valley precursors. However, by the time the continental masses have separated, the tectonic extension that produced the faulted margin has more or less ceased. The continental margin is now a **passive margin;** that is, it is not a plate boundary but a part of the same plate as the adjoining oceanic crust.

Although passive margins are tectonically quiet, as marine sediment is deposited on the margin, it effectively weighs down the crust, causing it to sink. This sinking provides space for the deposition of more sediment, which causes further sinking, and so on. Thus, the general lack of tectonic activity with some large-scale subsidence in passive margins allows the gradual accumulation of thick sediment deposits, which drape over, and subdue, the rifted basement topography (Figure 13.6).

The eastern continental margins of North and South America and the western margins of Europe and Africa are all passive margins that were ultimately formed during the rifting and breakup of the supercontinent Pangaea. On each of these margins, deposition of sediment on the continental shelf produces a thick wedge of shallow-water sandstones, limestones, and shales (Figure 13.7A). Beyond the continental shelf, turbidity currents deposit sediments on the continental slope and rise (see Chapter 11).

MOUNTAINS IN CONVERGENT MARGIN SETTINGS

Earlier we illustrated how the relative elevations of wooden blocks floating on water relate to their relative thicknesses: Thick blocks stand higher than thin blocks by virtue of having deep "roots." Now visualize what would happen if another small block of wood were placed atop one of the blocks in Figure 13.2. The combined block would sink until a new isostatic balance was reached. However, the top of the combined block would be higher than before, and the bottom would be lower. This process of establishing a new level of gravitational equilibrium is called **isostatic adjustment**. In a similar manner, many mountain belts stand high above the surface because they have buoyant crustal roots that extend deeper into the supporting material below.

Simple Subduction: Andean- and Aleutian-Type Mountain Building

When a subduction zone is established at the edge of a continent, a passive margin is transformed into an active margin. The resulting convergence zone involving an oceanic plate and a plate whose leading edge contains continental crust leads to the formation of a volcanic arc and compressional tectonic features inland of the continental margin (Figure 13.7). This type of convergence zone is said to be of *Andean-type* because it is typified by the Andean region of South America, where the Nazca plate is currently being subducted beneath the South American plate along the Peru–Chile Trench (see Figure 11.7). This scenario differs from that of an *Aleutian-type* convergence zone, which involves the convergence of two

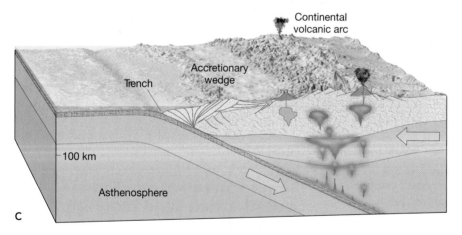

Figure 13.7 Orogenesis along an Andean-type subduction zone. **A.** Original passive continental margin with extensive wedge of sediments. **B.** Plate convergence generates a subduction zone, and partial melting produces a developing volcanic arc. **C.** Continued convergence and igneous activity further deform and thicken the crust, elevating the mountain belt, while the accretionary wedge grows.

oceanic plates and the formation of an island arc (Figure 13.8), as typified by the Aleutian Islands (Figure 13.9).

In an idealized Andean-type convergence zone, the subduction of an oceanic plate under a continental block leads to the deformation, metamorphism, and uplift of the continental margin. Once the oceanic plate descends to about 100 kilometres, partial melting of mantle rock above the subducting slab generates magma that migrates upward and further thickens the continental crust (Figure 13.7B). During the development of this continental volcanic arc, sediments derived from the land are scraped from the

subducting plate and plastered against the landward side of the trench (Figure 13.7B). As described in Chapter 11, this chaotic accumulation of sedimentary and metamorphic rocks with occasional scraps of ocean crust is called an *accretionary wedge*. Prolonged subduction can build an accretionary wedge that is thick enough to stand above sea level (Figure 13.7C).

Andean-type mountain belts therefore contain two roughly parallel zones, each containing distinctive suites of rock types. The continental block hosts volcanic rocks and large intrusive bodies intermixed with high-temperature metamorphic rocks, whereas the accretionary wedge that lies on the oceanic slab

Figure 13.8 The development of a volcanic island arc by the convergence of two oceanic plates. Continuous subduction along these Aleutian-type convergent zones results in the development of thick units of continental-type crust.

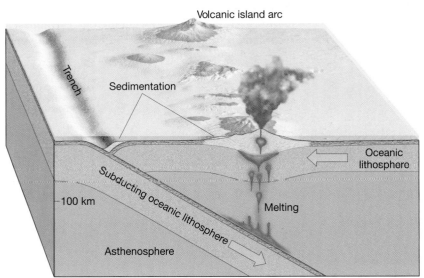

Figure 13.9 Three of the many volcanic islands that compose the Aleutian arc. This narrow band of volcanism results from the subduction of the Pacific plate. In the distance is the Great Sitkin volcano (1772 metres), which the Aleuts call the "Great Emptier of Bowels," because of its frequent activity.
(Photo by Bruce D. Marsh)

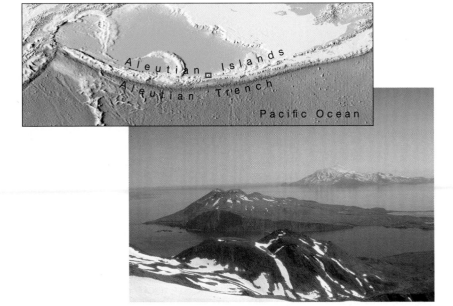

consists of folded, faulted, and metamorphosed sediments and volcanic debris (Figure 13.7C). North American examples of Andean-type mountain belts include the Coast Mountains of British Columbia and the Sierra Nevada of California.

Continental Collisions

Collisions of much greater magnitude are produced when two lithospheric plates carrying continental crust are brought into contact as the oceanic lithosphere on one plate is subducted under the other (Figure 13.10). Because continental crust is too buoyant to undergo any appreciable subduction, a spectacular collision between the continental masses results, and the two continental blocks fuse to become one. The mechanics of continental collision, crustal thickening, and the associated uplift are well displayed by the genesis of the Himalayas and the Tibetan Plateau.

THE HIMALAYAS India, once part of Antarctica, split from that continent about 130 million years ago, and over millions of years slowly drifted northward toward Eurasia (Figure 13.10A). The voyage of this continental block culminated in a head-on collision between India and Eurasia about 10 million years ago (Figure 13.10B). Although most of the oceanic crust that separated these land masses before the collision was subducted, some was caught up in the squeeze, along with sediment that lay offshore. Today these sedimentary rocks and slivers of oceanic crust are elevated high above sea level. Geologists believe that following such a collision, the subducted oceanic plate decouples from the rigid continental plate and continues its descent into the mantle.

The spreading centre that propelled India northward is still active; hence, India continues to be thrust into Asia at an estimated rate of a few centimetres each year. However, numerous earthquakes recorded off the southern coast of India indicate that

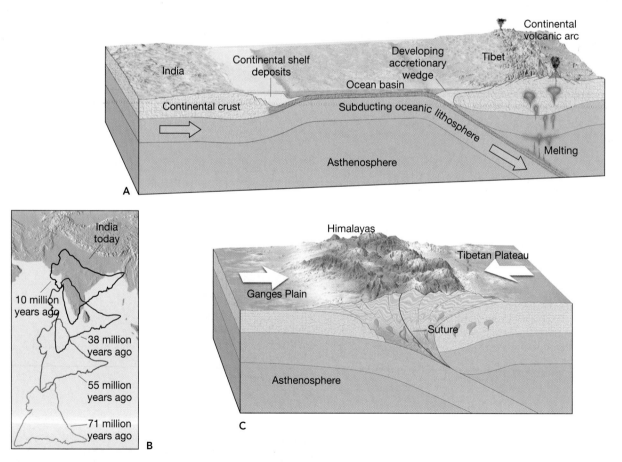

Figure 13.10   Simplified diagrams showing the northward migration and collision of India with the Eurasian plate. **A.** Converging plates generated a subduction zone, while partial melting of the subducting oceanic slab produced a continental volcanic arc. Sediments scraped from the subducting plate were added to the accretionary wedge. **B.** Position of India in relation to Eurasia at various times. **C.** Eventually, the two land masses collided, deforming and elevating the accretionary wedge and continental shelf deposits. In addition, slices of the Indian crust were thrust up onto the Indian plate. (Modified after Peter Molnar)

a new subduction zone may be in the making. If formed, it would provide a subduction site for the floor of the Indian Ocean, which is continually being produced at a spreading centre located to the southwest. Should this occur, India's northward journey, relative to Asia, would come to an end and the growth of the Himalayas would cease. A new orogen would then begin to form along the coast of India.

A similar but much older collision is believed to have taken place when the European continent collided with the Asian continent to produce the Ural Mountains, which extend in a north–south direction through Russia. Before the discovery of plate tectonics, geologists had difficulty explaining the existence of such mountain ranges as the Urals, which are located deep within continental interiors.

Accreted Terranes

Andean-type convergence is fairly straightforward in that nearly all of the material composing the subducting oceanic slab glides downward into the mantle and is consumed. Subduction is so efficient at such margins that the only traces of the subducted plate left at the surface are the small slivers of mafic oceanic crust and overlying sediments that have been shaved off and incorporated into the accretionary wedge. Convergence becomes more complicated when the leading edge of an oceanic plate carries features that are too thick and buoyant to be subducted. Such features vary widely in origin and include the following:

1. Micro-continents, small fragments of continental crust left over from continental rifting or sheared-off continental margins along transform faults, are rafted on oceanic plates. Recall that continental crust is thicker and more buoyant than oceanic crust and resists subduction.

2. Island arcs, produced by the convergence of two oceanic plates, are composed of crust that is largely andesitic in composition and therefore more buoyant than the adjacent mafic oceanic crust. As in the case of micro-continents, low crustal density and high crustal thickness prevent island arcs from being subducted.

3. Oceanic plateaus, as well as the hot-spot volcanoes and seamounts that compose such features as the Hawaiian Ridge, are prominent topographic features of the ocean floor produced by intraplate (mantle plume) volcanism. These features are mafic in composition and therefore of similar density to the crust of the surrounding ocean floor. However, because they are high-standing features, they are not readily forced under a continental plate by subduction.

The fate of a crustal component that resists subduction is to collide with, and become plastered against, the continental margin. Once the crustal fragment is firmly accreted to the continental margin and sheared off the subducting oceanic slab, it effectively becomes part of the continent itself. Packages of sedimentary deposits may also be added to the continent by virtue of being trapped between the crustal fragment and the continental margin.

Geologists refer to distinct units of material added to the edge of a continent as **terranes**. More formally, the term *terrane* designates any crustal fragment that has a geologic history distinct from that of the adjoining terranes. Some terranes are no larger than volcanic islands, whereas others, like the entire Indian subcontinent, are very large. Accreted terranes can compose substantial regions of continents, as observed along the western side of North America (Figure 13.11). British Columbia alone contains at least 39 distinct terranes that together compose more than 80 percent of the province's land area and that have been added to North America within the

Figure 13.11 Map showing terranes that have been added to western North America during the past 200 million years. Data from paleomagnetic and fossil evidence indicate that some of these terranes originated thousands of kilometres south of their present location.

CANADIAN PROFILE
Landscapes of the Canadian Rocky Mountains

The great compressional forces that accompanied the collision of terranes with the western margin of Canada resulted in a significant amount of crustal shortening that ultimately built the Canadian Rockies and their associated foothills (Figure 13.A). Huge sheets of rock bounded by westward dipping thrust faults were stacked atop one another and in some cases were deformed as they slid into their present positions. With progressive compression, older thrust sheets were carried in a piggyback fashion on younger thrust sheets that were generated successively eastward through time. In other words, thrust faults in the Rocky Mountain Foothills record the last stages of thrusting that occurred during the building of the mountain belt.

The landscapes of the Canadian Rockies and Rocky Mountain Foothills

reflect the structural characteristics of their underlying rocks as well as differences in the erosion rates of various rock types. A transect through southeast British Columbia and southwest Alberta reveals four basic physiographic components: the Western Ranges, the Main Ranges, the Front Ranges, and the Foothills (Figure 13.A).

The Western Ranges, located in southeast British Columbia, are characterized by intensely folded, thinly bedded Paleozoic shales and carbonates. Enhanced erosion of shale-rich beds, relative to the more resistant beds of carbonate, imparts a jagged appearance to the mountains.

East of the Western Ranges, the Rockies are dominated by thick, massive units of Proterozoic and Paleozoic carbonates. Instead of folding like the strata of the Western Ranges, these

rocks fractured and were thrust eastward in numerous fault-bounded sheets. The Main Ranges expose strata in a more or less horizontal orientation, reflecting the shallow dip of the thrust faults immediately underlying this area. Main Range peaks are characteristically castle-shaped, with steep cliffs on all sides.

East of the Main Ranges are the Front Ranges, which occur as well-defined, linear ridges separated by linear valleys. In these ranges, the strata within each thrust sheet are significantly upturned and their bounding thrust faults are more steeply inclined. Manifesting the inclined attitude of the thrust sheets, the southwest slopes of Front Range mountains have a distinct, slanted appearance.

Finally, the Rocky Mountain Foothills mark the easternmost extent

Figure 13.A Shapes of mountains and foothills of the Canadian Rockies partly reflect the structure of their contained rocks. The jagged peaks of Western Range Mountains, such as the Steeples, reflect intense folding of shale-rich strata. The flatter peaks of the Main Range Mountains, such as Castle Mountain, manifest the flat-lying attitude of strata within thrust sheets. Front Range Mountains, such as Mount Rundle, have a more slanted appearance because of steeper slopes of underlying thrust faults. The foothills southwest of Calgary have a more subdued topography because their underlying Mesozoic rock is easier to erode than the more resistant Paleozoic and Proterozoic rocks of the Rockies. The slightly greater resistance to erosion of sandstones and conglomerates (relative to adjacent shale) is indicated by protruding hogback ridges. Arrows indicate direction of movement along thrust faults. (Photo of Steeples © Sue McMurtrie/Fotolia; photo of Castle Mountain © Alec Pytlowany/Masterfile; photo of Mount Rundle by S. R. Hicock/Pearson Education; photo of foothills by BGSmith/Shutterstock)

of significant deformation associated with the building of the Canadian Rocky Mountains. Like the Front Ranges, strata of the Foothills are significantly upturned because of having been forced upward in sheets over the steeply inclined segments of thrust faults. However, strata of the Foothills are predominantly late Mesozoic to early Cenozoic in age and therefore much younger than those of the true Rockies. As these rocks are more prone to erosion than the Paleozoic strata of the Rockies, they have been worn down to form more subtle linear hills. Even so, hogback ridges, composed of Cretaceous sandstones and conglomerates that are more resistant than the intervening shales, occur in some places. The Foothills thus mark a topographic transition zone between the Rockies to the west and the Plains to the east.

past 200 million years. The Wrangellia Terrane (Figure 13.11) is one of the largest of these accreted terranes.

Terrane accretion produces significant topographic relief inboard of the collision zone. As the buoyant crustal material is peeled from the subducting plate, it is thrust in relatively thin sheets onto the adjacent continental block. The material may later be overridden or displaced farther inland by the addition of other fragments. In turn, the shortening and thickening of the continental margin caused by collision promotes uplift and the formation of a mountain belt. The uplift of the North American Cordillera is a classic example of mountain building associated with terrane accretion. The compression generated by terrane accretion on the western margin of Canada can be appreciated by considering the deformation experienced in the Rocky Mountains of British Columbia and Alberta (Box 13.1).

Mountain Belts with Complex Histories

Unsurprisingly, mountain belts can have extremely complex histories and can show evidence of more than one type of mountain-building process, including simple subduction, terrane accretion, and continent–continent collision. As such, each type of mountain building should be viewed as a potential stage in the evolution of a mature mountain belt. The complexity of mountain building is beautifully illustrated in the history of the Appalachian Mountain belt in eastern North America.

THE APPALACHIANS The Appalachian Mountain belt, stretching from Newfoundland and Labrador to the southeast coast of the United States, is the product of hundreds of millions of years of geologic activity. Through several decades of study, the evolution of the Appalachians has been interpreted to involve five basic phases of tectonic activity. In this section, the major events in the evolution of this complex mountain belt are briefly discussed, with an emphasis on Canadian features (Figure 13.12). The present-day distribution of major crustal components of the Appalachians is depicted in Figure 13.13.

PHASE 1: DIVERGENCE During the late Precambrian, a supercontinent called Rodinia was split apart by continental rifting. Land masses produced by this rifting included ancestral North America (part of Laurasia) and Africa (part of Gondwanaland), which drifted apart because of the spreading of the proto-Atlantic Ocean (Iapetus; Figures 13.12A and 13.12B). Smaller fragments of continental crust, also produced during the rifting process, were rafted on the diverging plates as isolated blocks, surrounded by larger expanses of oceanic crust. During this divergent phase, the edges of eastern North America and western Africa were occupied by passive margins that remained stable until the early Paleozoic.

PHASE 2: INITIAL CONVERGENCE Sometime during the Cambrian, convergence was initiated in Iapetus and the ocean basin had begun to shrink. Island arcs formed because of Aleutian-type (oceanic–oceanic) convergence (Figure 13.12C), and a microcontinent called Avalonia began to approach North America's eastern margin.

PHASE 3: ACCRETION OF TERRANES Continued closure of Iapetus brought eastern North America into contact with a number of crustal components that could not be consumed by subduction. The collision of these blocks with eastern North America is recorded in multiple mountain-building events. The first major event, called the Taconic Orogeny, involved the accretion of island arc complexes (Figure 13.12D) in the Ordovician (represented by rocks of the Dunnage Zone in the Canada Appalachians). A later mountain-building episode called the Acadian Orogeny resulted from the docking of Avalonia (represented by rocks of the Avalon Terrane) along eastern North America, beginning in the Silurian and reaching its maximum in the Devonian (Figure 13.12E).

PHASE 4: CONTINENTAL COLLISION Iapetus eventually closed, bringing the western margin of

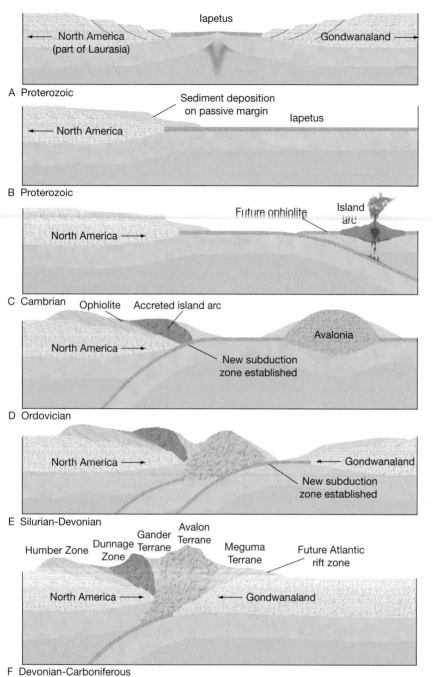

Accreted Terranes

- Island arc
- Submarine deposits
- Ancient ocean floor (ophiolite)
- Micro-continents

A Proterozoic

North America (part of Laurasia)

Iapetus

Gondwanaland

B Proterozoic

North America

Sediment deposition on passive margin

Iapetus

C Cambrian

North America

Future ophiolite

Island arc

D Ordovician

North America

Ophiolite   Accreted island arc

Avalonia

New subduction zone established

E Silurian-Devonian

North America

Gondwanaland

New subduction zone established

F Devonian-Carboniferous

Humber Zone   Dunnage Zone   Gander Terrane   Avalon Terrane   Meguma Terrane   Future Atlantic rift zone

North America   Gondwanaland

Figure 13.12 Principal tectonic events in the evolution of the northern Appalachian Mountains of eastern Canada. Arrows indicate movement direction. **A.** Rifting separates North America (then part of a continent called Laurasia) and Gondwanaland, forming the proto-Atlantic Ocean (Iapetus). **B.** With continued spreading of Iapetus, the eastern margin of North America exists as a passive margin on which land-derived sediments are deposited. **C.** Iapetus begins to close and Aleutian-type convergence is initiated in Iapetus, producing an island arc to the east of North America. **D.** With continued convergence, the volcanic arc is accreted to eastern North America, and a segment of its associated oceanic plate is plastered on as ophiolite. **E.** The micro-continent Avalonia is accreted to the eastern margin of North America in the Middle Devonian. **F.** Gondwanaland collides with eastern North America.

Gondwanaland against eastern North America. The Meguma Zone in Nova Scotia is believed to represent a remnant of the Gondwanaland continental margin (possibly part of Africa or South America) that was welded to the North American continent during early stages of the closure of Iapetus (Figure 13.12F) and that was left stranded on North America when later rifting produced the Atlantic Ocean basin. The Meguma Zone apparently came into contact with North America as early as the Devonian (Figure 13.12F), but it was during the Carboniferous and Permian that the main episode of continental collision occurred. The final collision between the African part of Gondwanaland and eastern North America was centred in the southeast United States and resulted in the Allegheny Orogeny, the last mountain-building event in the Appalachians. This continental collision was only one of several that ultimately resulted in the formation of the supercontinent Pangaea by the late Permian.

The Wilson Cycle

The Wilson Cycle, named after famous Canadian geophysicist J. Tuzo Wilson (see Chapter 12), incorporates the major events that occur during the splitting apart and coming together of continental land masses. The passage of a single Wilson cycle can be summarized as follows:

1. After the breakup of a continental land mass, a thick wedge of sediment is deposited along the passive continental margins, thereby increasing the size of the newly formed continent.

2. Because of a change in the direction of plate motion, the ocean basin begins to close and the continents begin to converge.

3. Plate convergence results in the subduction of the intervening oceanic slab and initiates an extended episode of igneous activity. This activity results in the formation of an Andean-type volcanic arc with associated intrusions.

4. Eventually the continental blocks collide. This event severely deforms and metamorphoses the entrapped sediments. Continental convergence causes these deformed materials to be displaced up onto the plates along thrust faults. This activity shortens and thickens the crustal rocks, producing an elevated mountain belt, and may be preceded by smaller-scale collisions involving the docking of terranes.

5. Finally, a change in the plate boundary ends the growth of the mountains. At this point erosional processes become the dominant forces in altering the landscape, and, over time, the mountain chain is worn down to its roots.

This sequence of events is thought to have repeated many times during Earth's long history.

However, the rate of deformation and geologic and climatic settings varied in each instance. Thus, the formation of each mountain chain must be regarded as a unique event.

Convergence and the Obduction of Oceanic Crust

Ophiolite complexes (Chapter 11) help us answer an important question: If continental crust stands high and oceanic crust stands low, how can oceanic crust end up exposed in some mountains, high above sea level? The answer appears to be that the subduction of oceanic crust is not always complete. In rare cases, pieces of the oceanic plate can be broken off, thrust onto the continent, and lifted high and dry above sea level during mountain building. This process is called *obduction*.

Ophiolites, although originally produced as sections of oceanic crust settings, are emplaced in convergent tectonic settings. Some ophiolites occur as disrupted multiple shavings of oceanic crust scraped off a subducted plate and incorporated into an accretionary wedge (e.g., Figure 13.7), like that of the Franciscan Complex of California (Figure 13.11). Others, like the Bay of Islands Ophiolite (Figure 13.13) in Newfoundland and Labrador, and the Thetford Mines Ophiolite (Figure 13.13) of Quebec (Canada's source of crysotile asbestos), appear to have been emplaced as thicker, more intact blocks of oceanic lithosphere that were thrust onto the edge of the continent during terrane accretion, and were eventually uplifted when the continental block rose upward to achieve isostatic equilibrium (Figure 13.12). In such places as Gros Morne National Park, Newfoundland and Labrador, the ophiolite sequence is so complete that the base of the oceanic crust can be observed (see Figure 11.12B).

Thick slices of ophiolites also occur in mountain ranges that mark the collision of two continents, as seen in the Alps and the Himalayas. The scientific

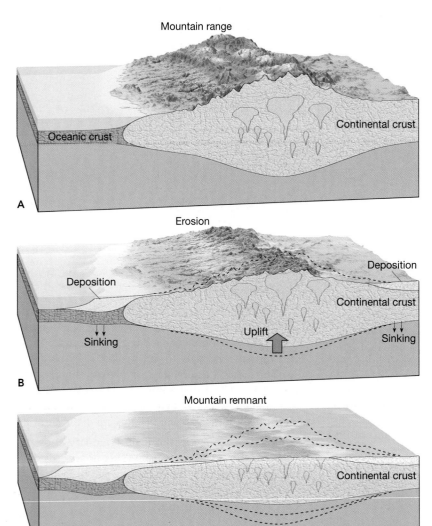

Figure 13.14 This sequence illustrates how the combined effect of erosion and isostatic adjustment results in a thinning of the crust in mountainous regions. **A.** When mountains are young, the continental crust is thickest. **B.** As erosion lowers the mountains, the crust rises in response to the reduced load. **C.** Erosion and uplift continue until the mountains reach "normal" crustal thickness.

value of ophiolites preserved in the suture zones of such mountain ranges is obvious, for they provide tangible evidence of ocean basins that separated the continents before their collision.

Isostatic Adjustment after Active Convergence

Applying the concept of isostasy, we should expect that when material is added to the top of a crustal block, such as the thrusted masses of rock piled up during mountain building, the root of the crustal block will subside to a deeper level. Accordingly, we should expect the original block to rebound and the thickness of its root to be reduced when weight is removed. (Visualize what happens to a ship as cargo is being loaded and unloaded.)

One of the consequences of isostatic adjustment is that as erosion lowers the summits of mountains, the crust will rise in response to the reduced load (Figures 13.14B and 13.14C). This will continue until the mountain block reaches "normal" crustal thickness, it is eroded to near sea level, and the once deeply buried interior of the mountain will be exposed at the surface. As mountains are worn down, the eroded sediment is deposited on adjacent landscapes, causing these areas to subside (Figure 13.14B). Isostatic adjustment is responsible for exposing the deep roots of the Appalachian Mountains in eastern North America and for contributing to the large amounts of sediment deposited along the Atlantic and Gulf Coastal Plain that now cover the older bedrock of accreted terranes (Figure 13.13).

BROAD VERTICAL MOVEMENTS IN CONTINENTS
Regions of Uplift

Based on studies of Earth's gravity, some form of up-and-down convective flow is occurring in the mantle that affects elevations of major landforms.

The buoyancy of hot rising material accounts for broad up-warping in the overlying lithosphere, whereas downward flow causes down-warping. Much of southern Africa exists as an expansive plateau that has an average elevation of nearly 1500 metres—much higher than would be expected for a stable continental platform. Seismic tomography indicates that a large mushroom-shaped mass of hot mantle rock is centred below the southern tip of Africa. This *super-plume* extends upward about 2900 kilometres from the mantle–core boundary and spreads out over several thousand square kilometres, with enough upward flow to elevate southern Africa.

Regions of Subsidence

Some down-warping is simply the result of an extra load being added to the crust, such as occurred during the last Ice Age (see Chapter 17). Other examples of crustal loading occur along the continental margins where sediments are being deposited. For example, the Mississippi River has dumped enormous quantities of sediment into the Gulf of Mexico. In the case of broad regional uplift, however, some down-warped areas may be linked to flow dynamics of the mantle.

FORELAND AND INTRACRATONIC BASINS Continental interiors, although having a more subdued topography than mountain belts along their margins, show a number of basins and intervening arches that manifest subtle deflections of the lithosphere. Of particular importance in North America are *foreland* and *intracratonic basins*, which have served as important catchment areas for sediments that now host significant volumes of oil and gas.

Foreland basins are elongate, asymmetrical, trough-like depressions (Figure 13.15) that are produced by the loading of a continental mass along one of its edges. Similar to the way the free end of a diving board bends in response to the load of a diver,

West / East
Canadian Rockies / Alberta Foothills / Alberta Plains

|← Fold and Thrust Belt →|←Western Canada Foreland Basin→|

Subsidence because of loading

Precambrian Basement

Mesozoic   Paleozoic

0   500 km

Figure 13.15 Simplified cross-section through Canadian Rocky Mountains, Alberta Foothills, and Alberta Plains. A foreland basin underlies the plains region because of loading by thrust sheets that accompanied the shortening of crust that formed the Rockies. Note that crustal shortening continued long after the main phase of foreland basin development. Thus, Mesozoic sedimentary rocks that originally accumulated in the western part of the foreland basin have been disturbed by thrust faulting.

Figure 13.16 Two possible mechanisms responsible for forming a circular intracratonic basin. **A.** The lithosphere thins and sags because of localized mantle upwelling. **B.** The lithosphere is weighed down locally by a mass of mantle material that has attached to the base of the lithosphere and has sunk because of increased density on cooling.

the lithosphere flexes downward under the increased mass of thickened crust. Among the best-known basins of this type in Canada is the Western Canada Foreland Basin.

This basin developed inland of the Rocky Mountains during the Mesozoic, in response to the crustal shortening and thickening that accompanied the accretion of terranes in British Columbia. Similarly, the Appalachian Foreland Basin in eastern Canada was produced by crustal thickening that

accompanied the accretion of terranes and uplift of the early Appalachian Mountains during the Paleozoic.

Intracratonic basins are circular bowl-shaped depressions that develop well within continental interiors. Two classic examples of intracratonic basins are the Williston Basin, which underlies the southern part of the Canadian Prairies, and the Michigan Basin, the northern part of which underlies southwest Ontario (Figures 13.16 and 9.17). The origin of intracratonic basins is somewhat

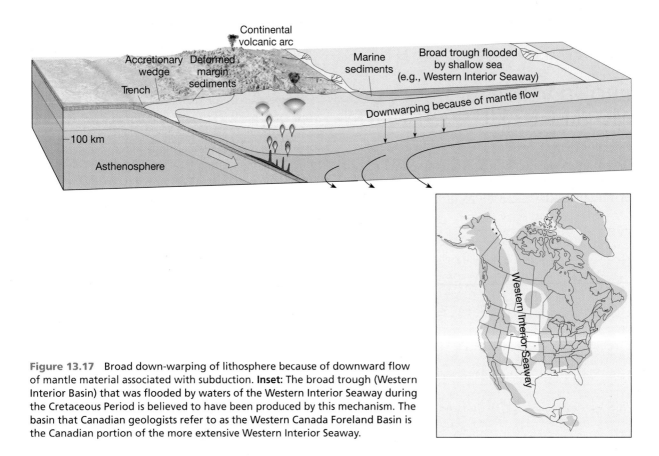

Figure 13.17 Broad down-warping of lithosphere because of downward flow of mantle material associated with subduction. **Inset:** The broad trough (Western Interior Basin) that was flooded by waters of the Western Interior Seaway during the Cretaceous Period is believed to have been produced by this mechanism. The basin that Canadian geologists refer to as the Western Canada Foreland Basin is the Canadian portion of the more extensive Western Interior Seaway.

obscure and remains a subject of significant debate. A few geologists believe that the formation of such basins is linked to far-field compressive forces related to plate convergence, but most assert that the circular basin shape must indicate a mantle-related phenomenon acting independently of plate interactions (Figure 13.16). In the latter camp, it has been suggested that an intracratonic basin forms by lithospheric thinning and subsequent sagging associated with the ascent of mantle plumes. Others have suggested that intracratonic basins represent circular dimples produced by blobs of dense mantle material that attached to the base of the lithosphere and later sank because of their increased density on cooling.

DOWN-WARPING OF CONTINENTAL MARGINS AND INTERIORS Evidence also suggests that much of the North American interior experienced a major episode of subsidence during the Cretaceous Period. Although sea level was no more than 120 metres higher than it is today, vast seas invaded much of the continent. The Cretaceous seas eventually retreated, leaving behind thick accumulations of marine sedimentary rocks. Today these largely undeformed strata are found hundreds of metres above sea level in the Canadian Prairies (Figure 13.17).

Similar episodes of large-scale down-warping are known on other continents, including Australia. The cause of these downward movements followed by rebound may be linked to subduction of oceanic lithosphere. One proposal suggests that when subduction ceases along a continental margin, the subducting slab detaches from the trailing lithosphere and continues its descent into the mantle. As this detached lithospheric slab sinks, it creates a downward flow in its wake that tugs on the base of the overriding continent. In some situations the crust is apparently pulled down enough to allow the ocean to extend inland. As the plate segment sinks deeper, the pull of the trailing wake weakens, and the continent "floats" back into isostatic balance. Although computer modelling supports this proposed mechanism, observational data to test this hypothesis have yet to be gathered.

THE ORIGIN AND EVOLUTION OF CONTINENTS

The lack of agreement on this topic among geologists can be partly attributed to the complex nature and antiquity of most continental material, which makes deciphering its history very difficult. Whereas oceanic crust has a relatively simple layered structure and a rather uniform composition, the much older continental crust consists of a collage of highly deformed and metamorphosed igneous and sedimentary rocks. Moreover, in many places, such as the Canadian Prairies, the basement rocks are mantled by thick accumulations of much younger sedimentary rocks—a fact that inhibits detailed study. Nevertheless, during the past few decades, great strides have been made in unravelling the secrets held by the rocks that make up the stable continental interiors.

Early Evolution of Continents

At one extreme is a proposal that the continental crust formed early in Earth's history, perhaps in the first billion years. During this period, chemical differentiation resulted in the upward migration of the less-dense, silica-rich constituents of the mantle to produce a "scum" of continental-type rocks. The more dense silicate minerals, those enriched in iron and magnesium, remained in the mantle.

Shortly after this period of chemical differentiation, a mechanism that may have resembled plate tectonics reworked and recycled the continental crust. Through such activity, the continental crust was deformed, metamorphosed, and even re-melted. However, because these silica-rich rocks were buoyant, they may not have been destroyed to any great extent or, if they were, they were replaced in roughly equal amounts by mantle-derived magmas. Thus, the essence of this hypothesis is that the total volume of continental crust has not changed appreciably since its origin—only the distribution and shape of the land masses have been modified by tectonic activity.

Gradual Evolution of Continents

An opposing view contends that the continents have gradually grown larger through geologic time by the addition of material derived from the upper mantle. A main tenet of this hypothesis is that the primitive crust was of an oceanic type and the continents were small or possibly nonexistent. Then, through magmatic differentiation of mantle-derived magmas, the continents slowly grew over vast spans of geologic time.

According to this scenario, the earliest continental rocks came into existence at a few, isolated island arcs. Once formed, these island arcs coalesced to form larger continental masses, while deforming the volcanic and sedimentary rocks that were deposited in the intervening oceans. Eventually, this process generated blocks of continental crust that had the size and thickness of modern continents.

We can consider the growth of continents, as described above, to be a two-stage process. The first stage involves the formation of silica-rich rocks, which are the major constituents of the upper continental crust. As stated earlier, this process typically occurs at subduction zones, where mantle-derived magmas form crustal rocks in such settings as island arcs. The second stage involves the accretion of these terranes into larger crustal areas (called provinces), which in turn are sutured together to form continent-size crustal blocks. The latter event is associated with a major episode of mountain building.

North America provides an excellent example of the development of continental crust and its piecemeal assembly into a continent. Notice in Figure 13.18 that very little continental crust exists that is older than 2.5 billion years. In contrast, between 2 billion and 1.5 billion years ago there was a period of major crustal growth. During this span, the accretion of numerous island arcs and other crustal fragments generated several large

crustal provinces. North America contains some of these crustal provinces, including the Superior and Hearne/Rae cratons shown in Figure 13.18. The locations of these ancient continental blocks during their formation are not known. However, about 1.9 billion years ago these crustal provinces collided to produce the Trans-Hudson mountain belt (Figure 13.18). (This mountain-building episode was not restricted to North America, because ancient deformed strata of similar age are found on other continents.) This event built the core of North America, around which several large and numerous small crustal fragments were later added. Examples of these late arrivals include the Blue Ridge and Piedmont provinces of the Appalachians and several terranes that were added to the western margin of North America during the Mesozoic and Cenozoic eras.

We do not know with certainty how many major periods of mountain building have occurred since the formation of Earth. Each of these events probably marks the formation of a supercontinent. The last major period evidently coincided with the closing of the ancestral Atlantic during the formation of the supercontinent Pangaea.

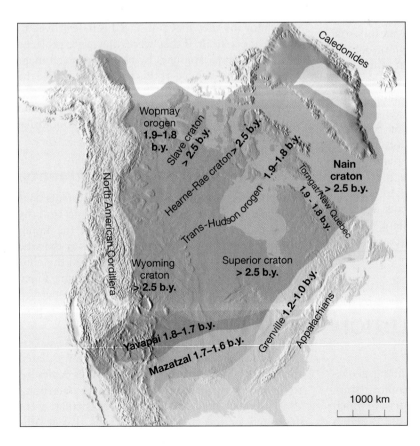

Figure 13.18 A map showing the major geologic provinces of North America and their ages in billions of years (b.y.). It appears that North America was constructed by crustal blocks that were assembled by processes very similar to modern plate tectonics. These ancient collisions produced mountainous belts that include remnant volcanic island arcs trapped by the colliding continental fragments.

CHAPTER SUMMARY

- *Isostasy* involves lighter crust "floating" on denser mantle; mountains have deep crustal roots. Erosion lowers mountain peaks while isostatic adjustment lifts their roots until the mountain block reaches "normal" crustal thickness.
- Major mountains form along convergent plate boundaries: *Andean-type*, where oceanic crust subducts under continental crust (continental volcanic arc); *Aleutian-type*, where oceanic crust subducts under oceanic crust (volcanic island arc); continental crust collisions (world's highest mountains); and accretion, where crustal frag-

ments are forcefully attached to continental margins as terranes.
- Upward flow of mantle plumes can uplift crust while sediment buildup on passive margins can cause crustal subsidence.
- There are two main schools of thought on the origin and growth of continents and their crust: Whereas some geologists assert that continental crust initially formed very early in Earth's history and was later reworked by plate tectonics, others favour the idea that continents grew more gradually via the accretion of mantle material.

MasteringGeology

www.masteringgeology.com

Looking for additional review and test prep materials? Visit the Study Area in MasteringGeology to enhance your understanding of this chapter's content by accessing a variety of resources, including

Self-Study Quizzes, Geoscience Animations, GEODe Tutorials, RSS feeds, flashcards, weblinks, self-study quizzes, and an optional Pearson eText.

REVIEW QUESTIONS

1. In the plate tectonics model, which type of plate boundary is most directly associated with the world's major mountain belts?

2. Describe how a volcanic island arc develops.

3. What is an accretionary wedge and how is it formed?

4. How does the plate tectonic theory help explain the existence of fossil marine life in rocks high in the Rocky Mountains?

5. In your own words, briefly describe the stages in the formation of a major mountain system according to the plate tectonic model.

6. What are terranes? How were they significant in the geologic evolution of both the eastern and western regions of what is now Canada?

7. What is the relationship between isostasy, the elevation of mountains, and the thickness of their roots?

8. Compare and contrast the currently opposing views on the origin and early evolution of continents.

14 MASS WASTING: THE WORK OF GRAVITY

This rock slide in a deep quarry at L'Épiphanie, Quebec, claimed three vehicles (one visible, partly buried) and two lives in January 2013. (Photo by THE CANADIAN PRESS/Graham Hughes)

CHAPTER OUTLINE

"We're sliding. We're going to die!" shouted a quarry worker as she and her truck were swept by a rock slide into a quarry about 100 metres deep (chapter-opening photo). Her body was recovered four days later, as well as that of a male co-worker who fell into the pit with his excavator. On a larger scale, in southwest Alberta in 1903 it took less than 100 seconds for more than 80 million tonnes (30 million cubic metres) of rock to tumble from the top of Turtle Mountain and spread out over three square kilometres of land at the base of the mountain. Within the path of the rock slide was the coal-mining town of Frank. At least 70 people died in this disaster.

Slope failures are hard to predict and Earth's surface is never perfectly flat; instead, it consists of slopes of different lengths and gradients. Slopes can be mantled with soil and vegetation or consist of barren rock and rubble. Although most of them may appear to be stable and unchanging, the force of gravity ultimately causes material to move downslope. At one extreme, the movement can be gradual and practically imperceptible. At the other extreme, it can consist of a roaring debris flow or a thundering rock slide. When these hazardous natural processes lead to loss of life and property, they become natural disasters (e.g. Hope Slide, Figure 14.1).

MASS WASTING AND LANDFORM DEVELOPMENT

Landslides (in the general sense) are examples of a basic geologic process called **mass wasting**, the downslope movement of rock, regolith, and soil under the direct influence of gravity. It is distinct from the erosional processes examined in subsequent chapters because mass wasting does not require a transporting medium, such as water, wind, or glacial ice.

The Role of Mass Wasting

As mentioned in Chapter 5, once weathering weakens and breaks rock apart, mass wasting carries the debris downslope, where a stream, acting as a conveyor belt, usually carries it away. Although it may make many intermediate stops along the way, the sediment may be eventually transported to the sea.

The combined effects of mass wasting and running water produce stream valleys, the most common and conspicuous of Earth's landforms. If streams alone created the valleys in which they flow, the valleys would be very narrow. The fact that most river valleys are much wider than they are deep indicates the significance of mass wasting processes in supplying material to streams. This fact is illustrated by the Fraser River Valley (Figure 14.2). The walls of the valley extend far from the Fraser River, owing to the transfer of weathered debris downslope to the river and its tributaries by mass wasting processes. In this manner, streams and mass wasting combine to sculpt the surface, along with groundwater, waves, and wind.

A B

Figure 14.1 The Hope Slide, the largest historic landslide in western Canada. **A.** Photo taken January 11, 1965, two days after the rock slide. **B.** Aerial view in 1988, when vegetation was re-established on the bottom part of the slide. In January 2011, another rock slide blocked traffic for a day north of here, near Yale in the Fraser Canyon.
(Photo **A** Reproduced with permission of Natural Resource Canada 2013, courtesy of Geological Survey of Canada (Photo 127297 by E.D. Kindle). photo **B** used with permission of John Clague)

Figure 14.2 The walls of the Fraser Valley west of Clinton, British Columbia, extend far from the channel of the Fraser River. This results partly from the transfer of weathered debris downslope to the river and its tributaries by mass wasting processes. (Photo © All Canada Photos/Alamy)

Slopes Change through Time

Clearly, if mass wasting is to occur, it needs slopes down which rock, soil, and regolith can move. It is Earth's mountain-building and volcanic processes that produce many of these slopes, sporadically changing the elevations of land masses and the ocean floor. If dynamic internal processes did not continually produce regions of higher elevations, the transfer of debris to lower elevations would gradually slow and eventually cease.

Most extreme mass wasting events occur in areas of rugged, geologically young mountains. Newly formed mountains are rapidly eroded by rivers and glaciers, which produce steep and unstable slopes. It is in such settings that massive destructive landslides occur, such as the Hope disaster (Figure 14.1). As mountain building subsides, mass wasting and erosional processes lower the land. Over time, steep and rugged mountains are worn down to form gentler, more subdued terrain with smaller, less dramatic downslope movements.

CONTROLS AND TRIGGERS OF MASS WASTING

Gravity is the controlling force of mass wasting, but several factors play an important role in promoting downslope movements. Long before a landslide occurs, various processes work to weaken slope material, gradually making it more and more susceptible to failure, and ultimately less stable. Eventually, the strength of the slope is weakened to the point that something **triggers**, or initiates, downslope movement. Remember that the trigger is not the sole cause of the mass wasting event but just "the last straw" among many causes. Among the common factors that trigger mass wasting processes are saturation of material with water, oversteepening of slopes, removal of anchoring vegetation, and ground vibrations from earthquakes.

The Role of Water

Mass wasting is sometimes triggered when heavy rains or periods of snowmelt saturate surface materials. This was the case in January 2011 when torrential downpours triggered devastating mudflows in Brazil (Figure 14.3).

When the pores in sediment become filled with water, the cohesion among particles is destroyed, allowing them to slide past one another with relative ease. For example, when sand is slightly moist, it sticks together quite well. However, if enough water is added to fill the openings between the grains, the strength of the sand is lost and it flows out in all directions (Figure 14.4). Thus, saturation reduces the internal strength of materials, and they are then easily set in motion by the force of gravity. When clay is wetted, it becomes very slick and can act as a lubricating agent. Water also adds considerable weight to a mass of material, which may be enough to cause the material to slide or flow downslope.

Oversteepened Slopes

Oversteepening of slopes can also trigger mass movements. A stream or glacier undercutting a valley wall

Figure 14.3 Torrential rains in January 2011 caused heavy damage by mudflows in Brazil. Water plays an important role in many mass wasting processes. (Photo by Ed Harp/U.S. Geological Survey)

Figure 14.4 The effect of water on mass wasting can be great. **A.** When little or no water is present, friction among the closely packed soil particles on the slope holds them in place. **B.** When the soil is saturated, the grains are forced apart and friction is reduced, allowing the soil to move downslope.

and waves pounding against the base of a cliff are two familiar examples. Furthermore, through their activities, people often create oversteepened and unstable slopes (chapter-opening photo; Figure 14.5) that become prime sites for mass wasting (see Box 14.1).

Unconsolidated granular particles (sand-sized or coarser) assume a stable slope called the **angle of repose** (*repose* = to be at rest). This is the steepest angle at which material remains stable. Depending on the size and shape of the particles, and the water content of the material, the angle varies from 25 to 40 degrees. The larger, more angular particles maintain the steepest slopes. If the angle is increased, the rock debris will adjust by moving downslope.

Oversteepening produces unstable slopes and mass movements in cohesive soils, regolith, and bedrock. The response will not be immediate, as with loose, granular material, but eventually one or more mass wasting processes will eliminate the oversteepening and restore stability to the slope.

Removal of Vegetation

Plants contribute to the stability of slopes because their root systems bind soil and regolith together and hold water. Their leaves can also protect the ground surface from the impact of raindrops. Where plants are lacking, mass wasting is enhanced, especially if slopes are steep and water is plentiful. When anchoring vegetation is removed by forest fires or by people (for timber, farming, or development), surface materials frequently move downslope.

Figure 14.5 Fractured rock was undercut and oversteepened to build this highway in British Columbia. Conspicuous joints dip parallel to the slope and are planes of weakness along which the rock can slide. (Photo © Dan Galic/Alamy)

BOX 14.1

PEOPLE AND THE ENVIRONMENT

Treacherous Slopes along the Sea-to-Sky Highway

During the 2010 Winter Olympics in Vancouver, Highway 99 from Vancouver to Whistler was heavily used to shuttle people to outdoor events at Whistler. The problem is the stretch between West Vancouver and Squamish (Figure 14.A), which has a history of landslides that became more frequent after construction of the Sea-to-Sky Highway in the 1950s. The road was routed along the east side of Howe Sound, where joints in heavily fractured rocks dip parallel to the mountain slope. This structural setting, made worse by oversteepening to build the road (Figure 14.5) and heavy rains and snowmelts, results in rockfalls, rock slides, and debris flows that damage the highway, property, and people (see examples below). Increased highway congestion can result in more lives lost and longer traffic delays to remove debris from the road.

Rockfalls occur where talus slopes are seen beside the road. Attempts to inhibit rockfalls include bolting fractured rock with metal rods, covering slopes with heavy, coarse metal mesh, spraying slopes with cement (shotcrete), retaining walls, and drilling holes through the rock to increase drainage.

In 1915 a rock slide killed 56 people in a field camp above the mine site at Britannia Beach, British Columbia, when 100 000 cubic metres of rock and snow slid away from the steep mountainside and plowed into the camp. It may have been triggered by a spring thaw, infiltration of water, and blasting in tunnels under the mountain.

Figure 14.A Map of the Howe Sound area between Vancouver and Squamish in British Columbia.

A classic debris flow (Figure 14.B) in British Columbia surged through Lions Bay in 1983, claiming two lives. It started as a slump into upper Alberta Creek, where water from an intense rainstorm and melting snow pooled behind a mass of logs and sediment that clogged the channel. When the dam broke, the slurry of debris grew to 10 000 cubic metres and travelled at 9 metres per second as it scoured more debris along its channel. Tongues of the debris flow over-topped the channel's banks, smashed into creekside homes, and took out culverts and bridges.

Along this highway, 2005 and 2008 were bad years for landslides. In July 2008, 16 000 cubic metres of rock and debris plunged into the sea near Furry Creek and Porteau Cove (see Figure 14.8), blocking the highway and taking out the railway tracks. All told, 30 000 tourists, commuters, and residents were delayed, but no one was killed.

An unusual example illustrating the anchoring effect of plants occurred on steep slopes near Menton, France. Farmers replaced olive trees, which have deep roots, with a more profitable but shallow-rooted crop of carnations. When the slope became unstable and failed, a landslide took 11 lives.

During the summers of 2009 and 2012 severe wildfires swept hillsides of British Columbia, denuding the slopes of vegetation (Figure 14.6) and making them more susceptible to mass wasting.

Figure 14.B Anatomy of a Canadian debris flow (based on Lions Bay event). Sequence of events: (1) Torrential rain swells streams near the mountain crest; (2) sediment slumps into a raging stream, triggering a debris flow that surges down the channel; (3) debris flow swells in volume as it picks up additional sediment and trees; and (4) debris flow emerges from the canyon onto a fan, where it damages houses, roads, bridges, and railways. (Reproduced with the permission of Natural Resources Canada 2013, courtesy of the Geological Survey of Canada.)

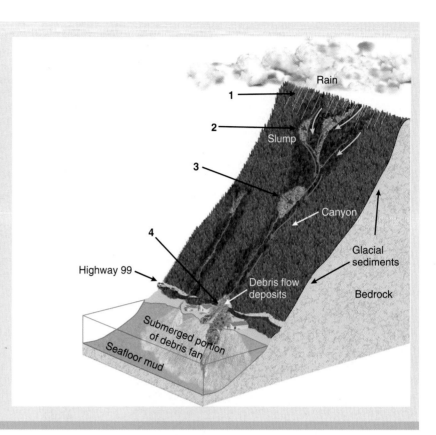

Earthquakes as Triggers

Conditions that favour mass wasting can exist in an area for a long time before movement occurs. An additional factor is sometimes necessary to trigger the movement. Among the more important and dramatic triggers are earthquakes. An earthquake and its aftershocks can set in motion enormous volumes of rock and unconsolidated material. Figure 14.7 illustrates the scale of devastation produced by but one of the hundreds of landslides triggered by the magnitude 7.9 earthquake that struck Sichuan Province, China, on May 12, 2008. On a smaller scale, the

Figure 14.6 During summer 2012, 1600 wildfires raged in British Columbia; almost 90 000 hectares were burned. The loss of anchoring vegetation sets the stage for accelerated mass wasting. This photo was taken on September 9, 2012, above Highway 97C near Peachland. (Photo by Jeff Bassett, Canadian Press)

Figure 14.7 The magnitude 7.9 earthquake that struck China's Sichuan Province on May 12, 2008, triggered hundreds of landslides that destroyed roads and bridges, and buried buildings and rail lines in debris. This aerial view shows the huge volume of landslide debris that dammed a river and created a lake. Had the natural dam burst under the increasing pressure of the water pooling behind it, catastrophic flooding would have occurred downstream. Thankfully, the lake was safely drained before this could happen. Note the heavy equipment for scale. (Photo by MARK/epa/Corbis)

1965 Hope Slide in British Columbia (Figure 14.1) may too have been triggered by earthquake activity.

Liquefaction

Intense ground shaking during earthquakes can cause water-saturated surface materials to lose their strength and behave as fluid-like masses that flow (see Chapter 10). This process, called liquefaction, is a major problem in the Ottawa-Gatineau region of eastern Ontario and western Quebec. In this area, Leda Clay (also known as quick clay) was deposited in the ancient Champlain Sea at the end of the last Ice Age. Slopes on this marine clay have failed many times, causing deaths, injuries, and property damage far beyond the site of failure. Even gentle slopes have failed because of liquefaction, in many cases induced by earthquakes, in others because of heavy rain, excavation, and overloading by heavy equipment and structures. The Fraser Delta in British Columbia is another example of potential failure because of liquefaction of its non-compacted fine sediments. The communities of Delta, Richmond, and Steveston are at risk, especially in the event of an earthquake.

Slope materials gradually weaken over time because of long-term weathering, infiltration of water, and other physical processes. Eventually, if the strength falls below what is necessary to maintain slope stability, a landslide will occur. The timing of such events is random, and thus accurate prediction is difficult at best.

CLASSIFICATION OF MASS WASTING PROCESSES

Geologists refer to a broad array of processes and classifications as mass wasting. Generally, the different types are based on the type of motion displayed, the type of material being moved, and the rate of movement.

Type of Motion

Usually, the kind of motion is described as either a fall, a slide, or a flow. Some classifications also include topples and spreads.

Figure 14.8 Rock slide blocking Highway 99 near Porteau Cove, British Columbia. (Photo by Jonathan Hayward/Canadian Press)

FALL When the movement involves detached individual particles of any size dropping through the air, it is termed a **fall**. A fall is a common form of movement on slopes that are so steep that loose material cannot remain on the surface. The rock may fall directly to the base of the slope or move in a series of leaps and bounds over other rocks along the way. Many falls result when freeze and thaw cycles or the action of plant roots (see Figure 5.7) loosen rock to the point that gravity takes over (Figure 14.8). Talus slopes are built and maintained by such events (Figures 5.3 and 14.10).

SLIDE Many mass wasting processes are described as **slides**, which occur whenever material remains fairly coherent (negligible internal deformation) and moves along a well-defined surface. Sometimes, as with rotational slide movement called slump (Figure 14.9A), the material moves as a block along a curved surface of failure. In others, the surface is a joint, a fault, or a bedding plane that parallels the slope and allows blocks of material, such as slabs of rock, to move by translational slide (e.g., the rock slide in Figure 14.9B). Sometimes the word *slide* is used in a general sense as a synonym for the word *landslide*, which has no specific definition in geology.

FLOW The third type of movement common to mass wasting processes is termed **flow**, which occurs when material moves downslope as a viscous fluid. Most flows are saturated with water and typically move as lobes or tongues that experience internal deformation (Figures 14.9C and 14.9D).

Type of Material

The descending mass may begin as unconsolidated material or as bedrock. If soil and regolith dominate (Figures 14.9C and 14.9D), such terms as *debris* and *earth* are used in the description. In contrast, when a mass of mainly bedrock breaks loose and moves downslope, the term *rock* is commonly part of the description (Figure 14.9B).

Rate of Movement

Rates of movement can be spectacularly sudden (Figure 14.9B) or exceptionally gradual (Figure 14.9D). Although various types of mass wasting are commonly classified as either rapid or slow, such a distinction is highly subjective because a wide range of rates exists between the two extremes. Even the velocity of a single process at a particular site can vary considerably. This is why we present the main

A Rotational slide (slump)

B Translational slide (rockslide)

C Rapid flow of soil, regolith, rock and water (debris flow)

D Sluggish flow of wet, muddy soil and regolith (earthflow)

Figure 14.9   In addition to falling, materials moved by mass wasting can, depending on their internal strength, slide as coherent blocks (with no internal deformation) or move viscously (with internal deformation). Slides can occur by **(A)** rotation along curved surfaces (as in a slump) or **(B)** translation parallel to the slope (as in a rock slide). Viscous movements include **(C)** rapid flows of saturated soil-regolith-rock mixtures (as in a debris flow) and **(D)** sluggish flows of wet, muddy mixtures of soil and regolith (as in an earthflow).

Figure 14.10   A talus is a slope built of angular rock fragments. Mechanical weathering, especially frost wedging, loosens the pieces of bedrock, which then fall to the base of the cliff. With time, a series of steep, cone-shaped accumulations build up at the base of the vertical slope. These talus cones are in Banff National Park, Alberta. (Photo by Marli Miller)

mass wasting processes according to the way they move: first those that move mainly by sliding, followed by those that move mainly viscously, then those that move very slowly, mainly by *creep*.

SLUMP

Slump refers to the downward sliding of a mass of rock or unconsolidated material rotating as a unit along a curved surface (rotational slide; Figures 14.9A and 14.11). Usually, the slumped material travels neither quickly nor very far. This form of mass wasting is common along river valleys and eroding shorelines, especially in thick accumulations of cohesive materials, such as clay. The ruptured surface is characteristically spoon shaped and concave upward and outward. As the movement occurs, a crescent-shaped scarp is created at the head, and the block's upper surface is usually tilted backward because of rotation. Although slump can involve a single mass, it commonly consists of multiple blocks. Sometimes water collects between the base of the scarp and the top of the tilted block. As this water percolates downward along the surface of rupture, it may lubricate this surface, ultimately promoting further instability and faster movement.

Slumping commonly occurs because a slope has been oversteepened. The material on the upper portion of a slope is held in place by the material at the bottom of the slope. As anchoring material at the

Figure 14.11   A. Slump occurs when material slips downslope en masse along a curved surface of rupture. Earthflows frequently form at the base of the slump. **B.** Tongue-shaped earthflow below a slump that occurred on a newly formed slope along a recently constructed highway. It formed in clay-rich material following a period of heavy rain. (Photo **B** by E. J. Tarbuck)

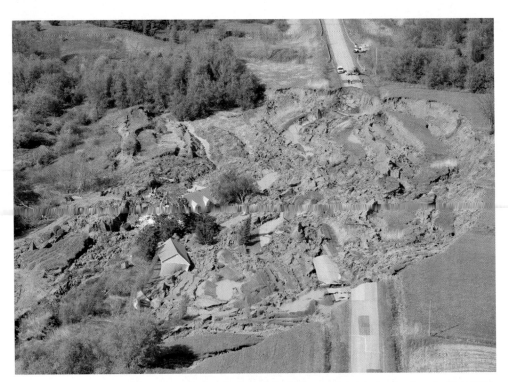

Figure 14.12   Fatal slump in the valley wall of the Salvail River at Saint-Jude, Quebec, in May 2010. A family of four was killed in their house as it was swallowed by the lower part of this muddy mass. (Photo by Graham Hughes/Canadian Press)

base is removed, the material above is made unstable and reacts to the pull of gravity. One relatively common example is a valley wall that becomes oversteepened by a meandering river (Figure 14.12). Slumping can also occur when a slope is overloaded, changing the weight on the material below. This type of slump commonly occurs where weak, clay-rich material (e.g., shale) underlies layers of stronger, more resistant rock, such as sandstone. The seepage of water through the upper layers reduces the strength of the shale below, resulting in slope failure. It is common for the lower parts of slumps to break up and flow (Figure 14.11B).

ROCK SLIDE

Rock slides occur when blocks of mainly bedrock break loose and travel rapidly down a slope (see Figure 14.9B). Such events are among the fastest and most destructive mass movements. Usually, rock slides take place in a geologic setting where the rock strata are inclined, or where joints and fractures parallel the slope. When such a rock unit is undercut at the base of the slope, it loses support and the rock eventually gives way. Sometimes the rock slide is triggered when rain or melting snow destabilizes the underlying surface to the point where friction is no longer sufficient to hold the rock unit in place. As a

result, rock slides tend to be more common during the spring, when heavy rains and melting snow are most prevalent. Commonly, rock-slide blocks break up soon after failure, and then move by flowing rapidly downslope.

Earthquakes can trigger rock slides and other mass movements. The 1811 earthquake at New Madrid, Missouri, for example, caused slides in an area of more than 13 000 square kilometres along the Mississippi River Valley. In a similar case, a strong earthquake that occurred west of Yellowstone National Park on August 17, 1959, triggered a massive slide that displaced some 27 million cubic metres of rock, soil, and trees into the canyon of the Madison River in southwest Montana.

Frank Slide, Canada's most famous rock-slide disaster, occurred at 4:10 a.m., April 29, 1903, when the failure and rapid downslope movement of an immense mass of rock from Turtle Mountain buried the village of Frank, a small mining community nestled in the Crowsnest Pass of Alberta (Figure 14.13).

Although Frank Slide probably started as a slide, it appears that on rock fragmentation, it evolved into a debris-like flow, travelling on a cushion of air and allowing the rock debris to travel partly up the opposite side of the valley.

The Frank Slide is difficult to attribute to a single cause, and it is quite possible that it simply manifests the combined effect of a number of

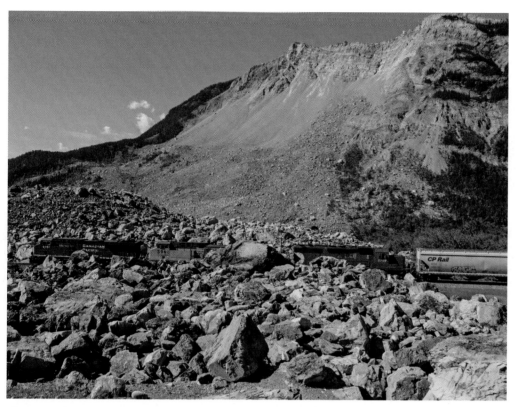

Figure 14.13   The Frank Slide event occurred in the early morning of April 29, 1903, in the Crowsnest Pass, Alberta. At least 70 people in the town of Frank were killed in this infamous Canadian disaster. (Photo © 2006 Gary Hebert)

geologic and human factors. Beginning in the Cretaceous Period, extensive thrusting and deformation led to the sliding and bending of hard Paleozoic carbonate rocks over soft Mesozoic rocks, ultimately forming the lofty peaks of the Alberta Rockies. Associated with this disturbance was the development of stress cracks in the Paleozoic carbonates that allowed the infiltration of water and the widening of fissures and cavities by dissolution, which led to the structural weakening of Turtle Mountain limestones. Considerably later, glacial activity during the last Ice Age removed a significant amount of carbonate rock near the base of Turtle Mountain, exposing the much softer underlying Mesozoic sandstones and shales, and leaving the remaining carbonates near the peak prone to sliding like a dinner plate on a slanted table (translational slide). It is suspected by some that deforestation and coal-mining activity (especially dynamite blasts) in the weak Mesozoic strata near the base of the slope contributed sufficient disturbance to trigger the mass wasting event. Then again, unseasonably warm weather (Chinook) preceding the event and unusually frigid conditions the night before the disaster suggest that frost wedging may have been the trigger.

This disaster, like many others, provides valuable information for the prevention of, or at least the reduction of, potential damage related to similar events in the future. Frank Slide also provides a reminder that Canadians are by no means immune to the types of natural disasters that we are so used to hearing about in other parts of the world. It is probably no coincidence that, long before the disaster that struck the town of Frank, the Blackfoot and Kutenai talked about Turtle Mountain as "the mountain that moves."

DEBRIS FLOW

Debris flow is a relatively rapid type of mass wasting that involves a flow of soil and regolith containing a large amount of water (Figure 14.9C). Debris flows are characteristic of mountainous regions, including some volcanoes. Because of their fluid properties, debris flows frequently follow canyons and stream channels. In populated areas, debris flows can pose a significant hazard to life and property (e.g., a 2012 Johnson's Landing debris flow in eastern British Columbia killed four people).

When a cloudburst or rapidly melting mountain snows create a sudden flood, large quantities of soil and regolith can be washed into nearby stream channels. The end product is a flowing

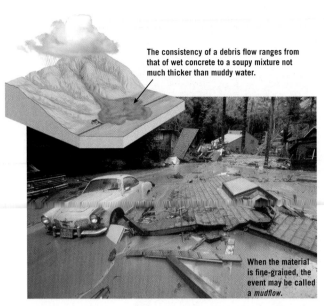

The consistency of a debris flow ranges from that of wet concrete to a soupy mixture not much thicker than muddy water.

When the material is fine-grained, the event may be called a *mudflow*.

Figure 14.14 A rapidly moving debris flow of well-mixed mud, soil, rock, and water did considerable damage in this community.
(Photo by Michael Collier)

Figure 14.15 A house damaged by a lahar along the Toutle River in Washington State, west-northwest of Mount St. Helens. The end section of the house was torn free and lodged against trees.
(Photo by D. R. Crandell/U.S. Geological Survey)

tongue of well-mixed mud, soil, rock, and water. Its consistency can range from that of wet concrete to that of soup. The rate of flow therefore depends not only on the slope but also on the water content. Dense debris flows are capable of carrying or pushing large boulders, trees, and even houses with relative ease.

Debris flows pose a serious hazard to development in mountainous areas, such as British Columbia (e.g., North and West Vancouver north to Pemberton; Box 14.1), Cape Breton Highlands of Nova Scotia, and southern California. The construction of homes on canyon hillsides and the removal of native vegetation by brush fires and other means have increased the frequency of these destructive events (Figure 14.14). When a debris flow reaches the end of a steep, narrow canyon, it spreads out into the area beyond the mouth of the canyon with a mixture of wet debris that contributes to the buildup of alluvial fans (discussed later in Chapter 15).

The fans are relatively easy to build on and commonly have nice views. However, because debris flows occur only sporadically, the public is often unaware of the potential hazard of such sites.

Lahars

As described in Chapter 4, debris flows composed mostly of volcanic materials on the flanks of volcanoes are called *lahars* (an Indonesian term). They can be deadly and occur either during an eruption or when a volcano is quiet. They take place when highly unstable layers of ash and debris become saturated with water and flow down steep volcanic slopes, generally following existing stream channels. Heavy rainfalls commonly trigger these flows. Others are initiated when large volumes of ice and snow are melted by heat flowing to the surface from within the volcano or by the hot gases and near-molten debris emitted during a violent eruption. The eruption of Mount St. Helens in May 1980 created several lahars (Figure 14.15).

EARTHFLOW

Slow, viscous earthflows most commonly form on hillsides in humid areas during times of heavy precipitation or snowmelt (see Figure 14.9D). When water saturates the soil and regolith on a hillside, the material may slump (Figure 14.11A), leaving a scarp on the upper part of a slope but rendering the material lower down on the slope unsupported and prone to viscous flow. Accordingly, earthflows are commonly observed at the bases of slump blocks, moving downslope in tongue- or teardrop-shaped masses (Figure 14.11B).

The materials most commonly involved are rich in clay and silt and contain only small proportions of sand and coarser particles. Earthflows range in size from bodies a few metres long, a few metres wide, and less than a metre deep to masses more than 1 kilometre long, several hundred metres wide, and more than 10 metres deep. They are characterized by a slow and persistent movement and can remain active for days or even years. Depending on the steepness of the slope and the material's consistency, measured velocities range from less than a millimetre a day up to several metres a day. Over the span that earthflows are active, movement is typically faster during wet intervals than during drier times.

SLOW MOVEMENTS

Movements, such as rock falls, rock slides, and lahars, are certainly the most spectacular and catastrophic forms of mass wasting. These dangerous events deserve intense study to enable more effective prediction, timely warnings, and better controls to save more lives. However, because of their large size and spectacular nature, they give us a false impression of their importance as a mass wasting process. Indeed, sudden movements are responsible for moving less material than the slower and far subtler action of creep. Whereas rapid types of mass wasting are characteristic of mountains and steep hillsides, creep takes place on both steep and gentle slopes and is thus much more widespread.

Creep

Creep is a type of mass wasting that involves the gradual downhill movement of soil and regolith. One factor that contributes to creep is the alternate expansion and contraction of surface material caused by freezing and thawing or wetting and drying. As shown in Figure 14.16, freezing or wetting lifts particles at right angles to the slope, and thawing or drying and gravity allow the particles to fall back vertically to a slightly lower level. Each cycle therefore moves the material a tiny distance downslope. Creep is aided by anything that disturbs the soil, such as raindrop impact, plant roots, burrowing animals, and water saturation. Following a heavy rain or snowmelt, waterlogged soil may lose its internal cohesion, allowing gravity to pull the material downslope. Because creep is imperceptibly slow, the process cannot be observed in action. What can be observed, however, are the effects of creep. Creep causes fences and utility poles to tilt and undrained retaining walls to be displaced (Figure 14.17A, B). Trees get tilted but continue to grow upward, resulting in J-shaped trunks.

Figure 14.16 The repeated expansion and contraction of the surface material causes a net downslope migration of rock particles—a process called creep.

Solifluction

When soil is saturated with water, the soggy mass may flow downslope at a rate of a few millimetres or a few centimetres per day or per year. Such a process is called **solifluction** (literally, "soil flow"). It is a type of mass wasting that is common wherever water cannot escape from the saturated surface layer by infiltrating to deeper levels. A dense clay hardpan in soil or an impermeable bedrock layer can promote solifluction.

Solifluction is also common in regions underlain by **permafrost**, the permanently frozen ground that occurs in association with Earth's harsh polar and alpine climates (see Box 14.2). Solifluction occurs in a zone above the permafrost called the **active layer**, which thaws during the high-latitude summer and then refreezes in winter. During the summer season, water is unable to percolate into the permafrost layer below. As a result, the active layer becomes saturated and slowly flows. The process can occur on slopes as gentle as two to three degrees. Where there is a well-developed mat of vegetation, a solifluction sheet may move in a series of well-defined lobes or partially overriding folds (Figure 14.18). More permafrost-related features follow in the next section.

Other Periglacial Features

Processes related to permafrost, and resulting features like solifluction lobes, are called **periglacial**. Because **periglacial** processes often initiate mass wasting events in cold environments, it is appropriate to mention them here. Box 14.2 explains continuous and discontinuous zones of permafrost and some associated environmental and industrial problems. Even in the continuous zone, unfrozen patches

A

B

Figure 14.17 Although creep is an imperceptibly slow movement, its effects (**A**) are commonly visible. **B** shows a failed retaining wall due to creep and excessive soil water pressure from melting snow. (Photo by S. R. Hicock)

A

B

Figure 14.18 **A.** Solifluction lobes northeast of Fairbanks, Alaska. Solifluction occurs in permafrost regions when the active layer thaws in summer. **B.** Solifluction lobes above Omega River near its mouth on north Baffin Island. (Photo **A** by J. E. Patterson; photo **B** by S. R. Hicock)

BOX
14.2

UNDERSTANDING EARTH
The Sensitive Permafrost Landscape

Many of the mass wasting events in this chapter have had sudden and disastrous impacts on people. When the activities of people cause ice contained in frozen ground to melt, the impact is more gradual and less deadly. Nevertheless, because permafrost regions are sensitive and fragile landscapes, the scars resulting from poorly planned actions can remain for generations.

Frozen ground, known as permafrost, occurs where summers are too cool to melt more than a shallow surface layer. Deeper ground remains frozen year-round. Strictly speaking, permafrost is defined only on the basis of temperature; that is, it is ground with temperatures that have remained below 0°C continuously for two years or more. The degree to which ice is present in the ground strongly affects the behaviour of the surface material. Knowing how much ice is present and where it is located is very important when it comes to constructing roads, buildings, and other projects in areas underlain by permafrost.

Permafrost underlies about 20 percent of Earth's land area. In addition to occurring in Antarctica and in some high mountain areas, permafrost is extensive in the lands surrounding the Arctic Ocean. It covers about 50 percent of Canada, a substantial portion of northern Siberia, and most of Alaska (Figure 14.C). Near the southern margins of the region, the permafrost consists of relatively thin, isolated masses. Farther north, the area and thickness gradually increase to the point where the permafrost is essentially continuous and its thickness may approach or even exceed 500 metres. In the discontinuous zone, land-use planning is more difficult than in the continuous zone farther north because discontinuous permafrost is patchy and difficult to predict.

When people disturb the surface, such as by removing the insulating vegetation mat or by building roads

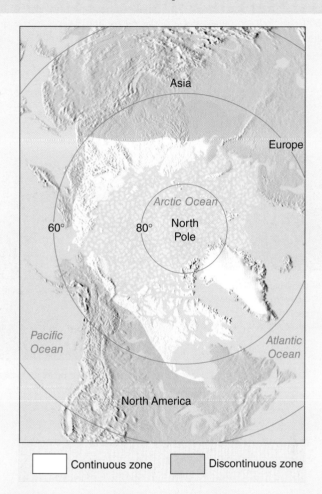

Continuous zone   Discontinuous zone

Figure 14.C   Distribution of permafrost in the Northern Hemisphere. About 50 percent of Canada and more than 80 percent of Alaska is underlain by permafrost, which is affected by global warming. Two zones are recognized. In the continuous zone, the only ice-free areas are beneath deep lakes or rivers. Higher latitude portions of the discontinuous zone have only scattered islands of thawed ground. Southward, the percentage of unfrozen ground increases until all the ground is unfrozen.
(From the U.S. Geological Survey)

and buildings, the delicate thermal balance is disturbed, and the permafrost can thaw (Figure 14.D). Thawing produces unstable ground that may slide, slump, subside, and undergo severe frost heaving.

As Figure 14.E illustrates, when a heated structure is built directly on permafrost that contains a high proportion of ice, thawing creates soggy material into which a building can sink.

One solution is to place buildings and other structures on piles, like stilts. Such piles allow subfreezing air to circulate between the floor of the building and the soil and thereby keep the ground frozen.

When oil was discovered on Alaska's North Slope, many people were concerned about the building of a pipeline linking the oil fields at Prudhoe Bay to the ice-free port of Valdez 1300 kilometres to the south. They voiced serious concern that such a massive project might damage the sensitive permafrost environment. Many also worried about possible oil spills and environmental consequences.

Because oil must be heated to about 60°C to flow properly, special engineering procedures had to be developed to isolate this heat from the permafrost. Methods included insulating the pipe, elevating portions of the pipeline above ground level, and even placing cooling devices in the ground to keep it frozen. The Alaskan pipeline is clearly one of the most complex and costly projects ever built in the Arctic tundra. Detailed studies and careful engineering helped minimize adverse effects resulting from the disturbance of frozen ground.

Figure 14.D When a rail line was built across this permafrost landscape in Alaska, the ground subsided.
(Photo by Lynn A. Yehle/U.S. Geological Survey)

Figure 14.E These buildings in Dawson, Yukon, are tilted because they rest directly on permafrost that is melting from the heat of the buildings.
(Photo by S. R. Hicock)

called talik can occur under the ground surface, usually under lakes. Some of these lakes gradually freeze to form ice-cored mounds covered with tundra vegetation, called **pingoes** (Figure 14.19A). Similar features are **palsas** (Figure 14.19B), but they are mounds of peat with ice lenses instead of a solid ice core. As you would expect, frost wedging (see Chapter 5) is common in periglacial environments. Bedrock can be so shattered, the shards cover the ground as **felsenmeer** (Figure 14.19C), also known as a block field.

During winter the active layer freezes, inducing frost heaving of the ground surface (which can cause creep and solifluction on slopes) and cryoturbation (ice mixing) of soil horizons below. In periglacial areas the ground often cracks; where water enters the cracks in summer, it freezes to form ice wedges. These cracks and ice wedges (Figure 14.19D) are commonly connected in geometric patterns called **patterned ground** that are distinctive when viewed from above (Figure 14.19E). Frost heaving and cryoturbation gradually raise stones to the surface, where they tend to concentrate in ice wedges to form sorted stone polygons shaped like nets or circles, and stripes where gravity pulls polygons downslope.

Where permafrost melts (because of climate change, talik expansion, or human activities), irregular features form on the surface, resulting in **thermokarst** topography (as opposed to karst developed in limestone terrain) that commonly includes thaw lakes (Figure 14.19F). Thermokarst formation can damage coastlines (lakes become bays), roads, railways (Figure 14.D), pipelines, power lines, and buildings (Figure 14.E). Preventing human-induced melting of permafrost in this sensitive environment (Box 14.2) requires innovative engineering solutions.

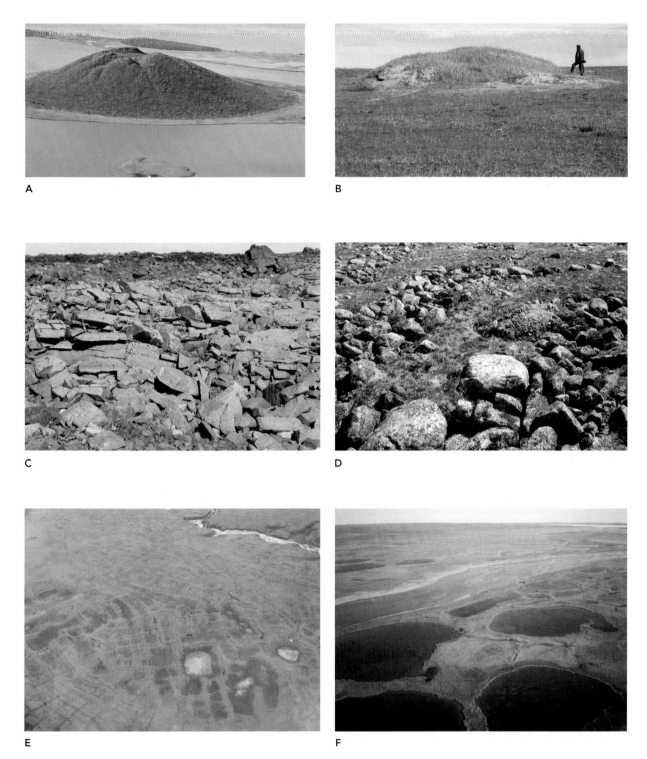

A

B

C

D

E

F

Figure 14.19 Selected periglacial features. **A.** Ice-cored pingo, Yukon. **B.** Small palsa on mainland Nunavut, south of Pelly Bay. **C.** Felsenmeer on north Baffin Island, south of Keele River. **D.** Ice wedge polygon near Kellet River, mainland Nunavut. **E.** Patterned ground near Pelly Bay, Nunavut. **F.** Thaw lakes west of Walker Lake, mainland Nunavut. (Photo **A** © eppic/Fotolia; photos **B–F** by S. R. Hicock)

CHAPTER SUMMARY

- *Mass wasting* is the downslope movement of rock, regolith, and soil driven by gravity. Other factors that can trigger movements are water saturation and oversteepening of slopes, removal of vegetation, and earthquakes.
- Mass wasting events are classified by 1) type of motion (fall, slide, flow); 2) material (debris, soil, rock), and 3) rate of movement.

- *Slumps* move as a unit along curved surfaces; *rock slides* of bedrock break loose and move downhill; debris flows of wet soil and regolith move rapidly downhill; and earthflows of saturated clay-rich soil move gradually downhill. *Creep* is the gradual downhill movement of soil and regolith; *solifluction* is the gradual flow of a saturated surface layer, usually over permafrost.

MasteringGeology
www.masteringgeology.com

Looking for additional review and test prep materials? Visit the Study Area in MasteringGeology to enhance your understanding of this chapter's content by accessing a variety of resources, including

Self-Study Quizzes, Geoscience Animations, GEODe Tutorials, RSS feeds, flashcards, weblinks, self-study quizzes, and an optional Pearson eText.

REVIEW QUESTIONS

1. What is the controlling force of mass wasting?
2. Describe how mass wasting processes contribute to the development of stream valleys.
3. How does water affect mass wasting processes?
4. Define "angle of repose" and describe its significance in mass wasting.
5. Describe the differences between a fall, a slide, and a flow.
6. How might the presence or absence of vegetation on a slope influence the potential for mass wasting to occur?
7. What factors are thought to have led to the massive rock slide at Frank, Alberta?
8. How does a slump differ from a debris flow?
9. Why are mass wasting events so commonly associated with volcanoes?
10. Describe the common association of mass wasting events with earthquakes.

CHAPTER OUTLINE

The Baleine River winds through the boreal landscape of northern Quebec. (Photo by Hemera Technologies/Thinkstock)

Rivers are very important. We use them as routes for moving goods, as sources of water for irrigation, and as an energy source. Their fertile floodplains have been cultivated since the dawn of civilization. When viewed as part of the Earth system, rivers and streams represent a basic link in the constant cycling of the planet's water. Moreover, running water is the dominant agent of landscape alteration, eroding more terrain and transporting more sediment than any other process. Because so many people live near rivers, **floods** are among the most destructive of all geologic hazards. Despite huge investments in levees and dams, rivers cannot always be controlled (Figure 15.1). Finally, geologists interpret ancient river systems preserved in the rock record based on observations of modern rivers; such interpretations can be valuable in the exploration for petroleum and mineral deposits.

EARTH AS A SYSTEM: THE HYDROLOGIC CYCLE

Water is continually on the move, from the ocean to the land and back again in an endless cycle. Water is just about everywhere on Earth—in the oceans, glaciers, rivers, lakes, air, and soil, and in tissues of living things. All of these reservoirs constitute Earth's hydrosphere. In all, the water content of the hydrosphere is about 1.36 billion cubic kilometres.

The vast bulk of it, about 96.5 percent, is stored in the global oceans (Figure 15.2). Ice sheets and glaciers account for another 1.74 percent, leaving less than 2 percent to be divided among lakes, streams, subsurface water, and the atmosphere

Figure 15.1 Most Canadians have witnessed stream flooding associated with the melting of snow during the spring. This photo shows a spring flood of the Thames River inundating a parking lot in London, Ontario. (Photo courtesy of S. R. Hicock)

(Figure 15.2). Although the percentages of Earth's water found in each of the latter sources (we could also add the biosphere) is just a small fraction of the total inventory, the absolute quantities are great.

The water found in each of the reservoirs depicted in Figure 15.2 does not remain in these places indefinitely. Water can readily change from one state of matter (solid, liquid, or gas) to another at the temperatures and pressures that occur at Earth's surface. Therefore, water is constantly moving among the hydrosphere, the atmosphere, the geosphere, and

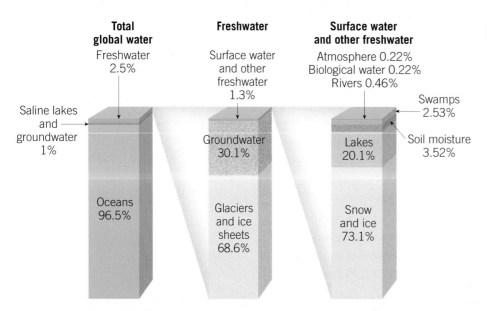

Figure 15.2 Distribution of Earth's water.

Total global water
Freshwater 2.5%
Saline lakes and groundwater 1%
Oceans 96.5%

Freshwater
Surface water and other freshwater 1.3%
Groundwater 30.1%
Glaciers and ice sheets 68.6%

Surface water and other freshwater
Atmosphere 0.22%
Biological water 0.22%
Rivers 0.46%
Swamps 2.53%
Soil moisture 3.52%
Lakes 20.1%
Snow and ice 73.1%

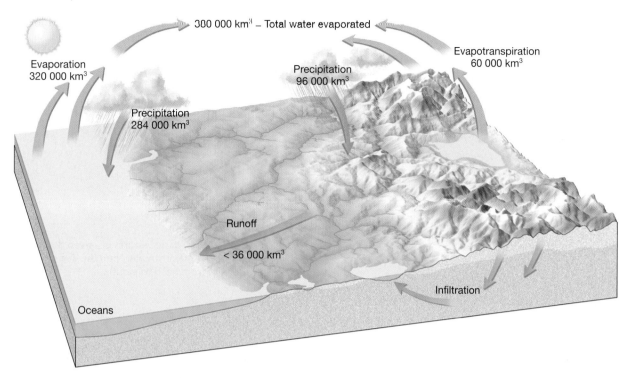

Figure 15.3 Earth's water balance. Each year, solar energy evaporates about 320 000 cubic kilometres of water from the oceans, while evaporation from the land (including lakes and streams) contributes 60 000 cubic kilometres of water. Of this total of 380 000 cubic kilometres of water, about 284 000 cubic kilometres falls back to the ocean, and the remaining 96 000 cubic kilometres falls on the land surface. Of that 96 000 cubic kilometres, approximately 60 000 cubic kilometres of water evaporates from the land. Assuming that not all of the water that infiltrated into the ground re-emerges as surface water, less than 36 000 cubic kilometres of water is left to erode the land during the journey back to the oceans.

the biosphere. This unending circulation of Earth's water supply is called the **hydrologic cycle**.

The hydrologic cycle is a gigantic world-wide system powered by energy from the Sun in which the atmosphere provides the vital link between the oceans and continents (Figure 15.3). Water evaporates into the atmosphere from the oceans and, to a much lesser extent, from the continents. Winds transport this moisture-laden air, often for great distances, until conditions cause the moisture to condense into clouds and precipitation to fall. The precipitation that falls into the ocean has completed its cycle and is ready to begin another.

A portion of the water soaks into the ground (called **infiltration**; see Chapter 16), moving downward, then laterally, and finally seeping into lakes and streams, or directly into the ocean. When the rate of rainfall is greater than the land's ability to absorb it, the additional water flows over the surface into lakes and streams, a process called **runoff**. Much of the water that infiltrates or runs off eventually finds its way back to the atmosphere because of

evaporation from soil, lakes, and streams. Also, some of the water that infiltrates the ground is absorbed by plants, which later release it into the atmosphere. This process is called **transpiration** (*trans* = across, *spiro* = to breathe). Because we cannot clearly distinguish between the amount of water that is evaporated and the amount that is transpired by plants, the term **evapotranspiration** is often used for the combined effect.

When precipitation falls in very cold areas—at high elevations or high latitudes—the water may not immediately soak in, run off, or evaporate. Instead, it may form snowfields and glaciers that store large quantities of water on land (see Chapter 17).

Figure 15.3 also shows that Earth's hydrologic cycle is balanced. Each year, solar energy evaporates about 320 000 cubic kilometres of water from the oceans, but only 284 000 cubic kilometres return to the oceans as precipitation. A balance is achieved by the 36 000 cubic kilometres that are carried to the ocean as runoff. Although runoff makes up a small percentage of the total, running water is *the single*

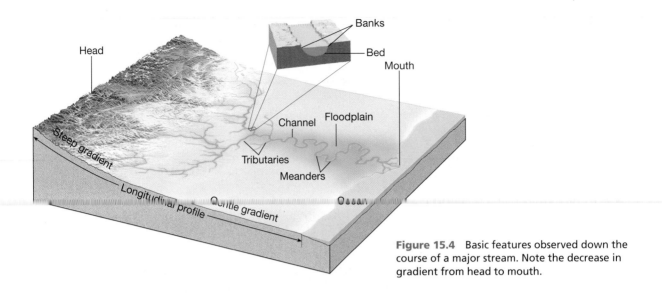

Figure 15.4 Basic features observed down the course of a major stream. Note the decrease in gradient from head to mouth.

most important natural erosional agent sculpting Earth's land surface.

From Sheet Flow to Channel Flow

The amount of water that runs off rather than sinking into the ground depends on the **infiltration capacity,** which is controlled by (1) the intensity and duration of the rainfall, (2) the prior wetted condition of the soil, (3) the soil texture, (4) the slope of the land, and (5) the nature of the vegetative cover. When the soil becomes saturated, **sheet flow** commences as a thin, unconfined sheet of water flowing over the ground for a short distance before threads of current typically develop, forming tiny channels called **rills.** Rills direct water flow to more prominent gullies that, in turn, feed larger and more stable channels of streams. A **stream** flows in a **channel**, regardless of size, whereas a river is a stream that carries large amounts of water and has numerous tributaries.

BASIC COMPONENTS OF A STREAM

Common to all major streams are a number of distinctive parts. Between its source area, called the **head** or **headwaters**, and its **mouth** (Figure 15.4), where it empties into another water body, a stream follows a well-defined path or **course**. Any given segment of a stream along its course is a **reach**. A major stream may be fed by several smaller streams or tributaries. Especially in low-lying areas, stream channels commonly develop snake-like bends or

loops called **meanders** (named after the sinuous river Menderes in Turkey).

The bottom, or **bed**, of a stream channel is bounded on either side by **banks**, which confine the flowing water during times of normal flow. Under flood conditions, water overtops the stream's banks, inundating areas of land beyond the channel. These areas, which are only submerged during floods, are commonly flatter than the surrounding landscape, forming a broad **floodplain** (Figure 15.4) on which sediment is deposited. This is especially true in the middle to lower reaches of a stream, where slopes tend to be low.

On a larger scale the **longitudinal profile** (or side view) of a major stream reveals that the slope or **gradient** of its channel is a concave-upward curve, with steep slopes near the headwaters and a progressive decrease in gradient toward the mouth (Figure 15.4).

STREAMFLOW

Water can flow either as **laminar flow** or as **turbulent flow** (Figure 15.5). In laminar flow, water molecules flow in straight paths that are parallel to the channel. By contrast, in turbulent flow, water commonly moves in a chaotic and erratic fashion as swirling, whirlpool-like eddies.

Laminar flow is possible only when water is moving very slowly through a smooth channel. If the velocity increases or the channel becomes rough, laminar flow changes to turbulent flow. Streams usually move fast enough for turbulent flow, which is effective in eroding a stream's channel and in

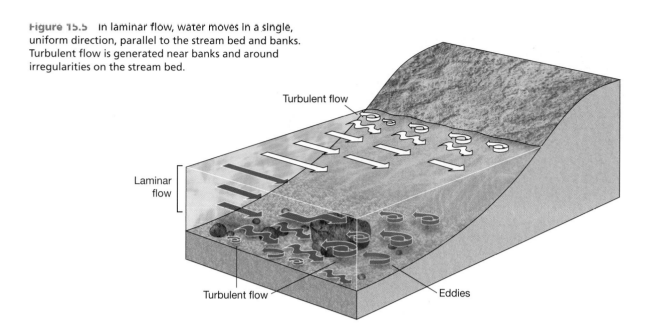

Figure 15.5 In laminar flow, water moves in a single, uniform direction, parallel to the stream bed and banks. Turbulent flow is generated near banks and around irregularities on the stream bed.

Turbulent flow

Laminar flow

Turbulent flow

Eddies

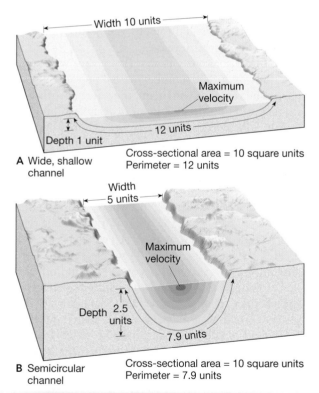

Width 10 units

Maximum velocity

12 units

Depth 1 unit

A Wide, shallow channel

Cross-sectional area = 10 square units
Perimeter = 12 units

Width 5 units

Maximum velocity

Depth 2.5 units

7.9 units

B Semicircular channel

Cross-sectional area = 10 square units
Perimeter = 7.9 units

Figure 15.6 Influence of channel shape on velocity. **A.** The stream in this wide, shallow channel moves more slowly than does water in the semicircular channel because of greater frictional drag. **B.** The cross-sectional area of this semicircular channel is the same as the one in part A, but it has less water in contact with its channel and therefore less frictional drag. Thus, water will flow more rapidly in channel B, all other factors being equal. In both cases, maximum velocity is farthest from the banks.

keeping sediment suspended in the water for transport downstream.

Flowing water makes its way to the sea under the influence of gravity. Some sluggish streams flow at less than 1 kilometre per hour, whereas a few rapid ones can exceed 30 kilometres per hour. Velocities are determined at gauging stations, where measurements are taken at several locations across the stream channel and then averaged. When the channel is straight, the highest velocities occur in the centre, just below the surface (Figure 15.6) where friction is least. Minimum velocities occur along the sides and bed of the channel, where friction is greatest. When a stream channel is crooked or curved, the fastest flow shifts toward the outside of each bend. This shift helps to erode the stream's channel on that side.

The ability of a stream to erode and transport material is directly related to its velocity, which depends on (1) the gradient; (2) the shape, size, and roughness of the channel; and (3) the discharge.

Gradient and Channel Characteristics

Gradient is expressed as the vertical drop of a stream over a fixed distance. Portions of the lower Mississippi River, for example, have very low gradients of less than 10 centimetres per kilometre, whereas some steep mountain stream channels drop more than 40 metres per kilometre, 400 times as abruptly as the lower Mississippi. The steeper the gradient, the

Figure 15.7 Whitewater rafters enjoy turbulent conditions in the Ottawa River rapids.
(Photo by Henry George/Jupiter-Images)

more gravitational energy is available for stream flow and higher velocity.

The *cross-sectional shape* of a channel determines the amount of water in contact with the channel and hence affects the frictional drag. The most efficient channel is one with the least perimeter for its cross-sectional area. Figure 15.6 compares two channel shapes. Although the cross-sectional areas of both are identical, the semicircular shape has less water in contact with the channel and therefore less frictional drag. As a result, if all other factors are equal, the water will flow more rapidly in the semicircular channel.

The size and roughness of the channel also affect the amount of friction. An increase in the size of a channel reduces the ratio of perimeter to cross-sectional area and therefore increases the efficiency of flow. A smooth channel promotes a more uniform flow, whereas an irregular channel creates enough turbulence to slow the stream's forward motion. In extreme cases, where turbulent flow extends all the way up to the water surface because of the violent collision and diversion of flowing water around irregularities (e.g., boulders) on the stream bed, **rapids** may form (Figure 15.7).

Discharge and Changes Downstream

The **discharge** of a stream is the amount of water flowing past a certain point in a given unit of time. This is usually measured in cubic metres per second.

The largest river in North America, the Mississippi, discharges an average of 17 300 cubic metres per second, but it is dwarfed by the world's largest river, the Amazon, which discharges 12 times as much water as the Mississippi. In fact, it has been estimated that the flow of the Amazon accounts for about 15 percent of all the fresh water discharged into the ocean by all of the world's rivers. Just one day's discharge would supply the water needs of Toronto for nearly 70 years!

The discharges of most rivers vary with rainfall, snowmelt, and number of tributaries. As discharge increases downstream, the width, depth, and velocity tend to increase in an orderly fashion. The stream will increase the size of its channel by widening and deepening it so that less water is in contact with the bed and banks of the channel. Consequently friction is reduced and the water flows faster.

In the headwaters region where the gradient is steepest (Figure 15.4), the water must flow in a relatively small and often boulder-strewn channel. This creates drag and turbulent flow. However, downstream, the bed material becomes smaller, offering less resistance to flow, and the width and depth of the channel increase to accommodate greater discharge. These factors permit water to flow more freely and rapidly and compensate for the decrease in gradient. A stream can therefore maintain a higher velocity near its mouth than upstream, because of the greater discharge, larger channel, and smoother bed.

STREAM EROSION

Streams erode their channels mainly by the plucking of loosened particles from their beds and by abrasion

Figure 15.8 **A.** Erosional processes in a stream. Sedimentary particles can be loosened and plucked from unconsolidated sediment on the stream's bed and from bedrock by the lifting action of strong currents. Abrasion occurs because of the impact of sedimentary particles with bedrock surfaces and other particles residing on the bed. Particles swept into swirling eddies that develop in depressions on the bed (especially where bedrock is exposed) cause localized abrasion that can lead to the formation of potholes. **B.** These potholes in the bed of Kanaka Creek, British Columbia, were produced by the drilling action of swirling pebbles. (Photo by S. R. Hicock)

(Figure 15.8A). Some erosion is also by the dissolution of soluble bedrock and channel debris; most dissolved material in a stream comes from inflows of groundwater.

An eddy in turbulent flow can dislodge particles from the channel and lift them into the water. The force of running water swiftly erodes poorly consolidated materials on the bed and banks of the stream. The stronger the current, the more effectively the stream will lift particles. In some instances, water is forced into cracks and bedding planes with sufficient strength to actually pry up pieces of rock from the bed. A stream can also erode solid rock in a manner similar to sandblasting as sand and gravel carried by a stream abrade a bedrock channel, including steep-sided gorges

(Figure 15.9). In addition, the individual sediment grains are also abraded by their many impacts with the channel and with one another. Thus, by scraping, rubbing, and bumping, abrasion erodes a bedrock channel and simultaneously smoothes and rounds the abrading particles.

Common features on some riverbeds are rounded depressions known as **potholes** (Figure 15.8B). They are created by the abrasive action of particles swirling in fast-moving eddies (Figure 15.8A). The rotational motion of the sand and pebbles acts like a drill to bore the holes. As the particles wear down to nothing, they are replaced by new ones that continue to drill the streambed. Eventually, smooth depressions several metres across and just as deep can result.

Figure 15.9 This steep-sided canyon in British Columbia has been cut through solid rock by stream erosion. Such canyons as this one are narrow because of a rapid rate of downcutting by the stream relative to the rate of mass wasting of the canyon walls. (Photo by Mike Schering)

TRANSPORT OF SEDIMENT BY STREAMS

Streams are Earth's most important erosional agent. Not only do they downcut their channels, they transport sediment produced by weathering. Weathered material is delivered to the stream by sheet flow, mass wasting, and groundwater.

Streams transport their loads of sediment in three ways: (1) in solution (**dissolved load**), (2) in suspension (**suspended load**), and (3) along the bottom of the channel (**bed load**). (See Figure 15.10.)

Dissolved Load

Most dissolved load is supplied by groundwater. As water percolates through the ground, it acquires soluble soil compounds, then ions, from deeper cracks and pores in bedrock. Eventually, much of this ion-rich water finds its way into streams.

The velocity of stream flow has essentially no effect on a stream's ability to carry its dissolved load. Once material is in solution, it goes wherever the stream goes, regardless of velocity. Precipitation occurs only when the chemistry of the water changes.

Suspended Load

Most streams carry the largest part of their load in *suspension* (Figure 15.10A). Indeed, the visible cloud of sediment suspended in the water is the most obvious portion of a stream's load (Figure 15.10B). Usually only fine sand, silt, and clay particles can be carried this way, but during flood stage, larger particles are suspended as well. Then the total quantity of material carried in suspension increases dramatically, as experienced by people whose homes have become sites for the deposition of this material. For example, the Hwang Ho (Yellow River) of China carries an amount of sediment equal in weight to the water that carries it. Rivers like this are appropriately described as "too thick to drink but too thin to cultivate." The type and amount of material carried in suspension are controlled by two factors: the velocity of the water and the settling velocity of each sediment grain.

Settling velocity is defined as the speed at which a particle falls through a stationary fluid. The larger the particle, the more rapidly it settles toward the streambed. Also the shape and specific gravity of particles influence settling velocity. Flat grains sink through water more slowly than spherical grains, and dense particles fall toward the bed more rapidly than do less dense particles. The slower the settling velocity and the higher the flow velocity, the longer a sediment particle will stay in suspension and the farther it will be carried downstream.

Bed Load

Coarser particles move along the bed of the channel as *bed load* (Figure 15.10A). The particles that make up the bed load move by rolling, sliding, and saltation. Sediment moving by **saltation** (*saltare* = to leap) appears to jump or skip along the streambed as particles are propelled upward by collisions or lifted by the current and then carried downstream a short distance until gravity pulls them back to the bed. Particles that are too large or heavy to move by saltation either roll or slide along the bottom, depending on their shapes.

A

B

Figure 15.10 **A.** Sediment transport processes in a stream channel. A stream carries sediment as ions in solution (dissolved load), in suspension (suspended load), and as bed load. Components of the bed load can move by rolling, sliding, and saltation (alternating between bed and suspended loads). **B.** The muddy suspended load of British Columbia's Fraser River contrasts sharply with the blue glacier-fed water of its tributary, the Bridge River. (Photo by S. R. Hicock)

Unlike the suspended and dissolved loads, the bed load moves intermittently when the force of the water is sufficient to move the larger particles (e.g., during floods). The bed load usually does not exceed 10 percent of a stream's total load. For example, of the 17 million tonnes of sediment carried to the Strait of Georgia by the Fraser River each year, most is carried in suspension and only 1 percent is bed load. Likewise, bed load constitutes a mere 1.5 percent of the 7 million tonnes of sediment transported down the St. Lawrence River.

Capacity and Competence

A stream's ability to carry solid particles is typically described by two criteria. The maximum load of solid particles that a stream can transport per unit of time is termed its **capacity**. The greater the discharge, the greater is the stream's capacity for hauling sediment. **Competence** of a stream is the maximum particle size that a stream can transport, based on its velocity: Fast streams have greater competence than slow streams. A stream's competence increases as the square of its velocity. Thus, if the velocity of a stream doubles, the impact force of the water increases four times; if the velocity triples, the force increases nine times, and so forth. Hence, the large boulders that are often visible during a low-water stage and that seem immovable can, in fact, be transported during flood stage because of the stream's increased competence (Figure 15.11).

Figure 15.11 Although the bed load of many rivers consists of sand, the bed load of this stream in British Columbia is made up of huge boulders. During floods, the seemingly immovable rocks in this channel are rolled along the bed of the stream and rounded by abrasion. The maximum size of particle a stream can move (its competence) is determined by the velocity of the water. (Photo by Mike Schering)

By now it should be clear why the greatest erosion and transportation of sediment occur during floods (Figure 15.12). The increase in discharge results in greater capacity; the increased velocity produces greater competence. With rising velocity the water becomes more turbulent, and larger and larger particles are set in motion. In just a few days, or perhaps just a few hours, a stream in flood stage can erode and transport more sediment than it does during normal flow.

DEPOSITION OF SEDIMENT BY STREAMS

Whenever a stream's velocity slows, its competence is reduced, and particles of sediment are deposited sequentially when their critical settling velocity is reached, based on their size. This process, called sorting, explains why particles of similar size are deposited together. Sediment deposited by streams is called **alluvium** and includes channel deposits, floodplain deposits (on the valley floor adjacent to the channel), or deposits near their mouths.

Channel Deposits

Alluvium deposited within a stream's channel comprises mostly sand and gravel, commonly called **bars**. Depending on sediment load and stream flow, sediment can locally accumulate on the channel bed as isolated mounds called **intrachannel bars**. Crescent-shaped buildups of sediment called **point bars** are constructed on the insides or *points* of meanders where streams lose competence.

Floodplain Deposits

A floodplain is that part of a valley that is inundated when stream flow overtops riverbanks during a flood (see Box 15.1). Floodplains range in width from a

Figure 15.12 During floods, both capacity and competence increase. Therefore, the greatest erosion and sediment transport occur during these high-water periods. Here we see the sediment-filled 2013 floodwaters of Alberta's Bow River eroding a bike path in Calgary. (Photo © Rosanne Tackaberry/Alamy)

15.1

PEOPLE AND THE ENVIRONMENT
Red River Floods

The Red River originates near the intersection of South Dakota, North Dakota, and Minnesota. It flows northward and empties into Manitoba's Lake Winnipeg (Figure 15.A).

In April 1997, Grand Forks, North Dakota, and other communities along the Red River experienced disastrous flooding—the worst ever recorded in the region. The flood was preceded by a very snowy winter. As April began, winter snows started melting when a spring storm pounded the northern Great Plains. The blizzard rebuilt snowdrifts to heights of 6 metres; however, the drifts melted quickly, causing rapid runoff into the Red River.

The discharge at Grand Forks jumped from about 70 cubic metres per second on April 1, 1997, to nearly 4200 three weeks later. Floodwaters at Grand Forks crested at 17.7 metres, almost 8 metres above flood level, which exceeded the previous record flood level set in 1897 by 1.2 metres. Two million hectares of land were under water, much of downtown Grand Forks was destroyed by water and fire, and more than 24 000 homes were damaged.

Farther downstream, the flood affected more than 200 000 hectares in southern Manitoba. After the 1950 flood that forced 100 000 Winnipegers from their homes, an artificial floodway was built in eastern Winnipeg to divert floodwaters from the city centre. The 1997 event displaced more than 25 000 people and caused $500 million in damages, which would have been much worse without the floodway.

The 1997 flood was a record-breaking 500-year flood (statistical probability of once in 500 years). The 2011 Red River flood (Figure 15.B) was a 300-year event that affected southwest Manitoba and southeast Saskatchewan.

Why do Red River floods occur so frequently and over such large areas? Four factors seem to contribute.

1. The Red River flows northward. Spring thaw also progresses from south to north and its runoff feeds the river. If the south-to-north thaw is perfectly synchronized, extensive floods occur in the northern portion of the valley.

2. Ice derived from the southern valley meets with freshly broken ice in the central and northern valley. Such ice concentrations can slow or block the water flow, causing river levels to swell.

3. The Red River flows across the broad, flat floor of a former lake. When the river floods onto this plain, the area covered can be extensive.

4. The river's gradient is low and decreases downstream into Manitoba. During floods the river's lack of slope causes it to form a gigantic shallow lake.

Figure 15.A   The Red River flows north into Manitoba's Lake Winnipeg.

Figure 15.B   A farm near St. Jean Baptiste, Manitoba, during the Red River flood in April 2011.
(Photo by Joe Bryksa/Winnipeg Free Press)

few metres to many kilometres. **Natural levees** (*lever* = to raise) are subtle, snake-like features that flank the channels of some streams. Although levees are not limited to a certain type of stream, they typically develop in those that have a large suspended load of sand, silt, and clay, and occupy broad, flat floodplain floors. Natural levees are built by recurring floods over many years. When a stream overflows its banks, the water flows over the floodplain surface as a broad sheet, which reduces the water's velocity and turbulence, and the coarser portion of the suspended load is deposited in strips bordering the channel. As the water spreads out over the flood plain, a lesser amount of finer sediment is laid down over the valley floor. This uneven distribution of material produces the gentle, almost imperceptible, slope of the natural levee (Figure 15.13).

A Normal stage

B Flood stage

C After many floods

Figure 15.13 Schematic diagram, showing how natural levees form in relation to a stream channel (topography highly exaggerated). **A.** Under normal conditions, stream flow is confined to the stream channel. **B.** When a stream overtops its banks during a flood, its flow velocity decreases rapidly, thus reducing its capacity and competence. Coarser grained material (usually sand) settles out closest to the channel, while finer grained material such as silt and clay settles farther away. The thickness of the resulting layer of sediment decreases with increasing distance from the channel banks. **C.** Over many years, repeated flood deposition leads to the development of a ridge on both sides of the stream channel.

THE GRADED STREAM CONCEPT AND BASE LEVEL

Like other complex systems, streams tend to naturally evolve toward a state of equilibrium, in which the parameters influencing their behaviour are in balance with one another and have reached their maximum efficiency. A stream that has (theoretically) attained such a balance is called a **graded stream**. In this condition, it is able to maintain just the amount of energy required to transport its load and experiences no net erosion or deposition.

The longitudinal profile of a stream (Figure 15.4) tends to be a smooth, concave-upward curve that progressively decreases in gradient from its headwaters to its mouth. Near its headwaters (where discharge is low and sediment is coarse), a stream must have a steep gradient to transport its load, whereas farther downstream (where discharge is high and sediment is finer), a gentle gradient provides sufficient energy for this task. Over time, local irregularities are smoothed out in a stream's longitudinal profile by eroding local topographic highs, where the stream's energy is above the optimum level for transporting sediment, and by depositing sediment in local depressions, where the stream's energy is below that level. The longer the time over which the stream has increased its load-carrying efficiency, the closer its longitudinal profile will be to its ideal grade. Thus time lets the stream approach equilibrium with its new conditions. If no subsequent erosional changes occurred, the profile would approach a flat gradient. Even though a natural stream may not attain true equilibrium, it will at least respond to disturbances in the same manner as the theoretical graded stream.

Stream profiles are strongly influenced by changes in **base level**—the lowest elevation to which a stream can erode its bed. Base level most commonly corresponds to the elevation at which a stream enters another water body, where, on escaping the confinement of its channel, it rapidly loses velocity and, in turn, loses its ability to erode. Along its course, a stream can encounter one or more **local (temporary) base levels** represented by the surface of a relatively small water body, such as a pond, a lake, or another stream. A resistant rock layer can also serve as a local base level by temporarily hindering the stream's ability to downcut. The Lockport Dolostone plays this role at Niagara Falls (Figure 15.14). Such a layer will commonly form a ledge that, because of undercutting and subsequent collapse, will maintain a steep slope over which water freely tumbles, producing a **waterfall**.

Niagara Falls exemplifies the effects of variations in bedrock erodibility (Figure 15.14). Here,

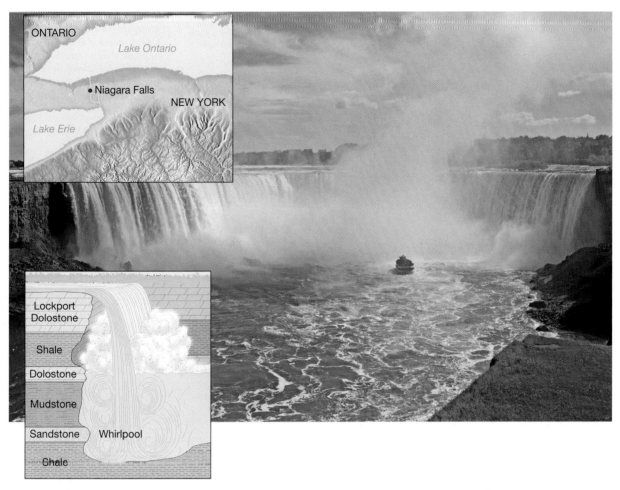

Figure 15.14   The larger Canadian Horseshoe Falls at Niagara Falls. The river plunges over the falls and erodes the shale beneath the more resistant Lockport Dolostone. As a section of dolostone is undercut, it loses support and breaks off. (Photo © digitex/Fotolia)

water falls over a resistant bed of dolostone that is underlain by less-resistant shale. As the water plunges over the lip of the falls, it erodes the weaker shale, undermining a section of dolostone, which eventually breaks off. In this manner the waterfall retains its vertical cliff while slowly but continually retreating upstream. Over the past 12 500 years, Niagara Falls has retreated more than 10 kilometres upstream. The course of the river itself has also changed substantially since pre-glacial times.

A waterfall can migrate upstream a significant distance by headward erosion, but when it is no longer an obstacle to flow, it ceases to be a local base level. Where a local change in gradient in the streambed disturbs stream flow, but not enough to produce a waterfall, the irregularity may become rapids. Both of these features occur where the stream profile drops rapidly. Once erosion has eliminated the resistant rock, the stream profile smoothes out again.

The lowest elevation to which any stream can erode is sea level, regarded as **ultimate base level**. In a stream close to grade, a rapid change in the base level, either local or ultimate, will cause a corresponding readjustment of the stream's activities in order to drive the system toward a new equilibrium. Sea level is a dynamic boundary that shifts relative to land with its own rise and fall (e.g., ice sheet expansion and melting; see Chapter 17) as well as tectonic movements of the land relative to it. If sea level falls relative to land, streams will tend to erode their bed until their longitudinal profile is adjusted to the lowered elevation of its mouth. If sea level rises relative to land, the stream will tend to raise its bed downstream by depositing more sediment, first at its mouth, then progressively upstream. For example, coastal streams carved deep valleys near their mouths as sea level dropped as much as 100 metres below its present position during the last Ice Age, when large

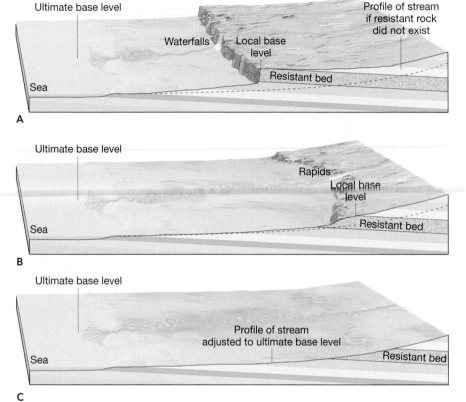

Figure 15.15 A resistant layer of rock can act as a local (temporary) base level. Because the durable layer is eroded more slowly, it limits the amount of downcutting upstream.

amounts of water were locked up in ice sheets. By the end of the Ice Age, the return of water from ice sheets into the oceans led to a rise in sea level, resulting in backfilling of the deep valleys.

Furthermore, a stream will gradually adjust its profile as it cuts through a resistant rock layer that formerly impeded its flow, and will then adjust to the next lowest base level (Figure 15.15). The construction of an artificial dam upstream of its mouth would represent a rise in base level (Figure 15.16). Because the stream would lose velocity and competence as it reached the reservoir behind the dam, it would deposit sediment, which is why dam reservoirs must be dredged. Meanwhile, water flowing downstream has more energy than it needs to transport its reduced sediment load and so it cuts into its bed. The resulting profile is effectively split into two smaller segments above and below the dam, each adjusting to its own base level (Figure 15.16).

STREAM VALLEYS

Valleys are perhaps the most common landforms on Earth's surface. Before the turn of the nineteenth century, it was generally believed that valleys were created by catastrophic events that pulled the crust apart and created troughs in which streams could flow. Today, however, we know that streams usually create their own valleys. However, some streams are very narrow compared with their valleys (called *misfit* streams) because their valleys were carved by glaciers or by glacial melt water. For example, few of Canada's major rivers fit their valleys because they occupy ancient *spillways* carved by former glacial meltwater streams that were much wider, and had much higher discharges, than those of the present rivers.

Stream valleys can be divided into two general types: narrow V-shaped valleys, and wide valleys with flat floors (floodplains) or U-shaped floors (carved by glaciers; see Chapter 17). These exist as the ideal forms, with many gradations in between.

Narrow Valleys

In some arid regions where weathering is slow and rock is resistant, narrow valleys with rapids and waterfalls can have nearly vertical walls (see Figure 15.9). A narrow V-shaped valley (Figure 15.17) indicates the stream's primary work has been downcutting. However, most valleys are much broader at the top than the bottom. This is because the sides of most valleys are shaped by weathering, sheet flow, and mass wasting, which deliver increased load to the stream.

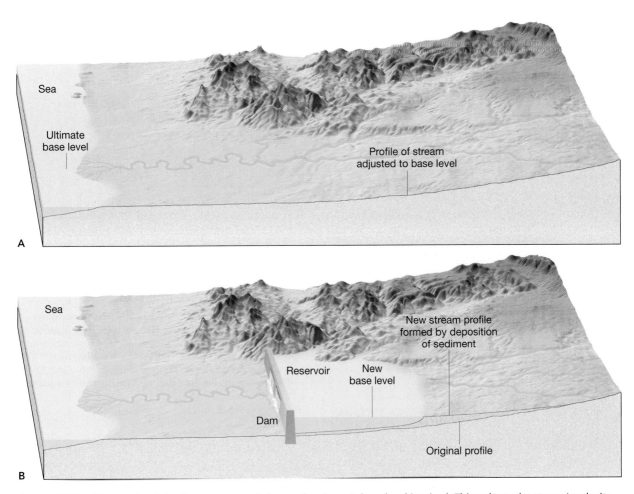

A

B

Figure 15.16 When a dam is built and a reservoir forms, the stream's base level is raised. This reduces the stream's velocity and leads to deposition and a reduction of the gradient upstream from the reservoir.

Figure 15.17 V-shaped valley opening in to Cambridge fjord, north Baffin Island. (Photo by S. R. Hicock)

Figure 15.18 **A.** When a stream lies well above base level, stream erosion is directed predominantly downward, producing a V-shaped valley. **B.** As a stream bed approaches base level, the stream channel begins to meander, eroding both downward and laterally, widening its floodplain. **C.** When a stream bed has been lowered to an elevation close to base level, lateral erosion predominates, leading to the development of a very broad floodplain. **D.** Photograph of the St. Mary River, near Lethbridge, Alberta, eroding its floodplain. Note also the well-developed point bars and cutbanks in the meanders of the river.
(Photo by C. Tsujita)

Wide Valleys

As a stream approaches base level and its gradient has decreased, less energy is expended in downcutting and more in lateral erosion. The result is the development of a meandering channel that widens the valley as it erodes first one bank and then the other (Figure 15.18). This side-to-side migration of the channel ultimately produces a broad *erosional floodplain*. If sediment is allowed to accumulate in an existing valley, as might be expected during a rise in base level, the valley floor aggrades and broadens, producing a *depositional floodplain*. The floodplain in British Columbia's Fraser Valley is one such feature; it was produced when a glacier gouged the former stream valley about 300 metres deeper than it had been. After the ice melted, the stream readjusted itself to its former base level by refilling the valley with alluvium. Further discussion of floodplain development in wide valleys is given in the next section.

TYPES OF STREAM SYSTEMS

Depending on flow rate, gradient, sediment load, climate, and a host of other factors, streams can take on a number of forms. In this section, three basic types—braided, meandering, and anastomosed—are discussed. Keep in mind, however, that a wide spectrum of forms exists among these basic types and that a single stream can theoretically show characteristics of all these forms at various points along its course.

Braided Streams

Sometimes a stream deposits materials on the floor of its channel. If these accumulations become thick enough to act as significant obstacles, they can split the flow into multiple paths. What results is a broad channel containing a complex network of converging and diverging flow paths that thread their way among the bars (Figure 15.19A). Such a stream is said to be **braided**. Braided patterns most commonly form when the load supplied to a stream exceeds its competence or capacity. For example, excessive load can occur at the terminus

A

B

Figure 15.19 **A.** Modern braided stream choked with sediment near the edge of a melting glacier. **B.** Ancient (Triassic) sandy braided river deposits, Blomidon Formation, Tenneycape, Nova Scotia. The conglomerate lenses were deposited by migrating gravel bars in the stream bed.
(Photo **A** by Bradford Washburn; photo **B** by Guy Plint)

of a glacier, where ice-eroded sediment is dumped into a meltwater stream flowing away from the glacier. By splitting its flow into multiple paths, a braided stream increases its ability to transport the load downstream.

Braided streams are dominated by coarse sediment (sand to gravel) bed load, the coarsest components commonly moulded into bars. Ancient deposits of braided rivers typically preserve crossbedded conglomerates that record the migration of such bars (Figure 15.19B).

Meandering Streams

Streams that occupy broad floodplains, whether erosional or depositional, commonly have a single channel with sweeping meanders. Meandering streams usually occur in areas of relatively low gradient, and their channels carry both fine-grained suspended sediment and coarser-grained bed load.

The manner in which meanders are maintained is well known (Figure 15.20). Erosion occurs on the outside of the meander where velocity and turbulence are greatest. Most often, the outside bank

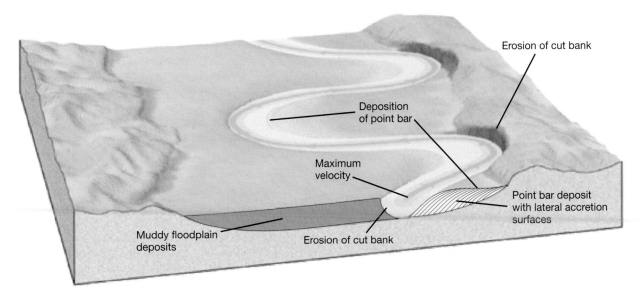

Figure 15.20 Schematic diagram showing the lateral migration of a meander by erosion of the cut bank and deposition on the point bar.

A

B

Figure 15.21   Erosion of a cut bank in action along the Newaukum River, Washington. **A.** January 1965. **B.** March 1965. Note the house about to be undermined by continued erosion of the cut bank. (Photos by P. A. Glancy/U.S. Geological Survey)

is undermined (cut), oversteepened, then fails by slumping into the channel. Because the outside of a meander is a zone of active erosion (Figure 15.21), it is called the **cut bank**. Much of the debris eroded by the stream at the cut bank moves downstream and is soon deposited as point bars in zones of decreased velocity on the insides of meanders, while coarser debris may be left in the channel as lag gravel. The channel meanders migrate laterally, while keeping

Figure 15.22   Lateral accretion surfaces of ancient point bar deposits (upper part of photograph) record the migration of a meandering river channel. The lateral accretion surfaces dip toward the left side of the photograph, indicating that the channel was migrating in that direction. (Photo by Guy Plint)

the same cross-sectional area, by eroding the outside of the bends and depositing on the inside. A point bar deposit can preserve **lateral accretion surfaces**, which mark the successive positions of the point bar surface as it is built out laterally (Figure 15.22). These surfaces, which resemble cross bedding but are significantly larger in scale, are hallmarks of meandering channels in ancient sedimentary deposits.

If we were to sample the floodplain alluvium associated with a meandering stream, we would find that some of it consists of coarse sands and gravels that were originally deposited as channel deposits and point bars by meanders shifting laterally across the valley floor. Other sediments would be composed of fine sands, silts, and clays that were spread across the floodplain whenever water overtopped the channel banks during floods. Thus, a vertical sequence can develop under a floodplain surface in which sediment gets finer as we move upward, changing from gravel to mud, as stream meanders migrate back and forth over time.

Due to the downslope gradient of the channel, erosion is more effective on the downstream side of a meander. Consequently, the bends also migrate down the valley as well as laterally. Sometimes the downstream migration of a meander is slowed when it reaches a more resistant portion of the floodplain. This allows the next meander upstream to "catch up." Gradually the neck of land between the meanders is narrowed. When they get close enough, the river may erode through the narrow neck of land to the next loop (Figure 15.23A). The new, shorter channel segment is called a **cutoff**, and because of its shape, the abandoned bend is called an **oxbow lake** (Figures 15.23A and 15.23B).

A

B

Figure 15.23   **A.** Formation of a cutoff and oxbow lake. **B.** Aerial view of Kenemich River at the foot of the Mealy Mountains, Newfoundland and Labrador, showing well-developed meanders, oxbow lakes, and meander scars. (Reproduced with the permission of Natural Resources Canada 2010, courtesy of the Geological Survey of Canada. Photo 2001-053H by Pat Pollock; photo **B** reproduced with the permission of Natural Resources Canada, 2013, Geological Survey of Canada [Photo 2001 053H by Pat Pollock])

The process of meander cutoff formation has the effect of shortening the river; however, the river also creates new meanders, thus lengthening its course by a similar amount.

Meandering streams commonly have well-developed natural levees (Figure 15.24C) that lie above the average level of their floodplains. For example, natural levees of the lower Mississippi River rise six metres above the lower portions of the valley floor. The area behind a natural levee is called a **back swamp** and is poorly drained because water cannot flow up over the levee and back into the river (Figures 15.24A and 15.24B). When a tributary stream enters a valley that has substantial natural levees, it may flow through the back swamp parallel to the main river for many kilometres before cutting through the natural levee and joining the river. Such streams are called **yazoo tributaries** (Figure 15.24B), after the Yazoo River, which parallels the lower Mississippi River for more than 300 kilometres.

Certain meandering rivers flow in steep, narrow valleys that probably developed on a floodplain that was near base level. Then, a change in base level, either when it dropped or when the land was uplifted, caused the stream to begin downcutting.

During the last Ice Age water was transferred from the ocean to glaciers on land (see Chapter 17), and sea level (ultimate base level) dropped, causing

Figure 15.24 **A.** Natural levees are commonly built during floods in meandering river systems. **B.** After floodwaters recede, water may be prevented from draining into the main channel, resulting in the development of back swamps and yazoo tributaries that flow parallel to the main stream. **C.** A meandering stream near Swan Hills in central Alberta, showing slightly raised natural levees (bright green vegetated strips on both sides of the channel) and poorly drained back swamps. (Reproduced with the permission of Natural Resources Canada 2010, courtesy of the Geological Survey of Canada; photo **c** by Denis St-Onge/Geological Survey of Canada)

rivers flowing into the ocean to downcut. This activity ceased when the glaciers melted and the ocean rose to its former level.

Regional uplift of the land is exemplified by the Fraser Plateau in south central British Columbia (Figure 15.25). As the plateau was gradually uplifted, meandering rivers adjusted to being higher above base level by downcutting.

After a river has adjusted to a relative drop in base level by downcutting, it may once again produce a floodplain at a level below the old one. The flat remnants of a former floodplain are sometimes preserved as **terraces** (Figure 15.26).

Anastomosed Streams

Anastomosed streams look like braided streams in some respects differ in their behaviour. Unlike a braided stream, which diverts flow around temporary bars of sediment in a single, shallow channel, an anastomosed stream has deep, interwoven, multiple channels separated by stable islands that are commonly heavily vegetated (Figure 15.27A). In other words, anastomosed streams are produced by the development of multiple true channels rather than by the local diversion of flow around temporary buildups of sediment within a single channel. Also, anastomosed streams tend to be dominated by fine-grained suspended load as opposed to coarse-grained bed load.

Anastomosed streams tend to occur in areas of extremely low gradient and possess little energy to carve their banks. Like meandering stream systems, they tend to have broad, muddy floodplains and levees along their channel banks.

The relatively small amounts of coarse-grained bed load in anastomosed systems are ultimately deposited in channels. However, unlike the channels of meandering streams that migrate laterally by eroding their outside bank and depositing sediment on point bars, those of anastomosed streams tend to become vertically filled with sediment with little or no lateral accretion and are ultimately abandoned. In the geologic record, channel deposits of anastomosed streams can be recognized as lens-shaped bodies of horizontally bedded sandstones or conglomerates encased in muddy (floodplain) sediments (Figure 15.27B).

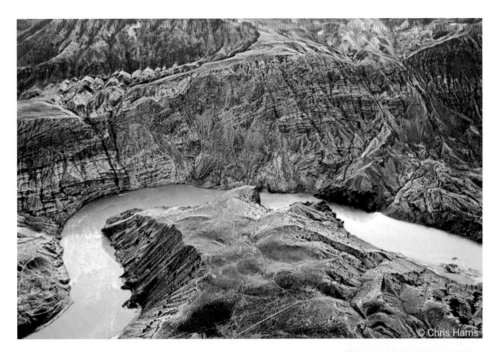

Figure 15.25 Incised meanders of the Fraser River in British Columbia that were formed in response to the uplift of the Fraser Plateau. (Photo by © Chris Harris Photography)

A

B

Figure 15.26 Terraces can form when a stream cuts down through previously deposited alluvium. This may occur in response to a lowering of elevation or as a result of regional uplift.

Figure 15.27 **A.** The upper Columbia River in southeast British Columbia is a good example of an anastomosing stream. Note the multiple active channels and intervening islands with wetlands. **B.** A sand-filled channel (lightest coloured) of an ancient anastomosed river (Cretaceous Dunvegan Formation, Pine River area, British Columbia), encased in muddy floodplain deposits. (Photo **A** by Norman D. Smith; photo **B** by Guy Plint)

ALLUVIAL FANS AND DELTAS

Two of the most common landforms composed of alluvium are alluvial fans and deltas. They are sometimes similar in shape and are deposited for essentially the same reason: an abrupt loss of competence in a stream. However, alluvial fans are deposited on land, whereas deltas are deposited in a body of water. In addition, alluvial fans can be quite steep, but deltas are relatively flat, barely protruding above the level surface of the ocean or lake in which they formed.

Alluvial Fans

Alluvial fans typically develop where a high-gradient stream leaves a narrow valley in mountainous terrain and comes out suddenly onto a broad, flat plain or valley floor (Figure 15.28). Alluvial fans form in response to the abrupt drop in gradient combined with the change from a narrow channel of a mountain stream to less confined channels at the base of the mountains. The sudden drop in velocity causes the stream to dump its load of sediment quickly in a distinctive cone- or fan-shaped accumulation. As illustrated by Figure 15.28, the surface of the fan slopes outward in a broad arc from an apex at the mouth of the steep valley. Usually, coarse material is dropped near the apex of the fan, while finer material is carried toward the base of the deposit. Many alluvial fans in arid areas have debris-flow deposits (Chapter 14) interbedded with the alluvium.

Deltas

A **delta** forms when a stream enters an ocean or a lake. Figure 15.29A depicts the structure of a simple delta built into a lake. As the stream's flow is checked on entering the lake, the dying current deposits its load of sediments in three types of beds. *Foreset beds* are composed of coarser particles that drop almost immediately on entering the lake to form layers that slope downcurrent on the *delta front*. The foreset beds are usually covered by thin, horizontal *topset beds*, which are deposited on the *delta plain* during floods. Topset beds tend to be dominated by mud and plant debris that accumulates in marshlands on the flat upper surface of the delta, but also contain the coarser grained material deposited within distributary channels. The finer silts and clays settle out some distance from the mouth in nearly horizontal layers called *bottomset beds* on an area called the *prodelta*.

As the delta grows outward, the stream's gradient continually lessens, eventually causing the channel to become choked with sediment from the slowing water. Consequently, the river seeks a shorter, higher-gradient route to base level, as illustrated in Figure 15.29B. This illustration shows the main channel dividing into several smaller ones, called **distributaries.** Most deltas are characterized by these shifting channels, which act in the opposite way to tributaries. Rather than carrying water into the main channel, distributaries carry water *away* from the main channel in varying paths. After numerous shifts of the channel, the simple delta may grow into the triangular shape of the Greek letter delta (Δ), for which it was named. The Nile Delta (Figure 15.30A) is affected by relatively strong wave activity that smears much of the sediment delivered to the river mouth against the shoreline; this has resulted in the development of the classic delta shape.

A   B

Figure 15.28 **A.** Alluvial fans develop where the gradient of a stream changes abruptly from steep to flat. Such a situation exists in Death Valley, California, where streams emerge from the mountains into a flat basin. As a result, Death Valley has many large alluvial fans. The highway will eventually be buried by fan buildup. **B.** Alluvial fan along Racing River, northern British Columbia.
(Photo **A** by Michael Collier; photo **B** by © Gunter Marx/Alamy)

Figure 15.29 **A.** Structure of a simple delta that forms in the relatively quiet waters of a lake. **B.** Growth of a simple delta. As a stream extends its channel, the gradient is reduced. Frequently, during flood stage the river is diverted to a higher-gradient route, forming a new distributary. Old abandoned distributaries are gradually invaded by aquatic vegetation and fill with sediment.
(After Ward's Natural Science Establishment, Inc., Rochester, NY)

Figure 15.30 The shapes of deltas vary and depend on such factors as a river's sediment load and the strength and nature of shoreline processes. **A.** The triangular shape of the Nile Delta was the basis for naming this feature; here, waves tend to re-shape what the river deposits. **B.** The present Mississippi Delta is called a *bird-foot delta*, where river deposition dominates over wave erosion.

Conversely, the Mississippi Delta (Figure 13.30B) is shaped more like a bird's foot, reflecting the high output of fine-grained, suspended sediment from its distributaries and relatively weak wave activity. Thus, depending on such factors as sediment load, shoreline shape, and variations in the nature and strength of wave activity, a delta can assume different shapes (Figure 15.30).

Although deltas that form in the ocean generally exhibit the same basic form as the simple lake-deposited feature just described, most large marine deltas are far more complex and have foreset beds that are inclined at a much lower angle than those depicted in Figure 15.29A. Indeed, many of the world's great rivers have created massive deltas, each with its own peculiarities.

DRAINAGE PATTERNS

A stream is just a small component of a larger system. Each system constitutes a **drainage basin**, the land area that contributes water to the stream. The drainage basin of one stream is separated from another by an elongated topographic high called a **divide** (Figures 15.31 and 15.32). Divides range in size from a ridge separating two small gullies to continental divides, which delineate enormous drainage basins. The Mississippi River has the largest drainage basin in North America. Extending between the Rocky Mountains in the

West and the Appalachian Mountains in the East, the Mississippi River and its tributaries collect water from more than 3.2 million square kilometres of the continent.

DRAINAGE PATTERNS Drainage systems are interconnected networks of streams that form a variety of patterns. A drainage pattern can vary in response to the kinds of rock on which the streams developed or the structural pattern of joints, faults, and folds.

The most common drainage pattern is **dendritic pattern** (tree-like; Figure 15.33A), characterized by irregular branching of tributaries that resembles the branches of a deciduous tree. It forms where underlying bedrock is relatively uniform in rock type and resistant to erosion, such as flat-lying sedimentary strata or massive igneous rocks. Structures in the substrate do not control the pattern of stream flow, which follows the slope of land.

When streams diverge from a central area, like spokes from the hub of a wheel, they produce a **radial pattern** (Figure 15.33B) that develops on isolated volcanic cones and domal uplifts.

Figure 15.33C illustrates a **rectangular pattern**, with many right-angle bends, where the bedrock is criss-crossed by a series of joints and faults. Because these structures are eroded more easily than unbroken rock, their geometric pattern guides the directions of streams as they carve their valleys.

Figure 15.33D illustrates a **trellis pattern**, in which tributary streams are nearly parallel to one

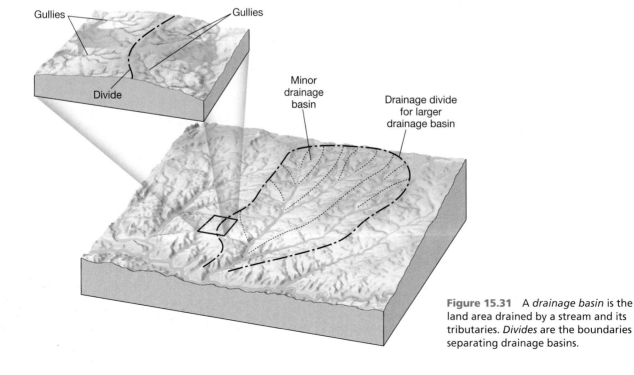

Figure 15.31 A *drainage basin* is the land area drained by a stream and its tributaries. *Divides* are the boundaries separating drainage basins.

Figure 15.32 All major river systems in Canada, with the exception of a few in the Prairie provinces, ultimately drain into the oceans surrounding North America. Note that streams in the southernmost areas of Alberta and Saskatchewan feed into the Mississippi drainage system that empties into the Gulf of Mexico more than 6000 kilometres to the southeast. The boundaries between the drainage basins are called divides.
(Map modified with permission from image courtesy of Ministry of Public Works and Government Services Canada, 2004, and courtesy of Natural Resources Canada, Geological Survey of Canada)

another and resemble a garden trellis. This pattern forms in areas with alternating parallel belts of resistant and less resistant rock and is particularly well displayed in the Front Ranges of the Canadian Rockies.

Headward Erosion and Stream Piracy

A stream can lengthen its course by **headward erosion**, extending the head of its valley upslope. As sheet flow converges and becomes concentrated at the head of a stream channel, its velocity and power to erode increase. Through headward erosion the valley becomes extended into previously undissected terrain (Figure 15.34).

Stream piracy is the diversion of the drainage of one stream because of the headward erosion of another stream. For example, if a stream on one side of a divide has a steeper gradient and more energy than a stream on the other side, it can extend its valley headward, eventually breaking down the divide and capturing part or all of the drainage of the slower stream.

Stream piracy also explains narrow, steep-sided gorges that have no active streams running through them. These abandoned water gaps (called *wind gaps*) form when the stream that cut the notch has its course changed by a pirate stream.

A Dendritic   B Radial   C Rectangular   D Trellis

Figure 15.33 Drainage patterns.

Figure 15.34 By headward erosion, valleys extend into previously undissected terrain. Aerial photo of the San Rafael River above its confluence with the Green River in Utah. (Photo by Michael Collier)

FLOODS AND FLOOD CONTROL

When the discharge of a stream exceeds the capacity of its channel, it overflows its banks as a flood. Floods are the most common and among the most destructive of geologic hazards. They are, nevertheless, simply part of the *natural* behaviour of streams. Just an hour or less of intense thunderstorm rainfall can trigger floods in small valleys. By contrast, major floods in large river valleys are commonly the result of an extraordinary series of precipitation events over a broad region for many days or weeks. Data collected at stream-gauging stations is useful for estimating the probability of various flood frequencies and magnitudes.

For a particular river, flood size tends to be related to flood frequency. The larger the flood, the less often it is expected to occur. A 100-year flood (or even the 500-year Red River flood in Box 15.1) describes the **recurrence interval** which is an estimate of how often a flood of a given size can be expected to occur. A 25-year event would be much smaller, but would be four times more likely to occur than a 100-year flood. For reasonable estimates, stream guage data must be collected for 10 to 30 years. Climate cycles like drought or excessive rain, and urbanization and damming of rural areas, influence the accuracy of flood recurrence estimates.

Causes and Types of Floods

Floods can be the result of several naturally occurring and human-induced factors. Among the common types of floods are regional floods, flash floods, ice-jam floods, and dam-failure floods.

REGIONAL FLOODS Most regional floods are seasonal. Rapid melting of snow in spring and heavy spring rains can overwhelm a river. The extensive 1948 flood of the Fraser River and the 1997 flood along the Red River (see Box 15.1) are notable examples of events triggered by rapid snowmelt. Early spring floods are sometimes made worse if the ground is frozen. This reduces infiltration into the soil, thereby increasing runoff. Extended wet periods any time of the year can create saturated soils, after which any additional rain runs off into streams until capacities are exceeded. Regional floods are commonly caused by slow-moving storm systems, including decaying hurricanes. For example, southern Alberta was subjected to torrential rain in June 2013, when a storm system stalled over the region. The Calgary area was particularly hard hit, receiving more than 100 millimetres of rain in 20 hours, causing $400 million in damage. Flooding of the Saguenay River and its tributaries in 1996 caused more than $700 million in damage to the area, largely because of widespread erosion in some parts of the drainage basin and significant sediment deposition in others (Figure 15.35).

FLASH FLOODS A flash flood can occur with little warning and can be deadly because it produces a rapid rise in water levels and can have a devastating flow velocity. Several factors influence flash flooding. Among them are rainfall intensity and duration, surface conditions, and topography. Mountainous areas are susceptible because steep slopes can funnel runoff into narrow canyons, as occurs along the Sea-to-Sky Highway between Vancouver and Squamish, British Columbia.

Urban areas are susceptible to flash floods because a high percentage of the surface area is composed of impervious roofs, streets, and parking lots, where runoff is very rapid. For example, in July 2013 the heaviest rain in Toronto's history combined with high winds to result in flash floods that set cars afloat, drowned subway stations, and cut power. To better understand the effect of urbanization on stream flow, examine Figure 15.36. The top part of the figure is a hypothetical hydrograph that shows the time relationship between a rainstorm and the occurrence of flooding. Notice that the water level in the stream does not rise at the onset of precipitation, because time is required for water to move from the place where it fell to the stream. This time difference is called the *lag time*. The hydrograph in the bottom part of Figure 15.36 depicts the same

Figure 15.35   Downstream along Ha! Ha! River, a tributary of the Saguenay River, several properties were covered by up to two metres of sediment during the flood of 1996. The sediment was derived from upstream areas that experienced severe erosion during the flood.
(Reproduced with the permission of Natural Resources Canada 2013, Geological Survey of Canada. Photo 1997-42KK by G.R. Brooks)

hypothetical area and rainfall event *after* urbanization. Notice that the peak discharge during a flood is greater and that the lag time between precipitation and flood peak is shorter than before urbanization. The explanation for this effect is straightforward. Streets, parking lots, and buildings cover the ground that once soaked up water. Thus, less water infiltrates, and the rate and amount of runoff increase. Further, because much less water soaks into the ground, the low-water (dry-season) flow in many urban streams, which is maintained by the movement of groundwater into the channel, is greatly reduced.

ICE-JAM FLOODS Frozen rivers are susceptible to ice-jam floods. As the level of a stream rises, it will break up the ice and create ice floes that can pile up on channel obstructions, even creating a dam across the channel. Water upstream from the ice dam can rise rapidly and overflow the channel banks. When the ice dam fails, the water stored behind the dam is released, causing a flash flood downstream.

DAM-FAILURE FLOODS Human interference with a stream system can cause floods. Dams and artificial levees are built for flood protection and are designed to contain floods of a certain magnitude. If a larger flood occurs, the dam or levee is overtopped. If the dam or levee fails or is washed out, the water behind it is released to become a flash flood.

Flood Control

Engineering efforts to eliminate or reduce the catastrophic effects of floods include the construction of artificial levees, flood-control dams, and river channellization.

ARTIFICIAL LEVEES *Artificial levees* are earthen mounds built on the banks of a river to increase the volume of water the channel can hold. When a river is confined by levees during periods of high water, it frequently deposits material in its channel as the discharge diminishes. Thus, each time there is a high flow, deposits are left on the riverbed, the bottom of the channel is built up, and less water is required to

Typical lag time between rainfall and runoff

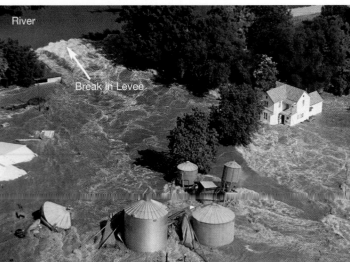

Figure 15.37 Water rushes through a break in an artificial levee in Monroe County, Illinois. During the record-breaking 1993 Midwest floods, many artificial levees could not withstand the force of the floodwaters. Sections of many weakened structures were overtopped or simply collapsed.
(Photo by James A. Finley/AP/Wide World Photos)

Lag time between rainfall and runoff after urbanization

Figure 15.36 When an area changes from rural to urban, the lag time between rainfall and flood peak is shortened. The flood peak is also higher following urbanization.
(L. B. Leopold, U.S. Geological Survey)

overflow the original levee. As a result, the height of the levee may have to be raised periodically to protect the floodplain. Moreover, many artificial levees are not built to withstand periods of extreme flooding (Figure 15.B). For example, levee failures were numerous in the U.S. Midwest during the summer of 1993, when the upper Mississippi and many of its tributaries experienced record floods (Figure 15.37), and on the Mississippi Delta in 2006 when Hurricane Katrina hit New Orleans. In some urban areas (e.g., Winnipeg) concrete floodwalls are constructed as artificial levees.

FLOOD-CONTROL DAMS *Flood-control dams* are built to store floodwater and then let it out slowly. This lowers the flood crest by spreading it out over a longer time. Many dams have significant non-flood-related functions, such as irrigation and

hydroelectric power generation. Many reservoirs are also major regional recreational facilities (e.g., Fanshawe and Wildwood in southern Ontario).

Building dams also has significant costs and consequences. For example, reservoirs created by dams may cover fertile farmland, useful forests, historic sites, and scenic valleys, and dams trap sediment. Therefore, deltas and floodplains downstream get eroded because they are no longer replenished with silt during floods. Large dams can also cause ecological damage to river environments that took thousands of years to establish. Furthermore, sedimentation behind a dam means that the volume of its reservoir will gradually diminish, reducing the effectiveness of this flood-control measure.

CHANNELLIZATION *Channellization* involves altering a stream channel to speed the flow of water and prevent it from reaching flood height. This may simply involve clearing a channel of obstructions or dredging a channel to make it wider and deeper.

Another approach, as exemplified by the Red River Floodway in Winnipeg, is to construct a floodway channel that is designed specifically to divert floodwaters away from urban centres (see Box 15.1).

A more radical alteration involves straightening a channel by creating *artificial cutoffs*. By shortening the stream, the gradient, velocity, discharge, and channel erosion increase, especially with flooding.

However, the river still tends to meander and tries to return to its previous course.

A NON-STRUCTURAL APPROACH Flood-control measures involve structural solutions aimed at controlling a river. These solutions are expensive and often give a false sense of security to people residing on the floodplain. Today, many scientists and engineers advocate *floodplain management*: identifying high-risk areas so that appropriate zoning regulations can be implemented to minimize development and promote more appropriate land use.

CHAPTER SUMMARY

- The *hydrologic* cycle refers to the continuous interchange of water among the oceans, atmosphere, and continents in the Earth system via the processes of precipitation, evaporation, infiltration, and runoff, as well as transpiration by plants. Of all the processes that operate within this cycle, it is the *runoff* of water over land that most influences the sculpting of Earth's varied landscapes.

- Runoff initially moves in a continuous layer of water by *sheet flow*, but soon separates into tiny *rills* that flow into larger *gullies* that, in turn, converge into larger *stream* channels.

- The flow velocity of a stream is dependent on characteristics of its channel (especially its slope or *gradient*, cross-sectional shape and size, and roughness) as well as its *discharge* (the volume of water passing a given point per unit of time).

- Water in a stream can flow in relatively straight paths (*laminar flow*) or more erratically (*turbulent flow*), depending on factors such as a stream's velocity and the roughness of its bed.

- Streams are capable of transporting particles above their beds as *suspended load* and along their channel floors as *bed load*. A stream's ability to transport solid particles depends on its capacity (maximum load of solid particles it can carry) and *competence* (maximum sediment particle size it can transport). Dissolved materials, transported in solution as *dissolved load*, are also considered as part of a stream's total sediment load.

- The two general types of *base level* (the lowest point to which a stream can erode its channel) are (1) *ultimate base level* (sea level) and (2) *temporary*, or *local, base level*. Lowering base level results in erosion; raising it induces deposition.

- Although many gradations exist, the two general types of stream valleys are (1) narrow V-shaped valleys dominated by downcutting and (2) wide valleys with flat floodplains produced by the lateral migration of meandering channels. Alluvial fans and *deltas* form at stream mouths.

- Based on attributes of stream channels, floodplains, and dominant sediment types, three basic forms of stream systems are recognized: *braided*, *meandering*, and *anastomosed*.

- A rapid decrease in a stream's flow velocity at the base of a steep slope causes sediment to be deposited as an *alluvial fan*. Similarly, when a stream enters a body of standing water, the resulting drop in its flow velocity leads to sediment deposition in a *delta*.

- The land area that contributes water to a stream is called a *drainage basin*. Patterns of stream networks within drainage basins include *dendritic*, *radial, rectangular,* and *trellis* arrangements.

- Floods are commonly triggered naturally by heavy rains or snowmelt. But human interference can worsen or even cause floods. Flood-control measures include the building of artificial levees and dams, and channellization. Many scientists and engineers advocate a non-structural approach to flood control that involves more appropriate land use.

MasteringGeology

www.masteringgeology.com

Looking for additional review and test prep materials? Visit the Study Area in MasteringGeology to enhance your understanding of this chapter's content by accessing a variety of resources, including

Self-Study Quizzes, Geoscience Animations, GEODe Tutorials, RSS feeds, flashcards, weblinks, self-study quizzes, and an optional Pearson eText.

REVIEW QUESTIONS

1. When the discharge of a stream increases, what happens to the stream's velocity?

2. What typically happens to channel width, channel depth, velocity, and discharge from the point where a stream begins to the point where it ends? Briefly explain why these changes take place.

3. Define *base level* and describe its importance in determining the characteristics of a stream.

4. Why do most streams have low gradients near their mouths?

5. Describe three ways in which a stream can erode its channel. Which one of these is responsible for creating potholes?

6. Describe the flow behaviour of water in the channel of a meandering stream.

7. At first glance, braided and anastomosed streams look very similar but are, in fact, very different in the nature of their channels and the materials they transport. Explain these differences.

8. Briefly describe the formation of natural levees and their relationship to floodplains.

9. Why do many small mountain streams look like they flow much faster than large, seemingly sluggish, lowland streams, even though the average velocity of the latter is often greater than the former?

10. List and briefly describe three basic flood-control strategies. What are some drawbacks of each?

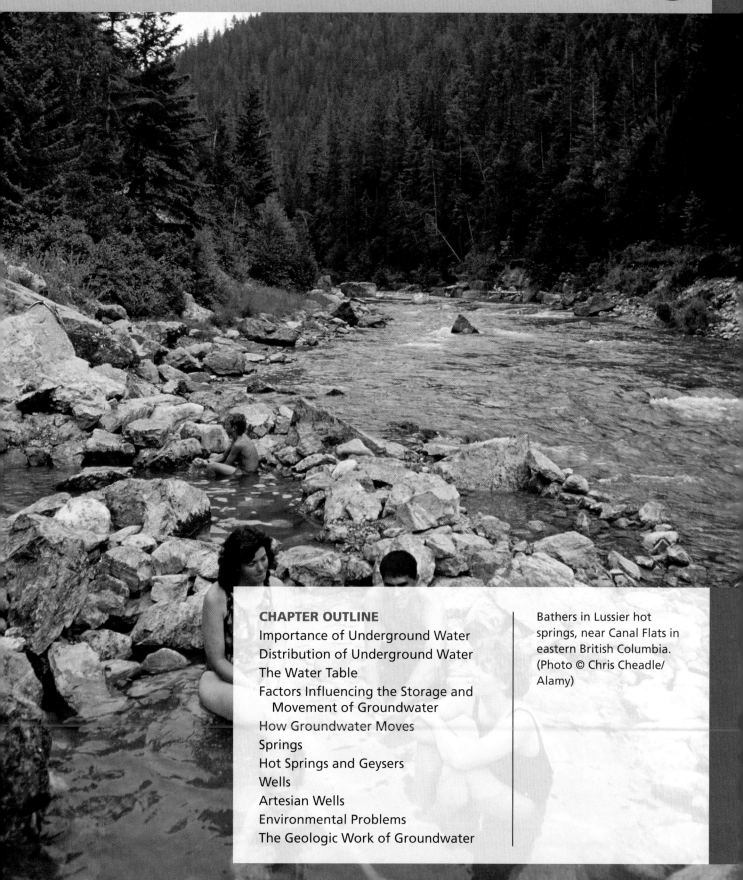

GROUNDWATER

Bathers in Lussier hot springs, near Canal Flats in eastern British Columbia. (Photo © Chris Cheadle/ Alamy)

Worldwide, wells and springs provide water for cities, crops, livestock, and industry. Groundwater is the drinking water for more than 50 percent of the population, is 40 percent of the water used for irrigation, and provides more than 25 percent of industry's needs. In some areas, however, overuse of this basic resource has resulted in water shortage, stream flow depletion, land subsidence, increased pumping cost, and groundwater pollution.

IMPORTANCE OF UNDERGROUND WATER

Groundwater is one of our most important and widely available resources, yet people's perceptions of the subsurface environment from which it comes are commonly unclear and incorrect. The reason is that the groundwater environment is largely hidden from view except in caves and mines, and the impressions people gain from these subsurface openings are misleading. Observations made on the land surface give an impression that Earth is solid. This view remains when we enter a cave and see water flowing in a channel that appears to have been cut into solid rock.

Because of such observations, many people believe that groundwater occurs only in underground rivers. In reality, most of the subsurface environment is not solid at all. It includes countless tiny *pore spaces* between grains of soil and sediment, and narrow joints and fractures in bedrock. It is in these small openings that groundwater collects and moves.

Considering all of Earth's water, only about 0.6 percent occurs underground, yet it is a vast quantity. When the oceans are excluded and only

sources of freshwater are considered, the significance of groundwater is more apparent.

Table 16.1 contains estimates of the distribution of fresh water in the hydrosphere. Clearly the largest volume occurs as glacial ice. Second in rank is groundwater, with slightly more than 14 percent of the total. However, when ice is excluded and just liquid water is considered, about 94 percent of all fresh water is groundwater. Without question, *groundwater represents the largest reservoir of fresh water that is readily available to humans.* Its value in terms of economics and human well-being is incalculable.

The dissolving action of groundwater slowly removes soluble rock, such as limestone, allowing surface depressions known as *sinkholes* to form and creating subterranean caverns (Figure 16.1). Groundwater also moderates stream flow: A large percentage of precipitation soaks in and then moves slowly underground to feed stream channels. Groundwater is thus a form of storage that sustains streams during times when rain does not fall. Thus, when we see water flowing in a river during a dry period, it represents rain that fell at some earlier time and was stored underground.

DISTRIBUTION OF UNDERGROUND WATER

When rain falls, some of the water runs off, some evaporates, and the remainder infiltrates the ground. This last path is the primary source of practically all water underground. The amount of water that takes each of these paths, however, varies greatly in both time and space. Influential factors include steepness of slope, nature of surface material, intensity of rainfall, and type and amount

TABLE 16.1   Fresh Water of the Hydrosphere

Parts of the Hydrosphere	Volume of Fresh Water (km³)	Share of Total Volume of Fresh Water (%)	Average Duration of Water Exchange
Ice sheets and glaciers	24 000 000	84.945	8000 years
Groundwater	4 000 000	14.158	280 years
Lakes and reservoirs	155 000	0.549	7 years
Soil moisture	83 000	0.294	1 year
Water vapour in the atmosphere	14 000	0.049	9.9 days
River water	1200	0.005	11.3 days
Total	28 253 200	100.000	

Source: U.S. Geological Survey Water Supply Paper 2220, 1987.

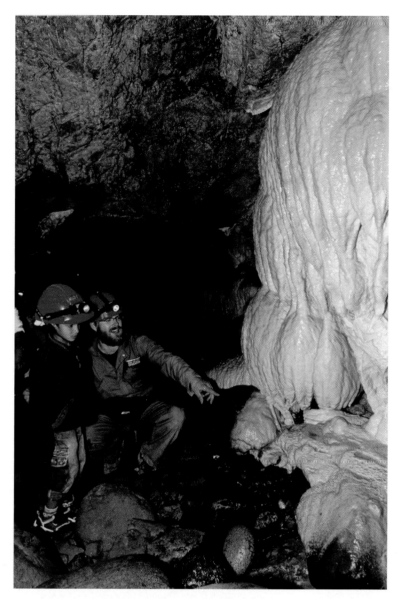

Figure 16.1 A view of the interior of the Lower Cave in Horne Lake Provincial Park, British Columbia. The dissolving action of groundwater created the caverns. Later, groundwater deposited the limestone decorations. (Photo by Chris Cheadle)

criss-crossed by roots, voids left by decayed roots, and animal and worm burrows that all enhance the infiltration of rainwater into the soil. Soil water is used in life functions and transpiration by plants. Some water also evaporates directly back into the atmosphere.

Water that is not held as soil moisture percolates downward until it reaches a zone where all of the open spaces in sediment and rock are completely filled with water (Figure 16.2). This is the **zone of saturation** or phreatic zone. Water within this zone is called **groundwater.**

The upper limit of this zone is known as the **water table.** Extending upward from the water table is the **capillary fringe** (*capillus* = hair). Here groundwater is held by surface tension in tiny passages between grains of soil or sediment. The area above the water table that includes the capillary fringe and the belt of soil moisture is called the **zone of aeration** or vadose zone. Although a considerable amount of water can be present in the zone of aeration, this water cannot be pumped by wells because it clings too tightly to rock and soil particles. By contrast, below the water table, the water pressure is great enough to allow water to enter wells, thus permitting groundwater to be withdrawn for use.

THE WATER TABLE

The water table level is important in predicting the productivity of wells, explaining the changes in the flow of springs and streams, and accounting for fluctuations in the levels of lakes.

The depth of the water table can range from zero at the surface to hundreds of metres in some places. The water table's configuration varies seasonally and yearly because the addition of water to the groundwater system is closely related to the quantity, distribution, and timing of precipitation. Its elevation can be mapped and studied in detail where wells are numerous because the water level in wells coincides with the water

of vegetation. Heavy rains falling on steep slopes underlain by impervious materials will obviously result in a high percentage of the water running off. Conversely, if rain falls steadily and gently on more gradual slopes composed of materials that are easily penetrated by the water, a much larger percentage of water soaks into the ground.

Some of the water that soaks in does not travel far because it is held by molecular attraction as a surface film on soil particles. This near-surface zone is called the **belt of soil moisture.** It is

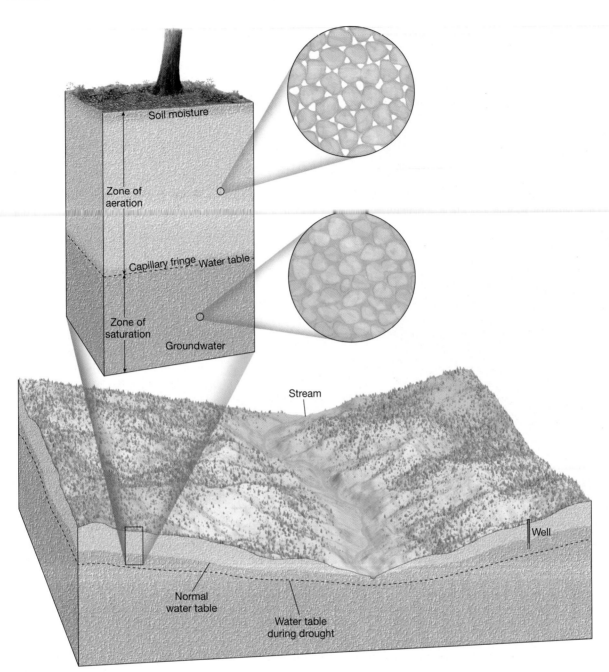

Figure 16.2 Distribution of underground water. The shape of the water table is usually a subdued replica of the surface topography. During periods of drought, the water table falls, reducing stream flow and drying up some wells.

table (Figure 16.3). Such maps reveal that its shape is usually a subdued replica of the surface topography, reaching its highest elevations beneath hills and then descending toward valleys (Figure 16.2). Wetlands (swamps) occur where the water table is right at the surface. Lakes and streams generally occupy areas low enough that the water table is above the land surface.

Groundwater moves very slowly and at varying rates under different conditions. Because of this, water tends to "pile up" beneath high areas between stream valleys, resulting in an uneven water table surface. If rainfall were to cease completely, these water-table hills would slowly subside and gradually approach the level of the valleys. However, new supplies of rainwater are usually added frequently enough to prevent this. Nevertheless, in times of extended drought, the water table may drop enough to dry up shallow wells (Figure 16.2). Other causes for the uneven water table are variations in rainfall and permeability from place to place.

EXPLANATION

- Location of well and elevation of water table above sea level, in metres
- *120* Water table contour shows elevation of water table, contour interval 10 metres
- ◄─ ─ ─ ─ Groundwater flow line

Figure 16.3 Preparing a map of the water table. The water level in wells coincides with the water table. **A.** First, the locations of wells and the elevation of the water table above sea level are plotted on a map. **B.** These data points are used to guide the drawing of water-table contour lines at regular intervals. On this sample map the interval is 10 metres. Groundwater flow lines can be added to show water movement in the upper portion of the zone of saturation. Groundwater tends to move approximately perpendicular to the contours and down the slope of the water table.

FACTORS INFLUENCING THE STORAGE AND MOVEMENT OF GROUNDWATER

The nature of subsurface materials strongly influences the rate of groundwater movement and the amount of groundwater that can be stored. Two factors are especially important: porosity and permeability.

Porosity

Water soaks into the ground because bedrock, sediment, and soil contain countless voids or openings called pore spaces. The quantity of groundwater that can be stored depends on the **porosity** of the material: the percentage of the total volume of rock or sediment that consists of pore spaces. Voids most often are spaces between sedimentary particles, but also common are joints; faults; cavities formed by the dissolving of soluble rock, such as limestone; and vesicles (voids left by gases escaping from lava).

Sediment is commonly porous, and open spaces may occupy 10 percent to 50 percent of the sediment's total volume. Pore space depends on the size and shape of the grains, how they are packed together, the degree of sorting, and, in sedimentary rocks, the amount of cementing material. For example, clay may have a porosity as high as 50 percent, whereas some gravels may have only 20 percent voids.

Where sediments of various sizes are mixed, the porosity is reduced because the finer particles tend to fill the openings among the larger grains. Most igneous and metamorphic rocks, as well as some sedimentary rocks, are composed of tightly interlocking crystals, so the voids between the grains may be negligible. In these rocks, fractures must provide the voids.

Permeability, Aquitards, and Aquifers

Rock or sediment may be very porous yet still not allow water to move through it. The pores must be *connected* to allow water flow, and they must be *large enough* to allow flow. Thus, the **permeability** (*permeare* = to penetrate) of a material is its ability to *transmit* a fluid.

Groundwater moves by twisting and turning through small, interconnected openings. The smaller the pore spaces, the slower the water moves. This idea is clearly illustrated by examining the information about the water-yielding potential of different materials in Table 16.2. Here groundwater

TABLE 16.2 Selected Values of Porosity, Specific Yield, and Specific Retention*

Material	Porosity	Specific Yield	Specific Retention
Clay	50	2	48
Sand	25	22	3
Gravel	20	19	1
Limestone	20	18	2
Sandstone (semiconsolidated)	11	6	5
Granite	0.1	0.09	0.01
Basalt (fresh)	11	8	3

*Values in percentage by volume
Source: U.S. Geological Survey Water Supply Paper 2220, 1987.

is divided into two categories: (1) the portion that will drain under the influence of gravity (called *specific yield*) and (2) the part that is retained as a film on particle and rock surfaces and in tiny openings (called *specific retention*). Specific yield indicates how much water is actually available for use, whereas specific retention indicates how much water remains bound in the material. For example, clay's ability to store water is great, owing to its high porosity, but its pore spaces are so small that water is unable to move through it. Thus, clay's porosity is high but because its permeability is poor, clay has a very low specific yield.

Impermeable layers that hinder or prevent water movement are termed **aquitards** (*aqua* = water, *tard* = slow). Clay is a good example. Conversely, larger particles, such as sand or gravel, have larger pore spaces. Therefore, the water moves with relative ease. Permeable rock strata or sediment that transmit groundwater freely are called **aquifers** (*aqua* = water, *fer* = carry). Sands and gravels are common examples.

In summary, you have seen that porosity is not always a reliable guide to the amount of groundwater that can be produced, and permeability is significant in determining the rate of groundwater movement and the quantity of water that can be pumped from a well.

HOW GROUNDWATER MOVES

The movement of most groundwater from pore to pore is exceedingly slow—typically a few centimetres each day under the pull of gravity. Water moves from areas where the water table is high to zones where the water table is lower. This means that water gravitates toward a stream channel, lake, or spring. Although some water takes the most direct path down the slope of the water table, much of the water follows long, curving paths toward the zone of discharge.

Figure 16.4 shows how water percolates into a stream from all possible directions. Some paths actually turn upward, apparently against the force of gravity, and enter through the bottom of the channel. This is easily explained: The deeper you go into the zone of saturation, the greater is the water pressure. Thus, the looping curves water follows in the saturated zone can be thought of as a compromise between the downward pull of gravity and the tendency of water to move toward areas of reduced pressure. As a result, water at any given height is under greater pressure beneath a hill than beneath a stream channel, and the water tends to migrate toward points of lower pressure.

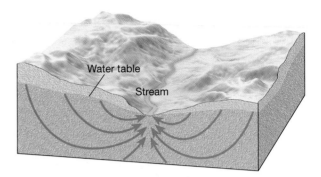

Figure 16.4 Arrows indicate groundwater movement through uniformly permeable material. The looping curves can be thought of as a compromise between the downward pull of gravity and the tendency of water to move toward areas of reduced pressure.

The foundations of our modern understanding of groundwater movement began in the mid-nineteenth century with the work of French engineer Henri Darcy. During this time, Darcy made measurements and conducted experiments in an attempt to determine whether the water needs of the city of Dijon in east-central France could be met by tapping local supplies of groundwater. He showed that the velocity of groundwater flow is proportional to the slope of the water table—the steeper the slope, the faster the water moves (because the steeper the slope, the greater the pressure difference between two points). The water-table slope, known as the **hydraulic gradient**, is determined by dividing the vertical difference between the recharge and discharge points (a quantity known as the **head**) by the length of flow between these points (Figure 16.5).

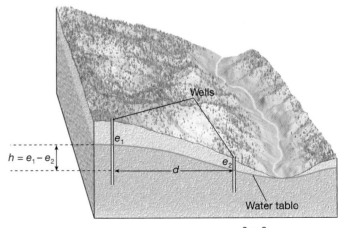

Hydraulic gradient $= \dfrac{e_1 - e_2}{d}$

Figure 16.5 The hydraulic gradient is determined by measuring the difference in elevation between two points on the water table ($e_1 - e_2$) divided by the distance between them, d. Wells are used to determine the elevation of the water table.

Darcy also experimented with different materials, such as coarse sand and fine sand, by measuring the rate of flow through sediment-filled tubes that were tilted at varying angles. He found that the flow velocity varied with the permeability of the sediment—groundwater flows more rapidly through sediments having greater permeability than through materials having lower permeability. This factor is known as **hydraulic conductivity** and is a coefficient that takes into account the permeability of the aquifer and the viscosity of the fluid. **Darcy's law**, named in his honour, can be expressed by the following formula:

$$V = \frac{K}{n} \cdot \frac{h}{l}$$

where V represents groundwater velocity, n the porosity, h the head ($e_1 - e_2$), l the length of flow, and K a coefficient that accounts for a material's permeability.

SPRINGS

Whenever the water table intersects Earth's surface, a natural outflow of groundwater results, which we call a **spring** (Figure 16.6). Springs typically form when an aquitard blocks the downward movement of groundwater and forces it to move laterally. Where the permeable bed crops out, a spring results. Another situation leading to the formation of a spring is illustrated in Figure 16.7. Here, an aquitard is situated above the main water table. As water percolates downward, a portion of it is intercepted by the aquitard, thereby creating a localized zone of saturation and a **perched water table**.

Springs are not confined to places where a perched water table creates a flow at the surface. Even in areas underlain by impermeable crystalline

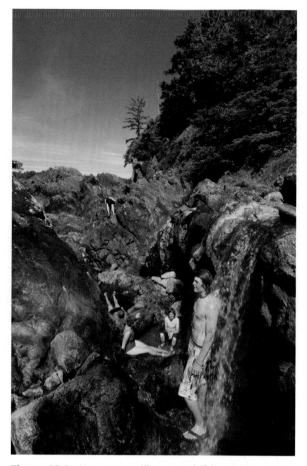

Figure 16.6 Hot water spills over a cliff from springs into pools below at Hot Springs Cove, Vancouver Island. (Photo © Chris Cheadle/Alamy)

rocks, permeable zones may exist in the form of fractures or solution channels. If these openings fill with water and intersect the ground surface along a slope, a spring will result.

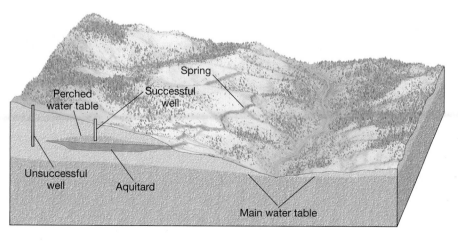

Figure 16.7 When an aquitard is situated above the main water table, a localized zone of saturation may result. Where the perched water table intersects the side of the valley, a spring flows. The perched water table also caused the well on the right to be successful, whereas the well on the left will be unsuccessful unless it is drilled to a greater depth.

Figure 16.8 The hot springs in Banff, Alberta, attract tourists from all over the world. The water feeding these springs enters faults in the Alberta Rockies, where it is gently heated because of the high geothermal gradient in this region. The heated water emerges in springs located at the base of the mountains. (Photo by Kristin Singh)

HOT SPRINGS AND GEYSERS

By definition, the water in **hot springs** is 6°C to 9°C warmer than the mean annual air temperature for the localities in which they occur. Temperatures in deep mines and oil wells usually rise with increasing depth, an average of about 2°C per 100 metres. Therefore, when groundwater circulates at great depths, it becomes heated. If it rises to the surface, the water may emerge as a hot spring. The water of some hot springs in the eastern United States is heated in this manner. However, the great majority (over 95 percent) of the hot springs (and geysers) in North America, including those in Banff, Alberta (Figure 16.8), and in Harrison, Lakelse, Liard, Radium, Fairmont, Hot Springs Cove (Figure 16.6), Hotspring Island (Figure 10.1), and Lussier (chapter-opening photo), British Columbia, are found in the west, where cooling igneous rocks occur.

Geysers are intermittent hot springs or fountains in which columns of water are ejected with great force at various intervals, often rising 30 to 60 metres into the air. After the jet of water ceases, a column of steam rushes out, usually with a thunderous roar. Perhaps the most famous geyser in the world is Old Faithful in Yellowstone National Park, Wyoming, which erupts about once each hour (Figure 16.9). Geysers are also found in other parts of the world, notably New Zealand and Iceland. In fact, the Icelandic word *geysa*, "to gush," gives us the name *geyser*.

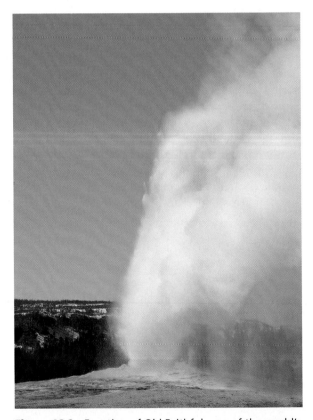

Figure 16.9 Eruption of Old Faithful, one of the world's most famous geysers. It emits as much as 45,000 litres of hot water and steam about once each hour. (Photo by Chris H. Galbraith/Shutterstock)

Geysers occur where extensive underground chambers exist within hot igneous rocks (Figure 16.10). As relatively cool groundwater enters the chambers, it is heated by the surrounding rock. At the bottom of the chambers, the water is under great pressure because of the weight of the overlying water. This great pressure prevents the water from boiling at the normal surface temperature of 100°C. For example, water at the bottom of a 300-metre water-filled chamber must attain nearly 230°C before it will boil. The heating causes the water to expand, with the result that some is forced out at the surface. This loss of water reduces the pressure on the remaining water in the chamber, which lowers the boiling point. A portion of the water deep within the chamber quickly turns to steam, and the geyser erupts (Figure 16.10). Following eruption, cool groundwater again seeps into the chamber and the cycle begins anew.

When groundwater from hot springs and geysers flows out at the surface, the material in solution is often precipitated, producing an accumulation of chemical sedimentary rock. When the erupting water contains dissolved silica, a material called *siliceous sinter* or *geyserite* is deposited around the spring.

When the water contains dissolved calcium carbonate, a form of limestone called *travertine* or *calcareous tufa* is deposited. The latter term is used if the material is spongy and porous, like the deposits at Coal River Springs, Yukon.

The deposits at Rabbitkettle Hotsprings in Nahanni National Park (Northwest Territories) are better developed than most (Figure 16.11). As the hot water flows upward through a series of channels and then out at the surface, the reduced pressure allows carbon dioxide to separate and escape from the water, which becomes supersaturated with calcium carbonate, which then precipitates. Some hot springs contain sulphur, which gives water a poor taste and unpleasant odour.

WELLS

The most common method for removing groundwater is the **well**, a hole bored into the zone of saturation. Wells serve as small reservoirs into which groundwater migrates and from which it can be pumped to the surface. By far the single greatest use of this water in North America is irrigation for agriculture. Industrial uses rank a distant second, followed by the amount used in city water systems and rural homes.

The water-table level may drop during dry seasons and rise following intervals of rain. Therefore, a well must penetrate below the water table to ensure

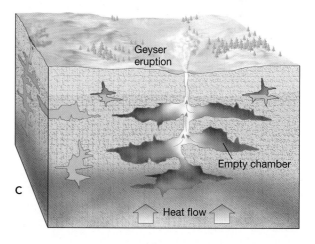

Figure 16.10 Idealized diagrams of a geyser. A geyser can form if the heat is not distributed by convection. **A.** In this figure, the water near the bottom is heated to near its boiling point. The boiling point is higher there than at the surface because the weight of the water above increases the pressure. **B.** The water higher in the geyser system is also heated; therefore, it expands and flows out at the top, reducing the pressure on the water at the bottom. **C.** At the reduced pressure on the bottom, boiling occurs. Some of the bottom water flashes into steam, and the expanding steam causes an eruption.

a continuous supply of water. Whenever water is withdrawn from a well, the water table around the well is lowered. This effect, termed **drawdown**, decreases with increasing distance from the well. The result is a depression in the water table, roughly conical in shape, known as a **cone of depression** (Figure 16.12). Because the cone of depression increases the hydraulic gradient near the well, groundwater will flow more rapidly toward the opening. For smaller domestic wells, the cone of depression is negligible. However, when wells are heavily pumped for irrigation or for industrial purposes, the withdrawal of water can be great enough to create a very wide and steep cone of depression. This may substantially lower the water table in an area and cause nearby shallow wells to become dry (Figure 16.12).

Digging a successful well is a familiar problem for people in areas where groundwater is the primary source of supply. One well may be successful at a depth of 10 metres whereas a neighbour may have to go twice as deep to find an adequate supply. When subsurface materials are heterogeneous, the amount of water a well is capable of providing may vary over short distances. For example, when two nearby wells are drilled to the same level and only one is successful, it may be caused by the presence of a perched water table beneath one of them (Figure 16.7). Massive igneous and metamorphic rocks provide a second example. These crystalline rocks are usually not very permeable except where they are cut by many intersecting joints and fractures. Therefore, when a well drilled into such rock does not intersect an adequate network of fractures, it is likely to be unproductive.

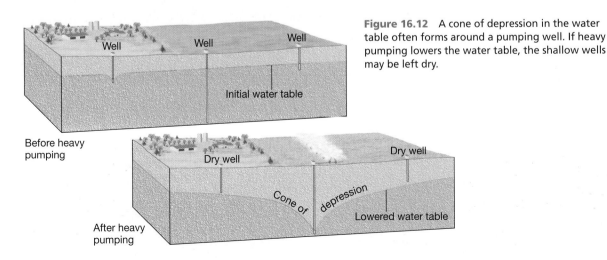

Figure 16.12   A cone of depression in the water table often forms around a pumping well. If heavy pumping lowers the water table, the shallow wells may be left dry.

ARTESIAN WELLS

In most wells, water cannot rise on its own. If water is first encountered at 30 metres depth, it remains at that level, fluctuating perhaps a metre or two with seasonal wet and dry periods. However, in some wells, water rises, sometimes overflowing at the surface. Such wells are abundant in the Artois region of northern France, and so we call these self-rising wells artesian.

To many people the term *artesian* is applied to any well drilled to great depths, which is incorrect. Others believe that an **artesian well** must flow freely at the surface (Figure 16.13), however term *artesian* applies to *any* situation in which groundwater under pressure rises above the level of the aquifer.

In an artesian system (Figure 16.14), (1) water must be confined to an aquifer that is inclined so that one end can receive water; and (2) aquitards, both above and below the aquifer (making it a *confined aquifer*) prevent the water from escaping. When such an aquifer is tapped, the pressure created by the weight of the water above will force the water to rise. If there were no friction, the water in the well would rise to the level of the water at the top of the aquifer.

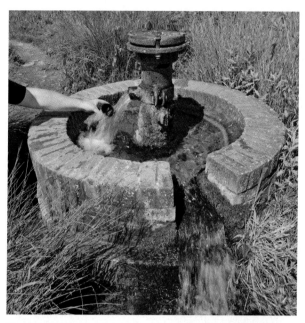

Figure 16.13   Sometimes water flows freely at the surface when an artesian well is developed. However, for most artesian wells, the water must be pumped to the surface. (Photo © Tony Watson/Alamy)

Figure 16.14   Artesian systems occur when an inclined aquifer is surrounded by impermeable beds.

Figure 16.15 A gusher-like flowing artesian well drilled into the Mirabel aquifer north of Montreal. (Reproduced with the permission of Natural Resources Canada 2014, courtesy of the Geological Survey of Canada)

However, friction reduces the height of the pressure surface. The greater the distance from the recharge area (where water enters the inclined aquifer), the greater the friction and the less the rise of water.

In Figure 16.14, well 1 is a **non-flowing artesian well**, because at this location the pressure surface is below ground level. When the pressure surface is above the ground and a well is drilled into the aquifer, a **flowing artesian well** is created (well 2, Figure 16.14, and Figure 16.15). *Artesian springs*

also exist in which groundwater reaches the surface by rising through a natural fracture rather than through an artificially produced hole. In deserts, artesian springs can create an oasis.

Artesian systems act as conduits, often transmitting water great distances from remote areas of recharge to points of discharge. In western South Dakota, the edges of sedimentary layers have been bent up to the surface along the flanks of the Black Hills, where permeable Dakota Sandstone is sandwiched between impermeable strata and gradually dips into the ground toward the east. When the aquifer was first tapped, water gushed many metres above the ground surface. Now thousands of additional wells tap the same aquifer, depleting the reservoir and lowering the water table. As a consequence, the pressure dropped to the point where many wells stopped flowing and had to be pumped.

On a different scale, city water systems can be considered examples of artificial artesian systems (Figure 16.16). The water tower, into which water is pumped, would represent the area of recharge, the pipes are the confined aquifer, and the faucets in homes are the flowing artesian wells.

ENVIRONMENTAL PROBLEMS
Mining Groundwater

The water table's height reflects a balance between the rate of infiltration and the rate of discharge and withdrawal. Any imbalance will either raise or lower the water table. Long-term imbalances can lead to a significant drop in the water table if either a decrease in recharge because of prolonged drought or an increase in groundwater discharge or withdrawal occurs. In some regions, groundwater is considered a *non-renewable* resource because the water available to recharge the aquifer is less than the amount being withdrawn.

The High Plains of the United States provide one example, where the agricultural economy is

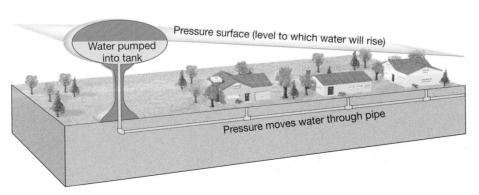

Figure 16.16 City water systems can be considered to be artificial artesian systems.

Figure 16.17 In some agricultural regions, water is pumped from the ground faster than it is replenished. In such instances, groundwater is being treated as a non-renewable resource. (Photo © Reed Kaestner/Corbis)

dependent on irrigation (Figure 16.17). Where intense irrigation has occurred over a long time, groundwater has been severely depleted and is literally being mined. Even if pumping were to cease immediately, it could take hundreds or thousands of years for the groundwater to be fully replenished. Fortunately, Canadian aquifers have not yet suffered these problems. To ensure this continues, the ambitious Okanagan Water Supply and Demand Project is modelling aquifers under the Okanagan Valley to guide future regulation of groundwater use by an increasing population.

Subsidence

The ground surface can sink when water is pumped from wells faster than natural recharge processes can replace it. This effect is pronounced in areas underlain by thick sediments. As the water is withdrawn, the water pressure drops and the weight of the overburden is transferred to the sediment. The greater pressure packs the sediment grains tightly together, and the ground subsides (e.g., Venice, Italy).

A classic example of subsidence due to overpumping occurred in the San Joaquin Valley of California, where the ground surface has subsided nine metres. Other cases include Las Vegas, Nevada; New Orleans and Baton Rouge, Louisiana; and the Houston-Galveston area of Texas. In the low-lying coastal area between Houston and Galveston, land subsidence ranges from 1.5 to 3 metres. The result is that about 78 square kilometres are permanently flooded.

One of the most spectacular examples of subsidence occurred in Mexico City, which is built on a former lakebed. In the first half of the twentieth century, thousands of wells were sunk into the water-saturated sediments beneath the city. As water was withdrawn, portions of the city subsided by as much as six to seven metres. In some places buildings have sunk so far that access to them from the street is located at what used to be the second-floor level!

Groundwater Contamination

The pollution of groundwater is a serious matter, particularly in areas where aquifers provide a large part of the water supply. One common source of groundwater pollution is sewage from septic tanks, inadequate or broken sewer systems, and farm wastes.

If sewage water that is contaminated with bacteria enters the groundwater system, it may become purified through natural processes. The harmful bacteria can be mechanically filtered by the sediment through which the water percolates, destroyed by chemical oxidation, or assimilated by other organisms. For purification to occur, however, the aquifer must be of the correct composition. For example, extremely permeable aquifers (such as highly fractured crystalline rock, coarse gravel, or cavernous limestone) have such large openings that contaminated groundwater can travel long distances without being cleansed. In this case, the water flows too rapidly and is not in contact with the surrounding material long enough for purification to occur. This is the problem at well 1 in Figure 16.18A. As learned by the people of Walkerton, Ontario, in 2000, such circumstances can lead to disaster (Box 16.1).

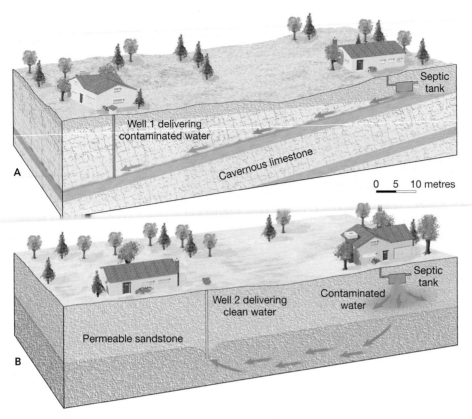

Figure 16.18 **A.** Although the contaminated water has travelled more than 100 metres before reaching well 1, the water moves too rapidly through the cavernous limestone to be purified. **B.** As the discharge from the septic tank percolates through the permeable sandstone, it is purified in a relatively short distance.

Well 1 delivering contaminated water

Septic tank

Cavernous limestone

A

0   5   10 metres

Well 2 delivering clean water

Contaminated water

Septic tank

Permeable sandstone

B

BOX 16.1

CANADIAN PROFILE

The Walkerton Tragedy: Geology Forms the Link

Robert A. Schincariol*

In May 2000 the people of Walkerton, Ontario, learned firsthand how their groundwater-derived water supply was directly linked to surface activities. Seven people died and 2300 fell ill when their water system became contaminated with deadly bacteria, primarily *Escherichia coli* (*E. coli* O157:H7). This virulent form of *E. coli* is known to originate in the digestive system of cattle. The causes of this outbreak were investigated by the Walkerton Inquiry and resulted in a major overhaul of Ontario's drinking water regulations.

Although the cause of contamination was manure spread on a farm near one of the town's wells (well 5; Figure 16.A), ultimately the mistakes of many people and agencies allowed the problems to go undetected. If they had been more aware of the

subsurface environment that provided the groundwater supply, the tragedy would not have happened. In fact, the inquiry report stated, "Both geology and hydrogeology are crucial factors in understanding why the contamination in May 2000 was able to enter well 5."[†]

The problem revolved around well 5, which obtained water from a very shallow and vulnerable bedrock aquifer that was shown to be susceptible to contamination by bacteria because it was under the *direct influence* of surface water. In a secure groundwater source (no direct influence), surface water will infiltrate through overburden materials (topsoil, clay, silt, sand) and through bedrock. This infiltration process is slow (months, years, or even decades) and bacteria and viruses are usually filtered out or die off. However, where these

overburden materials are thin or ineffective because of natural features (fractures, sand and gravel lenses) or human-induced features (fencepost holes, improperly abandoned or sealed wells) replenishment of the bedrock aquifer can be rapid. An interconnected network of fractures provides a ready pathway for groundwater flow. If the bedrock porosity of these fractured zones is very low, it can result in high groundwater velocities through fractures (see Darcy's law), allowing little time for filtration.

Well 5 was drilled in a weathered, fractured, and vertically jointed fine-grained dolostone. Overlying this shallow bedrock aquifer is as little as 2.4 metres of overburden deposits consisting of topsoil, till, sand, and gravel. Downhole testing at well 5 indicated that most pumped water was being derived from a zone between five and

Figure 16.A The Walkerton tragedy occurred due to the consumption of *E. coli*-contaminated water that was pumped from well 5 in a nearby farm. A combination of human negligence and geologic factors contributed to the tragedy. The *E. coli*, having been closely associated with manure, is believed to have been carried by water that rapidly infiltrated into the aquifer due to the highly permeable nature of both the sandy, glacial sediment (deposited during the last Ice Age) and the fractured bedrock underlying lot 20 near well 5 (inset). Lot 20 contains the livestock barn and yard on which approximately 70 tonnes of manure was spread.

(Cameron Tsujita/Pearson Education; inset photo by Marc Bolduc, RCMP)

seven metres below ground surface. The overburden and shallow bedrock aquifer are well interconnected, allowing rapid flow of groundwater and contaminants. In addition, a shallow water table existed at well 5 and heavy rainfall or ponded conditions resulted in the rapid downward migration of manure contaminants to the bedrock aquifer and into well 5.

Another avenue of surface water–groundwater connection was an unsealed test well, located only six metres from well 5, which provided a direct pathway for surface water or shallow groundwater to access the aquifer. This well likely provided a rapid route for groundwater flow, bypassing the natural aquifer materials that can filter out harmful microbes.

The incoming contamination overwhelmed the chlorine being added at the well and sufficient chlorine residuals were not maintained. This was aggravated by the fact that the operators of the Walkerton water system routinely used less chlorine than was required. Had continuous chlorine residual been maintained at well 5, the outbreak could have been prevented.

*Robert A. Schincariol is a professor in the Department of Earth Sciences at Western University. Used by permission.

†Walkerton Commission Report. Office of the Attorney General, Ontario, Canada. January 2002. © Queen's Printer for Ontario, 2002.

Conversely, when the aquifer is composed of sand or permeable sandstone, water can sometimes be purified after travelling only a few dozen metres through it. The openings between sand grains are large enough to permit water movement, yet the movement of the water is slow enough to allow ample time for its purification (well 2, Figure 16.18B).

Sometimes sinking a well can lead to groundwater pollution problems. If the well pumps a sufficient quantity of water, the cone of depression will locally increase the slope of the water table. In some instances the original slope can even be reversed. This could lead to the contamination of wells that yielded unpolluted water before heavy pumping

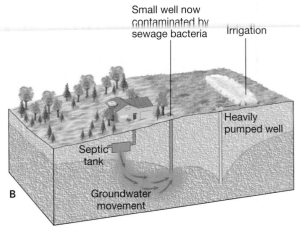

Figure 16.19 **A.** Originally the outflow from the septic tank moved away from the small well. **B.** The heavily pumped well changed the slope of the water table, causing contaminated groundwater to flow toward the small well.

began (Figure 16.19). Also recall that the rate of groundwater movement increases as the slope of the water table gets steeper. This could produce problems because a faster rate of movement allows less

time for the water to be purified in the aquifer before it is pumped to the surface.

Other sources and types of contamination also threaten groundwater supplies (Figure 16.20). These include widely used substances, such as highway salt, fertilizers that are spread across the land surface, and pesticides. In addition, a wide array of chemicals and industrial materials may leak from pipelines, storage tanks, landfills, and holding ponds. Some of these pollutants are classified as *hazardous*, meaning that they are flammable, corrosive, explosive, or toxic. In landfill disposal, potential contaminants are heaped onto mounds or spread directly over the ground. As rainwater oozes through the refuse, it may dissolve a variety of organic and inorganic materials. If the leached material reaches the water table, it will mix with the groundwater and contaminate the supply. Similar problems may result from leakage of shallow excavations, called holding ponds, into which a variety of liquid wastes are disposed.

Because groundwater movement is usually slow, polluted water can go undetected for a long time. In fact, contamination is commonly discovered only after drinking water has been affected and people become ill. By this time, the volume of polluted water may be very large, and even if the source of contamination is removed immediately, the problem is not solved.

Once the source of the problem has been identified and eliminated, the most common practice is simply to abandon the water supply and allow the pollutants to be flushed away gradually. This is the least costly and easiest solution, but the aquifer must remain unused for many years. To accelerate this process, polluted water is sometimes pumped out and treated. Following removal of the tainted water, the aquifer is allowed to recharge naturally, or in

Figure 16.20 Sometimes agricultural chemicals **(A)** and materials leached from landfills **(B)** find their way into groundwater. These are two of the potential sources of groundwater contamination.

some cases the treated water or other fresh water is pumped back in. This process is costly and time-consuming, and it may be risky because we have no way to be certain that all of the contamination has been removed. Clearly, the most effective solution to groundwater contamination is prevention.

THE GEOLOGIC WORK OF GROUNDWATER

Groundwater (weak carbonic acid; Chapter 5) dissolves soluble rocks, especially limestone that underlies millions of square kilometres of Earth's surface. It is here that groundwater carries on its important role as an erosional agent. Groundwater reacts with the calcite in the rocks to form calcium bicarbonate, a soluble material that is then carried away in solution.

Caverns

The most spectacular results of groundwater's erosional handiwork are limestone **caverns** (caves). In Canada and the United States, more than 18 300 caves have been discovered and new ones are found every year. Although most are relatively small, some have spectacular dimensions. Mammoth Cave in Kentucky and Carlsbad Caverns in New Mexico are famous examples. Mammoth is the world's largest cave system with 540 kilometres of passages, and Carlsbad's Big Room is large enough to accommodate Ottawa's Parliament buildings. Canada's largest cave system is Castleguard (> 20 kilometres) in the Alberta Rockies, while British Columbia's Arch network exceeds 10 kilometres. Quebec's Three Island cave is over 6 kilometres, and Nova Scotia's Hayes Cave extends about 400 metres through rock gypsum. Contrary to the fantastic fictional journey depicted by Jules Verne (featured in a Hollywood movie—see Box 16.2), caves do have a depth limit. Voronya Cave, the world's deepest known cave, located near the coast of the Black Sea, extends more than 2 kilometres below Earth's surface.

Most caverns are created at or just below the water table in the zone of saturation. Here acidic

---

GEOLOGY AND POPULAR MEDIA

Journey to the Centre of the Earth: When Jules Verne Met Geology

French author Jules Verne (1828–1905) was one of the true pioneers of science fiction, having written some of the earliest and greatest classics of the genre, including *Twenty Thousand Leagues Under the Sea, Around the World in Eighty Days, The Mysterious Island,* and, of course, *A Journey to the Centre of the Earth.* Verne was one of the few science fiction writers who successfully extrapolated the possibilities of the scientific progress made in his time, arguably having predicted forms of technology prior to their invention, including helicopters, automobiles, bullet trains, calculators, air conditioning, electricity, television—even a global communications network akin to the internet!

In the original version of Jules Verne's novel *A Journey to the Centre of the Earth* (published in 1864 as *Voyage au centre de la Terre*), Otto

Figure 16.B Nowhere near the centre of the earth (in fact, only about 240 metres deep), but bearing an uncanny resemblance to Jules Verne's deep subterranean world (as depicted in the 2008 movie version of *Journey to the Center of the Earth*), is the beautiful Reed Flute Cave. The cave is located in Guangxi Province, China, a region famous for its karst features. (Photo by gringos/Can Stock Photo Inc.)

Lidenbrock, an eccentric German professor, decodes the writings of a medieval alchemist that tell of a passageway to Earth's interior. Along with his nephew Axel and an Icelandic mountain guide, Lidenbrock hikes to a volcanic crater through which the men enter a volcanic tube leading to the centre of the planet. The story follows the men over several months in a hazardous descent that ultimately leads them to an ocean within a vast cavern illuminated by charged gas. As they explore further, they encounter a variety of life forms that have long been extinct at the surface. Toward the end of the story, the men are propelled back to the surface by a geyser, emerging from an active volcano in southern Italy.

The 2008 Hollywood film *Journey to the Center of the Earth* is but one of many adaptations of Jules Verne's famous novel to have appeared in television and cinema. And while extreme makeovers have been applied to both the characters and the plot for the sake of updating the story, the movie retains the basic elements of Verne's original vision—the trio of explorers (professor, nephew, and guide), the volcanic tubes, the subterranean ocean, encounters with prehistoric life, and the use of a geyser to return to the surface.

Jules Verne undoubtedly embellished elements of truth for the sake of entertaining his readers. For example, he would have certainly been aware of the impossibility of surviving the scalding temperatures of a geyser. However, it is intriguing to note that the concept of a hollow Earth, proposed by none other than Sir Edmund Halley in 1692, was actually taken seriously by a number of scientists in Verne's time; the true nature of Earth's inner structure was not to be revealed until the next century.

Today, we know very well that Earth's interior is not hollow, but that even with the necessary technology, anyone insane enough to attempt a Vernian voyage would be crushed and incinerated long before getting anywhere near the centre of the Earth. Moreover, contrary to what is depicted in the 2008 adaptation of the story, gem-grade diamonds do not typically occur in the same rocks as true rubies or emeralds, nor are they associated with the basaltic volcanoes of Iceland. We will assume that the movie's depiction of flawless, ice cube–sized diamonds decorating the "volcanic tubes" was intended to remind the viewer that none of the geologic content depicted in the movie is to be taken seriously.

An important conceptual component of Verne's original novel (but that was unfortunately lost in the movie version) is that of *fossil succession—* the definite and determinable order in which fossils succeed one another in time (see Chapter 8). This is represented metaphorically in a sequence of encounters with various prehistoric forms of life, beginning with land plants of the Paleozoic, followed by marine reptiles from the Mesozoic, and finally Cenozoic mastodons and primitive humans. The concept also appears in a dream sequence, in which Axel visualizes a journey back in time (see Chapter 8) that includes the glimpses of progressively older forms of life.

Jules Verne's *A Journey to the Centre of the Earth* not only serves as an intriguing snapshot of science as it existed in the mid-nineteenth century but, as exemplified by the success of the 2008 film adaptation of the novel, continues to influence popular culture to this day. Indeed, if you have either read the classic novel or seen the movie, it is difficult to enter an underground chamber such as Reed Flute Cave in China (Figure 16.B) without thinking of Jules Verne's epic tale.

As in the case of any other action film, one can expect a large number of scientific inaccuracies and must be prepared to simply suspend disbelief and enjoy the ride. That said, however, the film does hit one truth right on the head, courtesy of Brendan Fraser's portrayal of Professor Trevor Anderson, Hollywood's nutty answer to Verne's eccentric (and rather creepy) Professor Otto Lidenbrock—given the opportunity, a geologist will always be compelled to stop and identify a rock, regardless of how ridiculous the situation may appear to others.

---

groundwater follows joints and bedding planes. Dissolution slowly creates cavities and gradually enlarges them into caverns. Material that is dissolved by the groundwater is eventually discharged into streams and carried to the ocean.

In many caves, development has occurred at several levels, with modern cavern-forming activity occurring at the lowest elevation. As streams cut their valleys deeper, the water table drops as the elevation of the river drops. Consequently, when surface streams cut rapidly downward, surrounding groundwater levels drop rapidly and cave passages are abandoned by water while the passages are still relatively small. When streams cut slowly, there is time for large cave passages to form.

Within caverns, eye-catching depositional features are created by the seemingly endless dripping of water over great spans of time. The calcium carbonate that is left behind produces the limestone we call travertine. The cave deposits are also commonly called *dripstone*. Carbonate and salt minerals can also precipitate from water that forms pools on the cavern floor. Although the formation of caverns takes place in the zone of saturation, the deposition of calcium carbonate is not possible until the caverns are above the water table in the zone of aeration. As soon as the chamber is filled with air, the

Figure 16.21 Speleothems are of many types including these vertical strands of calcite formed from the cave's ceiling to its floor by dripping water. Horne Lake Caves, Vancouver Island, British Columbia. (Photo © Chris Cheadle/Alamy)

stage is set for the decoration phase of cavern building to begin.

The various cavern features produced by mineral precipitation are collectively called **speleothems** (*spelaion* = cave, *them* = put) (Figure 16.21). Perhaps the most familiar are **stalactites** (*stalaktos* = trickling). These icicle-like pendants hang from the ceiling of the cavern and form where water seeps through cracks above. When the water reaches air in the cave, some of the dissolved carbon dioxide escapes from the drop, and calcite precipitates. Deposition occurs as a ring around the edge of the water drop. As drop after drop follows, each leaves a trace of calcite behind, and a hollow limestone tube is created. Water then moves through the tube, remains suspended momentarily at the end, contributes a tiny ring of calcite, and falls to the cavern floor. The stalactite just described is appropriately called a *soda straw* (Figure 16.22). Often the hollow tube of the soda

Figure 16.22 Soda straw stalactites in Rat's Nest Cave, Alberta. (Photo courtesy of Mary Thomson)

straw becomes plugged or its supply of water increases. In either case, the water is forced to flow and hence deposit along the outside of the tube. As deposition continues, the stalactite takes on the more common conical shape.

Speleothems that form upward from the floor of a cavern are called **stalagmites** (*stalagmos* = dropping). The water supplying the calcite for stalagmite growth falls from the ceiling and splatters over the surface. As a result, stalagmites do not have a central tube and are usually more massive in appearance and rounded on their upper ends than stalactites. Given enough time, a downward-growing stalactite and an upward-growing stalagmite can join to form a *column*.

Karst Topography

Many areas of the world have landscapes that, to a large extent, have been shaped by the dissolving power of groundwater. Such areas are said to exhibit **karst topography**, named for the Kras Plateau in Slovenia where it is well developed. In North America karst landscapes occur in many areas that are underlain by limestone, including portions of the Atlantic provinces in Canada and Kentucky, Tennessee, Alabama, southern Indiana, and central and northern Florida in the United States. Generally, arid and semi-arid areas are too dry to develop karst topography. When solution features exist in such

regions, they are likely to be remnants of a time when rainier conditions prevailed.

Karst areas typically have irregular terrain punctuated with many depressions, called **sinkholes** or **sinks**. The limestone areas of Florida, Kentucky, and southern Indiana have tens of thousands of these depressions, varying in depth from just a metre or two to more than 50 metres (Figure 16.23A).

Some develop gradually over many years without any physical disturbance to the rock. The limestone immediately below the soil is dissolved by downward-seeping rainwater that is freshly charged with carbon dioxide. Over time the bedrock surface is lowered and the fractures into which the water seeps are enlarged. As the fractures grow, soil subsides into the widening voids, from which it is removed by groundwater flowing in the passages below. These depressions are usually shallow and have gentle slopes.

Sinkholes can also form abruptly and without warning when the roof of a cavern collapses under its own weight, resulting in steep-sided and deep depressions. In Canada, sinkholes are common in some parts of the Atlantic provinces that are underlain by easily dissolved evaporite and carbonate bedrock (Figure 16.23B).

Karst regions characteristically show a striking lack of surface streams. Following a rainfall, the runoff is quickly funnelled below ground through sinks then flows through caverns until it finally reaches

A

B

Figure 16.23 **A.** This high-altitude infrared image shows an area of karst topography in central Florida. The numerous lakes occupy sinkholes. **B.** The Angus Tower sinkhole in Wood Buffalo National Park, Northwest Territories. This sinkhole resulted from the collapse of a cave in limestone. (Photo **A** courtesy of U.S. Department of Agriculture; photo **B** © Cliff LeSergent/Alamy)

Figure 16.24 Development of a karst landscape. **A.** During early stages, groundwater percolates through limestone along joints and bedding planes. Solution activity creates and enlarges caverns at and below the water table. **B.** In this view, sinkholes are well developed and surface streams are funnelled below ground. **C.** With the passage of time, caverns grow larger and the number and size of sinkholes increase. The collapse of caverns and the coalescence of sinkholes form larger, flat-floored depressions.

the water table. Where streams do exist at the surface, their paths are usually short. Some sinkholes become plugged with clay and debris, creating small lakes or ponds. The development of a karst landscape is depicted in Figure 16.24.

In wet, tropical, and subtropical areas of the world, limestone bedrock tends to dissolve more rapidly than in other climates due to abundant rainfall and greater availability of carbon dioxide from the decay of lush tropical vegetation. The extra carbon dioxide in

Figure 16.25 One of the best-known and most distinctive regions of tower karst development is in the Guilin District of southeast China. (Philippe Michel/AGE Fotostock)

the soil means higher carbonic acid content and therefore higher rates of limestone dissolution. Among the most spectacular examples of extreme karst development is the tower karst of the Guilin District (Guangxi Province) in southeast China. Here, the collapse of interconnected caves (e.g., Reed Flute Cave in Figure 16.B, Box 16.2) and coalescence of sinkholes have left remnants of the formerly intervening limestone pillars—the distinctive, isolated, steep-sided hills depicted in many Chinese paintings (Figure 16.25).

CHAPTER SUMMARY

- *Groundwater* is the largest reservoir of fresh water. It fills pore spaces in the *zone of saturation*, which is separated from the *zone of aeration* by the *water table*.
- *Aquitards* hinder groundwater flow, whereas *aquifers* transmit groundwater readily. Groundwater moves in looping curves toward lower pressure areas.
- *Springs* occur where the water table intersects the surface, whereas *wells* are drilled into the zone of saturation, creating *cones of depressions* during pumping. In *artesian wells* water rises under natural pressure.

- *Hot springs* involve water rising from great depths, whereas *geysers* are eruptions of steam above hot igneous rock.
- Groundwater problems include over-pumping, which induces land subsidence and contamination.
- Most caverns form by dissolving limestone and contain speleothems precipitated from dripping water.
- *Karst topography* is an irregular terrain resulting from the dissolution of bedrock (usually limestone or dolostone). Among the most common karst features are *sinkholes* that can form when the roofs of underground caverns collapse.

MasteringGeology
www.masteringgeology.com

Looking for additional review and test prep materials? Visit the Study Area in MasteringGeology to enhance your understanding of this chapter's content by accessing a variety of resources, including

Self-Study Quizzes, Geoscience Animations, GEODe Tutorials, RSS feeds, flashcards, weblinks, self-study quizzes, and an optional Pearson eText.

REVIEW QUESTIONS

1. Approximately what percentage of Earth's fresh water (excluding that contained in glacial ice) is groundwater?

2. Explain the difference between the zones of aeration and saturation. Where does the water table lie in relation to these two zones?

3. Explain how permeability is different from porosity.

4. What is the difference between an aquitard and an aquifer?

5. Explain how geologic factors are believed to have rendered groundwater in the Walkerton area of Ontario prone to bacterial contamination and how geological factors ultimately contributed to the health disaster in that community in 2000 (see Box 16.1).

6. Based on what you have read in Chapter 15 as well as this chapter, explain why the rate of natural groundwater recharge tends to decrease as urban areas develop.

7. What are some possible negative consequences of pumping large volumes of groundwater out of an aquifer for irrigation purposes?

8. Areas whose landscapes largely reflect the erosional work of groundwater are said to exhibit what kind of topography? Describe the types of rocks that are most commonly associated with this type of topography and why they are prone to the development of caverns and sinkholes.

9. Why might it be appropriate to think of groundwater as a non-renewable rather than a renewable natural resource?

17 GLACIER AND GLACIATION

Athabasca Glacier in Jasper National Park, Alberta, is one of eight major glaciers draining the Columbia Icefield, which straddles the continental divide and the Alberta–British Columbia border. The Athabasca is readily accessible from Icefields Parkway and is the most visited glacier in North America. Columbia Icefield is the largest remnant of the ancient Cordilleran Ice Sheet. (Photo by James Randklev/Getty Images)

Climate has a strong influence on the nature and intensity of Earth's external processes. This fact is dramatically illustrated in this chapter because the existence and extent of glaciers are largely controlled by Earth's changing climate, as are permafrost and the periglacial phenomena reviewed in Chapter 14.

Today glaciers only cover about 10 percent of Earth's land surface. However, several nineteenth-century glacial geologists deduced that, in the recent geologic past (Pleistocene Epoch; see Figure 8.12), ice sheets were three times as extensive, covering vast areas with ice thousands of metres thick. Many regions still bear the mark of these ancient glaciers (Figure 17.1). The basic character of such diverse places as the Rocky Mountains, the Canadian Shield, and Gros Morne National Park was fashioned by now-vanished masses of glacial ice. In fact, approximately 95 percent of Canada's land mass has been covered and shaped by ancient ice sheets, especially the Cordilleran and Laurentide ice sheets (see Figure 17.28). Moreover, the Great Lakes and the fjords of Norway and British Columbia all owe their existence to glaciers. Glaciers, of course, are not just phenomena of the geologic past. As you will see, they are still sculpting the landscape and depositing debris in many regions today, creating spectacular scenery. However, glaciers are not just about climate and scenery—their deposits can help geologists find valuable minerals (Box 17.1).

GLACIERS: A PART OF TWO BASIC CYCLES

Glaciers are a part of two fundamental cycles in the Earth system: the hydrologic cycle and the rock cycle. In Chapter 15 you learned that the water of the hydrosphere is constantly cycled through the atmosphere, biosphere, and geosphere. Time and time again, the same water evaporates from the oceans into the atmosphere, precipitates on the land, and flows underground and in rivers back to the sea. However, when precipitation falls at high elevations or high latitudes, the water may become part of a glacier that can store ice for many tens, hundreds, or even thousands of years. During that time the glacier can be a powerful erosional force. Like rivers and other erosional processes, moving ice modifies the landscape as it transports and deposits sediment.

Figure 17.1 Moraine Lake and majestic peaks in Banff National Park, Alberta.
(Photo by © SuperStock/Alamy)

Even though he was being attacked from every angle by a cloud of mosquitoes, Chuck Fipke scrambled over the tundra like a crab, searching. He paid no attention to the buzzing pests as he assumed his usual prospecting pose: hands, knees, and nose to the ground, rear end in the air. "I worked really hard, seven days a week from 8 a.m. to 3 a.m. We drilled and drilled all winter when it was dark and the wind chill was 80 below. Everyone thought I was crazy. It was just me and Stewart and a floatplane. We took all the supplies in and all the samples out ourselves."*

Thus went a decade of prospecting that led to the 1991 discovery of Canada's first diamond mine in the Northwest Territories, 310 kilometres northeast of Yellowknife. Geologist Charles Fipke (Figure 17.A) and his partner, geologist and pilot Stewart Blusson (both graduates of the University of British Columbia), sampled ancient glacial sediments for "indicator" minerals commonly associated with diamonds: chrome diopside (pyroxene), pyrope garnet, olivine, and ilmenite (Figure 17.B). When others were convinced they were wasting their time, Fipke and Blusson sampled along frozen rivers and lakes, sleeping in tents on the open tundra, subsisting on canned food, and trudging long distances across stark barren terrain.

The persistent pair surmised that the indicators had been eroded and then dragged far from diamond-bearing igneous rock (called kimberlite) by ancient glaciers. They needed to find the kimberlite source "pipe" (carrot-shaped pluton) by looking "up-ice" from where they found the indicators—not a simple task as the ice had travelled in several directions over time. After years of poring over glacial maps, tracing directions of ice flow, and sampling thousands of square kilometres of glacial sediments, the trail of indicators intensified and then abruptly ended at Point Lake near Lac De Gras. They also noticed that the indicators became more jagged, with sharper corners, closer to the lake. "We can tell when we're getting closer to the source. If the edges are sharp, we know they haven't travelled far from the pipe,"* recalled Fipke. Flying over the lake with a magnetometer, they found the rock under the lake to be magnetically anomalous. They also noticed the lake was round and deep, like the craters above kimberlite pipes in Africa. Drilling into the lake produced a sample of kimberlite containing 81 diamonds, which started the largest staking rush in Canadian history.

Today the kimberlite under Point Lake (drained in the 1990s) hosts part of the Ekati diamond mine (see also

Figure 17.A Geologist Chuck Fipke at his lab in Kelowna, British Columbia. (Photo by Andrew Hetherington)

Chapter 20). The Ekati property contains over 150 kimberlite pipes, at least 20 of which contain gem quality diamonds (Figure 17.C). Seven pits are in operation, two of which have been converted to underground mining. The Ekati operation is the world's third largest diamond mine and produces 4 million carats of rough diamonds each year, which represents 4 percent by weight (6 percent by value) of the world's diamond production. It also employs more than 600 people, about half of whom are from northern Aboriginal communities. Since Ekati, the Diavik and Snap Lake diamond mines have also come into production northeast of Yellowknife—together making

A   B   C   D

Figure 17.B Indicator minerals associated with diamonds in kimberlite: **A.** chrome diopside, **B.** pyrope garnet (purple), **C.** olivine, and **D.** ilmenite. (Photos reproduced with the permission of Natural Resources Canada, 2013)

Canada the world's third-largest diamond-producing nation (by value) after Russia and Botswana. Canadian diamonds are uniquely beautiful and rival the quality of most other diamonds around the world. Furthermore, each Canadian diamond is laser-engraved with a microscopic serial number and comes with certificates authenticating its country of origin.

*Chuck Fipke, interviewed in Carl Hoffman, November 24, 2008, "How a rogue geologist discovered a diamond trove in the Canadian Arctic," Wired Magazine (November 24, 2008). (C) Condé Nast. www.wired.com/science/planetearth/magazine/16–12/ff_diamonds.

Figure 17.C Rough diamonds from Ekati mine. (Photo by Andrew Hetherington)

A **glacier** is a thick ice mass that originates on land from the accumulation, compaction, and re-crystallization of snow. Because glaciers are agents of erosion, they must *move*, even though they appear to be stationary. Although glaciers are found in many parts of the world today, most are located at high altitudes and in high latitudes. Basic types of glaciers are presented next.

Ice Sheets

Ice sheets exist on a continental scale. The low total annual solar radiation reaching the poles makes these regions prone to great ice accumulations. Although many ice sheets have existed in the past, just two achieve this status at present (Figure 17.2). In the area near the North Pole, Greenland is covered by an imposing ice sheet that occupies 1.7 million square kilometres, or about 80 percent of this large island. Averaging nearly 1500 metres thick, the ice extends 3000 metres above the island's bedrock floor in some places.

In the South Polar realm, the huge Antarctic Ice Sheet attains a maximum thickness of nearly 4300 metres and covers an area of more than 13.9 million square kilometres. Because of the proportions of these huge features, they commonly are called *continental ice sheets*. Indeed, the combined areas of present-day continental ice sheets represent almost 10 percent of Earth's land area.

These enormous ice masses flow out in all directions from one or more snow-accumulation areas and completely obscure all but the highest areas of underlying terrain. Indeed, the ancient Laurentide Ice Sheet covered most of Canada

(see Figure 17.28). Even sharp variations in the topography beneath the glacier usually appear as relatively subdued undulations on the surface of the ice. Such topographic differences, however, do affect the behaviour of the ice sheets, especially near their margins, by guiding flow in certain directions and creating zones of faster and slower flow.

Along portions of the Antarctic coast, glacial ice flows into bays, creating features called **ice shelves**. These are large, relatively flat masses of floating ice that extend seaward from the coast but remain attached to the land along one or more sides. The shelves are thickest on their landward sides, and they become thinner seaward. They are sustained by ice from the adjacent ice sheet as well as being nourished by snowfall and the freezing of seawater to their bases. Antarctica's ice shelves extend over approximately 1.4 million square kilometres. The Ross and Filchner ice shelves are the largest, with the Ross Ice Shelf alone covering an area approximately the size of Manitoba (Figure 17.2).

Valley (Alpine) Glaciers

Thousands of relatively small glaciers exist in lofty mountain areas, where they usually follow valleys that were originally occupied by streams. Unlike the rivers that previously flowed in these valleys, the glaciers advance slowly, perhaps only a few centimetres per day. Because of their setting, these moving ice masses are termed **valley glaciers** or **alpine glaciers** (Figure 17.3). Each glacier is like a stream of ice, commonly bounded by precipitous rock walls, that flows under its own weight down-valley from an accumulation area near its head. Like rivers, valley

Figure 17.3 Merging valley glaciers in British Columbia. (Photo by NASA Earth Observatory)

Figure 17.2 The only present-day ice sheets are those covering Greenland and Antarctica. Their combined areas represent almost 10 percent of Earth's land area. Greenland's ice sheet occupies 1.7 million square kilometres, or about 80 percent of the island. The area of the Antarctic Ice Sheet is almost 14 million square kilometres. Ice shelves occupy an additional 1.4 million square kilometres adjacent to the Antarctic Ice Sheet.

glaciers can be long or short, wide or narrow, single or with merging tributaries. Generally, the widths of alpine glaciers are small compared with their lengths. Some extend for just a fraction of a kilometre, whereas others go on for many tens of kilometres. The west branch of the Hubbard Glacier, for example, flows through 112 kilometres of mountainous terrain in Alaska and Yukon.

Other Types of Glaciers

In addition to valley glaciers and ice sheets, other types of glaciers are also identified. Covering some uplands and plateaus are masses of glacial ice called **ice caps**. Like ice sheets, ice caps completely bury the underlying landscape but are much smaller than the continental-scale features. Ice caps occur in many places, including Iceland (Figure 17.4A) and several of the large islands in Canada's Arctic Archipelago.

Often, ice caps and ice sheets feed **outlet glaciers**. These tongues of ice flow down valleys, extending outward from the margins of these larger ice masses. The tongues are avenues for ice movement from an ice cap or ice sheet through mountainous terrain to the sea. Some outlet glaciers become fast-flowing **ice streams** that drain most of an ice sheet. Where they encounter the ocean, some outlet glaciers and ice streams spread out as floating ice shelves, where they produce many icebergs.

Piedmont glaciers occupy broad lowlands at the bases of steep mountains and form when one or more alpine glaciers emerge from the confining walls of mountain valleys (Figure 17.4B). Here, the advancing ice spreads out to form a broad sheet. The size of individual piedmont glaciers varies greatly. Among the largest in Canada is the broad piedmont lobe west of Lake Hazen on Ellesmere Island.

B

Figure 17.4 **A.** Ice cap on Iceland. The volcano under Eyjafjallajokull spewed ash that drifted east, closing European airports in 2010. **B.** Piedmont glaciers on north Baffin Island. (Photo **A** *Landsat* image from NASA; photo **B** by S. R. Hicock)

FORMATION OF GLACIAL ICE

Snow is the raw material from which glacial ice originates; therefore, glaciers form in areas where more snow falls in winter than melts during the summer. Before a glacier is created, snow must be converted into glacial ice. This transformation is shown in Figure 17.5.

When temperatures remain below freezing following a snowfall, the fluffy accumulation of delicate hexagonal crystals soon changes. As air infiltrates the spaces between the crystals, the extremities of the crystals turn into water vapour, which condenses near the centres of the crystals. In this manner snowflakes become smaller, thicker, and more spherical, and the large pore spaces disappear. By this process, air is forced out and what was once light, fluffy snow is re-crystallized into a much denser mass of small grains having the consistency of coarse sand. This granular re-crystallized snow is called **firn**. As more snow is added, the pressure on the lower layers increases, compacting the ice grains at depth. Once the thickness of ice and snow exceeds 50 metres, the weight is sufficient to fuse firn into a solid mass of interlocking ice crystals—glacial ice.

Figure 17.5 The conversion of freshly fallen snow into dense, crystalline glacial ice.

MOVEMENT OF A GLACIER

The movement of glacial ice is generally referred to as *flow*, but is more realistically the total movement resulting from a combination of three distinct mechanisms: internal deformation, basal slip, and soft bed deformation.

Internal deformation involves movement *within* the ice. Ice behaves as a brittle solid until the pressure on it is equivalent to the weight of about 50 metres of ice. Once that load is surpassed, ice behaves as a plastic material and flow begins. Such flow occurs because of the molecular structure of ice. Glacial ice consists of layers of molecules stacked one on the other. The bonds between layers are weaker than those within each layer. Therefore, when a stress exceeds the strength of the bonds between the layers, the layers remain intact and slide over one another.

Basal slip occurs when the ice mass slips across the ground. Except where polar ice is frozen to bedrock, in this process meltwater probably acts as a hydraulic jack and lubricant, allowing the ice to lift and move over the rock. Liquid water is present because the melting point of ice decreases as pressure increases. Therefore, deep within a glacier the ice can be at the melting point even though its temperature is below 0°C. In fact, parts of a glacier bed can be wet and other parts can be dry, depending mainly on ice thickness.

In **soft bed deformation**, sediment and fractured rock deform by friction of the overriding glacier. Water-saturated sediment and weak bedrock, such as shale, are easily deformed and offer little resistance to the power of the glacier.

Figure 17.6 shows these three basic types of glacial movement. This vertical profile through a glacier also shows that not all the ice flows forward at the same rate. Frictional drag with the bedrock floor can cause the lower portions of the glacier to move more slowly.

In contrast to the lower portion of the glacier under pressure, the upper 50 metres or so are not under sufficient pressure to exhibit plastic flow. Rather, the ice in this uppermost zone is brittle and is appropriately named the **zone of fracture**. The ice in the zone of fracture is carried along piggyback style by the ice below. When the glacier moves over irregular terrain, the zone of fracture is subjected to tension, resulting in cracks called **crevasses** (chapter-opening photo and Figure 17.7). These gaping cracks can make travel across glaciers dangerous and can extend to depths of 50 metres. Below this depth, plastic flow seals them off.

Rates of Glacial Movement

Unlike stream flow, glacial movement is not obvious. If we could watch an alpine glacier move, we would

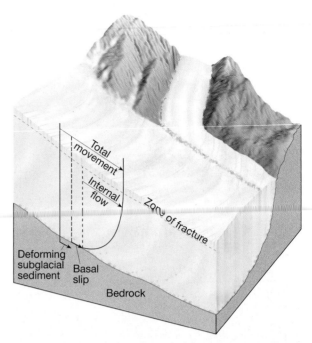

Figure 17.6 Cross-section through a glacier to illustrate ice movement, divided into three components. (1) Ice below approximately 50 metres behaves plastically and flows. Ice in the *zone of fracture* is carried passively on the main mass of ice. (2) Glacier ice can slip over its bed if wet under thick ice. (3) Soft material under the ice may deform by frictional drag of the ice. Often the rate of movement is slowest at the base of the glacier, where frictional drag is greatest.

see that, like the water in a river, not all of the ice in the valley moves at an equal rate. Just as friction with the valley floor can slow the movement of the ice at the bottom of the glacier, the drag created by the valley walls causes the rate of flow to be greatest in the centre of the glacier. This was first demonstrated by experiments during the nineteenth century, in which markers were carefully placed in a straight line across the top of a valley glacier. Periodically, the positions of the stakes were recorded, revealing the type of movement just described.

Average velocities vary considerably from one glacier to another. Some move so slowly that trees and other vegetation may become well established in the debris that has accumulated on the glacier's surface, whereas others may move at rates of up to several metres per day. Satellite radar images of Antarctica show that some outlet glaciers move at rates greater than 800 metres per year, whereas ice in some interior Antarctic ice creeps along at less than 2 metres per year.

The advance of some glaciers is characterized by episodes of extremely rapid movements called **surges**. Glaciers that exhibit such movement

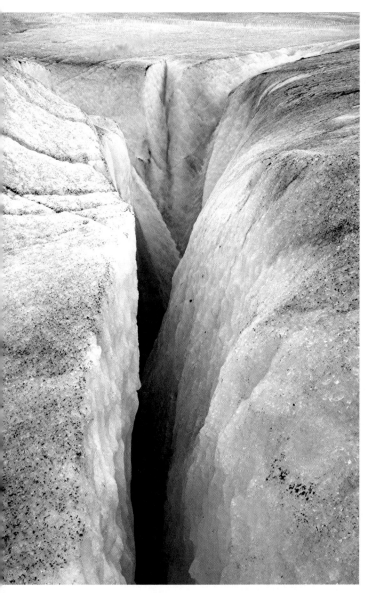

Figure 17.7 Crevasses form in the brittle ice of the zone of fracture. They can extend to depths of 50 metres and can make travel across glaciers dangerous. (Photo by Steve Faber/Shutterstock)

occur in the **zone of accumulation**. Its lower limit is defined by the **equilibrium line**. The elevation of the *snowline* (above which snow remains year-round) varies greatly. In polar regions it may be at sea level, whereas in tropical areas, the snowline exists only in high mountain areas, often at altitudes approaching 5000 metres. Above the equilibrium line, in the zone of accumulation, the addition of snow thickens the glacier and promotes flow. The equilibrium line separates the zone of accumulation from the **zone of ablation** or wastage. Here, the glacier experiences a net loss, as all of the snow from the previous winter melts, as does some of the glacial ice (Figure 17.8).

In addition to melting, some glaciers also waste as large pieces of ice break off the front of the glacier in a process called **calving**. Calving creates icebergs in places where the glacier has reached the sea or a lake (Figure 17.9). Because icebergs are just slightly less dense than seawater, they float very low in the water, with more than 80 to 90 percent of their mass submerged. Along the margins of Antarctica's ice shelves, calving is the primary means by which these masses lose ice. The relatively flat icebergs produced here can be several kilometres across and 600 metres thick. By comparison, thousands of irregularly shaped icebergs are produced by outlet glaciers and ice streams flowing from the margins of the Greenland Ice Sheet. Many drift southward and find their way into the North Atlantic, where they can pose a hazard to navigation, as the captain of the *Titanic* discovered in 1912.

Whether the margin of a glacier is advancing, retreating, or remaining stationary depends on the budget of the glacier. The **glacial budget** or **mass balance** is the balance, or lack of balance, between accumulation at the upper end of the glacier and ablation (loss) at the lower end. If ice accumulation exceeds ablation, the glacial front advances until the two factors again come into balance. When this happens, the terminus (front edge) of the glacier becomes stationary.

If a warming trend increases ablation or if a drop in snowfall decreases accumulation, the ice front will retreat (note exposed foreground in chapter-opening photo). As the terminus of the glacier retreats, the extent of the zone of ablation diminishes. Therefore, in time a new balance will be reached between accumulation and ablation, and the ice front will again become stationary.

Whether the margin of a glacier is advancing, retreating, or stationary, the ice within the glacier continues to flow forward. In the case of a receding glacier, the ice still flows forward but not rapidly enough to offset ablation.

flow along in an apparently normal manner, then speed up for a relatively short time, before returning to the normal rate again. The flow rates during surges are as much as 100 times the normal rate.

Budget of a Glacier

Snow is the raw material from which glacial ice originates; therefore, as mentioned, glaciers form in areas where more snow falls in winter than melts during the summer. Glaciers are constantly gaining and losing ice. Net accumulation and ice formation

Figure 17.8   The equilibrium line separates the zone of accumulation and the zone of ablation. Above the equilibrium line, more snow falls each winter than melts each summer. Below the equilibrium line, the snow from the previous winter completely melts, as does some of the underlying ice. Whether the margin of a glacier advances, retreats, or remains stationary depends on the balance between accumulation and ablation. In any case internal flow (blue arrows) is toward the terminus. When a glacier moves across irregular terrain, crevasses form in the upper brittle portion.

Figure 17.9   Icebergs are created when large pieces calve from the front of a glacier after it reaches a water body. In this photo, ice pinnacles are about to calve from the terminus of a small outlet glacier in Greenland. Ten to 20 percent of an iceberg protrudes above the water line. (Photo by S. R. Hicock)

GLACIAL EROSION

Glaciers are capable of great erosion. At a modern glacier terminus, as the ice melts, you can witness firsthand the release of rock material of various sizes; the ice has scraped, scoured, and torn rock from the floor and walls of the valley and carried it down-valley. Indeed, as a medium of sediment transport, ice has no equal.

Once rock debris is acquired by the glacier, the enormous competence of ice will not allow the debris to settle out like the load carried by a stream or by the wind. Consequently, glaciers can carry huge blocks that no other erosional agent could possibly budge (Figure 17.10). Although today's glaciers are of limited importance as erosional agents, much of the Canadian landscape was greatly modified by the Laurentide and Cordilleran ice sheets of the last Ice Age.

Glaciers erode the land primarily in two ways—plucking and abrasion. First, as a glacier flows over a fractured bedrock surface, it loosens and lifts blocks of rock and incorporates them into the ice. This process, known as **plucking**, occurs when melt-water penetrates the cracks and joints of bedrock beneath a glacier and freezes. As the water expands while turning to ice, it exerts tremendous leverage that pries the rock loose (see "Frost Wedging" in Chapter 5), and then freezes rock fragments to the base of the ice. In this manner sediment of all sizes becomes part of the glacier's load.

The second major erosional process is **abrasion** (Figure 17.11). As the ice with its load of rock

Figure 17.11 Glacial abrasion created the striations and larger grooves in this basalt outcrop at Yellowknife, Northwest Territories. (Photo by S.R. Hicock)

fragments slides over bedrock, it functions like sandpaper to smooth and polish the surface below. The pulverized rock produced by the glacial gristmill is appropriately called **rock flour**. Abrasion can produce so much rock flour that meltwater streams flowing out of a glacier have the appearance of milk and offer visible evidence of the grinding power of ice.

When the ice at the bottom of a glacier contains large rock fragments, long, linear scratches called **glacial striations** can be gouged into the bedrock (Figure 17.11). By mapping the orientations of striations over large areas, patterns of glacial flow can be reconstructed. However, not all abrasion produces distinct striations. The rock surfaces over which the glacier moves may also become highly polished by the ice and its load of finer particles. The broad expanses of smoothly polished rock exposures in many parts of the Canadian Shield provide excellent examples.

As is the case with other agents of erosion, the rate of glacial erosion is highly variable. This differential erosion by ice is largely controlled by four factors: (1) rate of glacial movement; (2) thickness of the ice; (3) shape, abundance, and hardness of the rock fragments contained in the ice at the base of the glacier; and (4) the erodibility of the surface beneath the glacier.

Figure 17.10 Large, glacially transported rocks at Okotoks, Alberta. Such big rocks are called glacial erratics (note fence for scale). (Photo © Cliff LeSergent/Alamy)

Variations in any or all of these factors from time to time or from place to place mean that the features, effects, and degree of landscape modification in glaciated regions can vary greatly.

LANDFORMS CREATED BY GLACIAL EROSION

The erosional effects of valley glaciers and ice sheets are quite different. A visitor to a glaciated mountain region like the Canadian Rockies is likely to see a sharp and angular topography (see Figure 17.1). The reason is that as alpine glaciers move down-valley, they tend to accentuate the irregularities of the mountain landscape by creating steeper canyon walls and making bold peaks even more jagged. By contrast, ice sheets override the terrain and hence subdue rather than accentuate the irregularities they encounter (such as the Canadian Shield). Although the erosional power of ice sheets is enormous, landforms carved by these huge ice masses usually do not inspire the same wonderment and awe that the erosional features created by valley glaciers do. Because much of the rugged mountain scenery so celebrated for its majestic beauty is the product of erosion by alpine glaciers, they are featured below. Figure 17.12 shows a hypothetical mountain area before, during, and after glaciation.

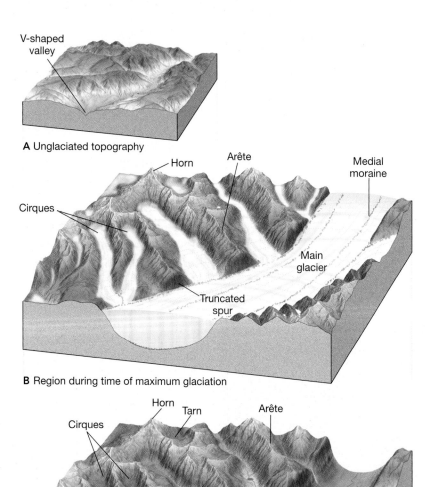

Figure 17.12 Erosional landforms created by alpine glaciers. The unglaciated landscape in part **A** is modified by valley glaciers in part **B**. After the ice recedes, in part **C**, the terrain looks very different than it did before glaciation.

V-shaped valley

A Unglaciated topography

Horn
Arête
Medial moraine
Cirques
Main glacier
Truncated spur

B Region during time of maximum glaciation

Horn
Tarn
Arête
Cirques
Hanging valley
Glacial trough

C Glaciated topography

Figure 17.13 Before glaciation, a mountain valley is typically narrow and V-shaped. During glaciation, a valley glacier widens, deepens, and straightens the valley, creating the U-shaped glacial trough seen on north Baffin island. (Photo by S. R. Hicock)

Glaciated Valleys

Unlike streams, which create their own valleys, glaciers take the path of least resistance by following the course of existing stream valleys. Before glaciation, mountain valleys are characteristically narrow and V-shaped because streams are downcutting. However, during glaciation these narrow valleys undergo a transformation as the glacier widens and deepens them, creating a U-shaped **glacial trough** (Figures 17.12C and 17.13). In addition to producing a broader and deeper valley, the glacier also straightens the valley. As ice flows around sharp curves, its great erosional force removes the spurs of land that extend into the valley. The results of this activity are triangular-shaped cliffs called **truncated spurs** (Figures 17.12B and 17.1).

The intensity of glacial erosion depends in part on the thickness of the ice. Consequently, main glaciers, also called *trunk glaciers*, cut their valleys deeper than do their smaller tributary glaciers. Thus, when the glaciers eventually recede, the valleys of tributary glaciers are left standing above the main glacial trough and are termed **hanging valleys** (Figure 17.12C). Rivers flowing through hanging valleys can produce spectacular waterfalls, such as those in Butte Inlet, Toba Inlet, Knight Inlet, British Columbia, and on Baffin Island (Figure 17.14).

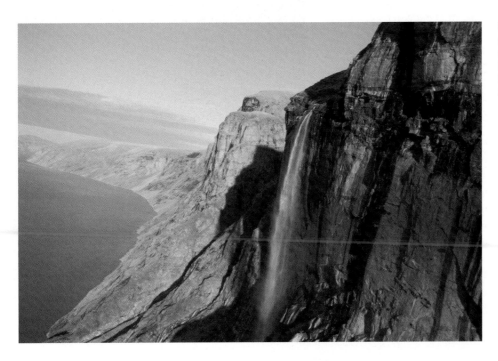

Figure 17.14 Waterfall cascades from a hanging valley into Itirbilung Fjord, Baffin Island, Nunavut. (Photo by Danita Delimont)

Figure 17.15 Glacier flowing from a cirque in Kluane National Park, Yukon. These bowl-shaped depressions are found at the heads of glacial valleys and represent a focal point of ice formation. (Photo by Marli Miller)

Before leaving the topic of glacial troughs and their associated features, we should discuss one more type of well-known feature: fjords. **Fjords** are deep, commonly spectacular, steep-sided inlets of the sea that occur at high latitudes where mountains are adjacent to the ocean (Figures 17.17 and 17.4B background). They are drowned glacial troughs that were scoured then deeply submerged as sea level rose following the Ice Age. The depths of fjords can exceed 1000 metres because glaciers are capable of eroding their beds far below the surface of the sea. For example, a 300-metre-thick glacier can carve its valley floor more than 250 metres below sea level before downward erosion ceases and the ice begins to float. Norway, British Columbia, Greenland, New Zealand, Chile, and Alaska, for example, all have coastlines characterized by fjords.

At the head of a glacial valley is a very characteristic and often imposing feature called a **cirque**. As Figures 17.12B and Figure 17.15 illustrate, these bowl-shaped depressions have precipitous walls on three sides but are open on the down-valley side. The cirque is the focal point of the glacier's growth because it is the area of snow accumulation and ice formation. Cirques begin as irregularities (e.g., faults) in the mountainside that are subsequently enlarged by the frost wedging and plucking that occurs along the sides and bottom of the glacier. After the glacier has melted away, the cirque basin is commonly occupied by a small lake called a **tarn** (Figures 17.12C and 17.16).

Sometimes when two glaciers exist on opposite sides of a divide, each flowing away from the other, the dividing ridge between their cirques is largely eliminated as plucking and frost action enlarge each one. When this occurs, the two glacial troughs come to intersect, creating a gap or pass from one valley into the other. Such a feature is termed a **col**. Some important and well-known mountain passes that are cols include St. Gotthard Pass in the Swiss Alps, Chilkoot Pass ("the golden staircase") that gold miners had to scale during the Klondike gold rush in Yukon in 1898, and Tioga Pass in California's Sierra Nevada.

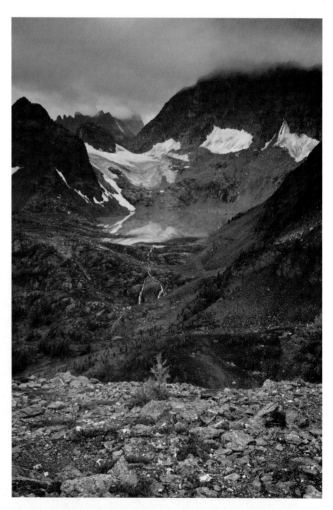

Figure 17.16 A small lake occupying a cirque is called a tarn. Cobalt Lake in Bugaboo Provincial Park, British Columbia. The sharp ridge above is an arete and the low pass, a col. (Photo © Roy LANGSTAFF/Alamy)

Figure 17.17 Like other fjords, this one in the northeast coast of Baffin Island is a drowned glacial trough. (Photo by S. R. Hicock)

Arêtes and Horns

During a visit to the European Alps, the Canadian Rockies, or other scenic mountain landscapes carved by valley glaciers, you are likely to see glacial troughs, cirques, and the other related features just discussed. You also are likely to see sinuous sharp edged ridges called **arêtes** (French for "knife-edge") and sharp pyramid-like peaks called **horns** projecting above the surroundings. Both features can originate from the same basic process: the enlargement of cirques produced by plucking and frost wedging (Figures 17.12B and 17.12C). In the case of horns, groups of cirques around a single high mountain enlarge and converge to produce an isolated horn. Noteworthy Canadian examples include Peyto Peak, Mount Thompson, Mt. Assiniboine of the Alberta Rockies (Figure 17.18).

Arêtes can be formed in a similar manner, except that the cirques are not clustered around a point but rather exist on opposite sides of a divide. As the cirques grow, the divide separating

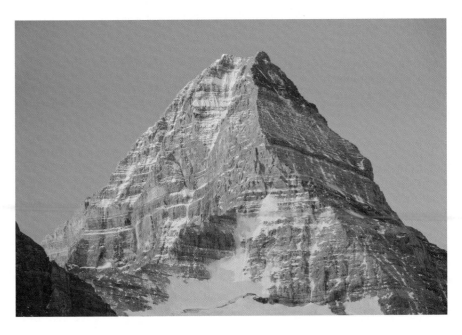

Figure 17.18 Horns are sharp pyramid-like peaks shaped by cirque glaciers. This example is Mt. Assiniboine, Alberta. (Photo © Kevin Schafer/Alamy)

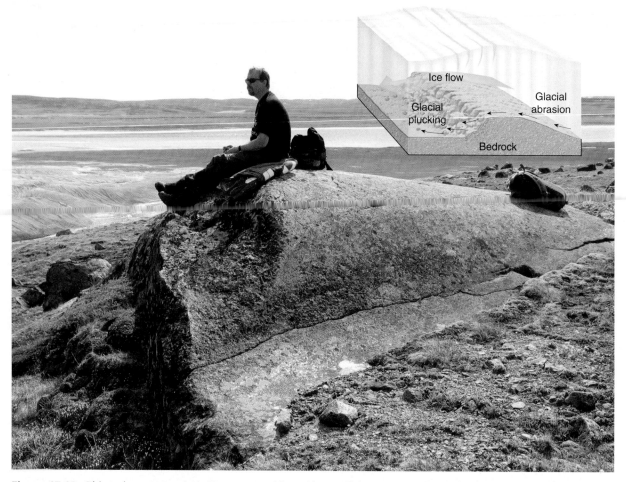

Figure 17.19 This roche moutonnée in Nunavut provides evidence of the direction of glacial ice movement. The gentle slope (under the backpack) was abraded and the steep side (under the geologist) was plucked, so the ice moved from right to left. (Photo by S. R. Hicock)

them is reduced to a narrow knifelike partition (Figures 17.12B, 17.12C, and 17.16). An arête, however, can also be created in another way: When two glaciers occupy parallel valleys, an arête can form when the divide separating the moving tongues of ice is progressively narrowed as the glaciers scour and widen their adjacent valleys (Figure 17.15; the glacier on the right is out of view).

Roches Moutonnées

In many glaciated landscapes, but most frequently where continental ice sheets have modified the terrain, the ice carves small streamlined hills from protruding bedrock knobs. Such an asymmetrical knob of bedrock is known by a French term, **roche moutonnée** ("sheep rock"). They are formed when glacial abrasion smoothes the gentle slope facing the oncoming ice sheet and plucking steepens the opposite side as the ice rides over the knob (Figure 17.19). Roches moutonnées indicate the direction of glacial

flow because the gentler slope is generally on the side from which the ice advanced.

GLACIAL DEPOSITS

Glaciers pick up and transport a huge load of debris as they slowly advance across the land. Ultimately these materials are deposited where the ice melts. Glacial deposits play a truly significant role in forming the landscape. For example, in many areas once covered by the Laurentide and Cordilleran ice sheets of the last Ice Age, the bedrock is rarely exposed because glacial deposits completely mantle the terrain. The general effect of these deposits is to reduce the local relief and thus level the topography. Indeed, rural country scenes familiar to many of us—rocky pastures in Ontario, wheat fields in Manitoba and Saskatchewan, rolling farmland in Alberta—result directly from glacial deposition by ancient ice sheets.

Long before the theory of an extensive Ice Age was ever proposed, much of the soil and rock debris covering portions of Europe was recognized as coming from somewhere else. At the time, these foreign materials were believed to have drifted into their present positions by floating ice during an ancient flood. As a consequence, the term *drift* was applied to this sediment. Although rooted in an incorrect concept, this term was so well established by the time the true glacial origin of the debris became widely recognized that it remained in the basic glacial vocabulary. Today **glacial drift** is an all-embracing term for sediments of glacial origin, no matter how, where, or in what shape they were deposited.

One of the features distinguishing drift from sediments deposited by other erosional agents is that glacial deposits consist primarily of mechanically weathered rock debris that underwent little or no chemical weathering before deposition. Thus, minerals that are notably prone to chemical decomposition, such as hornblende and the plagioclase feldspars, are commonly conspicuous components in glacial sediments.

Glacial drift is divided by geologists into two main types: (1) materials deposited directly by the glacier, known as **till**; and (2) sediments deposited by glacial meltwater, called **stratified drift**. We will now look at landforms made of each type.

LANDFORMS MADE OF TILL

Till is deposited as glacial ice melts and releases its load of rock fragments. Unlike moving water and wind, ice cannot sort the sediment it carries; therefore, deposits of till are characteristically poorly sorted mixtures of many particle sizes (Figure 17.20A). Close examination of this sediment shows that many of the stones are scratched and polished as the result of being dragged by the glacier. Such stones help distinguish tills from nonglacial stony muds (e.g., debris flows, rock slides); all are various types of diamicton.

Earlier ice ages are indicated by deposits called **tillite**, a sedimentary rock formed when till becomes lithified (Figure 17.20B). Such deposits, found in strata of different ages, usually contain striated rock fragments, and some overlie grooved and polished bedrock surfaces or are associated with sandstones and conglomerates that show features of meltwater deposits. For example, two Precambrian glacial episodes have been identified in the geologic record, the first approximately 2 billion years ago (including evidence from the Canadian Shield) and the second about 600 million years ago (Box 17.2).

Close up of cobble

A

B

Figure 17.20 **A.** Till is a poorly sorted mixture of many different sediment sizes. A close examination reveals cobbles that have been scratched as they were dragged by the glacier. **B.** Rocks with virtually identical textural characteristics to till produced by modern glaciers occur in the geologic record and represent ice ages of Earth's deep past. This example of tillite from northern Ontario records a Precambrian glacial episode. Tillite and similar nonglacial rocks are types of diamictite. (Photo **A** by E. J. Tarbuck; photo **B** by Grant Young)

CANADIAN PROFILE
Snowball Earth: Canadian Cryospheric Controversy

Once Earth scientists had developed criteria for the recognition of recent glacial activity, they quickly realized that those same criteria could also be applied to ancient rocks. The Precambrian represents almost 90 percent of the 4.6 billion years of Earth history, but extensive glacial deposits have been recognized only at the beginning and end of the Proterozoic. The oldest extensive glacial deposits occur in Early Proterozoic rocks of North America, Finland, South Africa, and Western Australia, which are about 2.3 billion years old (Figure 17.D). Late Proterozoic glacial deposits occur on every continent.

The widespread nature of Late Proterozoic glacial deposits suggested to Canadian scientist Paul Hoffman (currently at the University of Victoria) that the entire surface of Earth could have been frozen (the snowball Earth hypothesis, or SEH). Hoffman suggested that as its surface was progressively frozen, Earth lost heat by reflection of solar radiation from ice-covered areas, causing rapid cooling and eventually leading to the planet being encapsulated in ice. Escape from the deep freeze is explained by release of greenhouse gases into the atmosphere from volcanoes, reversing the deep freeze into a "deep fry" interval. The appeal of this idea lies in its simplicity.

The SEH, however, has many problems. For example, the SEH calls for synchronous global-scale glaciation, but among the few glacial deposits that have been accurately dated are significant differences in age. Also, the thickness (many kilometres in some cases) and subaqueous origin of many Precambrian glacial deposits are difficult to reconcile with a totally frozen planet because moving ice requires an active hydrologic cycle. Yet another problem concerns the limestone and dolostone cap carbonates that occur above many Late Proterozoic glacial deposits. According to the SEH, high levels of atmospheric CO_2 caused extreme global warming and increased weathering of silicate minerals, leading to saturation of the world's oceans

with bicarbonate ions and widespread deposition of carbonate sediments. Mudstones deposited immediately after the glaciations ended should show signs of intense weathering. Field evidence, however, indicates the opposite—glacial muds that directly overlie the cap carbonates show less evidence of weathering than those that are stratigraphically higher.

Remnant magnetism in some rocks can be used to determine the latitude at which they formed. Several ancient glacial deposits appear to have formed at sea level in equatorial latitudes. Does this indicate that the entire planet was glaciated? The presence of varves (mudstones with annual layers) and fossil ice-wedge structures is puzzling because both require significant seasonal temperature variations that are not found in equatorial regions today. One possible

explanation is the big tilt hypothesis, which invokes a highly tilted Earth (axis at greater than 54 degrees to the orbital plane) in the Precambrian. If Earth's axis was tilted at an extreme angle, equatorial regions would have experienced greater seasonality, possibly initiating glaciation on land masses at low latitudes. Unfortunately, a mechanism that adequately explains *how* such a radical change in tilt could have been accomplished, and independent evidence substantiating this hypothesis, remain to be found.

Despite its shortcomings, the snowball Earth concept has stimulated lively discussions on other aspects of Precambrian history. For example, Canadian paleontologist Guy Narbonne and others suggest the evolution of complex life forms that eventually colonized Earth may be closely tied to these climatic and environmental changes.

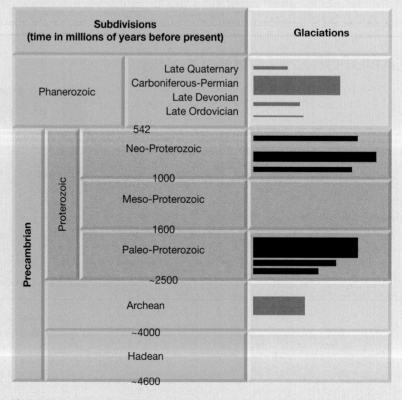

Figure 17.D Major glacial episodes in Earth's history as indicated by horizontal bars. Black bars emphasize glacial episodes of the Proterozoic for which widespread glacial deposits are known. (Reprinted by permission of Grant Young)

Boulders found in the till or lying free on the surface are called **glacial erratics** if they are different from the local bedrock (see Figure 17.10). This means that they must have been derived from a source outside the area where they are found. Although the locality of origin for most erratics is unknown, the origin of some can be determined. In many cases, boulders were transported as far as 500 kilometres from their source area and, in a few instances, more than 1000 kilometres. Big Rock near Okotoks (after the Blackfoot word for *rock*) is its most famous erratic (and reputedly the world's largest, weighing about 16 500 tonnes and standing 9 metres high; see Figure 17.10). The Foothills Erratics Train of southern Alberta is a classic example. The train is more than 600 kilometres long, made of a string of quartzite blocks derived from bedrock near Mt. Edith Cavell in Jasper National Park. A landslide dumped quartzite blocks onto a valley glacier that then carried the blocks eastward until the glacier merged with the edge of the last Laurentide Ice Sheet. Their combined southward flow and subsequent melting left the train of erratics that extends as far as Montana in the United States. Therefore, by studying glacial erratics as well as the mineral composition of the remaining till, geologists are sometimes able to trace the path of a lobe of ice.

In much of Canada, erratics dot pastures and farm fields once covered by ice sheets. In fact, in some places these large rocks were cleared from fields and piled to make fences, walls, and even houses (Figure 17.21). Keeping the fields clear, however, is an ongoing chore because each spring newly exposed erratics appear. Wintertime *frost heaving* has lifted them to the surface (see Chapter 14).

Figure 17.21 Many older houses in the Prairies and southern Ontario are constructed of fieldstones (glacial erratics). This one is near Edenwold, Saskatchewan. (Photo by Lorraine Brecht)

Figure 17.22 Well-developed lateral moraines deposited by the shrinking Athabasca Glacier in Jasper National Park. (Photo © Jon Arnold Images Ltd/Alamy)

Lateral and Medial Moraines

The most common term for landforms made primarily of till is *moraine*. Originally this term was used by French peasants when referring to the ridges and embankments of rock debris found near the margins of glaciers in the French Alps.

Alpine glaciers produce two types of moraines that occur exclusively in mountain valleys. The first of these is called a **lateral moraine** (Figure 17.22). As we learned earlier, when an alpine glacier moves down-valley, the ice erodes the sides of the valley with great efficiency. In addition, large quantities of debris are added to the glacier's surface as rubble falls or slides from higher on the valley walls and collects on the edges of the moving ice (see chapter-opening photo). When the ice eventually melts, this accumulation of debris is dropped next to the valley walls. These ridges of till parallel the sides of the valley and constitute the lateral moraines.

The second type of moraine that is unique to alpine glaciers is the **medial moraine** (Figures 17.3, 17.12B, and 17.23). Medial moraines are created when two alpine glaciers coalesce to form a wider valley glacier but the ice does not mix. The debris that was once carried along the sides of each glacier joins to form a single dark stripe of debris within the newly enlarged glacier. The creation of these dark stripes within the larger glacier is one obvious proof that glacial ice moves, because the moraine could not form if the ice did not flow down-valley.

Figure 17.23 Medial moraines form when the lateral moraines of merging valley glaciers join. Kluane National Park, Yukon. (Photo by Marli Miller)

It is quite common to see several medial moraines within a single alpine glacier, because a streak of debris will form whenever a tributary glacier joins the main glacier.

End and Ground Moraines

An **end moraine** is a ridge of mainly till that forms at the terminus of an alpine glacier or ice sheet. These relatively common landforms are deposited when a state of equilibrium is attained between ice ablation and accumulation. That is, the end moraine forms when the ice is melting and evaporating near the end of the glacier at a rate equal to the forward advance of the glacier from its zone of accumulation. Although the terminus of the glacier is now stationary, the ice continues to flow forward internally (see Figure 17.8), delivering a continuous supply of debris in the same manner as a conveyor belt delivers goods to the end of a production line. As the ice melts, the debris is dropped and the end moraine grows. The longer the ice front remains stationary, the larger the ridge of till will become. The glacier can also spread a sheet of till on the ground as it moves over it.

Eventually, ablation exceeds accumulation. At this point, the front of the glacier begins to recede in the direction from which it advanced. However, as the ice front retreats, the conveyor-belt action of the glacier continues to provide fresh supplies of debris to the terminus. In this manner a large quantity of till is deposited as the ice melts, creating a rock-strewn, undulating plain. This gently rolling layer of till deposited as the ice front advances, then recedes, is termed **ground moraine**. Ground moraine has a levelling effect, filling in low spots and clogging old

stream channels, often leading to a derangement of the existing drainage system. The area between lateral moraines in Figure 17.22 is a mix of ground moraine and meltwater deposits. In areas where this layer of till is still relatively fresh, such as the northern Great Lakes region, poorly drained, swampy lands are common.

Periodically, a glacier will retreat to a point where ablation and accumulation once again balance. When this happens, the ice front stabilizes and a new end moraine forms.

The pattern of end moraine formation and ground moraine deposition may be repeated many times before the glacier completely vanishes. Such a pattern is illustrated by Figure 17.24, part of the legacy of the last Laurentide Ice Sheet. The outermost end moraine marks the limit of the glacial advance. Because of its special status, this end moraine is also called the **terminal moraine**. Conversely, the end moraines that were created as the ice front occasionally stabilized during retreat are termed **recessional moraines**. Note that both terminal and recessional moraines are identical in origin; the only difference between them is their relative positions.

End moraines deposited during the last Ice Age are prominent features in many parts of Ontario. A well-known example north of Lake Ontario is the Oak Ridges Moraine that formed between two lobes of the Laurentide Ice Sheet. This hilly strip of glacial sediment extends westward from Trenton to Orangeville and is an important groundwater resource for the greater Toronto area (Figure 17.25). The moraine formed between the Simcoe and Ontario glacial lobes of the Laurentide Ice Sheet (Figure 17.24) and contains thick channel fills of sand and gravel that compose a large aquifer within and between till aquitards. It is a domestic source of water for greater Toronto and also stores and discharges clean cool water that is vital to aquatic life in the area.

Figure 17.26 represents a hypothetical area during glaciation and following the retreat of Canadian ice sheets. This figure depicts landscape features similar to what might be encountered if you were travelling in southern Canada during the last Ice Age or in Nunavut or Northwest Territories today. As you read the sections dealing with other glacial deposits, you will be referred to this figure several times.

Drumlins

In some areas that were once covered by continental ice sheets, a special variety of glacial landscape exists—one characterized by smooth, teardrop-shaped, parallel hills called **drumlins** (Figure 17.26). Good examples occur on islands off the Saanich

Figure 17.24   End moraines of central North America recording farthest advance of the Laurentide Ice Sheet during the last Ice Age. Moraines deposited during the most recent (Wisconsin) glaciation are shaded. **Inset:** Close-up view of eastern Great Lakes region showing flow directions of major ice lobes; note that "ORM" marks the location of the Oak Ridges Moraine (shown in more detail in Figure 17.25, below).

Figure 17.25   Oak Ridges Moraine (pink) depicted in a digital elevation model image. The moraine is an important aquifer and aggregate reserve for the greater Toronto area. (Reproduced with the permission of Natural Resources Canada, 2010, courtesy of the Geological Survey of Canada; Kenny et al., 1999)

Figure 17.26   This hypothetical area in Canada illustrates many common landforms deposited by an ice sheet. **A.** Esker in Nunavut. **B.** Drumlin at Morley flats near Calgary. **C.** Kame in Nunavut. **D.** Kettle hole in Northwest Territories. (Photos **A** S. R. Hicock; photo **B** © Bruce Martin; photo **C** by S. R. Hicock/Pearson Education; photo **D** reproduced with the permission of Natural Resources Canada 2013, courtesy of the Geological Survey of Canada; Photo 2001-178 by Lynda Dredge)

Peninsula of southern Vancouver Island, British Columbia; on the Morley Flats near Calgary, Alberta (Figure 17.26B); in the Guelph and Peterborough areas of Ontario; and Gaetz Head near Halifax, Nova Scotia.

These streamlined asymmetrical hills are composed largely of till but can also contain sand and gravel. They range in height from about 15 to 50 metres and can be up to 1 kilometre long. The steep side of the hill faces the direction from which the ice advanced, whereas the gentler, longer slope points in the direction the ice moved. Drumlins are occasionally found as isolated landforms but usually occur in clusters called *drumlin fields* (Figure 17.27). Two such clusters occur near Peterborough and Guelph, Ontario. The Peterborough drumlin field alone is estimated to contain about 3000 drumlins. Although drumlin formation is not fully understood, their streamlined shape indicates that they were moulded under the zone of plastic flow of an active glacier. It is thought that many drumlins originate when glaciers advance over previously deposited drift and reshape the material (e.g., James and Sidney islands, British Columbia).

LANDFORMS MADE OF STRATIFIED DRIFT

As the name implies, stratified drift is sorted according to the size and weight of the particles. Because ice is not capable of such sorting activity, these materials are not deposited directly by the glacier as till but instead reflect the sorting action of glacial meltwater. Accumulations of stratified drift commonly comprise sand and gravel—that is, bed-load material—because the finer rock flour remains suspended and therefore is carried far from the glacier by the meltwater streams. The rock flour may settle in seawater or in freshwater ponds and lakes, where it becomes laminated (called *varves* if they are annual layers). The laminations may be deformed by larger *dropstones* that melted out of icebergs and landed on the bottom of the lake. The sand and gravel provides aggregate for the construction industry to make concrete and asphalt (see Chapter 20). Buried deposits of sand and gravel make excellent aquifers, and clay from glacial lake deposits is used to make bricks and tile.

Figure 17.27 Map of part of the Peterborough, Ontario, drumlin field.

Outwash Plains and Valley Trains

At the same time as an end moraine is forming, water from the melting glacier cascades over the till, sweeping some of it out in front of the growing ridge of poorly sorted debris. Meltwater generally emerges from the ice in rapidly moving streams that are commonly choked with suspended material and carry a substantial bed load as well. As the water leaves the glacier, it moves onto the relatively flat surface beyond and rapidly loses velocity. As a consequence, much of its bed load is dropped and the meltwater begins weaving a complex pattern of braided channels (Figures 17.26 and 15.19A). In this way, a broad, ramplike surface composed of stratified drift is built adjacent to the downstream edge of most end moraines. When the feature is formed in association with an ice sheet, it is termed an **outwash plain**, and when largely confined to a mountain valley, it is usually referred to as a **valley train**.

Outwash plains and valley trains commonly are pockmarked with basins or depressions known as **kettles** (Figure 17.26). Kettles also occur in deposits of till. Kettles are formed when blocks of stagnant ice become wholly or partly buried in drift and eventually melt, leaving pits in the glacial sediment. Although most kettles do not exceed 2 kilometres in diameter, some with diameters exceeding 10 kilometres are known. In many cases water eventually fills the depression and forms a pond or lake. A good example is Sifton Bog in London, Ontario, the most southern large acidic bog in Canada.

Ice-Contact Deposits

When the melting terminus of a glacier shrinks to a critical point, flow virtually stops and the ice becomes stagnant. Meltwater that flows over, within, and at the base of the motionless ice deposits stratified drift. Then, as the supporting ice melts away, the stratified sediment is left behind in the form of hills, terraces, and ridges. Such accumulations are collectively termed **ice-contact deposits** and are classified according to their shapes.

When the ice-contact stratified drift is in the form of a mound or steep-sided hill, it is called a **kame** (Figure 17.26). Some kames represent bodies of sediment deposited by meltwater in openings within, or in depressions on top of, the ice. Others originate as deltas or fans built outward from the ice by meltwater streams. Later, when the stagnant ice melts away, these various accumulations of sediment collapse to form isolated, irregular mounds.

When glacial ice occupies a valley, **kame terraces** may be built along the sides of the valley. These features commonly are narrow masses of stratified drift deposited between the glacier and the side of the valley by streams that drop debris along the margins of the shrinking ice mass.

A third type of ice-contact deposit is a long, narrow, sinuous ridge composed largely of sand and gravel. Some are more than 100 metres high, with lengths exceeding 100 kilometres. The dimensions of many others are far less spectacular. Known as **eskers**, these ridges are deposited by meltwater rivers flowing within, on top of, and beneath a mass of motionless, stagnant glacial ice (Figure 17.26). Many sediment sizes are carried by the torrents of meltwater in the ice-banked channels, but only the coarser material can settle out of the turbulent stream.

THE GLACIAL THEORY AND THE ICE AGE

In the preceding pages we referred to the last Ice Age, a time when ice sheets and alpine glaciers were far more extensive than they are today. This idea evolved over many years. In 1821, a Swiss engineer, Ignaz Venetz, presented a paper suggesting that glacial landscape features occurred at considerable distances from the existing glaciers in the Alps. This implied that the glaciers had once been larger and occupied positions farther down-valley. Another Swiss scientist, Louis Agassiz, doubted the proposal of widespread glacial activity put forth by Venetz. He set out to prove that the idea was not valid. Ironically, his 1836 fieldwork in the Alps convinced him of the merits of his colleague's hypothesis. In fact, a year later Agassiz hypothesized a great ice age that had extensive and far-reaching effects—an idea that was to give Agassiz widespread fame.

The proof of the glacial theory proposed by Agassiz and others constitutes a classic example of applying the principle of uniformitarianism (see Chapter 1). Realizing that certain features are produced by no other known process but glacial action, they were able to begin reconstructing the extent of now-vanished ice sheets based on the presence of features and deposits found far beyond the margins of present-day glaciers. In this manner, the development and verification of the glacial theory continued during the nineteenth century, and through the efforts of many scientists, knowledge of the nature and extent of former ice sheets became clear.

By the beginning of the twentieth century, geologists had largely determined the areal extent of the Ice Age glaciation. During their investigations, they had discovered that many glaciated regions had not one layer of drift but several. Moreover, close examination of these older deposits showed well-developed zones of chemical weathering and ancient soils, as well as the remains of plants that require warm temperatures. The evidence was clear: Not just one glacial advance but many had occurred, each separated by extended intervals when climates were as warm or warmer than the present. The Ice Age had not simply been a time when the ice advanced over the land, lingered for a while, and then receded. Rather, it was a very complex event, characterized by a number of advances and withdrawals of glacial ice.

By the early twentieth century, a fourfold division of the Ice Age had been established for both North America and Europe. The divisions were based largely on studies of glacial deposits. In North America each of the four major stages was named for the midwest state of the United States where deposits of that stage were well exposed or were first studied. These were, in order from oldest to youngest, the Nebraskan, Kansan, Illinoian, and Wisconsin. These traditional divisions remained in place through most of the twentieth century, until it was learned that sediment cores from the ocean floor and ice cores from ice sheets contain a much more complete record of climate change during the last Ice Age. Unlike the glacial record on land, which is punctuated by many unconformities (since glaciers tend to destroy early deposits), sea-floor sediments and ice cores provide an uninterrupted record of climatic cycles for the Ice Age because of minimal erosion. Studies of these cores showed that glacial/interglacial cycles had occurred about every 100 000 years. More than 20 such cycles of cooling and warming were identified for the span we call the Ice Age.

During the Ice Age, glaciers left their imprint on almost 30 percent of Earth's land area, including about 10 million square kilometres of North America, 5 million square kilometres of Europe, and 4 million square kilometres of Siberia (Figure 17.28). The amount of glacial ice in the Northern Hemisphere was roughly twice that of the Southern Hemisphere. The primary reason is that the southern polar ice could not spread far beyond the margins of Antarctica. By contrast, North America and Eurasia provided great expanses of land for the spread of ice sheets.

The last Ice Age may have begun as early as 4.5 million years ago. This means that most of the

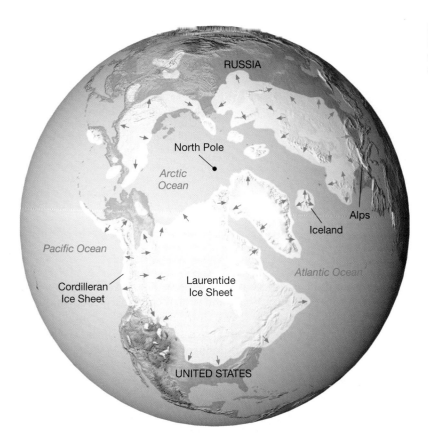

Figure 17.28   Maximum extent of ice sheets in the Northern Hemisphere during the last stage of the Ice Age, about 20 000 years ago.

major glacial stages occurred during a division of the geologic time scale called the Pleistocene Epoch (Chapter 8). Although the Pleistocene is commonly used as a synonym for the Ice Age, note that this epoch does not encompass all of the last glacial episode. The Antarctic Ice Sheet, for example, probably formed at least 38 million years ago.

OTHER EFFECTS OF ICE-AGE GLACIERS

In addition to the massive erosional and depositional work carried on by Ice Age glaciers (Figure 17.28), the ice sheets had other, sometimes profound, effects on the landscape. For example, as the ice advanced and retreated, animals and plants were forced to migrate. This led to stresses that some organisms could not tolerate. Hence, a number of plants and animals became extinct. One such stress in North America was the southward expansion of permafrost and periglacial features described in Chapter 14.

Furthermore, many present-day stream courses bear little resemblance to their pre-glacial routes. Other rivers, called misfit streams (Chapter 15), that today carry only a comparative trickle of water but nevertheless occupy broad channels called spillways (Chapter 15), are testimony to the fact that they once carried torrents of glacial meltwater.

In central areas of ice accumulation, such as Scandinavia and the Canadian Shield, the land has been slowly rising over the past several thousand years. Uplifting of almost 300 metres has occurred in the Hudson Bay region. We now understand that the land is rising because the added weight of a 3-kilometre-thick mass of ice such as the Laurentide Ice Sheet caused down-warping of Earth's crust. Ever since the removal of this immense load, the crust has been adjusting by gradually rebounding (Figure 17.29).*

Certainly one of the most interesting and perhaps dramatic effects of the Ice Age was the fall and rise of sea level that accompanied the advance and retreat of the ice sheets. Earlier in the chapter we pointed out that sea level would rise by an estimated 60 or 70 metres if the water locked up in the Antarctic Ice Sheet were to melt completely. Such an occurrence would flood many densely populated coastal areas.

Although the total volume of glacial ice today is great, exceeding 25 million cubic kilometres, during the Ice Age the volume of glacial ice amounted to about 70 million cubic kilometres (Figure 17.28), or 45 million cubic kilometres more than at present. Because we know that the snow from which glaciers are made ultimately comes from the evaporation of ocean water, the growth of ice sheets must have caused

*For a more complete discussion of this concept, termed isostatic adjustment, see the section on isostasy in Chapter 13.

Figure 17.29 Simplified illustration showing crustal subsidence and rebound resulting from the addition and removal of ice sheets. **A.** In northern Canada and Scandinavia, where the greatest accumulation of glacial ice occurred, the added weight caused down-warping of the crust. **B.** Ever since the ice melted, gradual uplift or rebound of the crust has been occurring.

a worldwide drop in sea level (Figure 17.30). Indeed, estimates suggest that sea level was at least 100 metres lower than today. Thus, land that is presently flooded by the oceans was dry. The Atlantic Coast of Canada lay more than 100 kilometres to the east of Nova Scotia; France and Britain were joined where the English Channel is today; Alaska and Siberia were connected across the Bering Strait; and Southeast Asia was tied by dry land to the islands of Indonesia.

Although formation and growth of ice sheets was an obvious response to significant changes in climate, the existence of the ice sheets triggered important climatic changes in the regions beyond their margins. In central Canada, glacial Lake

Agassiz was the largest lake in North America (Figure 17.31) and probably discharged down the St. Lawrence River into the North Atlantic. It was dammed by the retreating margin of the Laurentide Ice Sheet and drained down the Mississippi into the Gulf of Mexico for most of its life. Lake Winnipeg is the largest remnant of Lake Agassiz. About the time of Lake Agassiz, strong winds blowing off the retreating Laurentide Ice Sheet picked up fine dust from freshly exposed ground moraine and stratified drift, and then deposited the dust in what is now the northern United States. These aeolian dust deposits are referred to as loess, and today they make fertile farmland (more details in Chapter 18).

CAUSES OF ICE AGES

Although the literature of science contains a vast array of hypotheses relating to the possible *causes* of glacial episodes, we will discuss only a few major ideas to summarize current thought.

Plate Tectonics

Probably the most attractive proposal for explaining the fact that extensive ice ages of Earth have occurred only a few times in the geologic past comes from the theory of plate tectonics.*

Because glaciers can form only on land, we know that land masses must exist somewhere in the higher latitudes before an ice age can commence. Many scientists suggest that ice ages have occurred only when Earth's shifting lithospheric plates have carried the continents from tropical latitudes to more pole-ward positions.

Glacial features in present-day Africa, Australia, South America, and India indicate that these regions,

Figure 17.30 Changing global sea level during the past 20 000 (radiocarbon-based) years. The lowest level shown on the graph represents the time when the most recent Ice Age was at its maximum.

*A brief overview of the theory appears in Chapter 1, and a more extensive discussion is presented in Chapter 12.

Figure 17.31 Glacial Lake Agassiz, near its greatest extent in central Canada. (Copyright 1997 Minnesota Department of Natural Resources Reprinted with Permission)

which are now tropical or subtropical, experienced an Ice Age near the end of the Paleozoic Era, about 250 million years ago (see Chapter 1). However, no evidence shows that ice sheets existed during this same episode in what are today the higher latitudes of North America and Eurasia. Until the theory of plate tectonics was formulated, we had no reasonable explanation.

Today scientists understand that the areas containing these ancient glacial features were joined together as a single supercontinent (Pangaea) located at latitudes far to the south of their present positions. Later this land mass broke apart, and its pieces, each moving on a different plate, migrated toward their present locations (see Figure 1.15). Now we know that during the geologic past, plate movements accounted for many dramatic climatic changes as land masses shifted in relation to one another and moved to different latitudinal positions. Changes in oceanic circulation also must have occurred, altering the transport of heat and moisture and consequently the climate as well. Because the rate of plate movement is very slow—a few centimetres annually—appreciable changes in the positions of the continents occur only over great spans of geologic time. Thus, climatic changes triggered by shifting plates are extremely gradual and happen on a scale of millions of years.

Variations in Earth's Orbit

Because climatic changes brought about by moving plates are extremely gradual, the plate tectonics theory cannot be used to explain the alternation between glacial and interglacial climates that occurred during the Pleistocene Epoch. Therefore, we must look to some other triggering mechanism that might cause climatic change on a scale of thousands rather than millions of years. Many scientists today strongly suspect that the climatic oscillations that characterized the Pleistocene were linked to variations in Earth's orbit. This hypothesis was first developed by Scottish scientist James Croll in the nineteenth century and later strongly advocated in the early twentieth century by Serbian scientist Milutin Milankovitch. It is based on the premise that variations in incoming solar radiation are principal factors in controlling Earth's climate.

Milankovitch formulated a comprehensive mathematical model based on the following elements (Figure 17.32):

1. Variations in the shape (*eccentricity*) of Earth's orbit about the Sun

2. Changes in obliquity; that is, changes in the angle that Earth's rotational axis makes with the plane of its orbit

3. The wobbling of Earth's axis, called *precession*

By using these factors, Milankovitch calculated variations in the receipt of solar energy and the corresponding surface temperature of Earth back into time in an attempt to correlate these changes with the climatic fluctuations of the Pleistocene. In explaining climatic changes that result from these three variables, note they cause little variation in the total solar energy reaching the ground. Instead, their impact is felt because they change the degree of contrast between the seasons. Somewhat milder winters in the middle to high latitudes means greater snowfall totals, whereas cooler summers bring a reduction in snowmelt.

Later in the twentieth century, international teams of scientists added credibility to the astronomic theory of Milankovitch. Deep-sea sediments containing certain climatically sensitive microorganisms were analyzed to establish a chronology of temperature changes going back nearly half a million years. Ice cores containing remnant bubbles of Pleistocene greenhouse gases were also analyzed to corroborate the later part of that chronology.

This geologic time scale of climatic change was then compared with Milankovitch's calculations of eccentricity, obliquity, and precession to determine whether a correlation did indeed exist. Although the comparison was very involved and mathematically complex, the conclusions were straightforward. The researchers found that major variations in climate over the past several hundred thousand years were closely associated with changes in the geometry of Earth's orbit; that is, cycles of climatic change were shown to correspond closely with the periods of obliquity, precession, and orbital eccentricity.

Let us briefly summarize the ideas that we just described. The theory of plate tectonics provides us with an explanation for the widely spaced and nonperiodic onset of glacial conditions at various times in the geologic past, whereas the theory proposed by Milankovitch (and supported by later work) furnishes an explanation for the alternating glacial and interglacial episodes *within* the Pleistocene Epoch. Interdisciplinary research of the twenty-first century has been refining the details based on further analyses of terrestrial sediments, ice and deep-sea cores, and ancient and modern greenhouse gases (indicators of global warming). These data are used in constructing computer models of ice sheet behaviour, and oceanic and atmospheric circulation patterns, in order to predict changes in global climate and sea level.

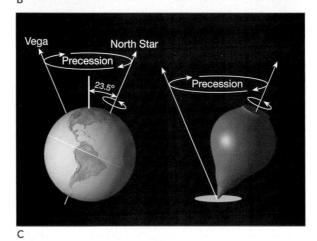

Figure 17.32 Orbital variations. **A.** Eccentricity. The shape of Earth's orbit changes during a cycle that spans about 100 000 years. It gradually changes from nearly circular to one that is more elliptical and back again. This diagram greatly exaggerates the amount of change. **B.** Obliquity. Today the axis of rotation is tilted about 23.5 degrees to the plane of Earth's orbit. During a cycle of 41 000 years, this angle varies from 22.5 degrees to 24.5 degrees. **C.** Precession. Earth's axis wobbles like that of a spinning top. Consequently, the axis points to different spots in the sky during a cycle of about 26 000 years.

CHAPTER SUMMARY

- A *glacier* is a thick mass of ice forming on land by compaction and re-crystallization of snow. Ice sheets are continental in scale; valley glaciers usually follow mountain valleys formed by streams.
- In the zone of fracture ice is brittle. Below about 50 metres ice flows like plastic. Ice can also slip across its bed or deform it. Glacial flow is slow except during rapid surges.
- Glaciers form where more snow falls in winter than melts in summer. Ice and snow are gained in the *zone of accumulation* and lost in the *zone of ablation*. Glacial budget is the net gain or loss between the zones.
- Glaciers erode by *plucking* (lifting) and *abrasion* (scraping). Valley glaciers produce glacial troughs, hanging valleys, fjords, cirques, arêtes, horns, and roches moutonnées.
- Glacial drift includes *till*, poorly sorted sediment deposited by ice, and *stratified drift*, well-sorted sediment deposited by meltwater.

- Lateral moraines form along valley sides and medial moraines form between two merging glaciers. An end moraine is a ridge-shaped deposit of till that forms at the front of a glacier, whereas ground moraine is formed as a sheet-like deposit beneath a moving glacier and is sometimes moulded into streamlined, teardrop-shaped hills called *drumlins*.
- An outwash plain of sand and gravel forms beyond an end moraine, and a similar valley train occupies a valley. *Eskers* are sinuous gravelly ridges formed in tunnels under the ice, and *kames* are deposited as gravelly hills.
- Ice Age glaciers forced migration of organisms; changed stream courses; depressed the crust, which rebounded after ice sheet removal; and affected climate and sea level changes.
- Ice ages are probably caused primarily by plate tectonics moving continents near poles, and by Earth's cyclical orbital variations, including eccentricity, obliquity, and precession.

REVIEW QUESTIONS

1. Describe how glaciers fit into the hydrologic cycle and the rock cycle.

2. Describe the three main components of glacial flow. Within a vertical profile of a glacier, does all of the ice move at the same rate?

3. What are the two main processes involved in the erosion of material underlying flowing glacial ice?

4. Explain what controls the margin of a glacier to advance, retreat, or remain stationary.

5. Describe five landform features associated with alpine glaciers that you would not expect to be associated with a continental ice sheet.

6. What is the difference between ground moraine and an end moraine? What is unique about terminal and recessional moraines?

7. What is glacial drift? What is the difference between till and stratified drift?

8. What are drumlins, and how is their shape believed to reflect ice flow direction?

9. Eskers characteristically have a snake-like shape and are composed of well-sorted sand and gravel deposits. How do these attributes relate to how eskers are formed? In what way are kames related to eskers?

10. In parts of Scandinavia and Canada, land has risen tens to a few hundreds of metres since the end of the Ice Age. How is this uplift believed to be related to glaciation?

18 DESERTS AND WINDS

Sagebrush dots the desert landscape behind an early settler's barn north of Osoyoos, British Columbia. (Photo by Max Lindenthaler/Shutterstock)

CHAPTER OUTLINE

Distribution and Causes of Dry Lands
Geologic Processes in Arid Climates
Transportation of Sediment by Wind
Wind Erosion
Wind Deposits

Climate has a strong influence on the nature and intensity of Earth's external processes, as was clearly demonstrated in the preceding chapter on glaciers. Another excellent example of the strong link between climate and geology is seen when we examine the development of arid landscapes. The word *desert* literally means "deserted" or "unoccupied." For many dry regions this is a very appropriate description, although where water is available in deserts, plants and animals thrive. Nevertheless, the world's dry regions are probably the least familiar land areas on Earth outside the polar realm.

Desert landscapes frequently appear stark. Their profiles are not softened by a carpet of soil and abundant plant life. Instead, barren rocky outcrops with steep, angular slopes are common. At some places the rocks are tinted orange and red. At others they are grey and brown and streaked with black. For many visitors, desert scenery exhibits a striking beauty; to others, the terrain seems bleak. Indeed, deserts are very different from the more humid places where most people live.

Arid regions display the effects of tectonic forces, running water, and wind. Because these processes combine in different ways from place to place, the appearance of desert landscapes varies a great deal (Figure 18.1).

DISTRIBUTION AND CAUSES OF DRY LANDS

The dry regions of the world encompass about 42 million square kilometres, a surprising 30 percent of Earth's land surface. No other climatic group covers so large a land area. Within these water-deficient regions, two climatic types are commonly recognized: **desert,** or arid, and **steppe,** or semi-arid. The two share many features; their differences are primarily a matter of degree (see Box 18.1). The steppe is a marginal and more humid variant of the desert and is a transition zone that surrounds the desert and separates it from bordering humid climates. Figure 18.2 shows that dry lands are concentrated in the subtropics and in the middle latitudes.

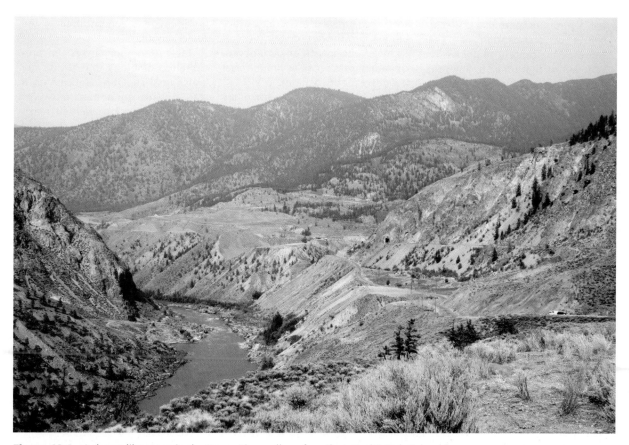

Figure 18.1   A desert-like scene in the Fraser River valley of south-central British Columbia. (Photo by Rolf Meinow/Shutterstock)

BOX 18.1

UNDERSTANDING EARTH

What Is Meant by *Dry*?

Albuquerque, New Mexico, in the southwest United States, receives an average of 20.7 centimetres of rainfall annually. As you might expect, because Albuquerque's precipitation total is modest, this location is classified as a desert when standard climate classification is applied. The Russian city of Verkhoyansk is a remote location located near the Arctic Circle in Siberia. There, the yearly precipitation total averages 15.5 centimetres, about 5 centimetres less than Albuquerque's. Although Verkhoyansk receives less precipitation than Albuquerque, its classification is that of a humid climate. How can this occur?

We all recognize that deserts are dry places, but just what is meant by the term *dry*? That is, how much rain defines the boundary between humid and dry regions? Sometimes it is arbitrarily defined by a single rainfall figure; for example, 25 centimetres of precipitation per year. However, the concept of dryness is a relative one that refers to any situation in which a water deficiency exists. Hence, climatologists define *dry climate* as one in which yearly precipitation is not as great as the potential loss of water by evaporation. Dryness, then, not only is related to annual rainfall totals but also is a function of evaporation, which in turn is closely dependent on temperature.

As temperatures climb, potential evaporation also increases. Fifteen to

TABLE 18.A	Average Annual Precipitation Defining the Boundary between Dry and Humid Climates		
Average Annual Temperature (C°)	Winter Rainfall Maximum (centimetres)	Even Distribution (centimetres)	Summer Rainfall Maximum (centimetres)
5	10	24	38
10	20	34	48
15	30	44	58
20	40	54	68
25	50	64	78
30	60	74	88

25 centimetres of precipitation may be sufficient to support coniferous forests in northern Scandinavia or Siberia, where evaporation into the cool, humid air is slight and a surplus of water remains in the soil. However, the same amount of rain falling on New Mexico or Iran supports only a sparse vegetative cover because evaporation into the hot, dry air is great. So, clearly, no specific amount of precipitation can serve as a universal boundary for dry climates.

To establish the boundary between dry and humid climates, the widely used Köppen classification system uses formulas that involve three variables: average annual precipitation, average annual temperature, and seasonal distribution of precipitation. The use of average annual temperature reflects its importance as an index of evaporation. The amount of rainfall defining the

humid–dry boundary is larger where mean annual temperatures are high, and smaller where temperatures are low. The use of seasonal precipitation distribution as a variable is also related to this idea. If rain is concentrated in the warmest months, loss to evaporation is greater than if the precipitation is concentrated in the cooler months.

Table 18.A summarizes the precipitation amounts that divide dry and humid climates. Notice that a station with an annual mean of 20°C and a summer rainfall maximum of 68 centimetres is classified as dry. If the rain falls primarily in winter, however, the station need receive only 40 centimetres or more to be considered humid. If the precipitation is more evenly distributed, the figure defining the humid–dry boundary is in between the other two.

Subtropical Deserts and Steppes

The heart of the low-latitude dry climates lies in the vicinities of the tropics of Cancer and Capricorn. Figure 18.2 shows a virtually unbroken desert environment stretching for more than 9300 kilometres from the Atlantic coast of North Africa to the dry lands of northwest India. The Northern Hemisphere contains another, much smaller, area of

tropical desert and steppe in northern Mexico and the southwest United States. In the Southern Hemisphere, dry climates dominate Australia. Almost 40 percent of the continent is desert, and much of the remainder is steppe. Arid and semi-arid areas also occur in southern Africa and minor parts of coastal Chile and Peru.

Figure 18.3 is an idealized visualization of Earth's general circulation of air pressure and

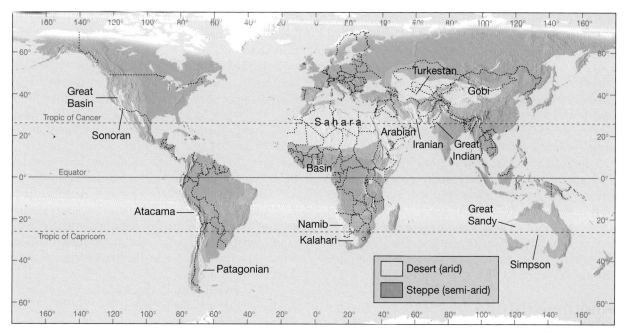

Figure 18.2   Arid and semi-arid climates cover about 30 percent of Earth's land surface. No other climate group covers so large an area.

Figure 18.3   **A.** Idealized diagram of Earth's general atmospheric circulation. The deserts and steppes that are centred in the latitude belt between 20° and 30° north and south coincide with the subtropical high-pressure belts. Here, dry subsiding air inhibits cloud formation and precipitation. By contrast, the pressure belt known as the equatorial low is associated with areas that are among the rainiest on Earth. **B.** In this view of Earth from space, North Africa's Sahara Desert, the adjacent Arabian Desert, and the Kalahari and Namib deserts in southern Africa are clearly visible as tan-coloured, cloud-free zones. The band of clouds that extends across central Africa and the adjacent oceans coincides with the equatorial low-pressure belt. (Photo courtesy of NASA)

winds. Heated air in the pressure belt known as the *equatorial low* rises between 15 and 20 kilometres and then spreads out. As the upper-level flow reaches 20° to 30° latitude, north or south, it sinks toward the surface. Air that rises into lower pressure areas in the atmosphere expands, cools, and leads to the development of clouds and precipitation. Areas under the influence of the equatorial low are among the rainiest on Earth. Just the opposite is true for the regions near 30° north and south latitude, where high pressure dominates as *subtropical highs* and air is subsiding. When air sinks, it is compressed and warmed—the opposite of what is needed to produce clouds and precipitation. Consequently, highs are known for their clear skies, sunshine, and ongoing drought (Figure 18.3B).

Middle-Latitude Deserts

Middle-latitude deserts and steppes are sheltered in the deep interiors of large land masses, far removed from the ocean, which is the ultimate source of moisture for cloud formation and precipitation. One well-known example is the Gobi Desert of central Asia, north of India (Figure 18.2).

High mountains across the paths of prevailing winds further separate these areas from water-bearing, maritime air masses; the mountains force the air to lose much of its water as it ascends. When air rises, it expands and cools, producing clouds and precipitation on the windward sides of mountains. By contrast, the leeward sides of mountains are usually much drier (Figure 18.4) because air reaching the leeward side has lost much of its moisture. As the air descends, it is compressed and

warmed, making cloud formation even less likely. The dry region that results is often referred to as a **rain shadow**.

In North America, the foremost mountain barriers to moisture from the Pacific are the Coast Ranges, Sierra Nevada, and Cascades (Figure 18.4). The Okanagan Valley of British Columbia lies in such a rain shadow area (chapter-opening photo; Box 18.2). In Asia, the great Himalayan chain prevents the summertime monsoon flow of moist Indian Ocean air from reaching the interior.

Because the Southern Hemisphere lacks extensive land areas in the middle latitudes, only a small area of desert and steppe occurs in this latitude range, existing primarily near the southern tip of South America in the rain shadow of the towering Andes.

The middle-latitude deserts provide an example of how tectonic processes affect climate. Rain shadow deserts exist by virtue of the mountains produced when plates collide. Without such mountain-building episodes, wetter climates would prevail where many dry regions exist today.

Polar Deserts

The coldest of the world's deserts occur in the Earth's polar regions, where the constant descent of cold, dry air associated with stable high-pressure cells prevents the formation of rain clouds.

Much of Canada's Arctic region is polar desert (Figure 18.5). Polar desert conditions dominate most of the northern Arctic Archipelago, including most of Axel Heiberg and Ellesmere islands, a significant portion of Baffin Island, the majority of Somerset Island, and all of the remaining Queen

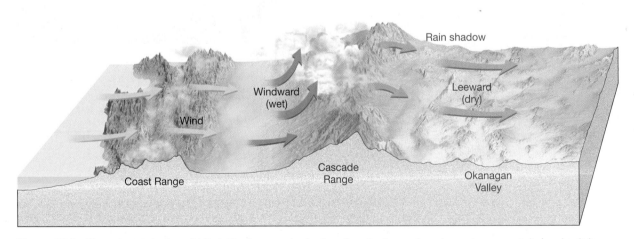

Figure 18.4 Many deserts in the middle latitudes are rain shadow deserts. As moving air meets a mountain barrier, it is forced to rise. Clouds and precipitation on the windward side often result. Air descending the leeward side is much drier. The mountains effectively cut the leeward side off from the sources of moisture, producing a rain shadow desert. The southern Okanagan desert of British Columbia occurs in the rain shadow of the Cascade Mountains.

CANADIAN PROFILE
The Okanagan Valley: A Canadian Desert

The Okanagan Valley in the interior of British Columbia is familiar to most Canadians as a fruit-growing and popular tourist region. However, many Canadians don't realize that the Okanagan Valley is also Canada's only non-polar desert. The valley, carved out by glaciers during the last Ice Age, is approximately 20 kilometres wide and about 250 kilometres long and extends from the British Columbia–Washington border to Vernon (see Figure 18.A).

Arid conditions prevail in the Okanagan Valley because of the rain-shadow effect of the Cascade Mountains to the west, characterized by an average annual precipitation of about 25 centimetres. Because much of the moisture from westerly winds is depleted from the air by the time it reaches the Okanagan Valley, cloud cover tends to be minimal. Consequently, the region experiences about 2000 hours of sunshine per year.

An assortment of typical desert plants, such as sagebrush and prickly pear cactus, are found in the very dry, southern sector of the valley. The northern Okanagan is less arid and supports grasslands and scattered forests of Ponderosa pine.

Even though the region is a desert, it hosts a number of elongate lakes that include the Okanagan, Swan, Kalamalka, and Wood lakes. In fact, the very word *Okanagan* means "place of water" in Salish (the language of the First Nations people who settled in the valley). The successful agricultural and tourist industries of the region owe their existence to the water supplied from these lakes and associated

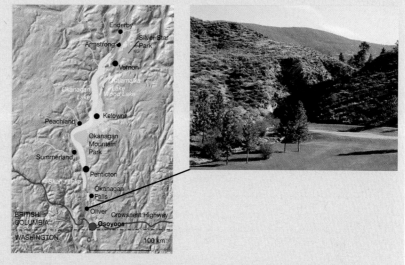

Figure 18.A Nk'Mip Canyon Desert Golf Course, southern Okanagan Valley. Note how irrigation has transformed part of the desert landscape into a lush, green fairway (foreground). Map: Location of the Okanagan Valley area. (Photo courtesy of Dave George, Nk'Mip Canyon Desert Golf Course)

rivers. The elongate shape of the lakes attests to the scouring action of glaciers during the last Ice Age.

The striking contrast between the lush green of a golf course and the nearly barren slopes of the surrounding hills in Figure 18.A illustrates the importance of irrigation in the Okanagan Valley. In addition to the availability of water, soil fertility contributes greatly to the success of agriculture in the region. Unlike many desert soils, those of the Okanagan are rich in nutrients, as their parent materials include the nutrient-rich deltaic sediments deposited after the last Ice Age.

Dairy and beef farming were established early in the settlement of the valley and remain important industries

today. These activities are concentrated in the semi-arid, northern sector of the valley where little or no irrigation is required to support plant growth for grazing cattle. Fruit growing in the Okanagan was first established by missionaries in 1862 near Kelowna but only became significant in the 1890s when the Government of Canada provided incentives to develop the fruit-growing industry. At present, much Canadian fruit that is available in supermarkets across Canada, such as apricots, cherries, peaches, pears, and plums, comes from the Okanagan Valley. The Okanagan Valley has also become one of Canada's most successful wine regions and accounts for most of British Columbia's wine production.

Elizabeth Islands. The climate is very dry and cold, and mean summer temperatures in the northern reaches of the region are as low as –1.5°C (and as high as 2°C in the south, on the Lancaster Plateau in western Baffin Island). Winter mean temperatures range between –32°C in the north and –23°C in the south. Annual precipitation is also very low, ranging

mostly between 10 and 20 centimetres, with a few sites registering greater values (up to 40 centimetres) in the Baffin Island Uplands. The northern portions of the region, such as Ellesmere Island, generally receive less precipitation than anywhere else in Canada, sometimes as little as 5 centimetres in a single year.

Figure 18.5   Typical polar desert landscape on Cornwallis Island, Arctic Canada. (Photo by Alfred Lenz)

GEOLOGIC PROCESSES IN ARID CLIMATES

The angular hills, sheer canyon walls, and desert surface of pebbles or sand contrast sharply with the rounded hills and curving slopes of more humid places. Although the contrasts may be striking, they do not reflect different processes. They merely reveal the different effects of the same processes that operate under contrasting climatic conditions.

Weathering

In humid regions, relatively fine-textured soils support an almost continuous cover of vegetation that mantles the surface. Here the slopes and rock edges are rounded, reflecting the strong influence of chemical weathering in a humid climate. By contrast, much of the weathered debris in deserts consists of unaltered rock and mineral fragments—the result of mechanical weathering processes. In dry lands, rock weathering of any type is greatly reduced because of the lack of moisture and the scarcity of organic acids from decaying plants. However, chemical weathering is not completely lacking in deserts. Over long spans

of time, clays and thin soils do form, and many iron-bearing silicate minerals oxidize, producing the rust-coloured stain (desert varnish) that tints some desert landscapes.

The Role of Water

Permanent streams are normal in humid regions, but practically all desert stream beds are dry most of the time (Figure 18.6A). Deserts have **ephemeral** (*ephemero* = short-lived) **streams,** which means they carry water only in response to specific episodes of rainfall. A typical ephemeral stream might flow for only a few days or perhaps just a few hours during the year. In some years the channel might carry no water at all (Figure 18.7).

This fact is obvious even to the casual traveller who notices numerous bridges with no streams beneath them or numerous dips in the road where dry channels cross. However, when the rare heavy showers do come, so much rain falls in such a short time that not all of it can soak in. Because desert vegetative cover is sparse, runoff is largely unhindered and consequently rapid, often creating flash floods along valley floors (Figure 18.6B). Because much

A   B

Figure 18.6 **A.** Most of the time, desert stream channels are dry. **B.** An ephemeral stream shortly after a heavy shower. Although such floods are short-lived, large amounts of erosion occur. (Photos by E. J. Tarbuck)

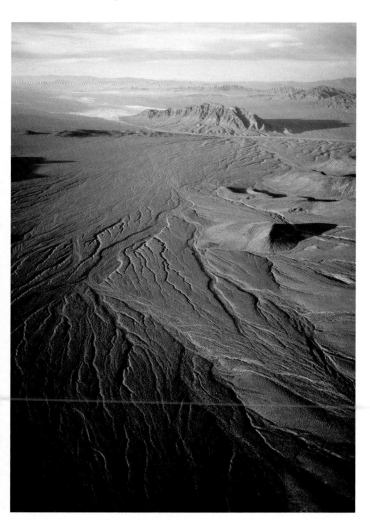

surface material in a desert is not anchored by vegetation, the amount of erosional work that occurs during a single short-lived rain event is impressive.

Humid regions are notable for their integrated drainage systems. But in arid regions, streams usually lack an extensive system of tributaries. In fact, a basic characteristic of desert streams is that they are small and die out before reaching the sea. Because the water table is usually far below the surface, few desert streams can draw on it as streams do in humid regions. Without a steady supply of water, the combination of evaporation and infiltration soon depletes the stream.

The few permanent streams that do cross arid regions, such as the Colorado and Nile rivers, originate *outside* the desert, commonly in well-watered mountains. Here the water supply must be great to compensate for the losses occurring as the stream crosses the desert. For example, after the Nile leaves its headwaters in the lakes and mountains of central Africa, it traverses almost 3000 kilometres of the Sahara without a single tributary.

It should be emphasized that *running water, although infrequent, nevertheless does most of the erosional work in deserts.* This is contrary to the common belief that wind is the most important erosional

Figure 18.7 Dry channels of ephemeral streams cover this parched desert surface. Desert rains are infrequent but when they occur, they are often heavy, short-lived, and erosive. (Photo by Michael Collier)

agent sculpting desert landscapes. Although wind erosion is indeed more significant in dry areas than elsewhere, most desert landforms are carved by running water. The main role of wind is in the transportation and deposition of sediment, which creates and shapes the ridges and mounds we call dunes.

TRANSPORTATION OF SEDIMENT BY WIND

Moving air, like moving water, is turbulent and able to pick up loose debris and transport it to other locations. Just as in a stream, the velocity of wind increases with height above the surface so that wind transports fine particles in suspension while heavier ones are carried as bed load (Figure 18.8). However, the transport of sediment by wind differs from that of running water in two significant ways. First, wind's lower density compared with water renders it less capable of picking up and transporting coarse materials. Second, because wind is not confined to channels, it can spread sediment over large areas, as well as high into the atmosphere.

Bed Load

The bed load carried by wind consists of sand grains. Observations in the field and experiments that use wind tunnels indicate that windblown sand moves by skipping and bouncing along the surface—a process termed saltation (Chapter 15).

The movement of sand grains begins when wind reaches a velocity sufficient to overcome the inertia of the resting particles. At first the sand rolls along the surface. When a moving sand grain strikes another grain, one or both of them may jump into the air. Once in the air, the grains are carried forward by the wind until gravity pulls them back toward the surface. When the sand hits the surface, it either bounces back into the air or dislodges other grains, which then jump upward. In this manner, a chain reaction is established, filling the air near the ground with saltating sand grains in a short interval of time (Figure 18.8).

Bouncing sand grains never travel far from the surface. Even when winds are very strong, the height of the saltating sand seldom exceeds a metre and usually is no greater than a half metre. Some sand grains are too large to be thrown into the air by impact from other particles. When this is the case, the energy provided by the impact of the smaller saltating grains drives the larger grains forward. This is called surface creep. Estimates indicate that between 20 and 25 percent of the sand transported in a sandstorm is moved in this way.

Figure 18.8 Schematic diagram illustrating suspended load, rolling bed load, and saltation. Inset: A cloud of saltating sand grains moving up the gentle slope of a dune. (Photo © Dennis Frates/Alamy)

Figure 18.9 Dust blackens the sky over Pearce, southern Alberta. Because of storms like this, portions of the Canadian and American prairies were called the Dust Bowl in the 1930s.
Photo by Chris Gibson from the collection of the Sir Alexander Galt Museum and Archives

Suspended Load

Unlike sand, finer particles of dust can be swept high into the atmosphere by the wind. Because dust is commonly composed of rather flat particles that have large surface areas compared with their weight, it is relatively easy for turbulent air to counterbalance the pull of gravity and keep these fine particles airborne for hours or even days. Although both silt and clay can be carried in suspension, silt commonly makes up the bulk of the suspended load because the reduced level of chemical weathering in deserts provides only small amounts of clay.

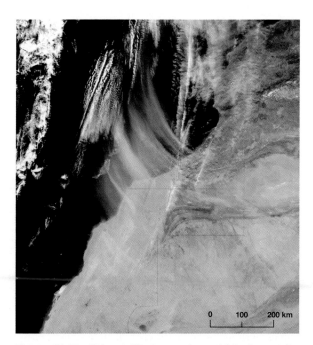

Figure 18.10 This satellite image shows thick plumes of dust from the Sahara Desert blowing northwestward over the Canary Islands. Dust storms can cover huge areas. (Photo courtesy of NASA)

Fine particles are easily carried by the wind, but they are not so easily picked up. Wind velocity is practically zero within a very thin layer close to the ground. Thus, the wind cannot lift the sediment by itself. Instead, the dust must be ejected or spattered into the moving air by bouncing sand grains or other disturbances. This idea is illustrated nicely on a dry unpaved country road on a windy day. Left undisturbed, little dust is raised by the wind. However, as a car or truck moves over the road, the layer of silt is kicked up, creating a thick cloud of dust.

Although the suspended load is usually deposited relatively near its source, high winds are capable of carrying large quantities of dust great distances (Figure 18.9). In the 1930s, silt that was picked up in Kansas was transported to New England and beyond into the North Atlantic. Similarly, dust blown from the Sahara has been traced as far as the West Indies (Figure 18.10).

WIND EROSION

Compared with running water and glaciers, wind is a relatively insignificant erosional agent. It is more effective in arid lands where dryness and scanty vegetation exist. Wind can pick up, transport, and deposit great quantities of fine sediment. During the 1930s, parts of the Prairies experienced vast dust storms. The plowing under of the natural vegetative cover for farming, followed by severe drought, exposed the land to wind erosion and led to the area being labelled the Dust Bowl (see Box 5.2).

Deflation, Blowouts, and Desert Pavement

One way that wind erodes is by **deflation** (*de* = out, *flat* = blow), the lifting and removal of loose material.

Figure 18.11 Formation of a blowout. **A.** Area before deflation. **B.** Area after deflation has created a shallow depression. **C.** This photo was taken in Saskatchewan in the 1930s during a prolonged drought. Strong winds removed the soil that was not anchored by vegetation. The mounds are more than 1 metre high and show the level of the land before deflation.
(Photo courtesy of the Saskatchewan Archives Board, photo R-A15082-3)

In portions of the 1930s Dust Bowl, vast areas of land were lowered by as much as a metre in only a few years.

The most noticeable results of deflation in some places are shallow depressions appropriately called **blowouts** (Figure 18.11). In the Great Plains region, from Alberta south to Texas, thousands of blowouts range from small dimples less than 1 metre deep and 3 metres wide to depressions that approach 50 metres deep and several kilometres across. The local water table controls the depths of these basins as damp ground and vegetation prevent further deflation.

In portions of many deserts the surface is a closely packed layer of coarse pebbles and cobbles too large to be moved by the wind, called a **desert pavement**. The common explanation for its formation is that deflation lowers the surface by removing sand

and silt until eventually only a continuous cover of coarse particles remains (Figure 18.12). Once desert pavement becomes established (which can take hundreds of years) the surface is protected from further deflation if left undisturbed. However, because the layer is only one or two stones thick, disruption by vehicles or animals can dislodge the pavement and expose the fine-grained material below to deflation once again.

Ventifacts and Yardangs

Like glaciers and streams, wind also erodes by abrasion. In dry regions, as well as along some beaches, windblown sand cuts and polishes exposed rock surfaces. Abrasion sometimes creates interestingly

Figure 18.12 **A.** Formation of desert pavement. As these cross-sections illustrate, coarse particles gradually become concentrated into a tightly packed layer as deflation lowers the surface by removing sand and silt. **B.** If left undisturbed, desert pavement, such as this in Antarctica's Allan Hills, will protect the surface from further deflation (light-coloured boulder at the left edge of the photograph is about 30 centimetres across).
(Photo by S. R. Hicock)

Figure 18.13 Ventifacts are rocks that are polished and shaped by sandblasting, like these basalt boulders in the Allan Hills of Antarctica.
(Photo by S. R. Hicock)

shaped stones called **ventifacts** (Figure 18.13). The side of the stone exposed to the prevailing wind is abraded, leaving it polished, pitted, and with sharp edges. If the wind is not consistently from one direction, or if the pebble becomes reoriented, it may have several faceted surfaces.

Sometimes abrasion is attributed to balanced rocks that stand high atop narrow pedestals and intricate detailing on tall pinnacles. However, sand seldom travels more than a metre above the surface, so the wind's vertical sandblasting effect is obviously limited.

Wind erosion is responsible for creating much larger features, called **yardangs** (from the Turkistani word *yar*, meaning "steep bank"). A yardang is a streamlined, wind-sculpted ridge (like an inverted ship's hull) oriented parallel to the prevailing wind. Individual yardangs tend to be less than 5 metres high and 10 metres or so long, but can reach up to 10 times that size.

WIND DEPOSITS

Although wind is relatively unimportant in producing *erosional* landforms, significant *depositional* landforms can be created in the world's dry lands and along many sandy coasts. Wind deposits are of two distinctive types: (1) mounds and ridges of sand from the wind's bed load, which we call dunes, and (2) extensive blankets of silt, called loess, that once were carried in suspension.

Sand Deposits

As is the case with running water, wind drops its load of sediment when velocity falls. Sand begins to accumulate wherever an obstruction across the path of the wind slows its movement. Winds commonly deposit sand in mounds or ridges called **dunes** (Figure 18.14).

As moving air encounters an object (e.g., clump of vegetation or rock) the wind sweeps around and

Figure 18.14 Sand sliding down the steep slip face of a dune in White Sands National Monument, New Mexico. (Photo by Michael Collier)

over it, leaving a shadow of slower-moving air behind the obstacle, as well as a smaller zone of quieter air just in front of the obstacle. Some of the saltating sand grains come to rest in these wind shadows. As sand accumulates it becomes a barrier to the wind and thus a more efficient trap for more sand. If the supply of sand is sufficient and the wind blows steadily long enough, the mound of sand grows into a dune.

Many dunes have an asymmetric profile, with the leeward (sheltered) slope being steep and the windward slope more gently inclined (Figure 18.15). Sand moves up the gentler slope on the windward side by saltation. Just beyond the crest of the dune, where the wind velocity is reduced, the sand accumulates. As more sand collects, the slope steepens and eventually some of it slides under the pull of gravity (Figure 18.14). In this way, the leeward slope of the dune, called the **slip face**, maintains an angle of about 34 degrees, the angle of repose for loose dry sand (see Chapter 14). Continued sand accumulation, coupled with periodic slides down the slip face, results in the slow migration of the dune in the direction of air movement.

As sand is deposited on the slip face, inclined cross-beds form in the direction the wind is blowing (Figure 18.15; also the Athabasca dunes in Saskatchewan). When the dunes are eventually buried under other layers of sediment and become part of the sedimentary rock record, their asymmetric shape

is destroyed, but the cross-beds remain as testimony to their origin. Cross-bedding is well displayed in the sandstone walls of Zion Canyon in southern Utah (Figure 18.15D) and in southern Alberta's badlands.

In some areas, moving sand is troublesome. For example, in Figure 18.16 dunes are advancing across irrigated fields in Egypt. In portions of the Middle East, valuable oil-rigs must be protected from encroaching dunes. In some cases, fences are built far enough upwind of the dunes to stop their migration. As sand continues to collect, however, the fences must be built higher. In Kuwait, protective fences extend for almost 10 kilometres around one important oil field. To keep a portion of Highway 95 near Winnemucca, Nevada, open to traffic, 1500 and 4000 cubic metres of sand must be taken away about three times a year. Attempts at stabilizing dunes by planting different varieties of grasses have been unsuccessful because the meagre rainfall cannot support the plants.

Types of Sand Dunes

Dunes are sand accumulations that usually assume consistent patterns. Figure 18.17 shows six different types and gradations exist among them, as do irregular dunes that do not fit any type. Wind direction, velocity, availability of sand, and amount of vegetation are the main factors determining dune form and size.

D

Figure 18.15   As parts **A** and **B** illustrate, dunes commonly have an asymmetrical shape. The steeper leeward side is called the slip face. Sand grains deposited on the slip face at the angle of repose create the cross-bedding of the dunes. **C.** A complex pattern develops in response to changes in wind direction. Also notice that when dunes are buried and become part of the sedimentary record, the cross-bedded structure is preserved. **D.** Cross-beds are an obvious characteristic of the Navajo Sandstone in Zion National Park, Utah.
(Photo by Marli Miller)

Figure 18.16 These desert dunes (called barchans) in Australia are advancing from left to right. (Photo © Atmotu Images/Alamy)

BARCHAN DUNES Solitary sand dunes shaped like crescents and with their tips pointing downwind are called **barchan dunes** (Figure 18.17A). They form where supplies of sand are limited and the surface is relatively flat, hard, and lacking vegetation. They migrate slowly with the wind up to 15 metres per year. The largest barchans reach 30 metres high while the maximum spread between their horns approaches 300 metres. When the wind direction is nearly constant, the crescent form of these dunes is nearly symmetrical. However, when the wind direction is not perfectly fixed, one tip becomes larger than the other.

TRANSVERSE DUNES Where prevailing winds are steady, sand is plentiful, and when vegetation is sparse or absent, dunes form a series of long ridges separated by troughs and oriented at right angles to the prevailing wind, called **transverse dunes** (Figure 18.17B). Many coastal dunes are of this type. Transverse dunes are common in many arid regions where the extensive surface of wavy sand is sometimes called a *sand sea*. In some parts of the Sahara and Arabian deserts, transverse dunes reach heights of 200 metres, are 1 to 3 kilometres across, and can extend for distances of 100 kilometres or more.

A relatively common dune form is intermediate between isolated barchans and extensive waves of transverse dunes. Such dunes, called **barchanoid dunes**, form scalloped rows of sand oriented at right angles to the wind (Figures 18.17C). The rows resemble a series of barchans that have been positioned side by side.

LONGITUDINAL DUNES **Longitudinal dunes** are long ridges of sand that form parallel to the prevailing wind where sand supplies are moderate (Figure 18.17D). Apparently, the prevailing wind direction must vary somewhat but still remain in the same quadrant of the compass. Smaller dunes are only 3 or 4 metres high and several dozens of metres long; in portions of North Africa, Arabia, and central Australia, longitudinal dunes can reach 100 metres high and extend for more than 100 kilometres.

PARABOLIC DUNES **Parabolic dunes** form where vegetation partially covers the sand. The shape of these dunes resembles barchans except that their tips point into the wind (Figure 18.17E). Parabolic dunes often form along coasts where there are strong onshore winds and abundant sand. If the sand's sparse vegetative cover is disturbed at some spot, deflation creates a blowout. Sand is then transported out of the depression and deposited as a curved rim, which grows higher as deflation enlarges the blowout.

STAR DUNES Confined largely to parts of the Sahara and Arabian deserts, **star dunes** are isolated hills of sand that exhibit a complex form (Figure 18.17F). Their name is derived from their bases, which resemble multi-pointed stars. Usually three or four sharp-crested ridges diverge from a central high point that in

Figure 18.17 Sand dune types.

some cases can approach 90 metres high. Star dunes develop where wind directions are variable.

Loess (Silt) Deposits

In some parts of the world the surface topography is mantled with deposits of windblown silt, called **loess**. Over thousands of years, dust storms deposited this material. When loess is breached by streams or road cuts, it tends to maintain vertical cliffs and lacks visible layers (Figure 18.18).

The distribution of loess worldwide indicates that this sediment has two primary sources: deserts and glacial outwash deposits. The thickest and most extensive deposits of loess on Earth occur in western and northern China. They were blown there from the extensive desert basins of central Asia.

Accumulations of 30 metres are common, and thicknesses of more than 100 metres have been measured. It is this fine buff-coloured sediment that gives the Yellow River (Hwang Ho) its name.

In North America, deposits of loess are significant in many areas, including South Dakota, Nebraska, Iowa, Missouri, and Illinois, as well as portions of the Columbia Plateau in the Pacific Northwest. Soils derived from this wind-deposited sediment are among the most fertile in the world.

A

B

Figure 18.18 **A.** This vertical loess bluff near the Mississippi River in southern Illinois is about three metres high. **B.** Vegetated loess on south Vancouver Island (shovel is for scale). (Photo **A** by James E. Patterson; photo **B** by S. R. Hicock)

Loess in North America (and Europe) was derived from deposits of stratified drift and till, much of it in ancestral Canada. During the retreat of the ice sheets, many river valleys were choked with sediment deposited by meltwater that was exposed to the air. Strong westerly winds sweeping across the barren floodplains and till plains picked up the finer sediment and dropped it as a blanket on the northern United States.

CHAPTER SUMMARY

- Two dry areas are *desert* (arid; low and mid latitudes) and *steppe* (semi-arid). Mechanical weathering dominates, and desert streams are ephemeral but do the most erosion. Wind also erodes, transports, and deposits sediment.
- Wind moves sand mainly by *saltation* (grain collisions). Wind erodes by deflation (removing fine sediment), leaving blowouts and desert pavements (stone layers); and by abrasion, creating *ventifacts* (stones) and *yardangs* (ridges).
- Wind deposits sand dunes (barchan, transverse, longitudinal, parabolic, star) and loess (silt from suspension). Downwind sides of dunes tend to be steeper.

MasteringGeology   www.masteringgeology.com

Looking for additional review and test prep materials? Visit the Study Area in MasteringGeology to enhance your understanding of this chapter's content by accessing a variety of resources, including

Self-Study Quizzes, Geoscience Animations, GEODe Tutorials, RSS feeds, flashcards, weblinks, self-study quizzes, and an optional Pearson eText.

REVIEW QUESTIONS

1. What criteria determine whether a given area is a desert or not?

2. How do sand dunes migrate, and how does the development of cross-beds relate to this process?

3. What are the primary factors responsible for the development of subtropical deserts, middle-latitude deserts, and polar deserts? Describe two places where true desert conditions occur in Canada.

4. Describe the way in which wind transports sand. How is this similar and different to the way sediment is transported in a stream?

5. Although sand dunes are the best-known wind deposits, accumulations of loess are significant in some parts of the world. What is loess, where are such deposits found, and what are the origins of this sediment?

6. Why is wind erosion relatively more important in arid regions than in more humid areas?

7. If it is so dry in deserts, why do they experience flash floods?

SHORELINES

19

Waves crash into rocks at Sombrio Point on Vancouver Island. (Photo © Josh McCulloch/Alamy)

Shorelines are dynamic environments. Their topography, geologic makeup, and climate vary greatly from place to place. Continental and oceanic processes converge along coasts to create landscapes that frequently undergo rapid change. When it comes to the deposition of sediment, they are transition zones between marine and continental environments. From an economic perspective, the interpretation of sedimentary processes from features in ancient shoreline deposits is important to searching for oil and gas reserves.

THE SHORELINE: A DYNAMIC INTERFACE

Nowhere is the restless nature of the ocean's water more noticeable than along the shore—the dynamic interface (common boundary) among air, land, and sea. Here we can see the rhythmic rise and fall of tides and observe waves constantly rolling in and breaking. Sometimes the waves are low and gentle. At other times they pound the shore with awesome fury. Although it may not be obvious, the shoreline is constantly being modified (Figure 19.1).

Present-day shorelines are not just formed by the relentless attack on the land by the sea but result from multiple geologic processes. For example, sea level dropped during ice ages, whereas coastal areas were inundated by the worldwide rise in sea level as glaciers melted at the close of the last Ice Age (Chapter 17). As the sea encroached landward, the shoreline retreated, becoming superimposed on existing landscapes. Thus shorelines have changed with sea level changes and will continue to do so.

Today the coastal zone is experiencing intensive human activity where people often assume it is a stable platform and well suited for constructing buildings. In fact many coastal landforms, especially beaches and barrier islands, are relatively fragile, short-lived features that are inappropriate sites for development. This is because they experience the full impact of waves.

WAVES

Wind-generated waves provide most of the energy that shapes and modifies shorelines. Where the land and sea meet, waves that may have travelled

A   B

Figure 19.1   A. Aerial photo of Sidney Spit, Sidney Spit Marine Park, British Columbia. This feature was produced by the reworking, transportation, and redeposition of sedimentary particles derived primarily from glacial materials that were deposited during the Pleistocene Epoch. Modern shoreline processes continue to modify this coastal landscape. **B.** Aerial photo of East Point Regional Park, Saturna Island, British Columbia. Rugged cliffs of this area are swept clean of sediment due to strong wave and current action. Although this promontory is composed of relatively resistant bedrock, erosional shoreline processes are slowly, but surely, wearing it away.
(Photo **A** © Chris Cheadle/Alamy; photo **B** © All Canada Photos/Alamy)

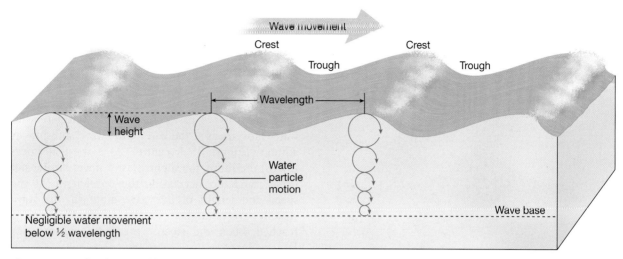

Figure 19.2 This diagram illustrates the basic parts of a wave as well as the movement of water particles with the passage of the wave. Negligible water movement occurs below a depth equal to one half the wavelength (the level of the dashed line).

unimpeded for hundreds or thousands of kilometres suddenly encounter a barrier that will not allow them to advance farther and that must absorb their energy.

Wave Characteristics

The undulations of the water surface (that we call waves) derive their energy and motion from the wind. In a breeze of less than three kilometres per hour, only small wavelets appear. At greater wind speeds more stable waves gradually form and advance with the wind.

All waves have the characteristics illustrated in Figure 19.2. The tops of the waves are *crests*, which are separated by *troughs*. The vertical distance between trough and crest is the **wave height**. The horizontal distance separating successive crests is the **wavelength**. The **wave period** is the time interval between the passage of two successive crests at a stationary point.

The height, length, and period that are eventually achieved by a wave depend on three factors: (1) the wind speed, (2) the length of time the wind has blown, and (3) the **fetch**, or distance that the wind has travelled across open water. As the quantity of energy transferred from the wind to the water increases, the height and steepness of the waves increase as well. Eventually a critical point is reached where waves grow so tall that they topple over, forming breakers called *whitecaps*.

A particular wind speed has a maximum fetch and duration of wind beyond which waves no longer increase in size. By this stage, waves lose as much energy through the breaking of whitecaps as they are receiving from the wind.

When wind stops or changes direction, or if waves leave the stormy area where they were created, they continue on without relation to local winds. The waves also undergo a gradual change to *swells*, which are lower and longer and can carry a storm's energy to distant shores. Because many independent wave systems exist at the same time, the sea surface acquires a complex, irregular pattern. Hence, the sea waves we watch from the shore are often a mixture of swells from faraway storms and waves created by local winds.

Circular Orbital Motion

When observing waves, you are watching *energy* travel through a medium (water). In open waters, it is the wave energy that moves forward, not the water itself. Each water particle moves in a circular path during the passage of a wave (Figures 19.2 and 19.3). When water is part of the wave crest, it moves in the same direction as the advancing waveform. In the trough, the water moves in the opposite direction. The toy boat in Figure 19.3 merely seems to bob up and down and sway slightly back and forth without advancing appreciably from its original position.

The energy contributed by the wind to the water is transmitted not only along the surface of the sea but also downward. However, beneath the surface, the circular motion rapidly diminishes until, at a depth equal to about half the wavelength, the movement of water particles becomes negligible; this depth is called *wave base* (Figure 19.2).

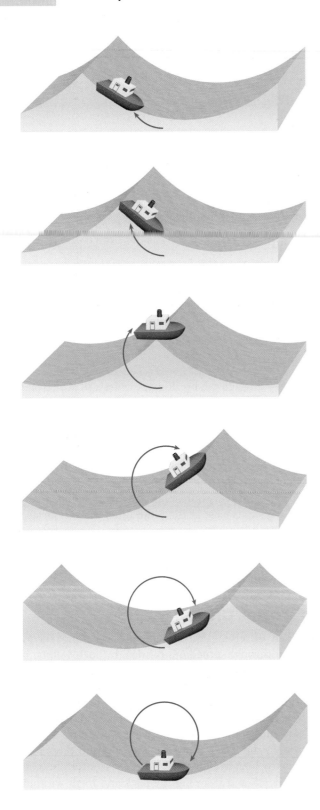

Figure 19.3 The movements of the toy boat illustrate that the wave energy advances but the water itself advances only slightly from its original position. In this sequence, the wave moves from left to right as the boat (and the water in which it is floating) rotates in a circular motion. The boat moves slightly to the left up the front of the approaching wave, and then, after reaching the crest, slides to the right down the back of the wave.

Waves in the Surf Zone

As long as a wave is in deep water, it is unaffected by water depth (Figure 19.4, left). However, when a wave approaches the shore, the water becomes shallower and influences wave behaviour. The wave begins to "feel bottom" at a water depth equal to about half its wavelength (wave base). Such depths interfere with water movement at the base of the wave and slow its advance (Figure 19.4, centre). As a wave advances toward the shore, the slightly faster waves farther out to sea catch up, decreasing the wavelength. As the speed and length of the wave diminish, the wave steadily grows higher. Finally, a critical point is reached when the steep wave front collapses, or *breaks.*

The turbulent water created by breaking waves is called **surf**. On the landward margin of the surf zone, the turbulent sheet of water from collapsing breakers, called *swash*, moves up the slope of the beach. When the energy of the swash has been expended, the water flows back down the beach toward the surf zone as *backwash*.

WAVE EROSION

During calm weather, wave action is minimal; it is during storms that waves accomplish most of their work (Figure 19.5). Each breaking wave can hurl thousands of tonnes of water against the land, sometimes causing the ground to literally tremble. The pressures exerted by Atlantic waves in wintertime, for example, average nearly 10 000 kilograms per square metre.

It is no wonder that cracks and crevices are quickly opened in cliffs, seawalls, breakwaters, and anything else that is subjected to these enormous shocks. Water is forced into every opening, causing air in the cracks to become highly compressed by the thrust of crashing waves. When the wave subsides, the air expands rapidly, dislodging rock fragments and enlarging and extending fractures.

Abrasion—the scouring and grinding action of the water armed with rock fragments (see Chapter 15)—is probably more intense in the surf zone than in any other environment. Smooth, rounded stones and pebbles along the shore attest to the relentless grinding action of rock against rock in the surf zone. Further, such fragments are used as tools by the waves as they cut horizontally into the land (Figure 19.6).

SAND MOVEMENT ON THE BEACH

Beaches are sometimes called "rivers of sand" because the energy from breaking waves often moves large

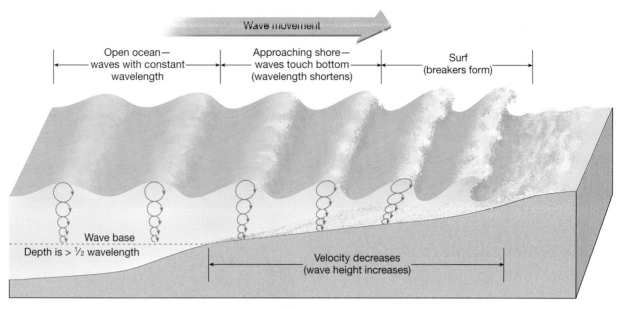

Figure 19.4   Changes that occur when a wave moves onto shore.

quantities of sand along the beach and in the surf zone, commonly by bending waves.

Wave Refraction

The bending of waves, called **wave refraction** (Figure 19.7), affects the distribution of energy along the shore and strongly influences where and how much erosion, sediment transport, and deposition will take place.

Waves seldom approach the shore straight on, and most move toward it at an angle. When they reach the shallow water of a smoothly sloping bottom, waves are bent and tend to become parallel to the shore. Such bending occurs because the part of the wave nearest the shore reaches shallow water and

Figure 19.5   When waves break against the shore, the force of the water can be powerful and the erosional work that is accomplished can be great. Mistaken Point, Newfoundland (note geologists for scale). (Photo by C. Tsujita)

Figure 19.6 **A.** Abrasion can be intense in the surf zone. Smooth, rounded rocks along the shore are an obvious reminder of this fact. Lawrencetown Beach Provincial Park, Nova Scotia. **B.** Sandstone cliff undercut by wave erosion at Gabriola Island, British Columbia.
(Photo **A** by Vadim.Petrov/Shutterstock; photo **B** by Fletcher and Baylis/Photo Researchers, Inc.)

A

B

slows first, whereas the part that is still in deep water continues forward at its full speed. The net result is a wave front that may approach nearly parallel to the shore regardless of the original direction of the wave.

Because of refraction, wave impact is concentrated against the sides and ends of headlands that project into the water, whereas wave attack is weakened in bays (Figure 19.8). As the waves reach the shallow water in front of the headland sooner than they do in adjacent bays, they are bent more nearly parallel to the protruding land and strike it from all three sides. By contrast, refraction in the bays causes

Figure 19.7 Waves bend as they approach Chesterman Beach near Tofino, British Columbia.
(Photo © Greg Vaughn/Alamy)

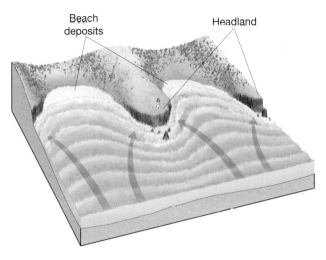

Beach deposits

Headland

Figure 19.8 Wave refraction along an irregular coastline. As waves first touch bottom in the shallows off the headlands, they are slowed, causing the waves to refract and align nearly parallel to the shoreline. This causes wave energy to be concentrated on the headlands (resulting in erosion) and dispersed in bays (resulting in deposition).

waves to diverge and expend less energy so that sediments can accumulate and form sandy beaches. Over time erosion of the headlands and deposition in the bays will straighten an irregular shoreline.

Longshore Transport

Most waves reach the shore at an angle, so the uprush of water from each breaking wave (swash) is oblique. However, returning backwash is straight down the slope of the beach. This zigzag pattern of water and sediment transport along the beach is called **beach drift** (Figure 19.9), which can transport sand and pebbles thousands of metres each day (typical rates are 5 to 10 metres per day).

Oblique waves also produce turbulent longshore currents within the surf zone that flow parallel to the shore and move substantially more sediment than beach drift. **Longshore currents** easily move the fine suspended sand and roll larger sand and gravel along the bottom. For many beaches, sediment-laden rivers

are the major sources of sand, and not eroded land behind the beach. Hence, if it were not for beach drift and longshore currents, many beaches would be nearly sandless.

TIDES

Tides are familiar to most people as the daily changes in the elevation of the ocean surface (Figure 19.10). They are controlled by the gravitational attraction between Earth and the Moon, with a smaller influence from the Sun.

Causes of Tides

The Moon's gravitational force causes ocean water to bulge on the side of Earth nearest the Moon (Figure 19.11). On the side of Earth farthest from the Moon, inertial force exceeds the gravitational attraction to the Moon, producing a net tidal force directed away from the Moon and forming another tidal bulge. So the tidal bulge nearest the Moon is due to the dominance of gravitational attraction over the opposing force of inertia, but the tidal bulge farthest from the Moon is due to the dominance of inertia over gravitational attraction.

Because the position of the Moon changes only moderately in a single day, the tidal bulges remain in place while Earth rotates through them. Thus if you stand on the seashore for 24 hours,

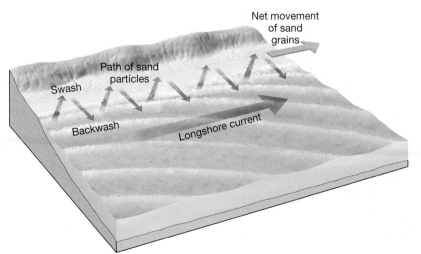

Net movement of sand grains

Path of sand particles

Swash

Backwash

Longshore current

Figure 19.9 Beach drift and longshore currents are created by obliquely breaking waves. Beach drift occurs as incoming waves carry sand obliquely up the beach (swash), while the water from spent waves carries it directly down the slope of the beach. Similar movements occur offshore in the surf zone to create the longshore current. These processes transport large quantities of material along the beach and in the surf zone.

Figure 19.10 Low to high tide on Nova Scotia's Hall's Harbour in the Bay of Fundy.
(Photo from © Laszlo Podor/Alamy)

Earth will rotate you through alternating areas of deeper and shallower water. Therefore, during one day you experience two high tides and two low tides.

Further, the tidal bulges migrate as the Moon revolves around Earth about every 29 days. As a result, the tides, like the time of moonrise, shift about 50 minutes later each day. After 29 days the cycle is complete and a new one begins. An inequality can exist between the high tides during a given day. Depending on the position of the Moon, the tidal bulges can be inclined to the equator (Figure 19.12). The first high tide experienced by an observer in the Northern Hemisphere is considerably lower than the high tide half a day later. Conversely, a Southern Hemisphere observer would experience the opposite effect.

Tidal Currents

Tidal current is the term used to describe the *horizontal* flow of water accompanying the rise and fall of the tide. These water movements, induced by tidal forces, are particularly impressive in the Bay of Fundy, where tidal currents can flow up to 25 million cubic metres per second. Tidal currents flow in one

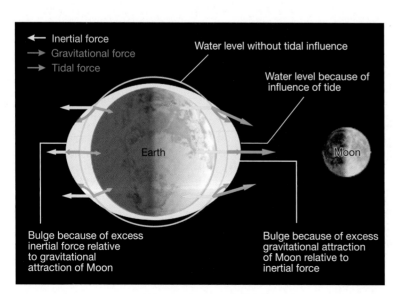

Figure 19.11 Schematic diagram showing the interaction of gravitational and inertial forces and the formation of tidal bulges in the ocean. Tidal forces are produced by the relative balance of gravitational attraction to the Moon and inertial forces of Earth. On the side of Earth facing the Moon, gravitational attraction is greater than the opposing inertial force and the reverse is true on the opposite side of Earth. Due to the ability of water to deform, the excess gravitational and inertial forces on opposing sides of Earth (in line with the Moon) produce two tidal bulges. These bulges are responsible for high tides.

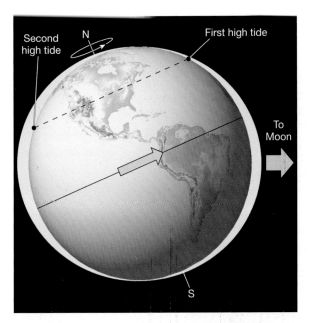

Figure 19.12 Tides on an Earth that is covered to a uniform depth with water. Depending on the Moon's position, tidal bulges can be inclined to the equator. In this situation, an observer will experience two unequal high tides.

direction during a portion of the tidal cycle and reverse their flow during the remainder. Tidal currents that advance into the coastal zone as the tide rises are called **flood currents.** As the tide falls, seaward-moving water generates **ebb currents.** Periods of little or no current, called *slack water,* separate flood and ebb. Areas affected by alternating tidal currents are **tidal flats** (see Figure 19.10) that vary from narrow coastal strips to extensive zones extending for several kilometres.

Tidal currents can be rapid in river **estuaries** (inlets of the sea formed at the mouths of streams),

Figure 19.13 This sandstone preserves herringbone cross-bedding, indicating that its deposition was influenced by tidal currents. Inferred current directions indicated by arrows.
(Photo by C. E. Jones)

straits, and bays. Off the coast of Brittany in France, for example, tidal currents are known to attain a speed of 20 kilometres per hour. Tidal currents can move through narrow inlets, where they constantly scour the small entrances to many good harbours that would otherwise be blocked.

As mentioned earlier in Chapters 6 and 18, cross-beds form via the migration of bedforms, such as ripples and dunes. A distinctive feature sometimes observed in ancient sandy tidal deposits is *herringbone cross-bedding* (Figure 19.13), in which cross-beds in alternating sedimentary layers dip in opposing directions (imparting the appearance of bones in a fish skeleton). This variety of cross-bedding records the back-and-forth migration of underwater bedforms in response to reversing current directions in the flood–ebb tidal cycle.

SHORELINE FEATURES

Erosional and depositional shoreline features vary depending on the type of rocks exposed along the shore, the intensity of wave activity, the nature of coastal currents, and whether the coast is stable, sinking, or rising.

Erosional Features

Whether along the rugged and irregular Newfoundland and Labrador coast or along the steep shorelines of the Pacific Coast, the effects of wave erosion are often easy to see. **Wave-cut cliffs** originate by the cutting action of the surf against the base of coastal land. As erosion progresses, rocks overhanging the notch at the base of the cliff crumble into the surf, and the cliff retreats (see Figure 19.6B). A relatively flat, bench-like surface, called the **wave-cut platform**, is left behind by the receding cliff (Figure 19.1B). The platform broadens as the wave attack continues. Some of the debris produced by the breaking waves remains along the water's edge as part of the beach, while the remainder is transported farther seaward.

Headlands that extend into the sea are vigorously attacked by waves because of refraction. The surf erodes the rock selectively, wearing away the softer or more highly fractured rock at the fastest rate. At first, sea caves may form. When caves on opposite sides of a headland unite, a **sea arch** results (Figure 19.14). Eventually the arch falls in, leaving an isolated remnant, or **sea stack** (Figure 19.15), on the wave-cut platform. In time it too will be consumed by the action of the waves.

Figure 19.14 Elephant Rock, a sea arch that formerly existed on the coast of Prince Edward Island. The arch ultimately succumbed to erosion and collapsed in 1999. (Photo by Brian Sytnyk/ Masterfile)

Depositional Features

Coastal regions dominated by deposition receive sediment primarily from river mouths (see Chapter 15) and erosion-dominated regions of the coast. Most coasts share a basic profile, including offshore, shoreface, and beach (foreshore and backshore; Figure 19.16).

The base of a coastal profile is marked by the flat *offshore zone*, which is permanently submerged underwater and lies below the average depth at which waves touch the sea bottom during normal fair-weather conditions. This depth limit is commonly referred to as *fair-weather wave base*.

A

B

Figure 19.15 **A.** Siwash Rock sea stack in Stanley Park, Vancouver, British Columbia. **B.** Elevated wave-cut platform and emergent sea stack near Trout River, Gros Morne area of Newfoundland and Labrador. (Photo **A** by S. R. Hicock; photo **B** reproduced with the permission of Natural Resources Canada, 2013, courtesy of the Geological Survey of Canada, photo 2002-092)

Figure 19.16 The coastal zone consists of several parts. The beach is an accumulation of sediment on the landward margin of the ocean or lake. It can be thought of as material in transit along the shore.

The *shoreface zone* lies landward of the offshore zone. It is characterized by constant day-to-day sediment transport in shallow water, between the fair-weather wave base and the low-tide mark. The shoreface normally has a concave-upward profile that is in equilibrium with the waves affecting it. The gradient of the shoreface ranges from nearly 0 degrees at its base to about 0.3 degrees at its upper boundary with the foreshore.

It is within the shoreface zone that most sediment is actively transported. Where waves approach the shore at an oblique angle, longshore currents transport sediment (usually sand) parallel to the shoreline landward of the breaker zone. In areas where wave approach is perpendicular to the shore, wave-generated currents form cells. In such cells, longshore currents converge and flow away from the shore as *rip currents*. Seaward of the surf zone, the rip currents diverge and dissipate, depositing sand in the lower shoreface.

A *beach* is an area of unconsolidated sediment that can be loosely considered to extend from the shoreface to the seaward limit of permanently vegetated land. In a more formal sense, the beach comprises two zones, called the foreshore and the backshore. In its simplest form, the beach is attached to, and runs parallel to, the mainland. Such a beach is called a *strand plain*. Most of the sediment composing Canadian beaches is supplied from rivers and reworked glacial deposits.

The *foreshore zone* is the area of the beach directly affected by the repeated swash and retreating backwash of breaking waves, between the low-tide and high-tide watermarks of the coastal zone. Waves transport water onshore. When they break, they drive a thin sheet of water rapidly up the slope of the shore, depositing sediment in thin laminae. The rate of deposition by swash is slightly higher than erosion by backwash, resulting in a net gain of sediment.

The *backshore zone* lies landward of the foreshore, above the normal high-tide level. In some modern settings, a flat-lying to landward-sloping area adjacent to the foreshore, called a *berm*, is produced. The berm marks the uppermost limit of the water line that is reached only during the most severe storms and highest tides. Because it is normally exposed well above water level, sand in the backshore area is commonly moulded into dunes by wind. Vegetation may be temporarily established in moist, low-lying areas of the backshore that are transitional to inland areas stabilized by permanent vegetation. A good example is Ontario's Pinery Provincial Park along the east shore of Lake Huron.

Ancient Coastal Deposits

Unlike erosional coastlines, which are rarely preserved in the geologic record, ancient examples of depositional coasts are common. Ancient counterparts to modern sandy coastal deposits commonly preserve sedimentary structures that can aid in the recognition of coastal zones in context of a basic coastal profile.

Offshore deposits commonly consist of alternating beds of sandstone (with hummocky cross-stratification) and shale (Figure 19.17A), the former recording storms (see Figure 6.26A) and the latter representing intervening periods of calm when mud was allowed to settle out on the sea floor below fair-weather wave base.

Figure 19.17 Sedimentary structures associated with ancient coastal deposits and their inferred coastal zones. The offshore zone is characterized by alternating beds of shale and hummocky stratified sandstone (**A**). The lower and upper portions of the shoreface are dominated by swaley cross-stratified sandstone (**B**) and cross-bedded sandstone (**C**), respectively. Beach deposits are dominated by tabular bedded, parallel-laminated sands in the foreshore zone (**D**). Although rarely preserved, sandstone with large-scale cross bedding (**E**) can indicate the migration of sand dunes. (Photos by C. Tsujita)

Shoreface deposits tend to be dominated by sandstone. That they contain little or no shale reflects the difficulty of mud to settle on the sea floor at water depths above fair-weather wave base. Lower shoreface sandstones commonly preserve evidence of storms in the form of *swaley cross-stratification* (Figure 19.17B). This is a variant of hummocky cross-stratification in which the convex-upward hummocks (and any sediment deposited between storms) are removed by erosion, leaving only concave-upward swales in the bottom remnants of sandstone beds that are directly stacked on one another.

Upper shoreface deposits record shallower water depths and transportation of larger volumes of sediment on a day-to-day basis than do those of the lower shoreface. Cross-bedding is common in upper shoreface sandstones (Figure 19.17C), indicating deposition associated with migrating ripples, dunes, and offshore bars under the influence of waves and nearshore currents.

Foreshore (beach) deposits typically consist of thin, tabular sandstone units with parallel lamination produced by swash in the foreshore (Figure 19.17D). The slight inclined nature of bed surfaces reflects the gentle dip of the foreshore toward the sea.

Backshore deposits vary greatly in their characteristics but in their simplest form are represented by sandstone units with large-scale cross-bedding, reflecting the migration of sand dunes by wind action well above high-tide level (Figure 19.17E).

SPITS, BARS, AND TOMBOLOS Where beach drift and longshore currents are active, several depositional features may develop. A **spit** (*spit* = spine) is an elongated ridge of sand that projects from the land into the mouth of an adjacent bay. The end in the water commonly hooks landward in response to the dominant direction of the longshore current (Figures 19.18B and 19.18C). The term **baymouth bar** is applied to a sandbar that completely crosses a bay, sealing it off from

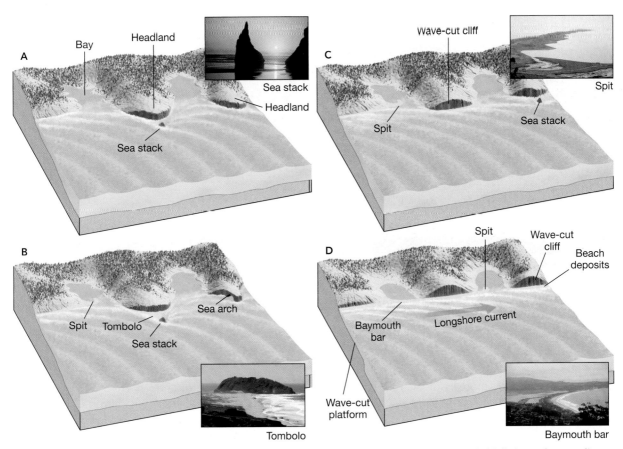

Figure 19.18 These diagrams illustrate the changes that can take place through time along an initially irregular coastline that remains relatively stable. The coastline shown in **A** gradually evolves to **B**, then **C**, and then **D**. The diagrams also serve to illustrate many of the features described in the section on shoreline features. (Photos by E. J. Tarbuck)

the open ocean (Figure 19.18D). Such a feature tends to form across bays where currents are weak, allowing a spit to extend to the other side. A **tombolo** (*tombolo* = mound) produces a ridge of sand that connects an island to the mainland or to another island (Figure 19.18B; see also Figure 19.7).

BARRIER ISLANDS The Atlantic and Gulf Coastal Plains are relatively flat and slope gently seaward. Rimming the shore zone from Cape Cod, Massachusetts, to Padre Island, Texas, are nearly 300 barrier islands. These are low ridges of land that parallel the coast at distances from 3 to 30 kilometres offshore, ranging from 15 to 30 kilometres in length and 1 to 5 kilometres in width. The tallest features on these large barrier islands are sand dunes, some of which reach heights of up to 30 metres. The lagoons separating these narrow islands from the shore represent zones of relatively quiet water that allow small craft travelling between New York and northern Florida to avoid the rough waters of the North Atlantic. Along with numerous baymouth bars and spits, barrier islands also occur along Canadian coasts

and are especially well-developed off the north shore of Prince Edward Island (Figure 19.19).

Barrier islands probably form in several ways. Some originate as spits that were subsequently severed from the mainland by wave erosion or by the general rise in sea level following the last Ice Age. Others are created when turbulent waters in the line of breakers heap up sand scoured from the bottom. Because these sand barriers rise above normal sea level, the piling of sand likely is the result of the work of storm waves at high tide. Finally, some barrier islands are former sand-dune ridges that originated along the shore during the last Ice Age, when sea level was lower. Associated with gaps along some barrier island (Figure 19.19A) and baymouth bar systems (Figure 19.19B) are **tidal deltas** maintained by tidal currents.

The Evolving Shore

Most coastlines start with an irregular shape. Along a coastline with varied geology, the pounding surf may at first increase its irregularity because the waves will

Figure 19.19 Well-developed barrier islands (**A**) and baymouth bars (**B**) occur on the northern coast of Prince Edward Island.
(Eric Augenstein/Earthstar Geographics)

erode the weaker rocks more easily than the stronger ones. However, if a shoreline remains stable, marine erosion and deposition will eventually produce a straighter, more regular coast (Figure 19.18). As waves erode the headlands, creating cliffs and a wave-cut platform, sediment is carried along the shore. Some material is deposited in the bays, while other debris is formed into spits and baymouth bars. At the same time, rivers fill the bays with sediment. Ultimately, a generally straight, smooth coast results.

STABILIZING THE SHORE

Today the coastal zone teems with human activity. Unfortunately, people often treat the shoreline as if it were permanently stable. One need only consider the incredible devastation left in the wake of Hurricane Katrina in 2005 to appreciate the fact that a shoreline is not always a safe place to live.

Compared with natural hazards such as earthquakes, volcanic eruptions, and landslides, shoreline erosion is commonly perceived to be a more continuous and predictable process that appears to cause relatively modest damage to limited areas. In reality, the shoreline is a dynamic place that can change rapidly in response to natural forces. Exceptional storms are capable of rapidly eroding beaches, cliffs, and property. Such bursts of accelerated erosion not only have a significant impact on the natural evolution of a coast but can also have a profound impact on people who reside in the coastal zone. Large sums are spent annually not only to repair damage but also

to prevent or control erosion. Already a problem at many sites, shoreline erosion is certain to become an increasingly serious problem as extensive coastal development continues.

During the past 100 years, growing affluence and increasing demands for recreation have brought unprecedented development to many coastal areas. As both the number and the value of buildings have increased, so too have efforts to protect property from storm waves by stabilizing the shore. Also, controlling the natural migration of sand is an ongoing struggle in many coastal areas. Such interference can result in unwanted changes that are difficult and expensive to correct.

Hard Stabilization

Structures built to protect a coast from erosion or to prevent the movement of sand along a beach are known as **hard stabilization**. Hard stabilization can take many forms, including jetties, groins, breakwaters, and seawalls.

JETTIES A principal goal in coastal areas is the development and maintenance of harbours involving jetty systems. **Jetties** are usually built in pairs and extend into the ocean at the entrances to rivers and harbours. With the flow of water confined to a narrow zone, the ebb and flow caused by the rise and fall of the tides keeps the sand in motion and prevents deposition in the channel. However, as illustrated in Figure 19.20, the jetty can act as a dam against which the longshore current and beach drift deposit sand.

Figure 19.20 **A.** Jetties are built at the entrances to rivers and harbours and are intended to prevent deposition in the navigation channel. Jetties interrupt the movement of sand by beach drift and longshore currents. Beach erosion often results downcurrent from the site of the structure. **B.** Stevenson Jetty at the mouth of the Fraser River, near Richmond, British Columbia. (Photo B by S. R. Hicock)

At the same time, wave activity removes sand on the other side. Because the other side is not receiving any new sand, it soon has no beach at all.

GROINS To maintain or widen beaches that are losing sand, groins are sometimes constructed. A **groin** (*groin* = ground) is a barrier built at a right angle to the beach to trap sand that is moving parallel to the shore (Figure 19.21). Groins are usually constructed of large rocks but can also be composed of wood. These structures often do their job so effectively that the longshore current beyond the groin becomes sand-starved. As a result, the current erodes sand from the beach on the downstream side of the groin.

To offset this effect, property owners downstream from the structure may erect a groin on their property. In this manner, the number of groins multiplies, resulting in a *groin field*. An example of such proliferation is the shoreline of New Jersey, where hundreds of these structures have been built. The north shore of Lake Ontario also has many groins. Because it has been shown that groins often

Figure 19.21 Groins along the shore near Powell River, British Columbia. (Photo © Troy and Mary Parlee/Alamy)

Figure 19.22 Aerial view of a breakwater of discarded ship hulls at Powell River, British Columbia. (Photo by Margaret L. Lutz, Powell River Books)

concrete hulls of wartime transport ships form a unique floating breakwater that protects the shoreline near the town's pulp mill (Figure 19.22).

Another type of hard stabilization built parallel to the shoreline is a **seawall**, which is designed to armour the coast and defend property from the force of breaking waves (Figure 19.23A). Waves expend much of their energy as they move across an open beach. Seawalls cut this process short by reflecting the force of unspent waves seaward. As a consequence, the beach to the seaward side of the seawall experiences significant erosion and can in some instances be eliminated entirely. Once the width of the beach is reduced, the seawall is subjected to even greater pounding by the waves (Figure 19.23B). Eventually this battering will cause the wall to fail, and a larger, more expensive wall must be built to take its place. Thus the wisdom of building what will become temporary protective structures along shorelines is increasingly questioned.

do not provide a satisfactory solution, they are no longer the preferred method of keeping beach erosion in check.

BREAKWATERS AND SEAWALLS Hard stabilization can also be built parallel to the shoreline. One such structure is a **breakwater**, the purpose of which is to protect boats from the force of large breaking waves by creating a quiet water zone near the shoreline. However, the reduced wave activity along the shore behind the structure can allow sand to accumulate and the marina will eventually fill with sand while the downstream beach erodes and retreats. At Powell River, British Columbia, decommissioned

Alternatives to Hard Stabilization

Armouring the coast with hard stabilization has several potential drawbacks, including the cost of the structure and the loss of sand on the beach. Alternatives to hard stabilization include beach nourishment and relocation.

BEACH NOURISHMENT This practice simply involves the addition of large quantities of sand to

A   B

Figure 19.23 **A.** Seawall around Stanley Park, Vancouver, British Columbia. **B.** West Vancouver once had a sandy beach. The seawall was built to protect the town but the beach narrowed dramatically. (Photo **A** by S. R. Hicock; photo **B** by Blair Kent)

Figure 19.24 Beach nourishment along the north shore of Lake Ontario. Orange machines are adding sand to widen the beach.
(Photo courtesy of the Toronto and Region Conservation Authority)

the beach system (Figure 19.24). By building beaches seaward, beach quality and storm protection are improved. **Beach nourishment**, however, is not a permanent solution to the problem of shrinking beaches. The same processes that removed the sand in the first place will eventually remove the replacement sand as well. In addition, beach nourishment is very expensive because huge volumes of sand must be transported to the beach from offshore areas, nearby rivers, or other source areas.

Beach nourishment appears to be an economically viable long-range solution to the beach preservation problem only in areas where dense development, large supplies of sand, relatively low-wave energy, and reconcilable environmental issues exist. Unfortunately, few areas possess all these attributes.

RELOCATION Many coastal scientists and planners are calling for a policy shift from defending and rebuilding beaches and coastal property in high hazard areas to *relocating* storm-damaged buildings in those places and letting nature reclaim the beach. Such proposals, of course, are controversial. People with significant near-shore investments shudder at the thought of not rebuilding and defending coastal developments from the erosional wrath of the sea. Others, however, argue that with sea level rising, the impact of coastal storms will only get worse in the decades to come. This group advocates that oft-damaged structures be abandoned or relocated to improve personal safety and to reduce costs. Such ideas will no doubt be the focus of much study and debate as communities evaluate and revise coastal land-use policies.

CHAPTER SUMMARY

- Wave height, wavelength, and period depend on wind speed, duration, and fetch. Wave forms advance as water particles move in circular orbits, except where waves break into surf near the shore.

- Waves erode by impact pressure and abrasion while wave refraction concentrates erosion on headlands.

- Wave *swash* and *backwash* move sediment by zigzag beach drift while longshore currents parallel the shore.

- Shoreline erosion creates receding wave-cut cliffs, wave-cut platforms, sea arches (caves joined), and sea stacks (arch collapses).

- Shoreline deposition creates spits (curl into bays), baymouth bars (across bays), tombolos (connect island to mainland), and barrier islands (parallel shore).

- Remedies for erosion include jetties, groins (right angle to shore), breakwaters (parallel to shore), seawalls (hug shore), beach nourishment (sand replacement), and relocation from worst storm areas.

MasteringGeology

www.masteringgeology.com

Looking for additional review and test prep materials? Visit the Study Area in MasteringGeology to enhance your understanding of this chapter's content by accessing a variety of resources, including

Self-Study Quizzes, Geoscience Animations, GEODe Tutorials, RSS feeds, flashcards, weblinks, self-study quizzes, and an optional Pearson eText.

REVIEW QUESTIONS

1. What are three factors that determine the height, length, and period of a wave?

2. Describe the motion of a water particle as a wave passes.

3. What causes waves to break when they reach the surf zone?

4. What are beach drift and longshore currents? How are these processes significant to the distribution of sediment along a shoreline?

5. Suppose a person watches the ocean from a beach for a full 24-hour day. Over that period, the person witnesses two high tides and two low tides. Why would two tidal cycles occur within the 24-hour period? Why not one or three?

6. Beach deposits are commonly preserved in the geologic record, yet some of the most impressive features seen along some modern shorelines, such as sea stacks and arches, are highly unlikely to be similarly preserved. Explain why.

7. Explain how the installation of jetties, groins, and breakwaters can help preserve beach areas locally. What are the shortcomings of such approaches (especially for neighbouring properties)?

8. What are the drawbacks of beach nourishment?

MINERAL AND ENERGY RESOURCES

20

CHAPTER OUTLINE

Renewable and Non-renewable
  Resources

Metallic Mineral Deposits and Geologic
  Processes

Non-metallic Resources

Non-renewable Energy Resources
  (Fossil Fuels)

Renewable Fuel Sources

Aerial view of the Ekati
diamond mine near Lac de
Gras, Northwest Territories,
about 300 kilometres
northeast of Yellowknife.
(Photo courtesy of BHP
Billiton)

A popular saying among geologists is "if it can't be grown, it's gotta be mined." Materials extracted from Earth are the basis for modern civilization (Figure 20.1). Everything we use in our lives that is not derived from living things or water comes from the geosphere. We depend on Earth's resources so much that we generally take this fact for granted. Chances are that most of the metals, plastics, and energy sources that you are using today are derived from Earth resources that were discovered and developed with the help of geoscientists. For example, when you turn on your television or computer, you are using materials derived from Earth. From the silicon chips to the copper in the wires, and from the glass screen to the energy that powers the computer, nearly all aspects of these high-tech devices are linked to mineral and energy resources. The economic uses of several minerals, both metallic and nonmetallic, are indicated in Table 2.2.

The mining industry is a vital contributor to the Canadian economy. The mining and mineral-processing industries contribute more than $35 billion annually to the economy, amounting to more than $1060 per person. Canada is also one of the world's largest exporters of minerals and mineral products. At least 80 percent of the country's mineral and metal production is exported. Canada ranks first in the world for the production of potash and uranium, is the second-largest producer of nickel and asbestos, and ranks in the top five for the production of diamonds, zinc, cadmium, titanium concentrate, aluminum, platinum group metals, salt, gold, molybdenum, copper, gypsum, cobalt, and lead. The five most important minerals in Canada with respect to production value are gold, nickel, potash, copper, and zinc.

The number of different **mineral resources** required by modern industries is immense (Figure 20.2), and although some countries, such as Canada and the United States, have rich supplies of many important minerals, no nation is completely self-sufficient. Consequently, the resources of Earth

Figure 20.1 Toronto at night. As this scene reminds us, mineral and energy resources are the basis of modern civilization. (Photo © Marcus/Fotolia)

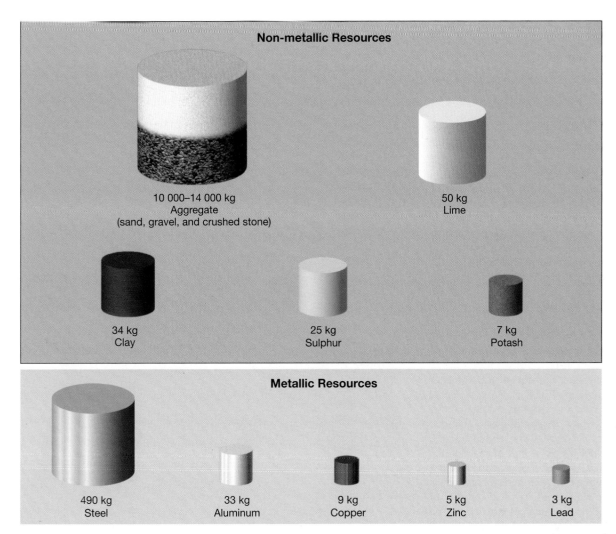

Figure 20.2   The annual per capita consumption of selected mineral resources for Canada.
(Based on data from Statistics Canada, Aggregate Producers of British Columbia, and Canadian Steel Producers Association.)

have long been the basis of world trade, have driven great waves of immigration, and have even generated wars.

Geoscientists are indispensable in many aspects of mineral and energy resource discovery, measurement, and management. These include predicting where an economically important resource might occur, determining the most effective way of extracting it, and determining the conditions of mineral deposit formation to aid in the discovery of similar deposits. At the same time, geoscientists are mindful of the great responsibilities nations face in their exploitation and utilization of natural resources (see Box 20.1), and they play crucial roles in assessing the possible environmental impacts of mineral extraction and in developing techniques for environmental remediation.

RENEWABLE AND NON-RENEWABLE RESOURCES

Resources are the endowment of materials held in reserve that are useful to people and are ultimately available commercially. Resources are commonly divided into two broad categories: renewable and non-renewable.

Renewable resources can be replenished over relatively short time spans, such as months, years, or decades. Common examples are plants and animals for food, natural fibres for clothing, and trees for lumber and paper. Energy from flowing water, wind, and the Sun are also considered renewable. By contrast, **non-renewable resources** continue to be formed in Earth, but the processes that create them are so slow that significant deposits may take

PEOPLE AND THE ENVIRONMENT

Resource Consumption and Sustainability: A Global Perspective

by Mike Powell*

In a global context, resources include not only minerals and fuel but also anything else held in reserve that can be used in the future. For many of us, resources are those things that we use in excess to maintain our quality of life or high standard of living (e.g., consumables, energy, and so on); this is a view embraced mainly by people living in developed countries. However, for most of the world's population, locally available resources are those things that simply maintain life on a daily basis (e.g., food and shelter). Many small countries possess a single resource (e.g., sandy white beaches or a pleasant climate), which translates into tourism dollars. From a global perspective, resources include the vast reservoirs of less tangible commodities, such as air, water, and soil quality, as well as plant and animal species. Global resource consumption is not equitable or evenly distributed on a per capita basis. The vast majority of worldwide resources are channelled into economies that have the financial capacity to buy commodities.

Earth can be thought of as a single mixed reservoir of all resources that are consumed mostly by a single component (people). The rate of resource consumption is a product of population size and rate of consumption. The rate of population growth has accelerated exponentially throughout history. It took more than 100 000 years for Earth to reach the 1 billion population mark. About 130 years later, population doubled to 2 billion. By 1975 it doubled again to 4 billion, and reached 7 billion in 2012. Increases in economic activity worldwide show that the richest 20 percent of people consume 85 percent of the resources, while the poorest 25 percent use less than 1.5 percent. To put this into perspective, consider a scenario where China consumed resources at the same rate as North America. Estimating conservatively, China would use the entire worldwide production of nearly all resources each

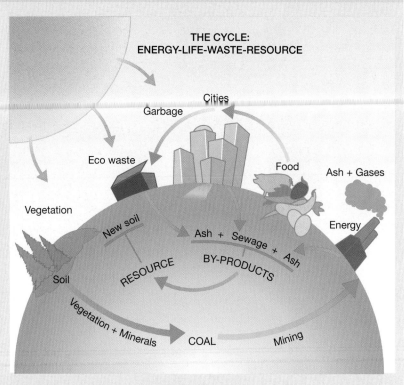

Figure 20.A   Uses of waste resources from by-products. (Courtesy of Mike Powell)

year! Another interesting perspective is to consider how long the total static resources would last if all the people in the world used resources at the same rate as North Americans—not very long, not even a generation.

Energy is the single most important resource. For any given nation, per capita energy consumption is a measure of the quality of life of its citizens and its global industrial status. Approximately 25 percent of the global population uses 75 percent of the total energy produced annually. North America (5 percent of the total population) and Western Europe (9 percent of the total population) each use about twice as much energy as all developing countries combined. On a per capita basis, people in developed countries use between 10 and 30 times as much energy as people in developing countries. Canada (sixth-largest consumer worldwide) uses 3.7 percent of the world's total generated electricity for a population of only

33 million. India (seventh-largest consumer worldwide), with a population of more than 1 billion, uses less.

How long global resources will last depends on future population growth and consumption trends. Even at a conservative across-the-board increase of 1 percent, most of our proven mineral and energy reserves will last for fewer than 200 years. If the rate of consumption increases by 2 percent, static levels of resources will last for fewer than 100 years. So, whether or not we use resources in a sustainable way will be a complicated issue in the future, and one of the greatest problems facing future generations. The question remains: Can we keep adding 100 million people to the surface of Earth each year and still pretend that resource consumption can be tailored to sustainability? Figure 20.A shows the relationship between some types of waste and the need for new resources.

Mike Powell is a consulting geoscientist.

millions of years to accumulate. For our purposes, Earth contains fixed quantities of these substances, which are the focus of this chapter.

When the present supplies have been mined or pumped from the ground, there will be no more. Examples are fuels (e.g., coal, oil, natural gas) and many important metals (e.g., iron, copper, uranium, gold). Some of these non-renewable resources, such as aluminum, can be used over and over again; others, such as coal, cannot be recycled. Some resources can be placed in either category, depending on how they are used. Groundwater is one such example. Where it is pumped from the ground at a rate that can be replenished, groundwater can be classified as a renewable resource. However, in places where groundwater is withdrawn faster than it is replenished, the water table drops steadily. In this case, the groundwater is being "mined" just like other non-renewable resources (see Chapter 16).

Resources include **reserves**, the already identified deposits from which minerals and fuel materials can be extracted profitably, and *known deposits* that are not yet economically or technologically recoverable. Resources can also include deposits that have not yet been discovered but are inferred to exist by some evidence.

METALLIC MINERAL DEPOSITS AND GEOLOGIC PROCESSES

An important point to be made about Earth's resources concerns the natural abundance of elements sought after; even the common metals, such as aluminum and iron, compose less than 10 percent of average continental crust. When we examine the distribution of mines and the primary mineral resources they extract, it becomes obvious that the various metals and other resources we rely on are not uniformly distributed across the globe—they are naturally concentrated only in particular areas. This uneven distribution is inherent in the Earth system. Not only does the composition of crust vary in different regions but the effects of tectonic processes, weathering, sedimentation rates, the movement of fluids, and various other factors are also expected to be subdued in some areas and enhanced in others. These circumstances, combined with the economics of extracting the resources, limit the localities on Earth where the mining of particular materials is practical.

Most of us have heard the term **ore**, which is generally used to denote those useful metallic minerals (and a few non-metallic minerals, such as fluorite

and sulphur) of sufficient concentrations to be mined at a profit. A rock body can be considered an ore one day and not the next because of economic factors. These can include fluctuations in the price of the material sought after, the price of fuel required for the running of machinery, and the efficiency of mining equipment. Note that the term *ore* is not applied to all materials of economic interest. Most non-metallic minerals used for such purposes as building stone, aggregate, abrasives, ceramics, and fertilizers are not usually called ores but are generally classified as **industrial minerals**.

In this section, a few of the most important types of metallic mineral deposits are discussed. The primary types of deposits discussed in this section and their contained metals are summarized in Table 20.1 and depicted in the context of plate tectonic environments in Figure 20.3. Canadian metallic mineral deposits of present and historical significance are shown in Figure 20.4.

Magmatic Deposits

Many of the world's most valuable metallic mineral resources are directly associated with magma that ultimately forms igneous rocks. Certain metals are naturally enriched in certain magmas, but most only reach economically viable concentrations on further enrichment during the cooling process. In both cases, it is the characteristics of the magma itself that are responsible for the formation of mineral deposits.

GRAVITATIONAL SETTLING The igneous processes that generate some metal deposits are fairly straightforward. For example, some economically important minerals are concentrated by simple gravitational settling within a magma chamber. In essence, crystals of heavy minerals that form during early stages of crystallization settle at the bottom of a magmatic body, such as a batholith or sill, concentrating layers of minerals (Figure 20.5). Such deposits, commonly called *cumulate* deposits, are important sources for chrome (in the mineral chromite), iron (in the mineral magnetite), and platinum. They typically form from mafic igneous magmas enriched in these elements. Examples of mafic intrusions that host such deposits are the Bird River Sill of Manitoba, the Muskox Intrusion of Northwest Territories, the Stillwater Complex of Montana, and the Bushveld Complex of South Africa.

IMMISCIBILITY Some metal deposits, such as the nickel deposits of Sudbury, Ontario, and Voisey's Bay, Newfoundland and Labrador, are probably produced by the separation of liquid components of magma in a manner similar to the separation of oil

TABLE **20.1** Occurrence of Metallic Minerals

Metal	Principal Ores	Geologic Occurrences
Aluminum	Bauxite	Residual product of weathering
Chromium	Chromite	Magmatic segregation
Copper	Chalcopyrite Bornite Chalcocite	Hydrothermal deposits; contact metamorphism; enrichment by weathering processes
Gold	Native gold	Hydrothermal deposits; placers
Iron	Hematite Magnetite Limonite	Banded sedimentary formations; magmatic segregation; residual product of weathering
Lead	Galena	Hydrothermal deposits
Magnesium	Magnesite Dolomite	Hydrothermal deposits
Manganese	Pyrolusite	Residual product of weathering
Mercury	Cinnabar	Hydrothermal deposits
Molybdenum	Molybdenite	Hydrothermal deposits
Nickel	Pentlandite	Magmatic segregation
Platinum	Native platinum	Magmatic segregation; placers
Silver	Native silver Argentite	Hydrothermal deposits; enrichment by weathering processes
Tin	Cassiterite	Hydrothermal deposits; placers
Titanium	Ilmenite Rutile	Magmatic segregation; placers
Tungsten	Wolframite Scheelite	Pegmatites; contact metamorphic deposits; placers
Uranium	Uraninite (pitchblende)	Pegmatites; sedimentary deposits
Zinc	Sphalerite	Hydrothermal deposits

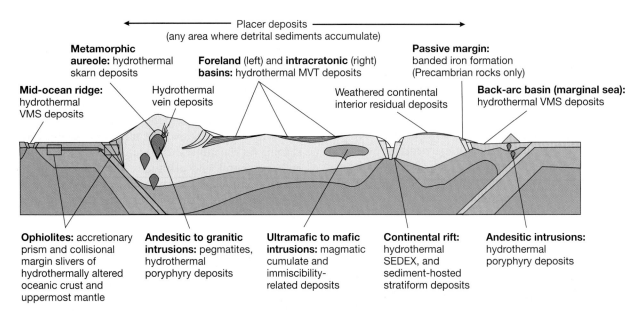

Figure 20.3 Distribution of common mineral deposit types and their contained metals with respect to plate tectonic environments (explained later in the chapter). Abbreviations used for types of hydrothermal deposits: VMS = volcanogenic massive sulphide, SEDEX = sedimentary exhalative, MVT = Mississippi Valley type.

Figure 20.4 Locations of important metallic resources and important mining centres in Canada.

and water in salad dressing left to stand on a kitchen counter. Such non-mixing of liquid phases is called *immiscibility*.

Mantle-sourced magmas of mafic to ultramafic composition are naturally enriched in elements, such as nickel and copper, relative to felsic magmas. Because these elements are readily incorporated into silicate minerals, such as olivine and pyroxene, substituting for atoms of iron and magnesium, they are usually too dispersed within mafic intrusive rocks to

be mined at a profit. In some cases, however, these elements can be scavenged from the melt by small droplets of immiscible iron sulphide liquid that eventually sink to the base of the intrusion and accumulate to form an orebody. The resulting deposit (Figure 20.6A) is dominated by the iron sulphide mineral *pyrrhotite*, with intergrowths of the nickel-bearing sulphide mineral *pentlandite* [$(Ni,Fe)_9S_8$], as well as *chalcopyrite* [$CuFeS_2$] and some precious metals such as platinum.

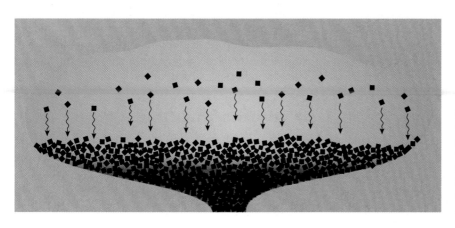

Figure 20.5 High-density minerals, such as chromite and magnetite, crystallize during the early stages of magma crystallization. The crystals can sink to the bottom of the magma chamber, forming concentrated layers of these minerals.

A

B

Figure 20.6 **A.** In Sudbury, Ontario, nickel-bearing liquid separated from mafic magma, eventually settling to form a sublayer beneath a silicate-dominated, mafic intrusive body and becoming injected into fractures that emanated from the impact structure. The magmatic materials are believed to have escaped from the mantle because of a meteorite impact during the Proterozoic. The Sudbury Basin impact structure has since been deformed into an oval shape. **B.** A sample of nickel-bearing rock from Sudbury. The nickel occurs in the rounded bodies of bronze-coloured sulphides that crystallized from immiscible fluid. Dark-coloured mafic silicate minerals surround the metal sulphide bodies. Scale bar: 5 millimetres.
(Photo courtesy of R. W. Hodder)

Although the nickel deposits of Sudbury and Voisey's Bay share similar origins from mantle-derived magma, the mechanisms believed to have triggered igneous activity in each case differ markedly. In Sudbury, the generation and emplacement of mafic magma is linked to the impact of a large meteorite that occurred about 1.9 billion years ago. The impact is believed to have produced fractures that penetrated into the mantle and acted as passageways for magma that contained the required sulphide droplets. The Sudbury orebody occurs at the base of a mafic igneous intrusion and is exposed at the surface as an oval ring-shaped structure (Figure 20.6B). In contrast, the Voisey's Bay orebody (1.3 billion years old) occurs at the base of a mafic igneous intrusion that appears to have been fed by mantle-penetrating fractures generated by an ascending mantle plume.

PEGMATITES As an igneous body cools, the most abundant components of the magma that are able to crystallize are removed from the magma. The melt remaining during the very last stages of cooling becomes enriched in volatile components (e.g., water) and rare elements that are not readily incorporated into common igneous minerals. Minerals that crystallize from such a melt may therefore be very unusual in their chemical composition, containing some of the least abundant elements found in Earth's crust. Because the melt is very fluid, it is readily injected into cracks surrounding the cooling igneous body and allows the growth of unusually large crystals (see Box 3.1).

The resulting rocks, called pegmatites, typically occur in dykes and small veins within and around plutons (Figures 20.7 and 20.9) and are generally felsic in composition. Elements of economic value that are mined from pegmatites include uranium, thorium, beryllium, lithium, tantalum, and niobium. Industrial minerals mined from pegmatites include feldspar and muscovite.

Hydrothermal Deposits

Among the best-known and most important ore deposits are those generated from **hydrothermal** (hot-water) **solutions**, which may be produced during the late-stage cooling of magma, by the heating of groundwater or seawater, or by metamorphic

Figure 20.7 Pegmatite dyke cuts through gneiss on mainland Nunavut, south of Pelly Bay. Note large orthoclase crystals at centre bottom. Knife is 20 centimetres long. Pegmatites, formed during the late stages of crystallization in felsic magmas, can be rich sources of rare earth elements, such as beryllium and lithium. (Photo by S. R. Hicock)

processes. A critical factor in the ability of hot water to dissolve metals appears to be the presence of dissolved salts, such as sodium chloride, potassium chloride, and calcium sulphate. Whereas metals are effectively insoluble in pure water, salt-rich *brines* are capable of dissolving at least small amounts of metallic elements (e.g., gold, silver, copper, lead, zinc, and mercury). High temperatures further increase the ability of brines to hold metals in solution. Because of their mobility, brines can migrate great distances before they eventually cool, lose their ability to keep metals in solution, and deposit the metals (usually in the form of sulphide minerals).

Companies mining hydrothermal ores must take great care in managing the waste materials (tailings) as the sulphide minerals contained in the ores readily react with water and produce substances that can be harmful to living things if released into the environment (Box 20.2).

Hydrothermal Deposits Associated with Igneous Activity

Studies of modern hydrothermal systems have shown that igneous activity serves as a powerful heat engine that drives the production and circulation of mineral-rich fluids. As is evident in the hot springs of Yellowstone National Park, Wyoming, ordinary groundwater can invade a zone of recent igneous activity and be heated to increase its capacity to dissolve minerals. In such an environment, migrating hot waters can remove metallic ions from intrusive igneous rocks and carry them upward, where they may be deposited as an orebody.

The role of igneous activity in producing ore deposits is also evident in the depths of the oceans. Since the mid-1970s, active hot springs and metal-rich sulphide deposits have been detected at several sites, including study areas along the East Pacific Rise and Juan de Fuca Ridge. The deposits are forming where heated seawater, rich in dissolved metals and sulphur, gushes from the sea floor as particle-filled clouds called *black smokers* (Box 11.3). As shown in Figure 20.8, seawater infiltrates the hot oceanic crust along the flanks of the ridge. As the water moves through the newly formed material, it is heated and chemically interacts with the basalt, extracting and transporting sulphur, iron, copper, and other metals. Near the ridge axis, the hot, metal-rich fluid rises along faults. On reaching the sea floor, the spewing liquid mixes with the cold seawater and the sulphides precipitate to form massive sulphide deposits.

VEIN DEPOSITS Hydrothermal fluids generated by cooling magmas can rise to the surface through fractures, faults, and other features that result from the brittle deformation of the overlying rocks. Fluids passing through the fractures eventually cool, allowing minerals to precipitate (Figure 20.9). The precipitated minerals, generally dominated by quartz or calcite, but sometimes including metallic minerals, fill the fractures to produce veins (Figure 20.10) that can range in width from a few centimetres to a few metres. The fluids can also react with the rocks immediately adjacent to the fractures to produce new minerals. Mineral deposits that occur in veins, or at least are intimately associated with vein systems, are called **vein** (*lode*) **deposits**. These are important sources of valuable ore minerals, such as native gold and silver, as well as copper and zinc sulphides. The hydrothermal environment in which some vein deposits were formed probably resembled that of Yellowstone. However, networks of metal-rich veins are also associated with fracture systems of other hydrothermal environments.

Mineral deposits of particular importance in Canada are vein gold deposits, which occur throughout the Archean greenstone belts of the Superior and Slave provinces of the Canadian Shield. More than 4000 tonnes of gold have been extracted from the many individual deposits in these areas. Among the most famous producers are the mines of the Porcupine, Red Lake, Kirkland Lake, Malartic-Val d'Or, and Yellowknife districts. Vein silver deposits are also important in some parts of Canada, particularly

BOX **20.2**
PEOPLE AND THE ENVIRONMENT
Acid Mine Drainage (AMD) in Canada

by Gordon Southam*

Base and precious metal mining in Canada (and globally) is focused on the recovery of metals (e.g., nickel, copper, or gold) from geologic deposits. In an existing mine, rock is blasted and brought to the surface or removed from an open pit and crushed in rod and ball mills. It then undergoes a series of flotation steps leading toward metal purification. After the minerals of economic interest—for example, millerite (NiS) or chalcopyrite ($CuFeS_2$)—are recovered, the gangue materials (waste rock) are disposed of in massive holding (waste) ponds. These wastes include silicates, base metals containing sulphide minerals that were not recovered during flotation, and, typically, pyrite. Mining can also result in the generation of waste rock possessing pyrite. On removal, this waste rock is usually stored above ground in large free-draining piles.

The disposal of sulphide-bearing mine wastes (rock and tailings) as open deposits results in the formation of unique acid-generating ecosystems (Figure 20.B). Acid formation is bio-catalyzed by acidophilic ("acid-loving") bacteria, (e.g., *Acidithiobacillus ferro-oxidans*), which oxidize sulphide minerals, generating dilute solutions of sulphuric acid that contain soluble, toxic heavy metals. This acid mine drainage (AMD) seeps into and damages surrounding aquatic and terrestrial environments.

Although abiotic chemical oxidation of pyrite can occur (see Reaction 1), it is slow and on its own will not lead to the formation of AMD. Under normal, natural water conditions (pH near 7), the iron that is released from Reaction 1 will oxidize (Reaction 2) to Fe^{3+}, which will then break down water molecules, producing three protons (acid; Reaction 3). The net acid generating capacity of Reactions 1–3 (4 protons) additionally cannot produce AMD.

$$FeS_2 + 3\tfrac{1}{2}O_2 + H_2O \rightarrow$$
$$Fe^{2+} + 2SO_4^{2-} + 2H^+ \quad (1)$$
$$Fe^{2+} + 1\tfrac{1}{4}O_2 + H^+ \rightarrow$$
$$Fe^{3+} + \tfrac{1}{2}H_2O \quad (2)$$
$$Fe^{3+} + 3H_2O \rightarrow$$
$$Fe(OH)_3 \text{ (iron hydroxide;}$$
$$\text{the rust colour)} + 3H^+ \quad (3)$$

Under acidic conditions (i.e., pH < 4) Fe^{2+} is generally stable and soluble (Reaction 2 slows down). Therefore, the net acid generation should slow as well, but it doesn't. This is where the acidophilic lithotrophic (*lithos* = rock, *trophic* = food or eating) bacteria become important. The key to the formation of acid mine drainage is the bacteria's ability to oxidize iron under acidic conditions. (They can also catalyze Reaction 2.) In the presence of water and acid conditions, Fe^{3+} will attack pyrite (Reaction 4), producing lots of Fe^{2+} (more food for the bacteria) and lots of acid.

$$FeS_2 + 14Fe^{3+} + 8H_2O \rightarrow$$
$$15Fe^{2+} + 2SO_4^{2-} + 16H^+ \quad (4)$$

The chemical oxidation of pyrite (Reaction 4) occurs extremely quickly under acid conditions—typically faster than the bacteria can oxidize the Fe^{2+}. Therefore, the rate-limiting step in the formation of AMD is the oxidation of Fe^{2+} by the bacteria (bio-catalyzed Reaction 2). It should be noted that Fe^{3+} can also chemically attack other base metals (e.g., Cu_2S) that will, in turn, release soluble toxic heavy metals (e.g., Cu^{2+}).

The Canadian mineral industry generates about 1 million tonnes of waste rock and 950 000 tonnes of tailings per day, exceeding 710 million tonnes of total waste per year. Canada has an estimated 351 million tonnes of waste rock, 510 million tonnes of sulphide tailings, and more than 55 million tonnes of other mining sources that have the potential to cause AMD.[1]

Once in a tailings pile, bacteria get their O_2 and CO_2 from the air (they're autotrophic, similar to plants) and their energy from the sulphide minerals (e.g., pyrite), ultimately forming AMD. Acid mine drainage is the mining industry's greatest environmental problem and its greatest liability.[2] The water pollution resulting from the bio-oxidation of mine wastes may need to be managed for centuries after mine closure; the cleanup at existing acid-generating mines in Canada will cost billions of dollars.

* Gordon Southam is an adjunct professor in the Department of Earth Sciences at Western University.

[1] Government of Canada, The State of Canada's Environment (Ottawa: Ministry of Supply and Services, 1991), pp. 11–19.

[2] P. C. Singer and W. Stumm, "Acidic Mine Drainage: The Rate-Determining Step," Science 167 (1970): 1121–1123.

Figure 20.B Metal mine tailings at the Lamoine mine near Chibougamau, Quebec, which appeared benign at first glance, were revealed to be highly oxidized immediately below the surface (inset). This zone of oxidation extended approximately 40 centimetres down into the tailings.
(Photos by Gordon Southam)

Figure 20.8   Massive sulphide deposits can result from the circulation of seawater through the oceanic crust along active spreading centres. As seawater infiltrates the hot mafic crust, it leaches out sulphur, iron, copper, and other metals. The hot, enriched fluid returns to the sea floor near the ridge axis along faults and fractures. Some metal sulphides may be precipitated in these channels as the rising fluid begins to cool. When the hot liquid emerges from the sea floor and mixes with cold seawater, the sulphides precipitate to form massive deposits. Photo shows a close-up view of a black smoker spewing hot, mineral-rich seawater along the East Pacific Rise. (Photo by OAR/National Undersea Research Program (NURP); NOAA)

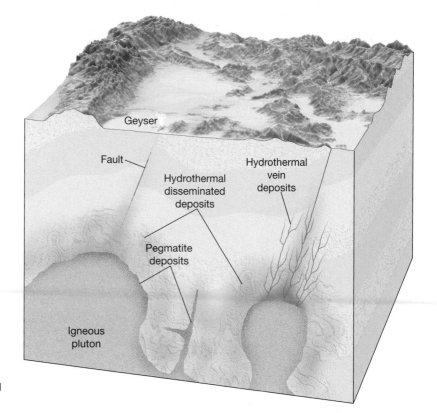

Figure 20.9   Illustration of the relationship between a parent igneous body and the associated pegmatite and hydrothermal deposits.

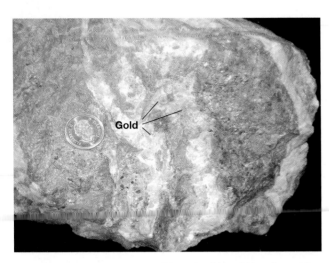

Figure 20.10 Metamorphic rock with gold-bearing white quartz veins from Timmins, Ontario. (Photo by C. Tsujita).

British Columbia. Historically significant to Canada are the lode silver deposits of Cobalt, Ontario, which spawned a remarkable mining boom in the early 1900s.

DISSEMINATED DEPOSITS Another important type of accumulation generated by magma-sourced hydrothermal fluids is called a **disseminated**

deposit. Rather than being concentrated in well-defined veins, these ores are distributed in small masses throughout a large rock body. Most of the world's copper and molybdenum, and smaller quantities of other metals, such as gold and silver, are mined from disseminated deposits called *porphyry deposits*. These are so named because of their close association with porphyritic igneous rocks.

When silicate minerals such as feldspars crystallize around the edges of an intrusion during the early cooling of a pluton, the water content of the remaining melt increases to the extent that steam pressure shatters the already crystallized rock and, in some cases, the surrounding host rock.

The fractures thus produced are then filled with the hydrothermal fluid condensed from the steam and, in turn, are filled with metal sulphides precipitated from the fluid. This cycle can be repeated several times until the plutonic rock and some of the host rock are riddled with minute sulphide-filled fractures rarely exceeding a few millimetres in thickness. The result is a swarm or *stockwork* of thin (at times microscopic) metal sulphide veinlets scattered throughout porphyritic rocks of the cooled pluton, as well as in the surrounding host rocks (Figures 20.9 and 20.11). Porphyry deposits are generally associated with magma chambers that feed stratovolcanoes (composite cones) and are found accordingly in convergent margin settings.

Figure 20.11 Sample of a porphyry molybdenum deposit from British Columbia. Mineralization has occurred in the dark groundmass of this andesitic igneous rock. (Photo by C. Tsujita/Pearson Education)

Porphyry deposits have a very low ore grade. For example, porphyry copper deposits contain only 0.4 percent to 0.8 percent copper. However, the ore occurs in such large volumes and so close to the surface that they are well worth mining. Large deposits of porphyry copper and molybdenum figure prominently in the mining industry of British Columbia.

VOLCANOGENIC MASSIVE SULPHIDE DEPOSITS

Some hydrothermal deposits form pod-shaped bodies of *massive sulphides* that are almost entirely composed of interlocking sulphide minerals and are intimately associated with volcanic (usually mafic) rock. These are called *volcanogenic massive sulphide* (VMS) *deposits*.

The hydrothermal systems associated with the black smokers we see in today's mid-ocean ridge settings are considered to be similar to those that produced VMS deposits in ancient rocks. As discussed earlier, the convective fluid flow that develops in centres of sea-floor spreading leaches metals from oceanic crust, transports them through fractures, and deposits them as sulphide minerals in mounds that surround volcanic vents (Figure 20.8). VMS deposits appear to represent these large sulphide bodies (Figure 20.12).

VMS deposits are extremely important worldwide as they commonly contain economically valuable concentrations of copper, zinc, lead, silver, and gold. VMS deposits occur in all provinces and territories of Canada, except Alberta and Prince Edward Island, and most of them are hosted in Precambrian greenstone belts. Among the better-known VMS deposits in Canada are those of Kidd Creek, Ontario; Matagami and Noranda, Quebec; Flin Flon, Manitoba; Bathurst, New Brunswick; and Buchans, Newfoundland and Labrador.

Sediment-Associated Hydrothermal Deposits

Some mineral deposits are intimately associated with sedimentary rocks and appear to have involved mineral precipitation from hydrothermal fluids at relatively low temperatures. For most of these deposits, the source of the metals is believed to be brine that was flushed from sediments buried deep within the sedimentary pile of a sedimentary basin, although deep-seated igneous activity (e.g., in rift basins) may be responsible for contributing heat to the hydrothermal system.

SEDIMENTARY EXHALATIVE (SEDEX) DEPOSITS

Some mineral deposits feature thin layers of massive sulphide that are interbedded with detrital or chemical sedimentary rocks (Figure 20.13A). These deposits are called *sedimentary exhalative* (SEDEX) *deposits*, as they are not only intimately related to sedimentary strata (most commonly mudrocks, chert, and fine-grained carbonates) but are also thought to be associated with the mineral precipitation from fluids that were "exhaled" from hydrothermal vents onto the sea floor. SEDEX deposits typically form sheet- to lens-like bodies that are vertically stacked within the sediment fill of failed continental rifts (Figure 20.13B) and fault-bounded basins of rifted continental margins. Hot brines, derived from deep areas within rift basins, are believed to have leached metallic ions from sediments and to have carried them in solution along faults, ultimately emerging at the sea floor from hydrothermal vents. It is further speculated that the brines formed dense pools in fault-bounded

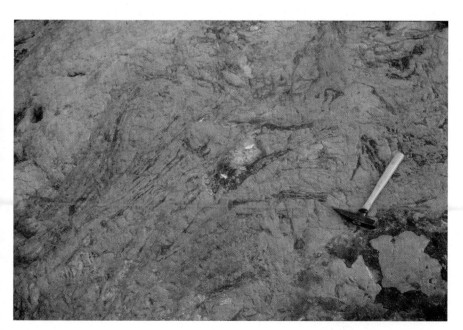

Figure 20.12 Massive sulphide deposit at Noranda, Quebec. This deposit contains mainly pyrite (light-coloured material), but thin, dark-coloured bands of galena are also visible. The rusty-coloured patches are iron oxides produced by the weathering of the pyrite.
(Photo courtesy of R. W. Hodder)

Figure 20.13   **A.** A sample of a SEDEX mineral deposit from the Sullivan mine near Kimberley, British Columbia, showing distinct, highly reflective beds of lead/zinc sulphides and dark-coloured beds of mudstone. **B.** Sedimentary-exhalative (SEDEX) deposits are interpreted to result from the precipitation of sulphide minerals from hydrothermal vents in fault-bounded depressions on the sea floor. SEDEX deposits typically occur in the sediment fill of rift basins. (Photo by C. Tsujita)

←1 cm→

A

Sulphides precipitate in fault-bounded depressions on seafloor near hydrothermal vents

Sediment

Metal-bearing brines rise up normal faults

B

depressions on the sea floor, ultimately precipitating metals in the form of sulphide minerals. The role of normal faults in the migration of hydrothermal fluids is indicated by the preservation of subvertical vein networks, apparently representing feeder vents, associated with some SEDEX deposits. In addition, concentrations of lead, zinc, and silver decrease with distance away from these vein networks. The floor of the present-day Red Sea bears pools of hydrothermal brines that are believed to be similar to those that formed ancient SEDEX deposits.

Canada's most famous SEDEX deposit of this type is an impressive lead-zinc deposit that was the foundation of the Sullivan mine in southwest British Columbia (Figure 20.13A). This mine closed in 2001 after 92 years of production.

SEDIMENT-HOSTED STRATIFORM DEPOSITS
Highly enigmatic in terms of their origin are strata-like bodies of metallic minerals called *sediment-hosted stratiform deposits*, which occur within sedimentary units of some ancient rift basins. A key characteristic of these deposits, most of which are rich in copper sulphides, is that the ore minerals occur as pore-filling material of the host rock, rather than as pure bands (Figure 20.14A). Also significant is the tendency of such deposits to occur in the basal portions of marine shales that abruptly overlie nearshore and non-marine sandstones.

Some geologists believe that sediment-hosted stratiform deposits are produced because of mineral precipitation from submarine brine pools, as envisaged for SEDEX deposits. However, more recent interpretations favour a mechanism by which oxygenated, copper-bearing brines travelling through a coarse-grained sedimentary unit are forced upward into an overlying unit of oxygen-poor, sulphide-rich mud, thereby promoting the precipitation of copper sulphide minerals among the tiny particles of clay and other detrital grains (Figure 20.14B). The most commonly cited deposit of this type is the Kupferschiefer of Germany (Figure 20.14A), but similar deposits are known in the Coppermine District in the Northwest Territories.

Metal-bearing brine reacts with sulphide in mud, precipitating sulphide minerals in sediment pores

Oxygenated, metal-bearing brine forced upward from permeable sedimentary unit

B

A

Figure 20.14 **A.** Sample of the Kupferschiefer shale from Germany. Note the greenish tinge in this sample imparted by copper oxide that was produced by the weathering of the contained copper sulphide minerals. **B.** Sediment-hosted stratiform copper deposits are formed by the interaction of oxygenated brine with overlying sulphide-rich sediment. (Photo by C. Tsujita)

MISSISSIPPI VALLEY–TYPE DEPOSITS *Mississippi Valley–type* (MVT) *deposits* are unusual hydrothermal deposits that, as their name implies, are well developed in southeast North America. Similar deposits have, however, also been found on nearly all other continents. It has been suggested that the compaction of shales deep within a sedimentary basin can release metal-bearing brines that migrate toward the edges of the basin, where they react with limestone (Figure 20.15A). More recently, it has been proposed that the mineralizing fluids are sourced from fractured Precambrian basement rocks. MVT deposits show evidence of significant calcite dissolution and replacement by other minerals, particularly sphalerite and galena (Figure 20.15B). Cavities developed in limestones hosting MVT deposits can be sufficiently large to permit the growth of huge crystals of sulphide minerals. In Canada, MVT deposits are actively mined for lead and zinc in Nunavut and the Northwest Territories.

Sedimentary Deposits

BANDED IRON FORMATIONS As already briefly mentioned in Chapter 6, a peculiar chemical sedimentary rock called **banded iron formation** was formed during the Archean and Proterozoic. The common *Superior-type banded iron formation* is Proterozoic in age and typically consists of alternating bands of iron oxides (magnetite or hematite) and chert (Figure 6.14B). Because of the generally reducing conditions that prevailed through much of the Precambrian, a great deal of iron occurred in the soluble ferrous state and was dissolved in large quantities from weathered rocks and delivered to the sea.

Large quantities of iron were probably also produced from hydrothermal vents.

It is believed that the oxygen liberated from photosynthesizing bacteria eventually accumulated in sufficient quantities in the oceans to oxidize some of the iron, resulting in the deposition of insoluble iron oxide minerals. It appears that such oxygenation occurred in pulses, such that the iron oxides were deposited in more or less distinct bands. During intervening periods when iron oxide precipitation was low, silica was deposited as a gel that eventually lithified to form chert.

Despite the presence of oxygen in the oceans when banded iron formations were formed, oxygen had not yet reached sufficient quantities to occur in a gaseous state in the atmosphere. Iron formations are not formed today because of our oxygen-rich atmosphere. In today's world, iron is immediately oxidized into the insoluble ferric state and therefore does not accumulate in a dissolved form to the degree it did during the Precambrian. In addition, much of the dissolved silica in today's oceans is taken up by organisms (e.g., radiolarians, diatoms, and sponges) to make their skeletons and therefore does not precipitate in large quantities to form chert.

In Canada and the northern United States, banded iron formations occur abundantly in the Lake Superior area of the Canadian Shield. They also reach ore grade in Newfoundland and Labrador. Banded iron formations presently compose the main sources of iron in North America.

PLACER DEPOSITS The formation of **placer** deposits relates to the sorting action of running water. As you will recall from Chapter 6, large,

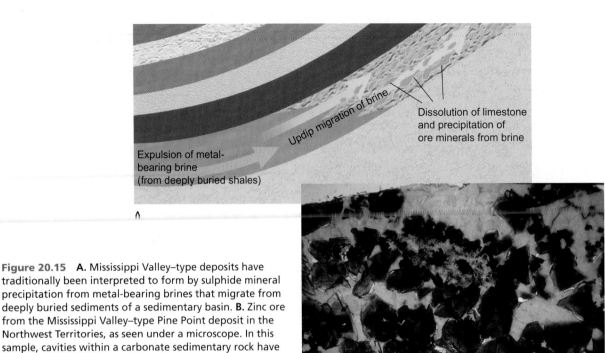

Updip migration of brine

Dissolution of limestone and precipitation of ore minerals from brine

Expulsion of metal-bearing brine (from deeply buried shales)

A

← 1 mm →

B

Figure 20.15 **A.** Mississippi Valley–type deposits have traditionally been interpreted to form by sulphide mineral precipitation from metal-bearing brines that migrate from deeply buried sediments of a sedimentary basin. **B.** Zinc ore from the Mississippi Valley–type Pine Point deposit in the Northwest Territories, as seen under a microscope. In this sample, cavities within a carbonate sedimentary rock have been filled with crystals of sphalerite (yellowish brown) and dolomite (white).
(Photo courtesy of R. W. Hodder)

heavy sediment grains tend to be deposited in more agitated water than do smaller, lighter ones. In the same sense, mineral particles of high density can be concentrated because of the sorting out and washing away of mineral particles of lower density. The concentrations of heavy minerals that form in this manner are called placers and are associated with areas of high water agitation, such as streams and beaches.

Placer deposits of gold were the foundation of the famous gold rushes in California and Yukon, and they continue to perpetuate images of old, haggard-looking prospectors panning river sediment, with their mules standing close by. It is in placer deposits that the familiar *nuggets* of gold are found, their commonly rounded appearance attesting to the rigours of sediment transport. It has traditionally been assumed that nuggets are sourced from hydro-thermal veins as large sedimentary particles and become increasingly smaller as they are transported away from their host rocks by water action. More recently, however, some geologists have pondered the possibility that gold nuggets might actually grow due to bacterially mediated gold precipitation from surface waters.

Panning is a simple, small-scale method of con-centrating gold that takes advantage of essentially the same process responsible for concentrating heavy minerals in natural deposits. Water and a bit of sediment are scooped into a pan and swirled to sus-pend the light rock particles. When the pan is tipped, the suspended sediment is dumped out with the water, and the heavy minerals are left behind in the pan as a residue. Most other methods of extracting heavy minerals, including sluicing and hydraulic monitoring, are based on the same prin-ciple (Figure 20.16).

Additional minerals extracted from placer deposits include magnetite, rutile and ilmenite (titanium oxides), platinum, and diamonds. Ancient placer deposits, such as conglomerate in the Witwatersrand of South Africa, are also mined for precious minerals.

Metamorphic Deposits

The role of metamorphism in producing mineral deposits is frequently tied to igneous processes. For example, many of the most important metamorphic ore deposits are produced by contact metamorphism. The host rock is re-crystallized and chemically altered by heat, pressure, and hydrothermal solu-tions emanating from an intruding igneous body. The extent to which the host rock is altered depends

A   B

Figure 20.16 **A.** It was placer deposits that led to the 1898 Klondike gold rush in Yukon. Here, a group of placer miners (in 1901 on Last Chance Creek) operate a sluice box that separates sand and gravel from flecks of gold by using running water. **B.** Gold mining in 2002 of a placer deposit along the same creek shown in **A.** Still using water, the hydraulic monitor thaws frozen gravel in the creek bank.
(Photo **A** courtesy of Yukon Archives, Adams and Larkin fonds, #9163; photo **B** by Peter Rotheisler)

on the nature of the intruding igneous mass as well as the nature of the host rock.

Some resistant materials, such as quartz sandstone, may show little alteration, whereas others, including limestone (readily metamorphosed to marble), may exhibit the effects of metamorphism for several kilometres from the igneous pluton. As hot, iron-rich fluids move through limestone, chemical reactions take place. These reactions release carbon dioxide, which greatly facilitates the mobilization of metallic ions. These extensive aureoles of metal-rich deposits are called *skarns* and commonly surround igneous plutons that have invaded limestone strata (Figure 20.17).

The most common metallic minerals associated with contact metamorphism are sphalerite (zinc), galena (lead), chalcopyrite (copper), magnetite (iron), and bornite (copper). The hydrothermal ore deposits may be disseminated throughout the altered zone or concentrated as masses either next to the intrusive body or along the margins of the metamorphic zone. Skarns can be closely associated with porphyry deposits. Two of Canada's best-known skarn deposits are the Copper Mountain deposit of British Columbia and Mines Gaspé copper deposits of Quebec. A number of tungsten and gold skarns occur in British Columbia and Yukon.

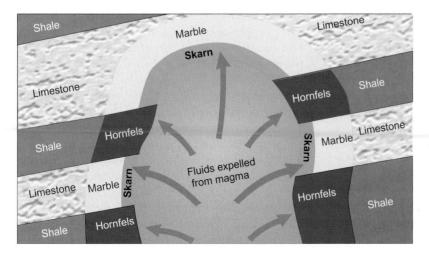

Figure 20.17 Skarns are associated with contact metamorphism. In this example, the intrusion of magma into sedimentary rock layers has metamorphosed limestone to marble and shale to hornfels. Infiltration of magmatic fluids into the zones of marble promotes the reaction of the fluids with minerals of the various intruded rocks, the dissolution of calcium carbonate, and the precipitation of metallic minerals in permeable zones. Hornfels lacks significant porosity and permeability and therefore does not host skarn deposits.

Weathering Deposits

Weathering creates many important mineral deposits by concentrating minor amounts of metals that are scattered through unweathered rock into economically valuable reserves. Such a transformation is often termed **secondary enrichment** and takes place in one of two ways. In one situation, chemical weathering coupled with downward-percolating water removes undesirable materials from decomposing rock, leaving the desirable elements enriched in the upper zones of the soil. The second situation is basically the reverse of the first. That is, the desirable elements that are found in low concentrations near the surface are removed and carried to lower zones, where they are redeposited and become more concentrated.

BAUXITE The formation of *bauxite*, the principal ore of aluminum, is one example of ore created by enrichment through weathering (Figure 20.18). Although aluminum is the third most abundant element in Earth's crust, economic concentrations of this metal are uncommon because most aluminum is tied up in silicate minerals, from which it is very difficult to extract.

Bauxite forms in wet tropical climates with deeply weathered soils called laterites. When aluminum-rich source rocks are subjected to intense and prolonged tropical chemical weathering, calcium, sodium, and silicon are removed by leaching. Because aluminum is insoluble, it becomes concentrated in the soil as bauxite, a hydrated aluminum oxide. Thus the formation of bauxite depends on a tropical climate weathering an aluminum-rich source rock. Also, nickel and cobalt deposits can form in laterite soils developing from igneous rocks rich in ferromagnesian silicate minerals.

OTHER DEPOSITS Many copper and silver deposits result when weathering processes concentrate metals that are dispersed through a low-grade primary ore. Usually, such enrichment occurs in deposits containing pyrite (FeS_2), the most common and widespread sulphide mineral. Pyrite is important because when it chemically weathers, sulphuric acid forms, which enables percolating waters to dissolve the ore minerals. Once dissolved, the metals gradually migrate downward through the primary orebody until they are precipitated. Deposition takes place because of changes that occur in the chemistry of the solution when it reaches the saturated zone (the zone beneath the surface where all pore spaces are filled with water; see Chapter 16). In this manner, the small percentage of dispersed metal can be removed from

Figure 20.18 Bauxite is the ore of aluminum and forms as a result of weathering processes under tropical conditions. Its colour varies from red or brown to nearly white. (Photo by E. J. Tarbuck)

a large volume of rock and redeposited as a higher-grade ore in a smaller volume of rock. This enrichment process is responsible for the economic success of some metallic mineral deposits, particularly those containing copper.

NON-METALLIC MINERAL RESOURCES

Earth materials that are not used as fuels, or processed for metals, are referred to as **non-metallic mineral resources**. Realize the use of the word *mineral* is very broad in the economic context and is quite different from the geologist's strict definition of *mineral* found in Chapter 2. Non-metallic mineral resources are extracted and processed either for the non-metallic elements they contain or for their desirable physical or chemical properties.

People often do not realize the importance of non-metallic minerals because they see only the products that result from their use, not the minerals themselves. That is, many non-metallics are used up in the process of creating other products. Examples include the fluorite and limestone that are part of the steelmaking process, the abrasives required to make a piece of machinery, and fertilizers needed to grow a food crop. The quantities of non-metallics used in construction and other applications are huge.

Non-metallic mineral resources are divided into two broad groups here: aggregate and stone, and industrial minerals. Because some substances have many uses, they can technically belong to either category.

Limestone, for example, is used as crushed rock and building stone in its raw form, but its main mineral constituent, calcite, is important in its own right as the key ingredient for the manufacture of cement and as a component in a score of other products, including cosmetics and pharmaceuticals.

Aggregate and Stone

Because most building materials are widely distributed and present in almost unlimited quantities, they have little intrinsic value. Their economic worth comes only after the materials are removed from the ground and processed. Because their per-tonne value compared with metals and industrial minerals is low, mining and quarrying operations are usually undertaken to satisfy local needs. Except for special types of cut stone used for building and monuments, transportation costs greatly limit the distance most building materials can be moved. The aggregate and stone industry is very important in the lives of Canadians, as reflected in the thousands of sand and gravel pits and stone quarries that exist in our country.

Natural aggregate consists of crushed stone, sand, and gravel. From the standpoint of quantity and value, aggregate is a very important building material. It is produced in all provinces and territories in Canada and is used in nearly all road and building construction (Figure 20.19A). Thanks to the large volume of sand and gravel in Canada deposited as glacial outwash during and at the end of the last Ice Age, every province and territory has an ample supply of aggregates for construction. Aggregate is used as-is in various construction applications and is also important in the manufacture of concrete and road asphalt. To appreciate the importance of aggregate in our daily lives, we only need to consider that just one kilometre of a four-lane highway, such as Highway 401 in Ontario, requires more than 40 tonnes of aggregate.

Attesting to the diversity of Canada's geologic makeup, many varieties of solid stone are quarried throughout the country, including rocks of igneous (e.g., granite and gabbro), metamorphic (e.g., marble, gneiss, and slate), and sedimentary (e.g., sandstone, limestone, and dolostone) origin. Cut stone is largely used for aesthetic applications in construction, such as decorative facings, walkways (Figure 20.19B), and countertops.

Industrial Minerals

Many non-metallic resources are classified as industrial minerals. In some instances these materials are important because they contain specific chemical elements or compounds used in fertilizers or industrial chemicals. Some minerals possess useful physical properties. For example, garnet is both relatively hard and fairly common, making it a handy substance for the manufacture of abrasive products, such as sandpaper. Other industrial minerals are used in the manufacture of products used in construction as fillers, coaters, and extenders in plastics, paints, and paper products and as heat-resistant materials, in

A

B

Figure 20.19 Examples of non-metallic resources. **A.** Aggregate pits are located in all provinces and territories of Canada. This pit is near Aldergrove, British Columbia. **B.** Cut stone set into the floor of a building in Iqaluit, capital city of Nunavut. (Photos by S. R. Hicock)

TABLE **20.2**   Occurrences and Uses of Non-metallic Minerals

Mineral	Uses	Geologic Occurrences
Apatite	Phosphorus fertilizers	Sedimentary deposits
Asbestos (chrysotile)	Incombustible fibres	Metamorphic alteration
Barite	Drilling mud; cement; paint; paper	Hydrothermal deposits
Calcite	Aggregate; steelmaking; soil conditioning; chemicals; cement; building stone	Sedimentary deposits
Clay minerals (kaolinite)	Ceramics; china	Residual product of weathering
Corundum	Gemstones; abrasives	Metamorphic deposits
Diamond	Gemstones; abrasives	Kimberlite pipes; placers
Fluorite	Steelmaking; aluminium refining; glass; chemicals	Hydrothermal deposits
Garnet	Abrasives; gemstones	Metamorphic deposits
Graphite	Pencil lead; lubricant; refractories	Metamorphic deposits
Gypsum	Plaster of Paris; drywall	Evaporite deposits
Halite	Table salt; chemicals; ice control	Evaporite deposits; salt domes
Muscovite	Insulator in electrical applications	Pegmatites
Quartz	Primary ingredient in glass	Igneous intrusions; sedimentary deposits
Sulphur	Chemicals; fertilizer manufacture	Sedimentary deposits; hydrothermal deposits
Sylvite	Potassium fertilizers	Evaporite deposits
Talc	Powder used in paints, cosmetics, etc.	Metamorphic deposits

addition to a host of other applications. Common industrial minerals and their uses are listed in Table 20.2. Some industrial minerals of particular importance in Canada, and their geologic occurrences, are indicated in Figure 20.20 and discussed next.

DIAMONDS Diamonds are familiar as gemstones, but diamond is also extremely valuable as an abrasive by virtue of being the hardest natural substance known. Only about one-quarter of all diamonds mined are used as gemstones.

The vast majority of diamonds are found in a unique ultramafic igneous rock called **kimberlite**. Magmas that produce kimberlite are believed to be generated by a small amount of partial melting in the asthenosphere at depths nearly 200 kilometres below Earth's surface. The diamonds themselves do not crystallize from kimberlitic magma. Rather, they are produced in the deep roots of the solid, lithospheric mantle beneath areas of old, stable continental crust at depths of more than 120 kilometres (Figure 20.21). It is only here that high temperatures (between 900°C and 1200°C) and pressures (more than 40 kilobars) remain stable for geologically long enough periods of time to allow the formation of diamonds.

Kimberlitic magma rapidly rises to the surface, acting as a sort of geologic elevator that picks up chunks of lithospheric mantle material and crustal rock during its ascent. If kimberlitic magma passes through the deep areas of lithospheric mantle where diamonds reside, diamonds can be naturally sampled from this material as xenocrysts (foreign crystals) and as crystal components of xenoliths (foreign rock fragments) and can be carried upward by the magma.

During the last stage of magma ascent, the rapid escape of carbon dioxide from the magma and the interaction of the hot kimberlitic magma with groundwater results in an explosive volcanic eruption from a pipe-shaped vent (Figure 20.21). The fractures and cavities within the vent are ultimately filled with kimberlite and shattered fragments of the surrounding rock. Associated with the main, carrot-shaped kimberlite pipe are ultramafic dykes and sills at depth and pyroclastic volcanic deposits at the surface.

Major producers of diamonds (by value) are Botswana, Russia, Canada, South Africa (the hub of the early diamond industry), and Angola. Canada's Ekati mine (chapter-opening photo) began production in 1998, and the nearby Diavik mine under Lac de Gras reached full production in 2004. More recent mining projects include Snap Lake, Jericho, and Victor (Figure 20.20). It is projected that Canada may supply 15 percent to 20 percent of the world's diamonds within the next decade.

CLAYS Clays, the fine-grained, platy minerals formed by the weathering and hydration of

Figure 20.20 Significant industrial mineral deposits in Canada. (Source: Natural Resources Canada)

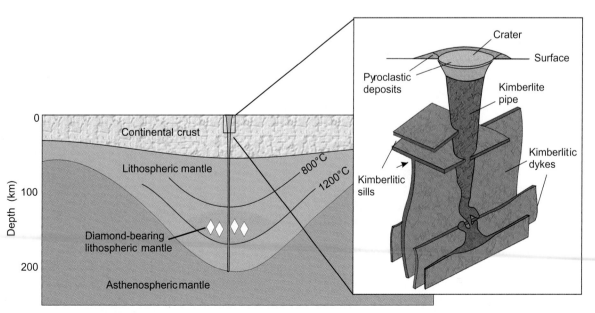

Figure 20.21 Kimberlite pipes are carrot-shaped igneous bodies that are formed when mantle-sourced magma is violently extruded to Earth's surface. At the Ekati mine in the Northwest Territories (see chapter-opening photo), diamonds are mined from this rare type of igneous body.

aluminosilicate minerals, are important industrial minerals. Certain clay minerals can form economically important deposits at the place of origin in masses of weathered material. However, much larger quantities of clay minerals occur in sedimentary deposits of seas and lakes, having been transported long distances by wind or water from their site of formation. Major Canadian producers of clay include Saskatchewan, Ontario, and British Columbia.

The diverse physical and chemical properties of clays make them extremely useful in many applications. For example, sediment dominated by the clay mineral kaolinite (but also generally containing minor amounts of other minerals) is extensively mined for the production of bricks, sewer pipes, and pottery. As an industrial mineral, kaolinite is also used in the production of wall and floor tiles, porcelain, insulation products, and ion-exchange products; as a filler (and natural whitener) for paint, adhesives, sealants, pharmaceuticals, and cosmetics; and as a coater in paper. It might surprise you that the glossy finish on the pages of magazines is actually a thin layer of kaolinite.

Clay minerals, such as *montmorillonite* (a weathering product of volcanic ash), readily absorb moisture and are therefore useful as absorbents in products such as clumping cat litter. Montmorillonite is also an important ingredient contributing to the lubricating properties of drilling mud in the petroleum industry. In addition, because of their high capacity for ion exchange, clays are used in oil refining and in waste treatment.

CARBONATE MINERALS As discussed in Chapter 6, calcium carbonate in the form of calcite (and to a lesser extent, aragonite) is an important component of many sedimentary rocks. Vast quantities of limestone, most representing accumulations of calcareous skeletal material secreted by organisms, are quarried worldwide. Although some limestone is quarried raw in the form of building stone, a great deal of it is extracted for its calcium carbonate content.

Large volumes of limestone are quarried and processed for the manufacture of cement. The principal raw materials used in the making of common cements are calcite (from limestone), with smaller amounts of silica (from sand), clay (from shale), and iron oxide. These provide the necessary ingredients—calcium, silica, alumina, and iron—that chemically interact to produce the desired qualities of cement. The raw materials are crushed into a powder and fed into the top of a tower containing a series of heating chambers. As the powdered substance drops through the series of chambers, it is heated to nearly 900°C, and then is fed through a kiln that heats the mixture

further, to about 1500°C–1600°C, and converts the raw material into a substance called clinker. The key substance formed during this heating process is calcium silicate. The clinker is cooled, mixed with a small amount of gypsum (a regulator of cement setting time), and milled into a fine powder that is then ready for use as cement. When water is added to the cement powder, crystals of calcium silicate hydrate form an interlocking network that gives concrete its strength for construction purposes.

Calcium carbonate is also used in a great many other applications. It is used as a filler in asphalt, fertilizers, insecticides, paints, rubber, and plastics; as a fluxing agent; as a mild abrasive in some toothpastes; as an acid neutralizer in a wide variety of cosmetic, medicinal, and paper products; and as a dietary supplement. In all likelihood, the very page you are reading in this text has a thin coat of calcium carbonate that has been added to the paper to provide a smooth, uniform surface for printing. People also use dolomite as a gentle abrasive and a dietary supplement.

EVAPORITE SALTS Evaporite deposits are important sources of many industrial minerals, particularly chloride and sulphate salts, and some carbonate minerals. During many times in Earth's past, widespread evaporite deposits were formed in shallow basins that were periodically flooded by seawater but dried up because of intense evaporation under arid conditions.

Normal seawater contains about 3.5 percent (by weight) dissolved matter that can be precipitated in mineral form when the water is evaporated. As observed in a glass of salty water left on the counter for several days, evaporation reduces the total volume of liquid, increasing the concentration of the dissolved matter to the point that salt can be precipitated. Partly because of differences in the relative concentrations of dissolved ions in seawater, minerals of different composition are precipitated sequentially as evaporation removes more and more water from the brine. In order of appearance, the principal minerals that form during progressive evaporation are calcite, gypsum, halite, and finally sylvite. Few evaporite deposits contain sylvite, probably because of the dilution of brines by episodic influxes of normal seawater from the adjacent ocean. Note that thick evaporite deposits represent several cycles of seawater influx, evaporation, and mineral precipitation rather than a single drying-up event in a basin.

Gypsum is primarily used for the manufacture of plaster products used in construction and other applications. Gypsum ($CaSO_4 \cdot 2H_2O$) is heated to about 180°C to drive off about three-quarters of its water (producing $CaSO_4 \cdot \frac{1}{2}H_2O$), milled to a fine powder, and sold as plaster. When water is added to the powder, it rehydrates the material to produce tiny, interlocking crystals of gypsum that give plaster products their strength for interior construction applications. A plaster product familiar to most people is drywall (also called wallboard or gyprock), which consists of a layer of plaster sandwiched between two sheets of paper. Physicians commonly use plaster to make casts for patients who require their limbs to be stabilized as their fractured bones heal. Gypsum is also widely used as a filler or additive in many products, including cosmetics, pharmaceuticals, fertilizers, paints, and plastics. Significant deposits of gypsum occur in British Columbia, Manitoba, Ontario, Nova Scotia, and Newfoundland and Labrador.

Halite, or salt, as it is more commonly known, is another important resource mined from evaporite deposits. The use of salt in Canada is very high, averaging about 360 kilograms of salt per person per year. This high figure reflects not only our liberal use of salt in the de-icing of roads but also the extensive use of halite in the manufacture of important substances used in the chemical industry, such as chlorine, caustic soda, baking soda, and washing soda. Halite, of course, is also used to season and preserve foods. Salt is a common evaporite and thick deposits are exploited by using conventional underground mining and brining, which involves dissolving salt underground and re-precipitating it at the surface. In Canada, extensive Paleozoic salt deposits occur in the sedimentary basins of the Prairie provinces, southwest Ontario, Quebec, and the Maritime provinces. Globally, salt is extracted directly from seawater in arid, coastal areas by using the natural evaporating abilities of the Sun's heat.

The mining of potash, an evaporite rock containing the potassium-bearing minerals sylvite (KCl) and carnallite ($KClMgCl_2 \cdot 6H_2O$), is a huge industry in Canada. Most of Canada's potash is mined from immense deposits in Saskatchewan, where it occurs in horizontal layers up to three metres thick (Figure 2.30). Potash deposits also occur in the Maritime provinces and are actively mined in New Brunswick. About 95 percent of all potash mined in Canada is exported to other countries, where it is primarily used in the production of fertilizers. It is also used in de-icing products, in the manufacture of soaps and detergents, and as an additive in glass and ceramic products.

PHOSPHATE Phosphate, contained in the mineral apatite, is mined primarily for the production of phosphoric acid for fertilizers, additives for livestock feed, industrial chemicals, and some home products. Although generally scarce in nature, phosphate can reach high concentrations in sedimentary rocks. The manner in which these deposits form is somewhat enigmatic, but appears to require a combination of high primary productivity, low oxygen, and low input rates of detrital sediment in a marine environment. Such conditions appear to be fairly common in oceanic environments influenced by upwelling cold, nutrient-rich seawater. North America's major phosphate mines are in the states of Florida, North Carolina, Idaho, and Utah, although sedimentary phosphate deposits are known to exist in British Columbia. Canada's only active phosphate mine is located in Kapuskasing, Ontario, where the weathering of an igneous intrusion has left a rich residue of apatite crystals.

SULPHUR Because of its many uses, sulphur is an important non-metallic resource. Sulphur is a major component of sulphuric acid and fertilizers; it is also used in matches and gunpowder. Sources of sulphur include deposits of native sulphur associated with salt domes and volcanic areas, and sulphide minerals such as pyrite. Canada's main source of sulphur is natural gas; huge amounts are scrubbed from natural gas as a measure to reduce the content of corrosive sulphur-bearing compounds and to ensure a cleaner-burning product.

OTHER INDUSTRIAL MINERAL DEPOSITS In addition to igneous and sedimentary deposits of industrial minerals, deposits of metamorphic origin also occur. Recall that, at convergent plate boundaries, the oceanic crust and sediments that have accumulated at the continental margins are carried to great depths. In these high-temperature, high-pressure environments, the mineralogy and texture of the subducted material are altered, producing deposits of non-metallic minerals, such as talc (used widely in cosmetic products) and graphite (used in the manufacture of steel products, lubricants, and pencils). Chrysotile asbestos is another product of metamorphism, resulting from the flushing of fluids through ultramafic rock. Zeolite minerals are used to extract ions in water softeners. Concentrations of industrial minerals can also be produced in association with skarns during contact metamorphism. These minerals include garnet and corundum, used in abrasive products.

NON-RENEWABLE ENERGY RESOURCES (FOSSIL FUELS)
Petroleum

Petroleum is the group of hydrocarbons that includes oil and gas, and is presently a vital resource for our daily activities. It is mainly used as fuel, but it also composes the main ingredients in plastics that find their way into synthetic fabrics, product packaging, casings, and a wide range of other products.

HOW PETROLEUM IS FORMED The origin of petroleum ultimately lies in organic matter contained in the tissues of living things. The vast majority of petroleum is derived from the remains of simple aquatic organisms (mostly planktonic algae) that constitute most of the plankton in the seas and other large bodies of water, although some land-derived organic matter may also contribute to petroleum generation. Organic matter has a rather low preservation potential in most aquatic environments, because scavenging organisms and aerobic microbes naturally recycle it. However, it often accumulates in the quiet-water environments of shallow seas and lakes, where low-oxygen conditions prevail. Accordingly, organic-rich sediments are typically fine-grained and are represented in ancient deposits by shales and fine-grained carbonate rocks. Because they are the principal sources of organic matter from which petroleum is generated, these organic-rich rocks are called *source rocks*.

Although organic matter stands a better chance of survival under low-oxygen conditions, it is by no means immune to microbial attack. Organic-rich sediment can initially yield significant quantities of *biogenic gas* (principally methane) because of the breakdown of organic matter by anaerobic microbes (Figure 20.22). This microbial attack also removes much of the oxygen, nitrogen, phosphorus, and sulphur from the organic matter, leaving a residue that is enriched in hydrocarbons. With progressive burial, the production of biogenic gas ceases, the organic-rich sediment undergoes lithification, and heat becomes the main agent in the breakdown of the organic matter.

As the hydrocarbon-rich organic matter of a source rock is subjected to higher and higher temperatures, it is transformed into a solid waxy substance called *kerogen*. At temperatures above about 50°C, carbon–carbon bonds within the kerogen break, producing the lighter, less complex hydrocarbon molecules. This process is called cracking. As the temperature rises, more carbon–carbon bonds are broken, both in the kerogen and in the hydrocarbon molecules that formed previously, generating oil (Figure 20.22). Oil generation peaks at a temperature of about 100°C, beyond which the kerogen is depleted of its hydrocarbon supply, and significant amounts of thermogenic natural gas are produced (Figure 20.22). The natural gas produced at temperatures just above that of peak oil generation is commonly called *wet gas* because, in addition to its primary constituent, methane, it contains gaseous

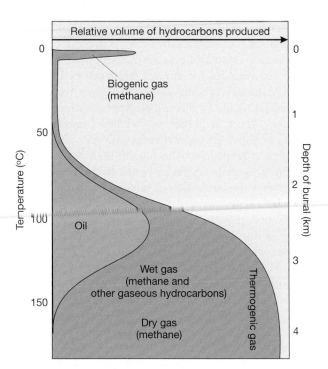

Figure 20.22 The temperatures and corresponding depths of burial at which oil and gas are generated. Note that biogenic gas is only produced at low temperatures, whereas thermogenic gas produced by the thermal cracking of organic molecules dominates at higher temperatures. Oil generation is restricted to a temperature window between approximately 50°C and 150°C. Note also the large amounts of natural gas produced at the expense of oil as hydrocarbons are cracked to progressively simpler molecular forms.

components, such as ethane, propane, and butane, that can be separated by condensation. At temperatures above about 150°C, only *dry gas*, consisting almost entirely of methane, is generated.

It should be noted that the specific proportions of oil and gas generated in any given source rock depend not only on burial depth and duration of cooking but also on the composition of the organic matter from which the hydrocarbons are derived. Whereas organic matter from marine sources is *oil prone*, land-derived organic matter tends to be more *gas prone*. Because land-derived organic matter can be transported into aquatic environments, some source rocks can be expected to be more gas prone than others.

PETROLEUM MIGRATION Unlike the organic matter from which they form, oil and gas are mobile. These fluids eventually migrate from the fine-grained source rocks where they originate into adjacent rocks of higher permeability. Because this occurs under the water table, the rock layers containing the oil and gas are saturated with water.

And since oil and gas are less dense than water, they migrate upward through the water-filled pore spaces of the enclosing rocks. Unless something halts this upward migration, the fluids will eventually reach the surface, at which point the volatile components will evaporate.

PETROLEUM TRAPS Sometimes the upward migration of oil and gas is halted. A geologic environment that enables economically significant amounts of oil and gas to accumulate underground is called a **petroleum trap**. Several geologic structures can act as petroleum traps, but all have two basic conditions in common: a porous, permeable **reservoir rock** that will yield oil and natural gas in sufficient quantities to make drilling worthwhile; and a **cap rock**, such as shale, that is virtually impermeable to oil and gas. The cap rock halts the upwardly mobile oil and gas and keeps them from escaping to the surface. Petroleum traps can be produced in a number of ways, but they can be separated into two groups: structural traps and stratigraphic traps.

Structural traps are petroleum traps that form because of the structural deformation of the rock layer that contains the hydrocarbons. One of the simplest structural traps is an anticline, an up-arched succession of sedimentary strata (Figure 20.23A). As the strata are bent, the rising oil and gas collect at the crest (top) of the fold. Because of its lower density, the natural gas collects above the oil. In turn, the oil rests on the denser water that saturates the reservoir rock. One of the world's largest oil fields, El Nala in Saudi Arabia, is the result of anticlinal traps, as is the famous Teapot Dome in Wyoming.

Fault traps form when strata are displaced in such a manner as to bring a dipping reservoir rock into position opposite an impermeable bed, as shown in Figure 20.23B. In this case the upward migration of the oil and gas is halted where it encounters the fault.

In the Gulf coastal plain region of the United States, important accumulations of oil occur in association with *salt domes*. Such areas have thick accumulations of sedimentary strata, including layers of rock salt. Salt occurring at great depths is ductile and has been forced to rise in columns by the pressure of overlying beds. These rising salt columns gradually deform the overlying strata, causing oil and gas to accumulate in the upturned sandstone beds adjacent to the salt column (Figure 20.23C).

Stratigraphic traps are petroleum traps that are formed because of lateral and vertical changes in rock type that reflect patterns of sediment deposition (Figure 20.24). A common type of stratigraphic trap is a pinch-out trap, characterized by the tapering off of a reservoir unit into a body of

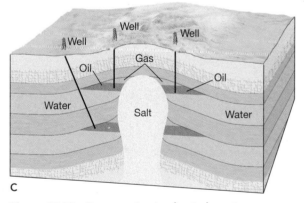

Figure 20.23 Common structural petroleum traps. **A.** Anticline. **B.** Fault trap. **C.** Salt dome.

impermeable rock. An unconformity trap results from the truncation of a reservoir unit by erosion, followed by the deposition of impermeable cap rock sediments. Reefs also form important stratigraphic traps, by virtue of representing lens-shaped bodies of porous, permeable limestone that are commonly encased by impermeable shales.

Coal

Whereas petroleum is generally sourced from organic matter provided by aquatic plankton, coal is largely derived from the fibrous and woody remains of land

Figure 20.24 Common stratigraphic petroleum traps.
A. Pinch-out trap. **B.** Unconformity trap. **C.** Limestone reef.

plants. Similar to petroleum, the organic remains that form coal can only accumulate in appreciable quantities in oxygen-poor environments. Accordingly, accumulations of coal-forming organic matter tend to be restricted to such areas as swamps. In a swamp, the decomposition of organic matter consumes so much oxygen from the water that much of the organic matter escapes decomposition. The organic matter that survives decomposition is buried to progressively greater depths, where it is gradually cooked and compressed to form coal. The resulting sedimentary rock was discussed in greater detail in Chapter 6.

Coal has been an important fuel for centuries. In the nineteenth and early twentieth centuries, cheap and plentiful coal powered the Industrial Revolution. Until the 1950s, coal was an important domestic fuel as well as a power source for industry. However, its direct use in the home has largely been replaced by oil, natural gas, and electricity. These fuels are preferred because they are more readily available (delivered via pipes, tanks, or wiring) and cleaner to use. Nevertheless, coal remains the major fuel used by many nations.

Although coal is plentiful, its recovery and use present a number of problems. Surface mining can turn the countryside into a scarred wasteland if careful (and costly) reclamation is not carried out to restore the land. Although underground mining does not scar the landscape to the same degree, it has been costly in terms of human life and health.

Underground mining long ago ceased to be a pick-and-shovel operation and is today a highly mechanized and computerized process (Figure 20.25). However, the hazards of collapsing roofs, gas explosions, and working with heavy equipment remain.

Air pollution is a major problem associated with the burning of coal. Much coal contains significant quantities of sulphur. Despite efforts to remove sulphur before it is burned, the sulphur is converted into noxious sulphur oxide gases. Through a series of complex chemical reactions in the atmosphere, the sulphur oxides are converted to sulphuric acid, which then falls to Earth's surface as rain or snow. This acid precipitation can have adverse ecological effects over widespread areas (see Box 5.1).

As none of the problems just mentioned is likely to prevent the increased use of this important and abundant fuel, stronger efforts must be made to correct the problems associated with the mining and use of coal. Disposal of fly ash produced by coal burning also poses problems. However, as indicated in Figure 20.A, this material may well prove to be a future resource in itself. For example, at Wabamun, Alberta, fly ash produced from coal burning for power generation is used in making high-quality cement.

Fossil Fuels in Canada

Canada is fortunate to host large quantities of coal and petroleum—so much that most of what is extracted is exported. The overwhelming majority of Canada's petroleum is produced in the southern areas of the Prairie provinces and British Columbia that overlie strata of the Western Canada Sedimentary Basin (Figure 20.26). Through much of Paleozoic and Mesozoic time, warm, shallow seas, within which organic-rich sediments were deposited, occupied this area of Canada. Hydrocarbons were generated from the organic-rich sediments and migrated

Figure 20.25   Modern underground coal mining is highly mechanized. Strip mining (**inset**) of coal at Estevan, Saskatchewan. Strip mining is common when coal seams are near the surface.
(**Main** photo by Melvin Grubb/Grubb Photo Services, Inc.; **inset** photo © JTB MEDIA CREATION, Inc./Alamy)

to the permeable, low-pressure areas of the rock column, such as Paleozoic reefs and units of Mesozoic sandstone. Similar circumstances allowed oil to be produced and trapped in basins and the continental shelf areas of Newfoundland and Labrador (Hibernia project), Yukon, Northwest Territories, Nunavut, and, to a lesser degree, British Columbia and Nova Scotia. Modest quantities of oil and gas are also extracted from Paleozoic sedimentary rocks of the Michigan Basin in Ontario (Figure 20.26), where North America's oil industry started. As discussed in Box 20.3, Canadians have played major roles in the development of the North American oil industry.

In the Prairie provinces, the shallow seas that supplied marine organic matter to form oil were rimmed with coastal lowlands where land plants thrived and supplied their fibrous remains to form coal. About 98 percent of Canada's coal is produced in British Columbia, Alberta, and Saskatchewan and is mostly of Mesozoic age (Figure 20.27). The famous coal beds of Nova Scotia are somewhat older, dating to the Late Paleozoic, and contributed greatly to the Canadian coal output for more than 100 years. By 2001, Canada's coal production was becoming a multibillion-dollar industry. Canada supplies more

than 20 countries (but mainly Japan and Korea) with coal and ranks as one of the world's leading coal exporters. A significant proportion of coal remains in Canada to supply energy required for steel production.

Environmental Effects of Fossil Fuel Use

We face a broad array of human-caused environmental problems. Among the most serious are the impacts on the atmosphere that occur because of fossil fuel combustion. As world population continues its explosive growth (Figure 20.28), environmental problems associated with fossil fuel emissions will continue to grow unless drastic measures are taken to decrease them. Rural and urban air pollution, acid rain, and global greenhouse warming are all closely linked to the use of these basic energy resources.

AIR POLLUTION *Air pollutants* are airborne particles and gases that occur in concentrations that endanger the health of organisms or disrupt the orderly function of the environment.

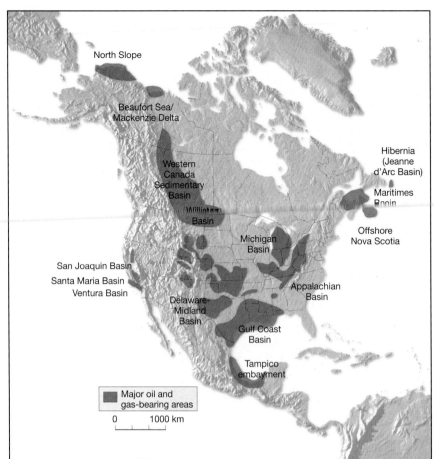

Figure 20.26 Distribution of important oil- and gas-bearing areas of North America. (Source: Natural Resources Canada)

Figure 20.27 Distribution of coal deposits in Canada. (Adapted from an image courtesy of the Coal Association of Canada)

BOX
20.3

CANADIAN PROFILE
The Hard Oilers of Enniskillen Township and Canada's Petroleum Industry

by Claudia Cochrane*

In the early 1850s, the Industrial Revolution was well under way in both Europe and the New World. As in ancient times, asphalt was needed for ship construction and for paving streets and sidewalks, and fuel was required for illumination. Although the Victorians had been using whale oil for their lamps, the great whales had been hunted almost to extinction. The world was desperate for a cheap source of petroleum. It was in the swampy hinterland of Lambton County's Enniskillen Township, Ontario, that the North American oil industry was born.

In response to the demand for oil, the enterprising Tripp Brothers, Henry and Charles, following their noses as well as reports from the Geological Survey of Canada, found their way to the site of the Lambton County oil seeps. In 1852 they started digging and manufacturing asphalt, which they sold for ships and roads. The International Mining & Manufacturing Company, chartered in 1854, was the first oil company in North America.

Initially, the Tripps were immensely successful. Only a year after incorporation, their asphalt was displayed at the Paris Universal Exhibition and received honourable mention from Emperor Napoleon III. More important, they received an order for asphalt to pave the streets of Paris. That winter the Enniskillen gum was transported overland by sled to Port Sarnia, and then by ship across the Atlantic Ocean to France.

In 1854, another enterprising Canadian and government geologist, Abraham Gesner, was experimenting with oil seeps in the colony of Nova Scotia. He had just invented and patented a method of extracting kerosene lamp fuel from the liquid oil component of natural seeps. When he set up a factory in New York the world suddenly lit up, and the search for crude oil was on.

Others, driven by dreams of profitable lighting, quickly followed the Tripps to Enniskillen Township and in 1858 James Miller Williams produced oil from sandy lenses at the base of the Tripp's gum bed. Initially pumped by hand and later by steam, his well yielded about 50 whiskey barrels a day. It was the first producing oil well in North America. By early winter, using a simple iron kettle distiller, he was refining kerosene. Although the resulting product was not very clean (it was called "skunk juice"), his was also the first oil refinery in North America. On the other side of Lake Erie, near Titusville in Pennsylvania, the Americans were exploiting gum beds as well, and a year later "Colonel" Edwin Drake, drilling all the way through into bedrock, encountered oil.

By 1860 word got out in both countries and the twin oil rush was on. In Enniskillen Township workers flocked to the new village of Oil Springs, and within a year there were 400 wells in the field; some of them also drilled into bedrock, each producing 50 to 500 barrels a day. In 1862 one of these wells brought in a gusher, reputed to produce 2000 barrels a day, and the rush compounded. Oil Springs boomed and soon 1000 wells covered 2.5 square kilometres around Black Creek (Figure 20.C). A forest of shifting ash-pole service-derricks replaced the native woodland. The oil flowed freely and there was often no need to pump. Indeed sometimes it flowed too freely, running into Black Creek and into Lake St. Clair, where it produced an oil slick several centimetres thick. Oil Springs and Titusville have often produced conflicting claims for the position of "first in North America," but neither has cared to take credit for the continent's first petroleum-related environmental debacle!

One of the more successful drillers, John Henry Fairbank, devised an ingenious method of pumping numerous wells efficiently and economically.

Figure 20.C   A photo taken in the late nineteenth century of drilling rigs in the Petrolia oilfield of southern Ontario, the birthplace of the Canadian oil industry.
(Photo courtesy of Charles Fairbank)

The well pumps were linked each to another, and thereby all were connected up to a central power source by a series of parallel wooden rods. Known as the "jerker rod system," it could pump more than 200 wells from one large central steam engine. Fairbank eventually expanded his operation over a large part of the Oil Springs field that is still operated by his descendants today. The Oil Springs boom was short-lived—less than eight years. The gushers "watered out" (depleted) and oil was discovered in Petrolia and farther afield in Texas. Production went up, the oil prices went down as the market became saturated, and Oil Springs became a ghost town.

But for Enniskillen Township, the story was not finished. The producers and the party simply moved several kilometres north to Petrolia, which produced its first gusher in 1866. This time, with a better infrastructure already in place, the boom was sustained for decades and Petrolia thrived as the oil capital of Canada. The only intrusion on this refined lifestyle was the indelicate smell of sour crude that wafted over the town when the wind was blowing in the wrong direction—the townspeople referred to it as "the smell of money."

It was in Petrolia that the energetic drillers came to call themselves "hard oilers." Although the exact origin of the label is obscure, it has been said that a team of resolute Petrolia oil workers were threatened by their opponents at a ball game with a "hard oil finish" and that the term was born on their victory. Many of the Petrolia Hard Oilers went on to open new oil fields abroad—in North Africa, Asia, and South America. Dubbed "the foreign drillers," they returned to Petrolia, full of exotic stories and souvenirs from strange lands. In all, they eventually went to 87 countries and were present in the 1920s and 1930s when giant oil fields were found in Iraq and other parts of the Middle East.

Price fluctuations were one of the greatest banes of the oil producers' lives. In an attempt to control supply,

Jacob Englehart bought up several refineries in Petrolia and the nearby city of London, where he and several other Ontario financiers established the Imperial Oil Company in 1880. Three years later, after a major fire in London, all of the operations were moved to Petrolia.

By 1893, Imperial Oil, still operating out of Petrolia, was a great refining success, with 23 branches all over Canada. But as demand outstripped supply, Imperial needed capital for expansion. As Canada was in a recession, the directors initially approached British investors, but were unsuccessful in securing funds. The only option left was to sell to the Americans. Standard Oil had already bought many small refineries in the United States, including Abraham Gesner's New York kerosene factory, and had been casting a covetous eye on Canada's flagship firm for several years. The conditions of the takeover, effected in 1898, were unequivocal: the Imperial name was kept; Canadian headquarters and refineries were moved from Petrolia to Sarnia; and Imperial Oil went on to participate in developing the industry in other parts of Canada over the next century.

One of the new frontiers of petroleum exploration was western Canada. The first exploration well in Alberta was drilled in 1902 at the site of an oil seep near Cameron Brook, which is now part of the Waterton Lakes National Park. It produced a brief boomtown of Oil Springs that suffered the same fate as its namesake in Ontario. But the nearby Turner Valley field, discovered in 1914 and drilled with the assistance of Petrolia Hard Oilers, established that Alberta was indeed a fertile ground for petroleum production.

After 20 years and 133 dry holes, Imperial Oil encountered Canada's first giant oil field at Leduc, Alberta, in 1947. Pipelines to Sarnia, Vancouver, and the United States were quickly built and Canada became a world-class oil-producing nation. But oil is not the only economically important hydrocarbon. In fact, natural gas is cleaner and requires no refining. Commercial natural gas

production was pioneered in Alberta and Ontario. In 1883, CPR workers, drilling for water for their steam engines at Langevin in southern Alberta, hit an unexpected flow of natural gas that ignited and destroyed their derrick. George Dawson of the Geological Survey of Canada, observing that the strata that contained the gas were continuous over much of western Canada, predicted large volumes of gas from the territory. Indeed, George Dawson's prediction was well fulfilled in that the reserves of the Western Canada Sedimentary Basin are 80 percent gas prone.

Looking farther afield for oil, Imperial pioneered exploration in the north with Canada's first Arctic discovery at Norman Wells in the Northwest Territories in 1920. The first well was drilled near another oil seep that was discovered by Alexander Mackenzie. The field was eventually connected to the Canadian pipeline system in 1985. The east coast of Canada was also considered to be prime exploration territory and, at about the same time as the Leduc discovery, drillers were exploring underwater in the Atlantic Ocean near Prince Edward Island. This first effort at offshore drilling in Canada was not economically encouraging, but the technology was off to a good start. A quarter century later, in 1979, the Hibernia Field was discovered 315 kilometres off the coast of Newfoundland and Labrador.

At the start of the twenty-first century, the fourth generation of Fairbank Oil celebrated its 140th anniversary in tiny Oil Springs, Ontario (population 800). North America's first oil discovery field remains a commercially viable operation as the fourteenth-largest oil producer in Ontario. Victorian technology is still largely utilized and, remarkably, the original jerker rod system, designed by J. H. Fairbank early in the 1860s, remains in place. This is the oldest continuously operated oil company in the world.

Claudia Cochrane is a consulting geologist with Cairnlins Resources Limited and an adjunct professor in the Department of Earth Sciences at Western University.

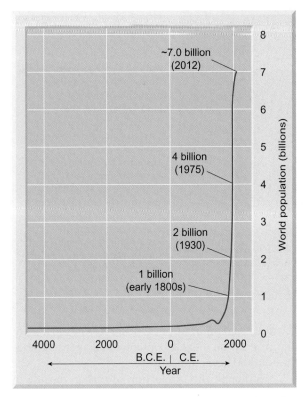

Figure 20.28 Growth of world population. It took until 1800 for the number to reach 1 billion. In 2013, more than 7 billion people inhabited the planet. The demand for basic resources is growing faster than the rate of population increase.
(Data from the Population Reference Bureau)

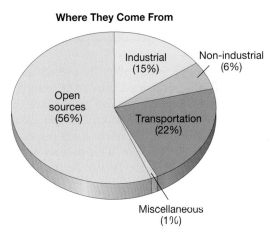

Figure 20.29 Principal types and sources of air pollution in Canada per unit mass. Although particulates from non-industrial sources, such as fields and roads, compose a large proportion of pollutants, the remaining pollutants can be linked largely to industrial and transportation-related emissions.
(Pie charts based on data from Criteria Air Contaminants Emission Summaries, Environment.)

The human population constitutes a giant chemical factory producing a remarkable variety of undesirable products. Figure 20.29 shows the major primary pollutants and their sources. *Primary pollutants* are emitted directly from identifiable sources. They pollute the air immediately on their emission. Much of the air pollution in Canada is particulate matter, most of which comes simply from dust blown from open sources, such as roads and fields. For the remainder of pollution sources, the significance of the industrial and transportation categories is obvious. Industry (including fuel-generating plants), the millions of vehicles on the roads, and airplanes in the skies are the greatest contributors in this category.

When chemical reactions take place among primary pollutants, *secondary pollutants* are formed. The noxious mixture of gases and particles that make up urban smog is an important example that is created when volatile organic compounds and sulphur and nitrogen oxides react in the presence of sunlight. The burning of fossil fuels by industry and various modes of transportation are the greatest contributors of these compounds.

CARBON DIOXIDE AND GLOBAL WARMING
Warming of the lower atmosphere is global in scale. Unlike acid rain and urban air pollution, this issue is not associated with any of the primary pollutants in Figure 20.29. Rather, the connection between global warming and burning of fossil fuels relates to a basic product of combustion: carbon dioxide.

Carbon dioxide (CO_2) is a gas that occurs naturally in the atmosphere and is augmented by fuel combustion. Although CO_2 represents only about 0.038 percent of clean, dry air, it is nevertheless meteorologically significant. The importance of carbon dioxide lies in the fact that it is transparent to incoming short-wave solar radiation but is not transparent to some of the longer wavelength outgoing radiation emitted by Earth. A portion of the energy

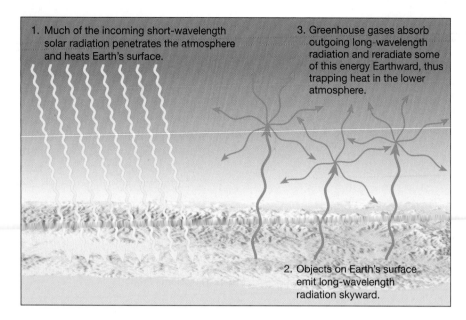

1. Much of the incoming short-wavelength solar radiation penetrates the atmosphere and heats Earth's surface.

3. Greenhouse gases absorb outgoing long-wavelength radiation and reradiate some of this energy Earthward, thus trapping heat in the lower atmosphere.

2. Objects on Earth's surface emit long-wavelength radiation skyward.

Figure 20.30 The heating of the atmosphere. Most of the short-wavelength radiation from the Sun that is not reflected back to space passes through the atmosphere and is absorbed by Earth's land-sea surface. This energy is then emitted from the surface as longer-wavelength radiation, much of which is absorbed by certain gases in the atmosphere. Some of the energy absorbed by the atmosphere is radiated Earthward. This so-called greenhouse effect is responsible for keeping Earth's surface much warmer than it would be otherwise.

leaving the ground is absorbed by carbon dioxide and subsequently re-emitted, part of it toward the surface, thereby keeping the air near the ground warmer than it would be without carbon dioxide. Thus, carbon dioxide is one of the gases responsible for warming the atmosphere. This process is called the *greenhouse effect* (Figure 20.30). Because carbon

dioxide is an important heat absorber, any change in the air's carbon dioxide content could alter temperatures in the lower atmosphere.

Although the proportion of carbon dioxide in the air is relatively uniform at any given time, its percentage has been rising steadily for more than a century (Figure 20.31). Much of this rise is the result of

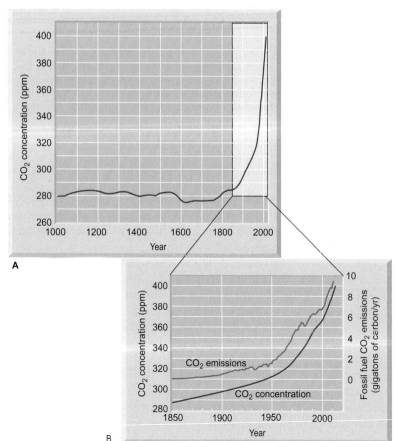

Figure 20.31 **A.** Carbon dioxide (CO_2) concentrations over the past 1000 years. Most of the record is based on data obtained from Antarctic ice cores. Bubbles of air trapped in the glacial ice provide samples of past atmospheres. The record since 1958 comes from direct measurements of atmospheric CO_2 taken at Mauna Loa Observatory, Hawaii. **B.** The rapid increase in CO_2 concentration since the onset of industrialization in the late eighteenth century is clear and has followed closely the rise in CO_2 emissions from fossil fuels. (Data from Mauna Loa Observatory, Hawaii [http://www.esrl.noaa.gov/gmd/], CDIAC website [http://cdiac.ornl.gov/trends/co2/graphics/lawdome.smooth75.gif], D.M. Etheridge, L.P. Steele, R.L. Langenfelds, R.J. Francey, J.-M. Barnola and V.I. Morgan. 1998. Historical CO_2 records from the Law Dome DE08, DE08-2, and DSS ice cores. In Trends: A Compendium of Data on Global Change. Carbon Dioxide Information Analysis Center, Oak Ridge National Laboratory, U.S. Department of Energy, Oak Ridge, Tenn., U.S.A, [CDIAC website: http://cdiac.ornl.gov/trends/emis/meth_reg.html].)

burning increasing quantities of fossil fuels. From the mid-nineteenth century until 2000, the carbon dioxide content of the air increased by more than 25 percent.

Have global temperatures already increased as a result of the rising carbon dioxide level? This appears to be the case, according to the Intergovernmental Panel on Climate Change (IPCC). During the twentieth century the increase was about 0.6°C. Moreover, recent years have been among the warmest on record. Other studies indicate that the increase in temperature in the twentieth century is likely to have been the largest of any century during the past millennium. Are these temperatures caused by human activities or would they have occurred anyway? In 2007 the IPCC declared that most of the observed warming over the past 50 years is likely due to the increase in carbon dioxide and other greenhouse gases that humans contribute to the atmosphere.

If fossil fuel use continues to increase at projected rates, the present carbon dioxide content of 360 parts per million (ppm) will climb to between 540 ppm and 970 ppm by 2100. With such an increase, the greenhouse effect would be much more dramatic and measurable than in the past. The predicted result would be an average global surface temperature increase of 1.5°C to 4.5°C. The warming of the lower atmosphere will not be the same everywhere. Rather, the temperature response in the polar regions could be much greater than the global average, while some low-latitude regions would experience much smaller fluctuations. According to the IPCC, the projected rate of warming during the next century will be much larger than the observed changes in the past century and is very likely without precedent during the past 10 000 years. However, the possible effects of aerosol emissions from fossil fuel combustion complicate this outlook considerably.

On a positive note, CO_2 from industrial plants is pumped into Saskatchewan's depleted Weyburn and Midale oil fields (carbon sequestration) to enhance oil recovery by increasing reservoir pressures and oil fluidity.

OIL SPILLS AND LEAKS Since North America's first commercial oil operation (in Oil Springs, Ontario) released its contents into Lake St. Clair (see Box 20.3), the environmental hazards posed by oil spills have been obvious. However, the sheer scale of oil spill disasters in recent times has significantly raised the level of international concern toward this unfortunate consequence of our dependence on petroleum. Causes of recent oil-related disasters have included unintentional oil spills from damaged oil tankers (e.g., the Exxon Valdez oil spill in 1989 that spilled

260 000 to 750 000 barrels of oil into Prince William Sound, Alaska), acts of war (e.g., the Iraqi sabotage of oil rigs, tankers, and pipelines in Kuwait during the Gulf War in 1991 that spilled 2 000 000 to 7 000 000 barrels of oil into the Persian Gulf); and oil rig blowouts (e.g., the 2010 Deepwater Horizon disaster in the Gulf of Mexico [see Box 20.4], in which 4 900 000 barrels of oil leaked into the Gulf of Mexico through a damaged wellhead).

The negative environmental impacts of oil spills and oil leaks are many. In the short term, crude oil released into the sea adversely affects wildlife (see discussion in Box 20.4). There are a number of methods used to clean up oil spills, including skimming (collection of surface oil), the application of dispersants, microbial biodegradation (using oil-consuming microbes to break down the oil), and controlled flaring. But while clean-up methods are improving, their effectiveness remains somewhat limited. The oil that is not collected or destroyed can remain in the environment and negatively impact wildlife for decades.

Unconventional Fossil Fuel Deposits

As supplies of petroleum and coal that can be extracted by conventional methods dwindle, we can expect that an increasing volume of fossil fuel will be produced from lower-grade deposits that require innovative, unconventional methods of extraction (Figure 20.32). Two main types of deposits that are being developed for hydrocarbon extraction are heavy oil sands and oil shales.

HEAVY OIL SANDS *Heavy oil sands*, also commonly called tar sands, are mixtures of sediment, water, and abundant black, tar-like bitumen. It is thought that such deposits result from a very high level of interaction between regular crude oil and groundwater linked to long-distance and near-surface oil migration. A popular explanation for the origin of the tarry oil is that cool, oxygen-rich groundwater provided optimal conditions for certain bacteria to preferentially consume light components of the oil, thus leaving behind a heavy residue. Exposure of petroleum to air at the surface of Earth also allows its light components to evaporate and could also contribute to enrichment of the heavier components of the petroleum. In any case, the hydrocarbons of the tar sands appear to represent degraded oil. Heavy oil sands occur in abundance in Alberta (Figure 20.32), the most famous of which are the Athabasca Oil Sands located northeast of Edmonton. Alberta's vast deposits are the source of approximately half of Canada's oil production.

Figure 20.32 Unconventional fossil fuel resources (oil sands, oil shales, and methane hydrates) in North America and uranium deposits of northern Saskatchewan.

Because of their high viscosity, hydrocarbons that occur in heavy oil sands cannot be pumped from a well like conventional oil can. The tar sand is effectively mined at the surface and heated to mobilize the hydrocarbons, which are upgraded to a synthetic crude with the addition of hydrogen and removal of impurities. Such projects as steam-assisted gravity drainage, whereby steam is injected directly into the oil sand deposit to mobilize the hydrocarbons, now bypass the mining process and oil is then recovered from pipes much like conventional crude oil. Much energy must be expended in the recovery process—about half as much as the end product yields. Nonetheless, Alberta's oil sands are a major source of petroleum and will undoubtedly play a major role in fossil-fuel production as global supplies inevitably decrease.

OIL SHALE In some cases, fine-grained, organic-rich sedimentary rocks have not been subjected to sufficiently high temperatures to liberate liquid and gas hydrocarbons, and they instead retain organic matter in the form of kerogen. A fine-grained sedimentary rock containing an abundance of kerogen is called an *oil shale*. Although widely used, this term is somewhat misleading because most oil shales are not shales at all, but fine-grained limestones (Figure 20.33). In any case, oil shales contain enormous amounts of hydrocarbons and can be artificially heated to crack their kerogen into liquid petroleum. Huge deposits of Cenozoic-age oil shale comprising the Green River Formation occur in Colorado, Utah, and Wyoming, and represent fine-grained lake sediments deposited during the Eocene Epoch. Paleozoic oil shales occur in a number of places in

20.4

The Other Oil Crisis—The Deepwater Horizon Oil Disaster

The precarious relationship between humans and the environment is never more apparent than those times when our hunger for oil collides with the consequences of human error and/or technological malfunction. As the human population and our corresponding demand for oil continue to climb, major oil spills and leaks are almost inevitable.

The recent environmental disaster in the Gulf of Mexico began on April 20, 2010, when an explosion occurred on the drilling platform of Deepwater Horizon, an offshore oil rig that had been leased by British Petroleum (BP) to drill an exploratory well approximately 400 kilometres southeast of Houston, Texas. The cause of the explosion was a blowout—a gusher of oil and gas that occurs when the pressure in an oil well is suddenly released at the surface. The blast killed 11 workers and injured 17 others, and ignited to produce a fireball that was visible tens of kilometres away. Despite strong efforts to douse the fire and save the platform (Figure 20.E), the rig eventually sank on April 22, 2010, damaging the wellhead and drill pipe and causing crude oil to leak into Gulf waters at a rate that, according to government officials, may have approached 60 000 barrels per day. Meanwhile, residents of the Gulf states watched helplessly as the edge of the oil slick slowly crept toward their shores; by June 4, 2010, the slick had reached beaches of Louisiana, Mississippi, Alabama, and Florida.

Initial attempts to shut down the leak focused on blocking, constricting, and diverting the flow of oil from the damaged blowout preventer; all failed. Later efforts to collect and pipe the leaking fluids to the surface had some success. On July 15,

Figure 20.D Tugboats fight the blaze produced by a platform explosion on the offshore oil rig Deepwater Horizon on April 20, 2010.
(Photo courtesy of US Coast Guard, File 100421-G-*L-Deepwater Horizon fire*)

2010, a temporary cap had been installed on the wellhead and the leak was successfully stopped. On August 4, 2010, drilling mud was pumped down the well to push the oil and gas back to the reservoir (a solution termed "static kill"). The well was permanently plugged by injecting cement into the well via multiple relief wells. The total amount of oil that had leaked into the Gulf was estimated at 4 900 000 barrels, making it the worst oil-related environmental disaster in North American history.

The potential damage inflicted by the release of oil into the natural environment, particularly in the aquatic realm, is far-reaching. One of the more obvious and immediate effects is the oiling of sea birds: The coating of a bird's feathers not only impedes a bird's ability to fly and insulate itself, but can poison the bird while it tries to rid itself of the oil. In addition to birds, petroleum toxicity affects all other marine biota, including mammals, reptiles (especially sea turtles), fish, countless invertebrate species, and a full range of aquatic plants—in other words, the entire food chain. Oil spills can also stimulate the population growth of microbes that consume oxygen and can ultimately deplete marine habitats of oxygen. From a human standpoint, oil spills can devastate the livelihoods of people dependent on local fisheries and tourism. The Gulf fisheries affected by the Deepwater Horizon leak will likely suffer for several years as the biota recover.

Figure 20.33 Outcrop of thinly bedded, kerogen-rich, Ordovician limestones ("oil shales") of the Collingwood Formation on the southern shore of Georgian Bay, Ontario.
(Photo by C. Tsujita)

Canada, including New Brunswick, Nova Scotia, and southern Ontario, and a few Mesozoic deposits have also been identified (Figure 20.32). Oil extraction from Canadian oil shales has been attempted but is not yet profitable. Similar to the case of heavy oil sands, the extraction of a liquid product from oil shale involves a high input of energy, both because it must be mined and because it must be heated to liberate oil. Accordingly, a considerable increase in the price of oil will be necessary for a profitable industry to be built around this resource.

METHANE HYDRATE *Methane hydrate* is a solid substance formed when water molecules form cages that surround molecules of methane. Methane hydrates, once thought to be oddities in the natural world, are now known to be common in permafrost areas associated with methane seeps. Even more significant are vast methane hydrate deposits found in deep areas of continental shelves of nearly every continent on Earth, including North America (Figure 20.34). In those places, the methane-ice complexes are kept stable because of high pressures and cold temperatures at the sea floor. At least some of these deposits are associated with communities of microbes that produce methane as part of their normal metabolic activities. Methane hydrates are sufficiently high in methane content to produce a flame when ignited with a match.

Although the thought of exploiting this large reservoir of methane is appealing, many concerns surround the use of this potential energy source. As with all unconventional hydrocarbon resources, the feasibility and cost of extraction is questionable at the present time. More serious, however, are the environmental impacts of extraction, both in terms of disturbing the sea floor and in terms of the potential leakage of methane into the atmosphere during extraction. The warming effect of methane in the atmosphere is at least 20 times as high as that of carbon dioxide, and thus methane leakage from sea-floor hydrates is a legitimate concern.

COAL-BED METHANE AND SHALE GAS The slow heating of fibrous organic matter derived from land plants not only produces solid coal but also liberates methane. This *coal-bed methane* is trapped in the pore spaces of coal seams and associated detrital sediments. Because it is confined in the pores of sedimentary rocks, it is difficult to extract by conventional means. However, many projects and wells are extracting the gas in Canada. It has been found that

Figure 20.34 A body of methane hydrate (yellowish-white) photographed on the sea floor some 850 metres below sea level, off the west coast of Vancouver Island, British Columbia.
(Photo courtesy of Ross Chapman)

coal-bed methane can be released by pumping large quantities of water from a coal seam through several wells. The merits of this practice have, however, been questioned because of concerns about surface-water and groundwater contamination, groundwater depletion, and the possible escape of the methane into the atmosphere. Still, coal-bed methane is attractive as a clean-burning alternative to conventional fossil fuels, such as oil and coal. As more efficient extraction technologies are developed, coal-bed methane is likely to become more important as a fuel source in the future.

Shale gas is natural gas (primarily methane) that has remained trapped in the pores and fractures of shale or other fine-grained sedimentary rock. This natural gas is produced when organic matter (typically aquatic in origin) contained in the rock undergoes thermal cracking and/or microbial degradation. Due to the low permeability of the rock, not all of the hydrocarbons generated as the organic matter decayed could be expelled. Until fairly recently, the development of shale gas as a resource has been hampered by its low profit potential in relation to conventional oil production—a function of both the low price of natural gas and the cost of its extraction. To extract shale gas, the permeability of the rock must be enhanced by fracturing the rock with pressurized fluid—a process called *hydrofracturing* or *fracking*. The development of shale gas is gaining in appeal as a result of the reduced recovery costs due to advances in technology, the immense volumes of shale gas estimated to occur in rocks worldwide, and the projected decrease in conventional oil production.

Nuclear Energy

Nuclear power plants generate roughly 12 percent of Canada's electricity supply. The fuel for these facilities comes from radioactive materials that release energy by the process of **nuclear fission**. Fission is accomplished by bombarding the nuclei of heavy atoms, commonly uranium-235, with neutrons. This causes the uranium nuclei to split into smaller nuclei and to emit neutrons and heat energy. The ejected neutrons, in turn, bombard the nuclei of adjacent uranium atoms, producing a chain reaction. If the supply of fissionable material is sufficient and if the reaction is allowed to proceed in an uncontrolled manner, an enormous amount of energy is released in the form of an atomic explosion. In most nuclear reactors, the chain reaction is regulated through the use of materials called *moderators*, which slow neutrons down to allow them to react with the uranium atoms in a controlled manner. Most reactors also use neutron-absorbing materials in control

rods to prevent the participation of too many neutrons in the reaction at any one time.

CANDU REACTORS The production of nuclear power in Canada is centred on the CANDU (Canadian Deuterium-Uranium) design, which uses natural uranium-235 as fuel and deuterium oxide as a moderator and heat transport medium (Figure 20.35).

Deuterium is a stable isotope of hydrogen containing a proton and a neutron. Because of the higher mass of deuterium, relative to the more common light hydrogen that contains a single proton and no neutrons, deuterium oxide is heavier than regular hydrogen oxide (water). Deuterium oxide is therefore commonly called *heavy water*. The CANDU design allows on-power refuelling, does not require fuel reprocessing, and can potentially use spent fuel from other reactors. The versatility of CANDU reactors is a major factor that has contributed to their use in a number of countries outside North America, including Argentina, India, Korea, Pakistan, and Romania.

URANIUM OCCURRENCES Although technically a metal, uranium is discussed in this section by virtue of being a fuel source. Uranium-235 is the only naturally occurring isotope that is readily fissionable and is therefore the primary fuel used in nuclear power plants. Although large quantities of uranium ore have been discovered, most contain less than 0.05 percent uranium. Of this small amount, 99.3 percent is the non-fissionable isotope uranium-238 and just 0.7 percent consists of the fissionable isotope uranium-235. Because most nuclear reactors operate with fuels that are at least 3 percent uranium-235, the two isotopes must be separated to concentrate the fissionable isotope. The process of separating the uranium isotopes is difficult, secretive, and substantially increases the cost of nuclear power.

In addition to being scarce, the size of the uranium atom generally prevents it from being incorporated into the crystal lattice of most rock-forming minerals. In addition, uranium is highly soluble in oxidizing environments and therefore requires unusual conditions to be precipitated in minerals at Earth's surface. Uranium ores are extremely diverse in their geologic settings, but it appears that a critical factor controlling the precipitation of uranium-bearing minerals is the absence of oxygen.

Uranium can be enriched in residual fluids of felsic magmas, reaching concentrations over a hundred parts per million and incorporated as a trace element in minerals such as zircon and apatite. In sufficient concentrations, however, uranium forms an oxide mineral (UO_2) called uraninite (pitchblende if

Figure 20.35 A significant amount of electricity in Canada is produced by nuclear fission. Canadian nuclear reactors, such as those at the Pickering Nuclear Power Plant in Ontario, are of CANDU (Canadian Deuterium-Uranium) design. (Photo by Kevin Frayer/Canadian Press)

very fine grained), which can occur in veins associated with felsic igneous intrusions. Ores of uranium-bearing minerals also occur as placers in Precambrian rocks, reflecting the oxygen-free atmosphere of those times. The uranium ores of Elliot Lake, Ontario, that formerly supplied a significant proportion of Canada's uranium represent such uranium placers.

The fact that uranium is soluble in oxidizing environments and insoluble in reducing environments can also contribute to the formation of uranium ores. For example, the rich uranium deposits of northern Saskatchewan's Athabasca Basin (Figure 20.32), which currently account for Canada's entire uranium production, appear to have been formed by the interaction of deep-sourced, oxygen-free fluid with shallow-sourced oxygenated fluid that carried dissolved uranium. In this case, this fluid interaction was focused in small areas where fault breccias intersect a nonconformity separating highly deformed metamorphic rocks from overlying sedimentary rocks. Uranium can also be dissolved near Earth's surface by oxygenated groundwater and carried through permeable, coarse-grained sedimentary rocks (e.g., sandstone). The uranium-charged fluid precipitates uranium in the mineral carnotite when it mixes with oxygen-poor water. Most of the uranium mined in Arizona, New Mexico, and Utah is

contained in this type of ore. The close association of uranium and organic matter is also apparent in the slightly elevated concentration of uranium in organic-rich shales and phosphate deposits, relative to other sedimentary rock types.

OBSTACLES TO DEVELOPMENT At one time, nuclear power was heralded as the clean, cheap source of energy to replace fossil fuels. However, several obstacles have emerged to hinder the development of nuclear power as a major energy source, not the least of which is the enormous cost of building the facilities that contain numerous safety features. More important, perhaps, is the concern over the possibility of a serious accident at one of the nearly 200 nuclear plants that exist worldwide. Japan's Fukushima nuclear power plant is an example. In 2011 an earthquake-generated tsunami devastated the coast where the plant was (Box 10.2) and caused a series of equipment failures, nuclear meltdowns, and leakage of radioactive waste.

We emphasize that the concentrations of fissionable uranium-235 and the design of reactors are such that nuclear power plants cannot explode like an atomic bomb. The dangers arise from the possible escape of radioactive debris during a meltdown of the core or other malfunction. In addition, hazards, such as the disposal of nuclear waste and the relationship that exists between nuclear energy programs and the proliferation of nuclear weapons, must be considered as we evaluate the pros and cons of employing nuclear power.

RENEWABLE FUEL SOURCES

Geothermal Energy

Geothermal energy is becoming popular for home and commercial heating, including greenhouses and fish farms year-round. In Springhill, Nova Scotia, water that has been warmed by the natural geothermal gradient in abandoned shafts of coal mines is pumped to provide space heating for industrial buildings. In fact, Canadian geothermal companies drill 1 to 3 kilometre-deep wells to tap the geothermal gradient and heat homes. Water is pumped through a simple piping system to heat and cool buildings such as office towers in Toronto and North Vancouver. Fort Liard, Northwest Territories, may become Canada's first community to be powered entirely by geothermal energy.

Most geothermal energy used to generate electricity is focused on areas where groundwater is heated by volcanic activity. Geothermal power plants are not yet available in Canada but are well established in Iceland (Figure 20.36A), Italy, New Zealand, and the United States. In these facilities, steam and superheated water generated by hot springs is piped to turbines that generate electric power. In Canada, the highest potential for generating electricity from geothermal energy on a large scale lies in British Columbia and the Yukon, where recent igneous activity has produced areas of high heat flow (Figure 20.36B). Pilot studies near Meager Creek (Figure 20.36B) suggest that developing a commercial geothermal power facility there could provide electricity for 90 000 homes a year.

Lower-grade geothermal potential exists in the Prairie provinces (Figure 20.36B), where deep aquifers of Western Canada Sedimentary Basin (see Chapter 13) hold immense volumes of warm water that could be tapped as an energy source.

As with other alternative methods of power production, geothermal sources are not expected to provide much of the world's growing energy needs in the immediate future. Nevertheless, their use will increase as the production of conventional resources decline.

Organic-Based Sources

LANDFILL METHANE Methane produced by the microbial decomposition of organic matter in landfills is a significant greenhouse gas that escapes to the atmosphere. Thus, with the continued rise in global population, methane production from landfills can only increase in total volume and production rate. One way to deal with both the volume of methane released to the atmosphere and the demand for energy is to use this methane as fuel. About one-quarter of all landfill methane is presently being collected in Canada, about 70 percent of which is converted to energy. However, carbon dioxide, another greenhouse gas, is produced from methane combustion.

BIOMASS ENERGY Biomass energy is derived from the tissues of plants, through photosynthesis. Plants produce their structural tissues and sugars with solar energy, and this stored energy can later be released through combustion. This kind of biomass energy is released when wood is burned in a campfire.

Biomass fuel is a primary source of energy in developing countries in the form of wood and dung, but has been largely replaced in developed countries by fossil fuels. A renewable biomass fuel is ethanol, a product of anaerobic (oxygen-free) fermentation. In Canada, the forestry industry generates lots of waste material that could support large ethanol-producing operations. Ethanol can be used as an additive to gasoline and reduces carbon monoxide and carbon dioxide emissions. A form of biodiesel has been developed from vegetable oils and could also be used as an additive to conventional fuel. Although biomass fuels are far from replacing conventional fossil fuels, they are renewable and can reduce greenhouse gas emissions.

Hydroelectric Power

The power generated by falling water drives turbines that produce electricity, hence the term *hydroelectric power*. Canada is a world leader in the production of hydroelectricity, as it contributes to the production of 58 percent of Canada's total electricity generation (Figure 20.37). Most of this energy is produced at large dams, which allow controlled flow of water (Figure 20.38). The water impounded in a reservoir is a form of stored (potential) energy that can be released at any time to produce electricity.

Although water power is considered a renewable resource, the dams built to provide hydroelectricity have finite lifetimes and there are always negative environmental effects (see Chapter 15). All rivers carry suspended sediment that is deposited behind the dam as soon as it is built. Eventually the sediment will completely fill the reservoir, which takes 50 to 300 years, depending on the

A

Geothermal Heat Sources

High-grade sources of geothermal heat with potential for electricity generation

■ Hot dry rock

■ Hot water/steam

Lower-grade (warm water) sources of geothermal heat

□ Fractured rock/high heat flow

□ Sedimentary basins

0 _____ 1000 km

Western Canada Sedimentary Basin resource estimate: 4.11 x 10⁸ Megawatt-years

Meager Creek Estimated energy yield: 300 Megawatt-years

Pebble Creek Estimated energy yield: 200 Megawatt-years

Regina test hole Estimated energy yield: 3 Megawatt-years

Springhill Mine annual heat exchange; 2440 Gigajoules

B

quantity of suspended material transported by the river. A good hydroelectric site provides a significant height for the water to fall and a high rate of flow. Canada still has many rivers that have not been dammed for hydroelectric power, but many of these are in remote areas that are particularly sensitive to environmental disturbance.

A newer strategy, called a *pumped water–storage system*, is actually a type of energy management. When demand for electricity is low, unneeded power produced by non-hydroelectric sources is used to pump water from a lower reservoir to a storage area at a higher elevation. When demand for electricity is high, the water stored in the higher reservoir is available to drive turbines and produce electricity to supplement the power supply.

Solar Energy

Solar energy has become popular as an alternative resource on a small scale. Many people use well-insulated south-facing windows in their homes as

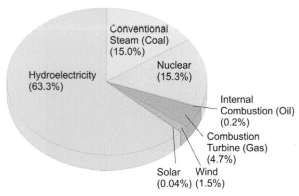

Figure 20.37 Electricity generation sources in Canada. Note the high contribution of electricity from hydroelectric sources compared with fossil fuels and nuclear power generation.
(Data for the pie chart from Canadian Electricity Association)

passive solar collectors that allow objects in a room to absorb the energy of the Sun's rays and to re-emit the energy as heat. More elaborate systems use large glass-covered boxes to collect energy, which heats air or water that is, in turn, circulated through the house in pipes to supply heat where it is needed.

The use of solar photovoltaic panels is increasing on farms and cottages in Ontario, Quebec, and the Prairie provinces, but is still minor compared to conventional fuels because although solar energy is free, the equipment required for its capture is expensive. Government studies suggest solar energy could provide 5 percent of Canada's electricity.

Research continues on improving the efficiency of solar collecting technologies, and the development of commercial solar power projects has

Figure 20.38 Daniel-Johnson Manicouagan (Manic) 5 Hydroelectric Dam in Quebec.
(Photo by Walter Muma)

been rapid in some parts of Canada. In 2009, Canada's first large-scale photovoltaic solar park, a 9.1-megawatt facility called First Light 1, was installed at Stone Mills, Ontario. Construction of the country's largest solar farm, the Sarnia Photovoltaic Power Plant (Figure 20.39), located near Sarnia, Ontario, was completed in 2010. Covering nearly 365 hectares of land (equivalent to 420 Canadian football fields), and utilizing some 1.3 million thin film solar panels, the plant has a generating capacity of 80 megawatts, capable of generating enough electricity to power 12 000 homes. Solar farms have also been established in Arnprior and Sault Ste. Marie, Ontario, and many other such facilities are in various stages of planning for Canadian localities.

Wind Energy

Wind turbines are now commonplace in Canada, with wind farms well established in British Columbia, Alberta (Figure 20.40), Saskatchewan, Ontario, Quebec, and Prince Edward Island. Wind power technology has improved, efficiency has increased, and the costs of turbines have dropped. However, wind turbines are controversial, as noise pollution and related health issues, land costs for turbine sites, and safety risks posed to birds and other wildlife have raised concerns.

Tidal Power

The ocean contains a huge amount of physical energy in tides. Although harnessing this energy involves sophisticated technology, the principle of electricity generation from tidal energy is fairly simple. The most common method involves trapping ocean water in reservoirs at high tide and later releasing it through hydroelectric turbines as the tide goes out (Figure 20.41). The largest tidal energy plant is located on the La Rance River in France, which generates 240 megawatts of power. The Annapolis Royal Generating Station in the Bay of Fundy, Nova Scotia, is the only tidal plant in North America and generates about 20 megawatts.

Envisioned for the future are in-stream technologies that will allow turbines installed on the sea floor to draw energy directly from tidal currents. In 2009, a $10-million prototype turbine was installed in the Bay of Fundy, but was quickly destroyed by currents more than twice as strong as it was designed to handle. The European company that installed the turbine estimates it will take until 2015 before it can try again.

Although tidal power is a good non-polluting form of energy, its use is limited to areas where the tidal range is high and water turbidity is low.

A

B

Figure 20.39   **A.** Sarnia Photovoltaic Power Plant, completed in 2010 with an 80-megawatt generating capacity, is Canada's largest solar power facility. **B.** Ground-level view of photovoltaic panel array at Sarnia facility. (Photo by Sarnia, Ontario, Canada [80MW]; First Solar, Inc.)

Figure 20.40   Blue Ridge Wind Turbine, Waterton Wind Turbines Facility near Hillspring, Alberta. (Photo courtesy of Vision Quest Windelectric Inc.)

Figure 20.41 The harnessing of tidal energy involves trapping ocean water behind a dam at high tide **(A)** and then releasing the water through hydroelectric turbines at low tide **(B)**. The turning of the turbines generates electricity that can be connected to a power grid. The Annapolis Royal Generating Station in Nova Scotia **(C)** generates approximately 20 megawatts of electricity. **D.** The deployment of seabed-mounted turbines may be the next major step in the development of tidal power.
(Photo **C** courtesy of Nova Scotia Power; photo **D** by James P. Blair/National Geographic Stock)

CHAPTER SUMMARY

- Mineral resources are commercially useful natural materials, including profitable reserves and ores.
- The formation of many metallic ores is associated with igneous activity. Metallic minerals can be concentrated by gravitational settling at the bottom of a magma chamber or by the separation of metal-rich fluid from a silicate melt due to immiscibility. The heat given off by igneous activity can also increase the capacity of water to dissolve metal ions. Hydrothermal (hot water) metallic ore deposits are formed when the metal ions dissolved in the hot water are forced to precipitate (commonly as sulphide minerals) once the water cools at or below Earth's surface.

- Metal ores formed by sedimentary processes include banded iron formation and placer gold deposits. Banded iron formations were deposited in the Precambrian seas as layers of precipitated iron oxides and silica. Placer gold deposits form by the sorting of sedimentary particles by running water.
- Skarn ores are produced by chemical processes associated with contact metamorphism, and the development of bauxite (aluminum ore) is dependent on the intense chemical weathering that occurs in the tropics.
- Non-metallic resources include aggregate (sand and gravel), stone, and industrial minerals (salt and sulphur).

- Oil and natural gas formed from organic matter supplied by marine organisms (largely planktonic algae) in ancient seas. Oil and gas are generated from organic-rich source rocks, migrate into permeable reservoir rocks (sandstone), where they accumulate, and are prevented from further migrating to the surface (i.e., are trapped) by impermeable cap rock (commonly shale). Coal formed from plants in ancient swamps.
- Burning fossil fuels causes air pollution (smog) and global warming (carbon dioxide). Oil spills and leaks also pose serious environmental hazards.
- Alberta's oil sands provide about 15 percent of Canada's oil. Hydroelectric power accounts for about 60 percent of Canada's electricity. Alternative energy sources include nuclear fission (of uranium) and geothermal and non-geologic sources, such as hydroelectric, solar, wind, and tidal power.

MasteringGeology

www.masteringgeology.com

Looking for additional review and test prep materials? Visit the Study Area in MasteringGeology to enhance your understanding of this chapter's content by accessing a variety of resources, including

Self-Study Quizzes, Geoscience Animations, GEODe Tutorials, RSS feeds, flashcards, weblinks, self-study quizzes, and an optional Pearson eText.

REVIEW QUESTIONS

1. Explain the difference between a renewable and non-renewable resource, providing at least one example of each.

2. What are reserves, and how are these related to resources?

3. Describe two kinds of hydrothermal deposits, explaining the differences in how they form.

4. Metamorphic ore deposits are often related to igneous processes. Provide an example.

5. Describe how bauxite, the primary ore of aluminum, is formed, and explain the agricultural and environmental concerns that surround the mining of this particular type of ore deposit.

6. Describe the ways in which placer deposits of heavy minerals can form.

7. Describe the effects of metal mining in Canada on the natural environment.

8. Identify at least three items and/or building materials that contain non-metallic minerals, stating the names of the specific minerals present in each.

9. How do petroleum and coal differ in terms of their source materials and in the processes involved in their formation?

10. Relative to many other countries, Canada has been slow to adopt geothermal energy for electricity generation. Explain why this might be.

GLOSSARY

Aa flow A type of lava flow that has a jagged, blocky surface.

Ablation A general term for the loss of ice and snow from a glacier.

Abrasion The grinding and scraping of a rock surface by the friction and impact of rock particles carried by water, wind, and ice.

Abyssal plain A very level area of the deep-ocean floor, usually lying at the foot of the continental rise.

Accretionary wedge A large wedge-shaped mass of sediment that accumulates in subduction zones. Sediment is scraped from the subducting oceanic plate and accreted to the overriding crustal block.

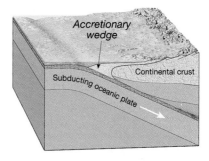

Active continental margin Usually narrow and consisting of highly deformed sediments. Such margins occur where oceanic lithosphere is being subducted beneath the margin of a continent.

Active layer The zone above the permafrost that thaws in summer and refreezes in winter.

Aftershock A smaller earthquake that follows the main earthquake.

Alluvial fan A fan-shaped deposit of sediment formed where a stream's slope abruptly reduces.

Alluvial fan

Alluvium The unconsolidated sediment deposited by a stream.

Alpine glacier A glacier confined to a mountain valley, which in most instances was previously a stream valley.

Anastomosed stream A stream with deep, interwoven, multiple channels

separated by stable islands that are commonly heavily vegetated.

Andesitic composition See _Intermediate composition_.

Angle of repose The steepest angle at which loose, dry material remains stationary without sliding downslope.

Angular unconformity An unconformity in which the older strata dip at an angle different from that of the younger beds.

Anticline A fold in sedimentary strata that most commonly resembles an arch.

Aphanitic texture A texture of igneous rocks in which the crystals are too small for individual minerals to be distinguished without magnification.

Aquifer The rock or sediment through which groundwater moves easily.

Aquitard An impermeable bed that hinders or prevents groundwater movement.

Archean Eon The second eon of Precambrian time. The eon following the Hadean and preceding the Proterozoic. It extends between approximately 4.0 billion and 2.5 billion years ago.

Arête A narrow, knife-like ridge separating two adjacent glaciated valleys.

Artesian well A well in which the water rises above the level where it was initially encountered.

Assimilation In igneous activity, the process of incorporating country rock into a magma body.

Asthenosphere The mechanically weak, ductile subdivision of the mantle that underlies the lithosphere.

Atmosphere The gaseous portion of a planet; the planet's envelope of air. One of the traditional subdivisions of Earth's physical environment.

Atoll A coral island consisting of a nearly continuous ring of coral reef surrounding a central lagoon.

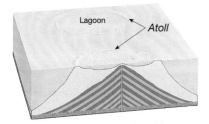

Atom The smallest particle that exists as an element.

Atomic number The number of protons in the nucleus of an atom.

Atomic weight The average of the atomic masses of the isotopes for a given element.

Aureole A zone or halo of contact metamorphism found in the country rock surrounding an igneous intrusion.

Back swamp A poorly drained area on a floodplain that results when natural levees are present.

Banded iron formation A chemical sedimentary rock consisting of alternating bands of iron oxide minerals and chert. Restricted to the Precambrian and most widespread in Proterozoic rock sequences.

Bank, stream The sides of a stream channel.

Bar A common term for sand and gravel deposits in a stream channel.

Barchan dune A solitary sand dune shaped like a crescent with its tips pointing downwind.

Barchanoid dunes Dunes that form scalloped rows of sand oriented at right angles to the wind. This form is intermediate between isolated barchans and extensive waves of transverse dunes.

Barrier island   A low, elongate ridge of sand that parallels the coast.

Basal slip   A mechanism of glacial movement in which the ice mass slides over the surface below.

Basaltic composition   See *Mafic composition*.

Base level   The level below which a stream cannot erode.

Basin   A circular downfolded structure.

Batholith   A large mass of igneous rock (exceeding 100 km² in areal extent) formed by the emplacement and crystallization of magma at depth.

Baymouth bar   A sandbar that completely crosses a bay, sealing it off from the main body of water.

Beach drift   The transport of sediment in a zigzag pattern along a beach, caused by the uprush of water from obliquely breaking waves.

Beach nourishment   The process in which large quantities of sand are added to the beach system to offset losses caused by wave erosion. Building beaches seaward improves beach quality and storm protection.

Bed   See *Strata*.

Bed load   Sediment moved along the bottom of a stream by moving water, or particles moved along the ground surface by wind.

Bed, stream   The bottom of a stream channel.

Bedding plane   A nearly flat surface separating two beds of sedimentary rock. Each bedding plane marks the end of one deposit and the beginning of another having different characteristics.

Belt of soil moisture   A zone in which water is held as a film on the surface of soil particles and can be used by plants or withdrawn by evaporation. The uppermost subdivision of the zone of aeration.

Biochemical   A type of chemical sediment that forms when material dissolved in water is precipitated by water-dwelling organisms. Shells are common examples.

Bioclastic   The texture of a sedimentary rock composed of (usually fragmented) skeletal remains of organisms.

Biogenous sediment   Sea-floor sediments consisting of material of marine-organic origin.

Biosphere   The totality of life forms on Earth.

Blowout   A depression excavated by wind in easily eroded materials.

Body wave   A seismic wave that travels through Earth's interior.

Bowen's reaction series   A concept proposed by N. L. Bowen that illustrates the relationships between magma and the minerals crystallizing from it during the formation of igneous rocks.

Braided stream   A stream consisting of numerous intertwining channels that are characteristically unstable.

Breakwater   A structure protecting a nearshore area from breaking waves.

Brittle deformation   Deformation that involves the fracturing of rock. Associated with rocks near the surface.

Brittle failure   See *Brittle deformation*.

Burial metamorphism   Low-grade metamorphism that occurs in the lowest layers of very thick accumulations of sedimentary strata.

Caldera   A large depression typically caused by collapse or ejection of the summit area of a volcano.

Caliche   A hard layer, rich in calcium carbonate, that forms beneath the *B* horizon in soils of arid regions.

Calving   Ablation of a glacier that occurs when large pieces of ice break into the water.

Cap rock   A necessary part of an oil trap. The cap rock is impermeable and hence keeps upwardly mobile oil and gas from escaping to the surface.

Capacity   The total amount of sediment a stream is able to transport.

Capillary fringe   A relatively narrow zone at the base of the zone of aeration. Water rises from the water table in tiny thread-like openings between grains of soil or sediment.

Catastrophism   The concept that Earth was shaped by catastrophic events of a short-term nature.

Cavern   A naturally formed underground chamber or series of chambers most commonly produced by solution activity in limestone.

Cementation   One way in which sedimentary rocks are lithified. As material precipitates from water that percolates through the sediment, open spaces are filled and particles are joined into a solid mass.

Cenozoic Era   A span on the geologic time scale beginning about 66 million years ago, following the Mesozoic Era.

Channel, stream   A natural passageway or depression of flowing water.

Chemical sedimentary rock   Sedimentary rock consisting of material that was precipitated from water by either inorganic or organic means.

Chemical weathering   The processes by which the internal structure of a mineral is altered by the removal or addition of elements.

Cinder cone   A rather small volcano built primarily of ejected lava fragments that consist mostly of pea- to walnut-size lapilli.

Cinder cone

Cirque   An amphitheatre-shaped basin at the head of a glaciated valley produced by frost wedging and plucking.

Clastic   A sedimentary rock texture consisting of broken fragments of pre-existing rock.

Cleavage   The tendency of a mineral to break along planes of weak bonding.

Col   A pass between mountain valleys where the headwalls of two cirques intersect.

Colour   A phenomenon of light by which otherwise identical objects can be differentiated.

Columnar joints   A pattern of cracks that form during cooling of molten rock to generate columns.

Compaction   A type of lithification in which the weight of overlying material compresses more deeply buried sediment. It is most important in fine-grained sedimentary rocks, such as shale.

Competence   A measure of the largest particle a stream can transport; a factor dependent on velocity.

Composite volcano   A volcano composed of both lava flows and pyroclastic material.

Composite volcano

Compound   A substance formed by the chemical combination of two or more elements in definite proportions and usually having properties different from those of its constituent elements.

Compressional stress   The differential stress that shortens a rock body.

Compressional stress

Concordant   A term used to describe intrusive igneous masses that form parallel to the bedding of the surrounding rock.

Conduit   A pipe-like opening through which magma moves toward Earth's surface. It terminates at a surface opening called a vent.

Cone of depression   A cone-shaped depression in the water table immediately surrounding a well.

Cone of depression

Confining pressure   See *Uniform stress.*

Conformable layers   Rock layers that were deposited without interruption.

Contact metamorphism   The changes in rock caused by the heat from a nearby magma body.

Continental drift   A hypothesis, credited largely to Alfred Wegener, that suggested all present continents once existed as a single supercontinent. Further, beginning about 200 million years ago, the supercontinent began breaking into smaller continents, which then drifted to their present positions.

Continental margin   That portion of the sea floor adjacent to the continents. It may include the continental shelf, continental slope, and continental rise.

Continental rise   The gently sloping surface at the base of the continental slope.

Continental shelf   The gently sloping submerged portion of the continental margin, extending from the shoreline to the continental slope.

Continental slope   The steep gradient that leads to the deep-ocean floor and marks the seaward edge of the continental shelf.

Continental volcanic arc   Mountains formed in part by igneous activity associated with the subduction of oceanic lithosphere beneath a continent. Examples include the Andes and the Cascades.

Convection   The transfer of heat by the mass movement or circulation of a substance.

Convergent plate boundary   A boundary in which two plates move together, resulting in oceanic lithosphere being thrust beneath an overriding plate, eventually to be reabsorbed into the mantle. It can also involve the collision of two continental plates to create a mountain system.

Convergent boundary

Coral reef   A structure formed in a warm, shallow, sunlit ocean environment that consists primarily of the calcite-rich remains of corals as well as the limy secretions of algae and the hard parts of many other small organisms.

Core   The innermost layer of Earth based on composition. It is thought to be largely an iron-nickel alloy with minor amounts of oxygen, silicon, and sulphur.

Correlation   The equivalence of rocks of similar age in different areas as determined by rock type, fossil content, radiometric ages, or other criteria.

Course, stream   The path or route of a stream.

Covalent bond   A chemical bond produced by the sharing of electrons.

Crater   The depression at the summit of a volcano or one produced by a meteorite impact.

Creep   The slow downhill movement of soil and regolith.

Creep

Crevasse   A deep crack in the brittle surface of a glacier.

Cross-beds or cross-bedding   A structure in which relatively thin layers are inclined at an angle to the main bedding. Formed by currents of wind or water.

Cross-cutting relations   A principle of relative dating. A rock or fault is younger than any rock (or fault) through which it cuts.

Crust   The very thin outermost layer of Earth.

Crystal habit   The external appearance of a mineral as determined by its internal arrangement of atoms.

Crystal settling During the crystallization of magma, the earlier-formed minerals are denser than the liquid portion and settle to the bottom of the magma chamber.

Crystallization The formation and growth of a crystalline solid from a liquid or gas.

Cut bank The area of active erosion on the outside of a meander.

Cutoff A short channel segment created when a river erodes through the narrow neck of land between meanders.

Darcy's law When permeability is uniform, the velocity of groundwater increases as the slope of the water table increases. It is expressed by the formula $V = \frac{K}{n} \cdot \frac{h}{l}$, where V is velocity, n the porosity, h the head, l the length of flow, and K the coefficient of permeability.

Dark silicate Silicate minerals that contain ions of iron or magnesium (or both) in their structure. They are dark in colour and have a higher specific gravity than nonferromagnesian silicates.

Debris flow A flow of soil and regolith containing a large amount of water. Most common in semi-arid mountainous regions and on the slopes of some volcanoes.

Decompression melting The melting that occurs because of a drop in confining pressure as rock ascends.

Deep-ocean basin The portion of sea floor that lies between the continental margin and the oceanic ridge system. This region composes almost 30 percent of Earth's surface.

Deep-sea fan A cone-shaped deposit at the base of the continental slope. The sediment is transported to the fan by turbidity currents that follow submarine canyons.

Deflation The lifting and removal of loose material by wind.

Deformation A general term for the processes of folding, faulting, shearing, compression, or extension of rocks as the result of various natural forces.

Delta An accumulation of sediment formed where a stream enters a lake or an ocean.

Dendritic pattern A stream system that resembles the pattern of a branching tree.

Dendritic pattern

Desert One of the two types of dry climate; the driest of the dry climates.

Desert pavement A layer of coarse pebbles and gravel created when wind removes the finer material.

Detrital sedimentary rocks Rocks that form from the accumulation of materials that originate and are transported as solid particles derived from both mechanical and chemical weathering.

Diagenesis A collective term for all the chemical, physical, and biologic changes that take place after sediments are deposited but before metamorphism.

Differential stress See *Directed pressure.*

Differential weathering The variation in the rate and degree of weathering caused by such factors as mineral makeup, degree of jointing, and climate.

Dip The angle at which a rock layer or fault is inclined from the horizontal. The direction of dip is at a right angle to the strike.

Dip-slip fault A fault in which the movement is parallel to the dip of the fault.

Directed pressure Forces that are unequal in different directions.

Discharge The quantity of water in a stream that passes a given point in a period of time.

Disconformity A type of unconformity in which the beds above and below are parallel.

Discontinuity A sudden change with depth in one or more of the physical properties of the material making up Earth's interior. The boundary between two dissimilar materials in Earth's interior as determined by the behaviour of seismic waves.

Discordant A term used to describe plutons that cut across existing rock structures, such as bedding planes.

Disseminated deposit Any economic mineral deposit in which the desired mineral occurs as scattered particles in the rock but in sufficient quantity to make the deposit an ore.

Dissolution A common form of chemical weathering, it is the process of dissolving into a homogeneous solution, as when an acidic solution dissolves limestone.

Dissolved load That portion of a stream's load carried in solution.

Distributary A section of a stream that leaves the main flow.

Divergent plate boundary A boundary in which two plates move apart, resulting in upwelling of material from the mantle to create new sea floor.

Divergent boundary

Divide An imaginary line that separates the drainage of two streams, often found along a ridge.

Dome A roughly circular upfolded structure.

Drainage basin The land area that contributes water to a stream.

Drawdown The difference in height between the bottom of a cone of depression and the original height of the water table.

Drumlin A streamlined, asymmetrical hill mainly composed of till. The steep side of the hill faces the direction from which the ice advanced.

Ductile deformation A type of solid-state flow that produces a change in the size and shape of a rock body without fracturing. It occurs at depths where temperatures and confining pressures are high.

Dune A hill or ridge of wind-deposited sand.

Dyke A tabular-shaped intrusive igneous feature that cuts through the surrounding rock.

Earthflow The downslope movement of water-saturated, clay-rich sediment. It is most characteristic of humid regions.

Earthflow

Earthquake The vibration of Earth produced by the rapid release of energy.

Ebb current The movement of tidal current away from the shore.

Echo sounder An instrument used to determine the depth of water by measuring the time interval between emission of a sound signal and the return of its echo from the bottom.

Elastic rebound The sudden release of stored stress in rocks that results in movement along a fault.

Electron A negatively charged subatomic particle that has a negligible mass and is found outside an atom's nucleus.

Element A substance that cannot be decomposed into simpler substances by ordinary chemical or physical means.

Eluviation The washing out of fine soil components from the *A* horizon by downward-percolating water.

End moraine A ridge of mainly till marking a former position of the front of a glacier.

Energy levels The spherically shaped, negatively charged zones that surround the nucleus of an atom.

Environment of deposition A geographic setting where sediment accumulates. Each site is characterized by a particular combination of geologic processes and environmental conditions.

Eon The largest time unit on the geologic time scale, next in hierarchy above era.

Ephemeral stream A stream that is usually dry because it carries water only in response to specific episodes of rainfall. Most desert streams are of this type.

Epicentre The location on Earth's surface that lies directly above the hypocentre/focus of an earthquake.

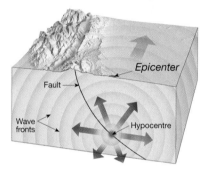

Epicenter
Fault
Wave fronts
Hypocentre

Epoch A unit of the geologic time scale that is a subdivision of a period.

Equilibrium line The lower limit of the zone of accumulation on a glacier.

Era A major division on the geologic time scale; eras are divided into shorter units called periods.

Erosion The incorporation and transportation of material by a mobile agent, such as water, wind, or ice.

Eruption column Buoyant plumes of hot, ash-laden gases that can extend thousands of metres into the atmosphere.

Esker A sinuous ridge composed largely of sand and gravel deposited by a stream flowing in contact with a glacier near its terminus.

Estuary A funnel-shaped inlet of the sea that formed when a rise in sea level or subsidence of land caused the mouth of a river to be flooded.

Estuary

Evaporite A sedimentary rock formed of material deposited from solution by evaporation of the water.

Evapotranspiration The combined effect of evaporation and transpiration.

Exfoliation dome A large, dome-shaped structure, usually composed of granite, formed by sheeting (unloading).

External process A process, such as weathering or erosion, that is powered by the Sun and contributes to the transformation of solid rock into sediment.

Extrusive The igneous activity that occurs at Earth's surface.

Fall A type of movement common to mass-wasting processes that refers to airborne pieces (of solid material) of any size.

Fault A break in a rock mass along which movement has occurred.

Fault scarp A cliff created by movement along a fault. It represents the exposed surface of the fault before modification by weathering and erosion.

Felsenmeer A thin accumulation of angular blocks on bedrock, produced by frost wedging, where no steep slopes (sources) occur nearby.

Felsic composition A compositional group of igneous rocks indicating the rock is composed almost entirely of light-coloured silicates.

Ferromagnesian silicate See *Dark silicate*.

Fetch The distance that the wind has travelled across the open water.

Firn Granular re-crystallized snow. A transitional stage between snow and glacial ice.

Fissility The property of splitting easily into thin layers along closely spaced, parallel surfaces, such as bedding planes in shale.

Fissure A crack in rock along which there is a distinct separation.

Fissure eruption An eruption in which lava is extruded from narrow fractures or cracks in the crust.

Fjord A steep-sided inlet of the sea formed when a glacial trough was deeply scoured then partially submerged.

Flood The overflow of a stream channel that occurs when discharge exceeds the channel's capacity. The most common and destructive geologic hazard.

Flood basalts The flows of basaltic lava that issue from numerous cracks or fissures and commonly cover extensive areas to thicknesses of hundreds of metres.

Flood current The tidal current associated with the increase in the height of the tide.

Floodplain   The flat, low-lying portion of a stream valley subject to periodic flooding.

Floodplain

Flow   A type of movement common to mass-wasting processes in which material moves downslope as a viscous fluid.

Flowing artesian well   An artesian well in which water flows freely at Earth's surface because the pressure surface is above ground level.

Focus   *See Hypocentre.*

Fold   A bent layer or a series of layers that were originally horizontal and subsequently deformed.

Foliation   A term for a planar arrangement of textural features often exhibited by metamorphic rocks.

Force   Any influence that tends to put stationary objects in motion or change the motion of moving bodies.

Foreshocks   Small earthquakes that often precede a major earthquake.

Fossil   The remains or traces of organisms preserved from the geologic past.

Fossil fuel   A general term for any hydrocarbon derived from organic matter that can be used as a fuel, including coal, oil, natural gas, bitumen from tar sands, and shale oil.

Fracture   Any break or rupture in rock along which no appreciable movement has taken place.

Fracture zone   A linear zone of irregular topography on the deep-ocean floor that follows transform faults and their inactive extensions.

Fragmental texture   See *Pyroclastic texture*.

Frost wedging   The mechanical breakup of rock caused by the expansion of freezing water in cracks and crevices.

Frost wedging

Fumarole   A vent in a volcanic area from which fumes or gases escape.

Geologic time scale   The division of Earth history into blocks of time: eons, eras, periods, and epochs. The time scale was created by using relative dating principles.

Geologist   A person who is trained in and works in the geologic sciences.

Geology   The science that examines Earth, its form and composition, and the changes that it has undergone and is undergoing.

Geothermal energy   Natural steam used for power generation.

Geothermal gradient   The gradual increase in temperature with depth in the crust. The average is 25°C per kilometre in the upper crust.

Geyser   A fountain of hot water ejected periodically from the ground.

Glacial budget   The balance, or lack of balance, between ice formation at the upper end of a glacier and ice loss in the zone of ablation.

Glacial drift   An all-embracing term for sediments of glacial origin, no matter how, where, or in what shape they were deposited.

Glacial erratic   An ice-transported boulder that was not derived from the bedrock near its present site.

Glacial striations   The scratches on bedrock caused by glacial abrasion.

Glacial trough   A mountain valley that has been widened, deepened, and straightened by a glacier.

Glacier   A thick mass of ice originating on land from the compaction and re-crystallization of snow that shows evidence of past or present flow.

Glass (volcanic)   The natural glass produced when molten lava cools too rapidly to permit crystallization. Volcanic glass is a solid composed of unordered atoms.

Glassy   A term used to describe the texture of certain igneous rocks, such as obsidian, that contain no crystals.

Gneissic texture   A texture of metamorphic rocks in which dark and light silicate minerals are separated, giving the rock a banded appearance.

Graben   A valley formed by the downward displacement of a normal fault-bounded block.

Graben

Grade (metamorphic)   The intensity of metamorphism as measured by the degree of difference between the original rock and the metamorphic rock.

Graded bed or graded bedding   A sediment layer characterized by a decrease in sediment size from bottom to top.

Graded stream   A stream that has the correct channel characteristics to maintain exactly the velocity required to transport the material supplied to it.

Gradient   The slope of a stream, generally expressed as the vertical drop over a fixed distance.

Granitic composition   See *Felsic composition*.

Groin   A short wall built at a right angle to the seashore to trap moving sand.

Groins

Ground moraine   An undulating layer of till deposited under a moving glacier.

Groundmass   The matrix of smaller crystals within an igneous rock that has porphyritic texture.

Groundwater   The water in the zone of saturation.

Guyot   A submerged flat-topped seamount.

Hadean Eon   The first eon on the geologic time scale; the eon ending about 4 billion years ago that preceded the Archean Eon.

Half-life   The time required for one-half of the atoms of a radioactive substance to decay.

Hanging valley   A tributary valley that enters a glacial trough at a considerable height above the floor of the trough.

Hanging valley

Hard stabilization The structures built to protect a coast from erosion or to prevent the movement of sand along a beach.

Hardness A mineral's resistance to scratching and abrasion.

Hardpan A general term for a relatively hard, impervious layer of sediment or soil just below the ground surface.

Head (headwaters) The beginning or source area for a stream.

Headward erosion The extension upslope of the head of a valley because of erosion.

Historical geology A major division of geology that deals with the origin of Earth and its development through time. It usually involves the study of fossils and their sequence in rock beds.

Hogback A narrow, sharp-crested ridge formed by the upturned edge of a steeply dipping bed of resistant rock.

Horizon A layer in a soil profile.

Horn A pyramid-like peak formed by glacial action in three or more cirques surrounding a mountain summit.

Horst An elongate, uplifted block of crust bounded by normal faults.

Horst

Hot spot A concentration of heat in the mantle capable of producing magma that, in turn, extrudes onto Earth's surface. The intraplate volcanism that produced the Hawaiian Islands is one example.

Hot spring A spring in which the water is 6°C to 9°C warmer than the mean annual air temperature of its locality.

Hummocky cross-stratification A sedimentary structure characterized by draped laminations that dip away from a central high (hummock). Hummocks

are typically about 1 metre in diameter and are believed to be produced by storm waves.

Humus The organic matter in soil produced by the decomposition of plants and animals.

Hydraulic conductivity The ability of a material to conduct groundwater based on its permeability (the higher the permeability, the greater the flow).

Hydraulic gradient The slope of the water table. Expressed as h/l, where h is the head and l the length of flow.

Hydroelectric power The electricity generated by falling water that is used to drive turbines.

Hydrologic cycle The circulation of Earth's water supply. The cycle is powered by energy from the Sun and is characterized by continuous exchanges of water among the hydrosphere, atmosphere, biosphere, and geosphere.

Hydrolysis A chemical weathering process in which minerals are altered by chemically reacting with water and acids.

Hydrosphere The water portion of our planet; one of the traditional subdivisions of Earth's physical environment.

Hydrothermal (hot-water) solution The hot, watery solution that escapes from a mass of magma during the latter stages of crystallization. Such solutions can alter the surrounding country rock and are commonly the source of ore deposits.

Hypocentre The place within Earth where rock displacement produces an earthquake.

Ice cap A mass of glacial ice covering a high upland or plateau and spreading out radially.

Ice sheet A very large, thick mass of glacial ice flowing outward in all directions from one or more accumulation centres.

Ice shelf Forming where glacial ice flows into bays, it is a large, relatively flat mass of floating ice that extends seaward from the coast but remains attached to the land along one or more sides.

Ice stream A zone of ice within an ice sheet or ice cap that flows more rapidly than the surrounding ice; it is usually not constrained by exposed bedrock.

Ice-contact deposit An accumulation of stratified drift deposited in contact with a supporting mass of ice.

Igneous rock Rock formed from the crystallization or solidification of magma or lava.

Inclusion A piece of one rock unit contained within another. Inclusions are used in relative dating. The rock mass adjacent to the one containing the inclusion must have been there first in order to provide the fragment.

Index fossil A fossil that is associated with a particular span of geologic time.

Index mineral A mineral that is a good indicator of the metamorphic environment in which it formed. It is used to distinguish different zones of regional metamorphism.

Industrial minerals Useful non-metallic resources.

Inertia Objects at rest tend to remain at rest, and objects in motion tend to stay in motion unless either is acted on by an outside force.

Infiltration The movement of surface water into rock or soil through cracks and pore spaces.

Infiltration capacity The maximum rate at which soil can absorb water.

Inner core The solid innermost layer of Earth, about 1216 kilometres in radius.

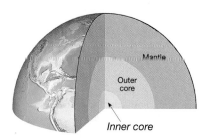

Intensity (earthquake) A measure of the degree of earthquake shaking at a given locale based on the amount of damage.

Intermediate composition A compositional group of igneous rocks, indicating that the rock contains at least 25 percent dark silicate minerals. The other dominant mineral is plagioclase feldspar.

Internal deformation The re-crystallization and ductile flow of ice within a glacier.

Internal process A process, such as mountain building or volcanism, that derives its energy from Earth's interior and elevates Earth's surface.

Intrachannel bar A sand and gravel bar within the channel of a stream.

Intraplate volcanism The igneous activity that occurs within a lithospheric plate away from plate boundaries.

Intrusive rock   The igneous rock that formed below Earth's surface.

Ion   An atom or a molecule that possesses an electrical charge.

Ionic bond   A chemical bond between two oppositely charged ions formed by the transfer of valence electrons from one atom to the other.

Isostasy   The concept that Earth's crust is floating in gravitational balance on the material of the mantle.

Isostatic adjustment   The compensation of the lithosphere when weight is added or removed. When weight is added, the lithosphere will respond by subsiding, and when weight is removed, there will be uplift.

Isotopes   The varieties of the same element that have different mass numbers; their nuclei contain the same number of protons but different numbers of neutrons.

Jetties   A pair of structures extending into the ocean at the entrance to a harbour or river that are built for the purpose of protecting against storm waves and sediment deposition.

Jetties

Joint   A fracture in rock along which no significant displacement has occurred.

Kame   A steep-sided hill composed of sand and gravel, originating when sediment collected in openings in stagnant glacial ice.

Kame terrace   A narrow, terrace-like mass of stratified drift deposited between a glacier and an adjacent valley wall.

Karst topography   A type of topography formed on soluble rock (especially limestone) primarily by dissolution. It is characterized by sinkholes, caves, and underground drainage.

Kettle   The depressions created when blocks of ice become detached in glacial deposits and subsequently melt.

Kimberlite   A rare ultramafic rock that commonly contains diamonds.

Klippe   A remnant of a thrust sheet that was isolated by erosion.

Laccolith   A massive igneous body intruded between pre-existing strata.

Laccolith

Lahar   The debris flows on the slopes of volcanoes that result when unstable layers of ash and debris become saturated and flow downslope, usually following stream channels.

Laminar flow   The movement of water particles in straight paths that are parallel to the channel. The water particles move downstream without mixing.

Lateral accretion surfaces   Gently dipping sedimentary structures preserved within point bar deposits of meandering streams. These surfaces mark former positions of an accreting point bar.

Lateral moraine   A ridge of till along the sides of a valley glacier composed primarily of debris that fell to the glacier from the valley walls.

Laterite   A red, highly leached soil type found in the tropics that is rich in oxides of iron and aluminum.

Lava   The magma that reaches Earth's surface.

Lava dome   A bulbous mass associated with an old-age volcano, produced when thick lava is slowly squeezed from the vent. Lava domes can act as plugs to deflect subsequent gaseous eruptions.

Lava dome

Lava tube   A tunnel in hardened lava that acts as a horizontal conduit for lava flowing from a volcanic vent. Lava tubes allow fluid lavas to advance great distances.

Law of superposition   In any undeformed sequence of sedimentary rocks, each bed is older than the one above and younger than the one below.

Leaching   The depletion of soluble materials from the upper soil by downward-percolating water.

Left-lateral strike-slip   Where the crustal block on the opposite side of a fault moved to the left as you faced the fault.

Light silicates   Silicate minerals that lack iron or magnesium. They are generally lighter in colour and have lower specific gravities than dark silicates.

Liquefaction   The transformation of a stable soil into a fluid that is often unable to support buildings or other structures.

Lithification   The process, generally cementation or compaction, of converting sediments to solid rock.

Lithosphere   The rigid outer layer of Earth, including the crust and uppermost mantle.

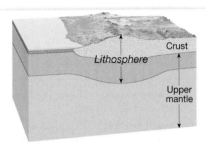

Local (temporary) base level   The level of a lake, resistant rock layer, or any other base level that stands above sea level.

Loess   The deposits of windblown silt that lack visible layers, are generally buff-coloured, and are capable of maintaining a nearly vertical cliff.

Long (L) waves   These earthquake-generated waves travel along the outer layer of Earth and are responsible for most of the surface damage. L waves have longer periods and wavelengths than other seismic waves.

Longitudinal dunes   Long ridges of sand oriented parallel to the prevailing wind; these dunes form where sand supplies are limited.

Longitudinal dunes

Longitudinal profile   A cross-section of a stream channel along its descending course from the head to the mouth.

Longshore current   A nearshore current that flows parallel to the shore.

Lower mantle   See *Mesosphere*.

Lustre   The appearance or quality of light reflected from the surface of a mineral.

Mafic composition   A compositional group of igneous rocks characterized by a substantial proportion of dark, magnesium- and iron-rich silicate minerals and calcium-rich plagioclase feldspar.

Magma   A body of molten material found at depth, including any dissolved gases and crystals.

Magma mixing   The process of altering the composition of a magma through the mixing of material from another magma body.

Magmatic differentiation   The process of generating more than one rock type from a single magma.

Magnetometer   A sensitive instrument used to measure the intensity of Earth's magnetic field at various points.

Magnitude (earthquake)   An estimate of the total amount of energy released during an earthquake, based on seismic records.

Manganese nodules   A type of hydrogenous sediment scattered on the ocean floor, consisting mainly of manganese and iron and usually containing small amounts of copper, nickel, and cobalt.

Mantle   One of Earth's compositional layers. The solid rocky shell that extends from the base of the crust to a depth of 2900 kilometres.

Mantle plume   A mass of hotter than normal mantle material that ascends toward the surface, where it may lead to igneous activity. These plumes of solid yet mobile material may originate as deep as the core–mantle boundary.

Mass balance   The difference between gain (accumulation) and loss (ablation) of ice in a glacier, determined as a change of mass over some time interval.

Mass number   The sum of the number of neutrons and protons in the nucleus of an atom.

Mass wasting   The downslope movement of rock, regolith, and soil under the direct influence of gravity.

Massive   An igneous pluton that is not tabular in shape.

Meander   A loop-like bend in the course of a stream.

Meander

Mechanical weathering   The physical disintegration of rock, resulting in

smaller fragments but no change in chemical composition.

Medial moraine   A ridge of till formed when lateral moraines from two coalescing alpine glaciers join.

Melt   The liquid portion of magma excluding the solid crystals.

Mesosphere   The part of the mantle that extends from the core–mantle boundary to a depth of 660 kilometres. It is also known as the lower mantle.

Mesozoic Era   A time span on the geologic time scale between the Paleozoic and Cenozoic Eras—from about 251 million to 66 million years ago.

Metallic bond   A chemical bond present in all metals that can be characterized as an extreme type of electron sharing in which the electrons move freely from atom to atom.

Metamorphic facies   A distinctive assemblage of minerals that can be used to designate a particular set of metamorphic environmental conditions recorded in a metamorphic rock.

Metamorphic grade   Intensity of metamorphism as measured by the degree of difference between the original rock and the metamorphic rock.

Metamorphic rock   Rock formed by the alteration of pre-existing rock deep within Earth (but still in the solid state) by heat, pressure, and/or chemically active fluids.

Metamorphism   The changes in mineral composition and texture of a rock subjected to elevated temperatures and pressures within Earth.

Mid-ocean ridge   A continuous mountainous ridge on the floor of all the major ocean basins and varying in width from 500 to 5000 kilometres. The rifts at the crests of these ridges represent divergent plate boundaries.

Mid-ocean ridge

Migmatite   A rock exhibiting both igneous and metamorphic rock characteristics. Such rocks can form when light-coloured silicate minerals melt and then crystallize while the dark silicate minerals remain solid.

Mineral   A naturally occurring, inorganic crystalline solid material with a specific chemical composition structure.

Mineral resource   All discovered and undiscovered deposits of a useful mineral that can be extracted presently or in the future.

Mineralogy   The study of minerals.

Modified Mercalli Intensity Scale   A 12-point scale developed to evaluate earthquake intensity based on the amount of damage to various structures.

Mohorovičić discontinuity (Moho)   The boundary separating the crust and the mantle, discernible by an increase in seismic velocity.

Mohs scale   A series of 10 minerals used as a standard in determining hardness.

Moment magnitude   A more precise measure of earthquake magnitude than the Richter scale that is derived from the amount of displacement that occurs along a fault zone.

Monocline   A one-limbed flexure in strata. The strata are usually flat-lying or very gently dipping on both sides of the monocline.

Mountain   A landform with an obvious peak that rises significantly above the land surrounding it, generally about 300 metres or more.

Mountain belt   A regionally extensive group of mountains composed of multiple mountain ranges.

Mountain range   A linked series of mountains.

Mouth   The point downstream where a river empties into another stream or water body.

Mud crack   A feature in some sedimentary rocks that forms when wet mud dries out, shrinks, and cracks.

Natural levee   An elevated landform composed of alluvium that parallels some streams and acts to confine their waters, except during floodstage.

Nebular theory   A model for the origin of the solar system that supposes a rotating nebula of dust and gases that contracted to form the Sun and planets.

Neutron   A subatomic particle found in the nucleus of an atom. The neutron is electrically neutral, with a mass approximately equal to that of a proton.

Nonclastic   A term for the texture of sedimentary rocks in which the minerals form a pattern of interlocking crystals.

Nonconformity   An unconformity in which older metamorphic or intrusive igneous rocks are overlain by younger sedimentary strata.

Nonferromagnesian silicates   See *Light silicates.*

Non-flowing artesian well   An artesian well in which water does not rise to the surface, because the pressure surface is below ground level.

Nonfoliated   Metamorphic rocks that do not exhibit foliation.

Nonmetallic mineral resource   A mineral resource that is not a fuel or processed for the metals it contains.

Non-renewable resource   A resource that forms or accumulates over such long time spans that it must be considered as fixed in total quantity.

Normal fault   A fault in which the rock above the fault plane has moved down relative to the rock below.

Normal fault

Normal polarity   A magnetic field with the same polarity as the one that presently exists.

Nuclear fission   The splitting of atomic nuclei into smaller nuclei, causing neutrons to be emitted and heat energy to be released.

Nucleus   The small, heavy core of an atom that contains all of its positive charge and most of its mass.

Nuée ardente   Incandescent volcanic debris buoyed up by hot gases that moves downslope in an avalanche fashion.

Numeric date   The number of years that have passed since an event occurred.

Oceanic ridge   See *Mid-ocean ridge*.

Octet rule   The order in which atoms combine so that each can have the electron arrangement of a noble gas; that is, the outer energy level contains eight electrons.

Ophiolite complex   The sequence of rocks that make up the oceanic crust. The three-layer sequence includes an upper layer of pillow basalts, a middle zone of sheeted dykes, and a lower layer of gabbro.

Ore   A useful metallic mineral that can be mined at a profit. The term is also applied to certain non-metallic minerals, such as fluorite and sulphur.

Orogenesis   The processes that collectively result in the formation of mountains.

Outcrops   The bedrock exposed at the ground surface.

Outer core   A layer beneath the mantle about 2270 kilometres thick, which has the properties of a liquid.

Outlet glacier   A tongue of ice normally flowing rapidly outward from an ice cap or ice sheet, usually through mountainous terrain to the sea.

Outwash plain   A relatively flat, gently sloping plain consisting of materials deposited by meltwater streams in front of the margin of an ice sheet.

Oxbow lake   A curved lake produced when a stream cuts off a meander.

Oxbow lake

Oxidation   The removal of one or more electrons from an atom or ion. So named because elements commonly combine with oxygen.

Pahoehoe flow   A lava flow with a smooth to ropy surface.

Paleomagnetism   The natural remnant magnetism in rock bodies. The permanent magnetization acquired by rock that can be used to determine the relative location of the magnetic poles and the latitude of the rock at the time it became magnetized.

Paleozoic Era   A time span on the geologic time scale between the Precambrian and Mesozoic Eras, from about 541 million to 252 million years ago.

Palsa   A domelike frost mound of peat with ice lenses, commonly found in the Arctic.

Pangaea   The proposed supercontinent that 200 million years ago began to break apart and form the present land masses.

Parabolic dune   A sand dune similar in shape to a barchan dune except that its tips point into the wind. These dunes often form along coasts that have strong onshore winds, abundant sand,

and vegetation that partly covers the sand.

Parabolic dunes

Paradigm   A theory that is held with a very high degree of confidence and is comprehensive in scope.

Parasitic cone   A volcanic cone that forms on the flank of a larger volcano.

Parent material   The material on which a soil develops.

Parent rock   The rock from which a metamorphic rock formed.

Partial melting   The process by which most igneous rocks melt. Because individual minerals have different melting points, most igneous rocks melt over a temperature range of a few hundred degrees.

Passive continental margin or passive margin   A margin that consists of a continental shelf, continental slope, and continental rise. It is not associated with plate boundaries and therefore experiences little volcanism and few earthquakes.

Patterned ground   The general term for circles, polygons, nets, and stripes in surface material subjected to intense frost action (e.g., frost wedging and heaving). It is common in polar regions.

Pedalfer   The soil of humid regions characterized by the accumulation of iron oxides and aluminum-rich clays in the B horizon.

Pedocal   The soil associated with drier regions and characterized by an accumulation of calcium carbonate in the upper horizons.

Pegmatite   A very coarse-grained igneous rock (typically granite) commonly found as a dyke associated with a large mass of plutonic rock that has smaller crystals. Crystallization in a water-rich environment is believed to be responsible for the very large crystals.

Pegmatitic texture   A texture of igneous rocks in which most of the interlocking crystals are all larger than 1 centimetre in diameter.

Perched water table   A localized zone of saturation above the main water table, created by an impermeable layer.

Periglacial   An environment in which frost action is the main process shaping the landscape.

Period   A basic unit of the geologic time scale that is a subdivision of an era. Periods can be divided into smaller units called epochs.

Permafrost   Subsoil that is frozen continuously for at least two years. It is usually found in the sub-Arctic and Arctic regions.

Permeability   A measure of a material's ability to transmit fluid.

Petroleum trap   A geologic structure that allows for significant amounts of oil and gas to accumulate.

Phaneritic texture   An igneous rock texture in which the crystals are roughly equal in size and large enough so the individual minerals can be identified without magnification.

Phanerozoic Eon   That part of geologic time represented by rocks that contain abundant fossil evidence. The eon extending from the end of the Proterozoic Eon (541 million years ago) to the present.

Phenocryst   A conspicuously large crystal embedded in a matrix of finer-grained crystals.

Physical geology   A major division of geology that examines the materials of Earth and seeks to understand the processes and forces acting beneath and on Earth's surface.

Piedmont glacier   A glacier that forms when one or more alpine glaciers emerge from the confining walls of mountain valleys and spread out to create a broad sheet in the lowlands at the base of the mountains.

Pillow lava   Basaltic lava that solidifies in an underwater environment and develops a structure that resembles a pile of pillows.

Pingo   A large conical mound of soil-covered ice raised mainly by water pressure within or below permafrost in Arctic regions.

Pipe   A vertical conduit through which magmatic materials have passed.

Placer   A deposit formed when heavy minerals are mechanically concentrated by currents, most commonly streams and waves. Placers are sources of gold, tin, platinum, diamonds, and other valuable minerals.

Plate   One of numerous rigid sections of the lithosphere that moves as a unit over the asthenosphere.

Plate tectonics   The theory that proposes that Earth's outer shell consists of individual plates that interact in various ways and thereby produce earthquakes, volcanoes, mountains, and the crust itself.

Plucking   The process by which pieces of bedrock are lifted out of place by a glacier.

Pluton   A structure that results from the emplacement and crystallization of magma beneath the surface of Earth.

Plutonic rock   The igneous rock that forms at depth. Named after Pluto, the god of the underworld in classical mythology.

Point bar   A crescent-shaped accumulation of sand and gravel deposited on the inside of a meander.

Point bar

Polymorphs   Two or more minerals that have the same chemical composition but different crystalline structures. They are exemplified by the diamond and graphite forms of carbon.

Pore space   The open spaces in a rock, in sediment, or in soil.

Porosity   The volume of open spaces in rock or soil, expressed as a percentage of the total volume of a body of rock or soil.

Porphyritic texture   An igneous rock texture characterized by two distinctively different crystal sizes. The larger crystals are called phenocrysts, whereas the matrix of smaller crystals is termed the groundmass.

Porphyroblastic texture   A texture of metamorphic rocks in which particularly large grains (porphyroblasts) are surrounded by a fine-grained matrix of other minerals.

Porphyry   An igneous rock with a porphyritic texture.

Pothole   A depression formed in a stream channel by the abrasive corkscrew action of the water's sediment load.

Precambrian   All geologic time before the Paleozoic Era.

Primary (P) wave   A type of seismic wave that involves alternating compression and expansion of the material through which it passes.

Principle of fossil succession   Fossil organisms succeed one another in a definite and determinable order, and any time period can be recognized by its fossil content.

Principle of original horizontality   Layers of sediment are generally deposited in a horizontal or nearly horizontal orientation.

Proterozoic Eon   The eon following the Archean and preceding the Phanerozoic. It extends between 2.5 billion and 541 million years ago.

Proton   A positively charged subatomic particle found in the nucleus of an atom.

Pumice   A light-coloured glassy vesicular rock commonly having a felsic composition.

P-wave shadow zone   The zone between 105 and 140 degrees distance from an earthquake epicentre, which direct waves do not reach because of refraction by Earth's core.

Pyroclastic flow   A highly heated mixture, largely of ash and pumice fragments, travelling down the flanks of a volcano or along the surface of the ground.

Pyroclastic material   The volcanic rock ejected during an eruption. Pyroclastics include ash, bombs, and blocks.

Pyroclastic texture   An igneous rock texture that results from the consolidation of individual rock fragments that are ejected during a violent volcanic eruption.

Radial pattern   A system of streams running in all directions away from a central elevated structure, such as a volcano.

Radial pattern

Radioactive decay   The spontaneous breakdown of an unstable isotope toward a more stable state, accompanied by energy emission.

Radioactivity   The property of energy emission exhibited by an unstable isotope undergoing radioactive decay.

Radiocarbon dating   Using the radioactive isotope of carbon to date organic materials of the recent geologic past.

Radiometric dating   The procedure of calculating the absolute ages of rocks and minerals that contain certain radioactive isotopes.

Rainshadow A dry area on the lee side of a mountain range. Many middle-latitude deserts are of this type.

Rainshadow

Rapids A part of a stream channel in which the water suddenly begins flowing more swiftly and turbulently because of an abrupt steepening of the gradient.

Reach, stream A relatively straight segment of a stream.

Recessional moraine An end moraine formed as the ice front stagnated during glacial retreat.

Rectangular pattern A drainage pattern that is characterized by numerous right-angle bends and that develops on jointed or fractured bedrock.

Rectangular pattern

Recurrence interval The average time between occurrences of hydrologic events, such as floods of a given or greater magnitude.

Regional metamorphism The metamorphism associated with large-scale mountain building.

Regolith The layer of weathered rock and mineral fragments that nearly everywhere covers Earth's land surface.

Relative dating The placing of rocks and structures in their proper sequence or order. Only the chronologic order of events is determined.

Renewable resource A resource that is virtually inexhaustible or that can be replenished over relatively short time spans.

Reserve The already identified deposits from which minerals can be extracted profitably.

Reservoir rock The porous, permeable portion of an oil trap that yields oil and gas.

Resources The endowment of materials held in reserve that are useful to people and are ultimately available commercially.

Return period See *Recurrence interval*.

Reverse fault A fault in which the material above the fault plane moves up in relation to the material below.

Reverse fault

Reverse polarity A magnetic field opposite to the one that presently exists.

Richter scale A scale of earthquake magnitude based on the amplitude of the largest seismic wave record.

Ridge-push A mechanism that can contribute to plate motion. It involves the oceanic lithosphere sliding down the oceanic ridge under the pull of gravity.

Ridge sliding Where oceanic plates slide downward and outward from a ridge crest under the influence of gravity.

Right-lateral strike-slip Where the crustal block on the opposite side of a fault moved to the right as you face the fault.

Rift valley A long, narrow trough bounded by normal faults. It represents a region where divergence is taking place.

Rift zone A zone of tension and normal faulting where two lithospheric plates move away from each other.

Rills The tiny channels that develop as unconfined flow begins producing threads of current.

Ripple marks The small waves of sand that develop on the surface of a sediment layer by the action of moving water or air.

Roche moutonnée An asymmetrical knob of bedrock formed when glacial abrasion smoothes the gentle slope facing the advancing ice sheet and plucking steepens the opposite side as the ice overrides the knob.

Rock A consolidated mixture of minerals.

Rock cleavage The tendency of rocks to split along parallel, closely spaced surfaces. These surfaces are often highly inclined to the bedding planes in the rock.

Rock cycle A model that illustrates the origin of the three basic rock types and the interrelatedness of Earth materials and processes.

Rock flour The ground-up rock produced by the grinding effect of a glacier.

Rock structure All features created by the processes of deformation, from minor fractures in bedrock to a major mountain chain.

Rock slide The rapid movement of a coherent mass of rock downslope along planes of weakness.

Rock slide

Runoff The water that flows over the land rather than infiltrating into the ground.

Salt flat A white crust on the ground produced when water evaporates and leaves its dissolved materials behind.

Saltation The transportation of sediment through a series of leaps or bounces.

Schistosity A type of foliation characteristic of coarser-grained metamorphic rocks. Such rocks have a parallel arrangement of platy minerals, such as the micas.

Scoria The vesicular ejecta that is the product of basaltic magma.

Scoria cone See *Cinder cone*.

Sea arch An arch formed by wave erosion when caves on opposite sides of a headland unite.

Sea arch

Sea stack An isolated mass of rock standing just offshore, produced by the collapse of a sea arch.

Sea stack

Sea-floor spreading   The hypothesis first proposed in the 1960s by Harry Hess that suggested that new oceanic crust is produced at mid-ocean ridges, which are the sites of divergence.

Seamount   An isolated volcanic peak that rises at least 1000 metres above the deep-ocean floor.

Seawall   A barrier constructed to prevent waves from reaching the area behind the wall. Its purpose is to defend property from the force of breaking waves.

Secondary (S) wave   A seismic wave that involves particle motion perpendicular to the direction of propagation.

Secondary enrichment   The concentration of minor amounts of metals that are scattered through unweathered rock into economically valuable concentrations by weathering processes.

Sediment   A material that settles out in particulate form from a fluid, either by gravitational factors or precipitation.

Sedimentary environment   See *Environment of deposition*.

Sedimentary facies   The characteristics of a rock unit that reflect its environment of deposition and differentiate the rock unit from time-equivalent units adjacent to it.

Sedimentary rock   The rock formed from the weathered products of pre-existing rocks that have been transported, deposited, and lithified.

Seismic gap   A segment of an active fault zone that has not experienced a major earthquake over a span when most other segments have. Such segments are probable sites for future major earthquakes.

Seismogram   The record made by a seismograph.

Seismograph   An instrument that records earthquake waves.

Seismology   The study of earthquakes and seismic waves.

Settling velocity   The speed at which a particle falls through a still fluid. The size, shape, and specific gravity of particles influence settling velocity.

Shatter cones   The sets of conical fractures present in rocks affected by the shock waves of an explosion. They are closely associated with meteorite impact structures.

Shear   The stress that causes two adjacent parts of a body to slide past each other.

Sheet flow   Runoff moving in unconfined thin sheets.

Sheeted dykes   A large group of nearly parallel dykes.

Sheeting   A mechanical weathering process characterized by the splitting off of slablike sheets of rock due to unloading.

Shells   See *Energy levels*.

Shield   A large, relatively flat expanse of ancient metamorphic and igneous rock within the stable continental interior.

Shield volcano   A broad, gently sloping volcano built from fluid basaltic lavas.

Shield volcano

Silicate   Any one of numerous minerals that have the silicon–oxygen tetrahedron as their basic structure.

Silicon–oxygen tetrahedron   A pyramid-shaped structure composed of four oxygen atoms surrounding a silicon atom that constitutes the basic building block of silicate minerals.

Sill   A tabular igneous body that was intruded parallel to the layering of pre-existing.

Sinkhole (sink)   A depression produced in a region where soluble rock has been removed by groundwater.

Sinkhole

Slab-pull   A mechanism that contributes to plate motion in which cool, dense oceanic lithosphere sinks into the mantle and pulls the trailing lithosphere along.

Slide   A movement common to mass-wasting processes in which the material moving downslope remains fairly coherent and moves along a well-defined surface.

Slip face   The steep, leeward surface of a sand dune that maintains a slope of about 34 degrees.

Slump   The downward slipping of a mass of rock or unconsolidated material moving as a unit along a curved surface.

Slump

Soft bed deformation   The deformation of water-saturated subglacial fine sediment or weak bedrock by frictional drag of the overriding glacier.

Soil   A combination of mineral and organic matter, water, and air; the portion of the regolith that supports plant growth.

Soil profile   A vertical section through a soil that shows its succession of horizons and the underlying parent material.

Solifluction   The slow downslope flow of water-saturated (thawed) materials common to permafrost areas.

Solum   The *O*, *A*, and *B* horizons in a soil profile. Living roots and other plant and animal life are largely confined to this zone.

Sorting   The degree of similarity in particle size in sediment or sedimentary rock.

Specific gravity   The ratio of a substance's weight to the weight of an equal volume of water.

Speleothem   A collective term for the dripstone features found in caverns.

Spheroidal weathering   Any weathering process that tends to produce a spherical shape from an initially blocky shape.

Spit   An elongate ridge of sand that projects from the land into the mouth of an adjacent bay.

Spring   A flow of groundwater that emerges naturally at the ground surface.

Stalactite   The icicle-like structure that hangs from the ceiling of a cavern.

Stalagmite   The column-like form that grows upward from the floor of a cavern.

Star dune   An isolated hill of sand that exhibits a complex form and develops where wind directions are variable.

Star dune

Steppe   One of the two types of dry climate. A marginal and more humid variant of the desert that separates it from bordering humid climates.

Stock   A pluton similar to but smaller than a batholith.

Strain   An irreversible change in the shape and size of a rock body caused by stress.

Strata   Parallel layers of sedimentary rock.

Stratified drift   The sediments deposited by glacial meltwater.

Stratovolcano   See *Composite cone*.

Streak   The colour of a mineral in powdered form.

Stream   A general term to denote the flow of water within any natural channel. Thus, a small creek and a large river are both streams.

Stream piracy   The diversion of the drainage of one stream, resulting from the headward erosion of another stream.

Stress   The force per unit area acting on any surface within a solid.

Strike   The compass direction of the line of intersection created by a dipping bed or fault and a horizontal surface. Strike is always perpendicular to the direction of dip.

Strike-slip fault   A fault along which the movement is horizontal.

Subduction   The process by which oceanic lithosphere plunges into the mantle along a convergent zone.

Subduction

Subduction zone   A long, narrow zone in which one lithospheric plate descends beneath another.

Subduction zone metamorphism   Metamorphism in the region of a subducted slab under very high pressures but relatively low temperatures.

Submarine canyon   A seaward extension of a valley that was cut on the continental shelf during a time when sea level was lower, or a canyon carved into the outer continental shelf, slope, and rise by turbidity currents.

Surf   A collective term for breakers; also the wave activity in the area

between the shoreline and the outer limit of breakers.

Surface waves   The seismic waves that travel along the outer layer of Earth.

Surge   An episode of rapid glacial advance. Surges are typically sporadic and short-lived.

Suspended load   The fine sediment carried within the body of flowing water or air.

Syncline   A linear downfold in sedimentary strata; the opposite of anticline.

Syncline

System   A group of interacting or interdependent parts that form a complex whole.

Tablemount   See *Guyot*.

Tabular   The description of a feature, such as an igneous pluton, that has two dimensions that are much longer than the third.

Talus slope   An accumulation of rock debris at the base of a cliff.

Talus slope

Tarn   A small lake in a cirque.

Tensional stress   The type of stress that tends to pull a body apart.

Terminal moraine   The end moraine marking the farthest advance of a glacier.

Terrace   A flat, bench-like structure produced by a stream, which was left elevated as the stream cut downward.

Terrane   A crustal block bounded by faults, whose geologic history is distinct from the histories of adjoining crustal blocks.

Terrigenous sediment   The sea-floor sediments derived from terrestrial weathering and erosion.

Texture   The size, shape, and distribution of the particles that collectively constitute a rock.

Thermokarst   The karst-like ponds produced in a permafrost region by the local melting of ground ice and resultant settling of the ground.

Thrust fault   A low-angle reverse fault.

Thrust fault

Tidal current   The alternating horizontal movement of water associated with the rise and fall of the tide.

Tidal delta   A delta-like feature created when a rapidly moving tidal current emerges from a narrow inlet and slows, depositing its load of sediment.

Tidal flat   A marshy or muddy area that is alternately covered and uncovered by the rise and fall of the tide.

Tide   The periodic change in the elevation of the ocean surface.

Till   The poorly sorted sediment deposited directly by a glacier.

Tillite   A rock formed when till is lithified.

Tombolo   A ridge of sand that connects an island to the mainland or to another island.

Tombolo

Transform boundary   A boundary in which two plates slide past each other without creating or destroying lithosphere.

Transform boundary

Transform fault boundary A major strike-slip fault that cuts through the lithosphere and accommodates motion between two plates.

Transpiration The release of water vapour to the atmosphere by plants.

Transverse dunes A series of long ridges oriented at right angles to the prevailing wind; these dunes form where vegetation is sparse and sand is very plentiful.

Trellis pattern A system of streams in which nearly parallel tributaries occupy valleys cut in folded strata.

Trellis pattern

Trench An elongate depression in the sea floor produced by bending of oceanic crust during subduction.

Trigger A factor that initiates an event, such as an episode of mass wasting.

Truncated spurs Triangular-shaped cliffs produced when spurs of land that extend into a valley are removed by the great erosional force of a valley glacier.

Tsunami A rapidly moving ocean wave generated by earthquake activity, which is capable of inflicting heavy damage in coastal regions.

Turbidite Turbidity current deposit characterized by graded bedding.

Turbidity current A downslope movement of dense, sediment-laden water created when sand and mud on the continental shelf and slope are dislodged and thrown into suspension.

Turbidity current

Turbulent flow The movement of water in an erratic fashion often characterized by swirling, whirlpool-like eddies. Most streamflow is of this type.

Ultimate base level Sea level; the lowest level to which stream erosion could lower the land.

Ultramafic composition A compositional group of igneous rocks that contain mostly olivine and/or pyroxene.

Unconformity A surface that represents a break in the rock record, caused by erosion and/or nondeposition.

Uniform stress Forces that are equal in all directions.

Uniformitarianism The concept that the processes that have shaped Earth in the geologic past are essentially the same as those operating today.

Valence electron The electrons involved in the bonding process; the electrons occupying the highest principal energy level of an atom.

Valley glacier See *Alpine glacier*.

Valley train A relatively narrow body of stratified drift deposited on a valley floor by meltwater streams that issue from the terminus of an alpine glacier.

Vein deposit A mineral filling a fracture or fault in a host rock. Such deposits have a sheet-like, or tabular, form.

Vent The surface opening of a conduit or pipe in a volcano.

Ventifact A cobble or pebble polished and shaped by the sandblasting effect of wind.

Vesicular texture A term applied to aphanitic igneous rocks that contain many small cavities called vesicles.

Viscosity A measure of a fluid's resistance to flow.

Volatiles The gaseous components of magma dissolved in the melt. Volatiles readily vaporize (form a gas) at surface pressures.

Volcanic Pertaining to the activities, structures, or rock types of a volcano.

Volcanic island arc A chain of volcanic islands generally located a few hundred kilometres from a trench, where there is active subduction of one oceanic plate beneath another.

Volcanic neck An isolated, steep-sided, erosional remnant consisting of solidified magma that once occupied the vent of a volcano.

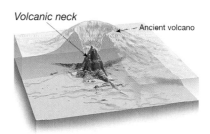

Volcanic neck — Ancient volcano

Volcano A mountain formed from lava or pyroclastics.

Water table The upper level of the saturated zone of groundwater.

Water table

Waterfall A precipitous drop in a stream channel that causes water to fall to a lower level.

Wave height The vertical distance between the trough and crest of a wave.

Wave period The time interval between the passage of successive crests at a stationary point.

Wave refraction A change in direction of waves as they enter shallow water. The portion of the wave in shallow water is slowed, which causes the waves to bend and align with the underwater contours.

Wave-cut cliff A seaward-facing cliff along a steep shoreline, formed by wave erosion at its base and mass wasting.

Wave-cut platform A bench or shelf along a shore at sea level, cut by wave erosion.

Wavelength The horizontal distance separating successive crests or troughs.

Weathering The disintegration and decomposition of rock at or near the surface of Earth.

Well An artificial opening bored into the zone of saturation.

Xenolith An inclusion of unmelted country rock in an igneous pluton.

Yardang A streamlined, wind-sculpted ridge that has the appearance of an inverted ship's hull oriented parallel to the prevailing wind.

Yazoo tributary A tributary that flows parallel to the main stream because a natural levee separates the two.

Yazoo tributary

Zone of ablation The part of a glacier below the equilibrium line where annually there is a net loss of ice.

Zone of accumulation The part of a glacier characterized by snow accumulation and ice formation. The lower limit of this zone is the equilibrium line.

Zone of aeration The area above the water table where openings in soil, sediment, and rock are not saturated with water but are filled mainly with air.

Zone of fracture The upper portion of a glacier that consists of brittle ice.

Zone of saturation The zone where all open spaces in sediment and rock are completely filled with water.

Zone of aeration

Water table

Zone of saturation

INDEX

Note: f denotes a figure, t denotes a table, and n denotes a footnote.